David M. Davison
Marsha Landau
Leah McCracken
Linda Thompson

PRENTICE HALL

Mathematics

Explorations & Applications

Needham, Massachusetts
Upper Saddle River, New Jersey

	A	B	C	D	E
1		Records	Tapes	CDs	
2	1983	208.6	238.8	0.6	
3	1984	204.6	332	5.8	
4	1985	167	339.1	22.6	
5	1986	125.2	344.5	53	
6	1987	107			
7	1988	72.4			
8	1989	34.6			
9	1990	11.7			
10	1991	4.8			
11	1992	2.3			
12					

AUTHORS

David M. Davison, *Eastern Montana College, Billings, Montana*

Marsha S. Landau, *National-Louis University, Evanston, Illinois*

Leah McCracken, *Lockwood Junior High School, Billings, Montana*

Linda Thompson, *Warrenton, Oregon*

REVIEWERS

Bettye C. Hall, *Director of Mathematics (retired), Houston Independent School District, Houston, Texas*

Joanne Martin, *Mathematics Teacher, New Prague, Minnesota*

Jeffrey S. McIntire, *Mathematics Teacher, Maumee High School, Maumee, Ohio*

Elizabeth C. McNair, *Mathematics Teacher, Burns Junior High School, Brandon, Florida*

Connie Bain, *Mathematics Teacher, Bonneville Junior High School, Salt Lake City, Utah*

Staff Credits

Editorial
Barbara A. Bertell
Judith Buice
Noralie V. Cox
Edward de Leon
Christine Deliee
Mimi Jigarjian
Caroline M. Power
Dennis Slattery
Mary Jane Wolfe

Marketing
Kathy Carter
Bridget A. Hadley
Christina Trinchero

Manufacturing
Therese Bräuer

Production
David Graham

Design
Russell Lappa
Stuart Wallace

ISBN 0-13-435820-1
Printed in the United States of America

6 7 8 9 02 01 00

PRENTICE HALL
dedicates
this mathematics program
to
all mathematics educators
and
their students

Contents

What is a proof set? see p. 93

How do fish live in a frozen pond? see p. 2

2 Solving Equations

IN EVERY CHAPTER, LOOK FOR:

PROJECT ▼ WRITE ▼ DATA ▼ CALCULATOR ▼ COMPUTER ▼ ESTIMATION

What makes up population change? see p. 139

▼ DATA ▼ CALCULATOR ▼ COMPUTER ▼ ESTIMATION ▼ MENTAL MATH ▼

How long do most teens study per day? see p. 230

6 Ratios, Proportions, and Percent

7 Equations and Inequalities

8 Graphing in the Coordinate Plane

IN EVERY CHAPTER, LOOK FOR:

PROJECT ▼ WRITE ▼ DATA ▼ CALCULATOR ▼ COMPUTER ▼ ESTIMATION

What is the loft of a golf club? see p. 360

9 Algebra in Geometry and Measurement

DATA FILE 9 *360*

10 Area and Volume Formulas

DATA FILE 10 *404*

What is an animal's home range? see p. 405

▼ DATA ▼ CALCULATOR ▼ COMPUTER ▼ ESTIMATION ▼ MENTAL MATH ▼

Who designed the 1495 parachute?   see p. 450

IN EVERY CHAPTER, LOOK FOR:

PROJECT ▼ WRITE ▼ DATA ▼ CALCULATOR ▼ COMPUTER ▼ ESTIMATION

IN EVERY CHAPTER LOOK FOR:

PROJECT ▼ DATA ▼ WRITE ▼ CALCULATOR ▼ COMPUTER ▼ ESTIMATION ▼ MENTAL MATH

**Just how
cold
is
it?**

IF YOU DROP a rubber ball into liquid nitrogen (-320°F), and then drop the ball from a height of 2 ft, the ball will be so brittle it will shatter.

PONDS IN WINTER

COOLING WATER becomes more dense until it reaches 39°F when it becomes less dense. Water at 39°F is always found at the bottom of ponds, which is why fish survive in the pond when the surface is frozen.

Icy Surface 32°F

33°F

35°F

37°F

39°F

Integers and Expressions

Think about it...

If you plunge a very cold glass into hot water, the glass will break. Why does this happen? How do engineers design products to withstand rapid changes in temperature?

FREEZING POINTS of common substances

Water

32°F

Vinegar

2°F

Gasoline

-70°F

Sugar

300°F

Salt

1,474°F

WIND CHILL

IN 1939, wind chill measurements were developed from experiments done in Antarctica. In 1943, Siple and Passell of the United States Army Climatic Research Unit used the concept of wind chill to help determine a soldier's clothing needs in very cold climates.

AIR TEMP (°F)	WIND SPEED IN MILES PER HOUR									
	0	5	10	15	20	25	30	35	40	
	Equivalent wind chill temperatures									
35	35	32	22	16	12	8	6	4	3	Little danger of frostbite
30	30	27	16	9	4	1	-2	-4	-5	
25	25	22	10	2	-3	-7	-10	-12	-13	
20	20	16	3	-5	-10	-15	-18	-20	-21	Increased danger of frostbite
15	15	11	-3	-11	-17	-22	-25	-27	-29	
10	10	6	-9	-18	-24	-29	-33	-35	-37	
5	5	0	-15	-25	-31	-36	-41	-43	-45	
0	0	-5	-22	-31	-39	-44	-49	-52	-53	
-5	-5	-10	-27	-38	-46	-51	-56	-58	-60	
-10	-10	-15	-34	-45	-53	-59	-64	-67	-69	
-15	-15	-21	-40	-51	-60	-66	-71	-74	-76	High danger of frostbite
-20	-20	-26	-46	-58	-67	-74	-79	-82	-84	
-25	-25	-31	-52	-65	-75	-81	-86	-89	-92	

Integers

▼ Suppose you earn $25 babysitting. The next week you spend $25 on sports equipment. You know that earning $25 is the *opposite* of spending $25. How can we represent this with numbers?

To represent earning $25, use a *positive integer*: +25, or 25.
To represent spending $25, use a *negative integer*: ‑25.

READ ‑25 as *negative 25* or *the opposite of 25*.

THINK What integer is neither negative nor positive?

Integers	The whole numbers and their opposites form the set of integers.

..., ‑4, ‑3, ‑2, ‑1, 0, 1, 2, 3, 4, ...

negative   zero   positive

Example 1 **Write an integer to represent each situation.**

  a. earning $50   **b.** a debt of $30

Solution   **a.** +50 or 50   **b.** ‑30

▼ You can represent integers on a number line.

Example 2 **Write the integer represented by each point on the number line.**

D   A   C   B

0

  a. *A*   **b.** *B*   **c.** *C*   **d.** *D*

Solution   **a.** ‑2   **b.** 3   **c.** 0   **d.** ‑4

Opposites	Opposites are two integers the same distance from zero on a number line, but in opposite directions.

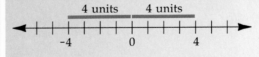

4 units   4 units

‑4   0   4

Example 3 Graph ⁻6 and its opposite on a number line.

Solution Draw a number line. Make sure the tic marks are evenly spaced. Mark points on the number line at ⁻6 and 6.

└── Mark zero on the number line first.

▼ Opposite integers are the same distance from zero on a number line. This means they have the same *absolute value*.

Absolute Value	The absolute value of an integer is its distance from zero on a number line.

THINK Why can't the absolute value of a number be negative?

Example 4 **a.** $|{-}5| = 5$ **b.** $|5| = 5$

⁻5 is 5 units from 0.
5 is 5 units from 0.

▼ You can also use situations and number lines to compare integers.

Example 5 On Monday the temperature was ⁻10°. On Tuesday it was ⁻15°. It was colder on Tuesday since 15° below zero is colder than 10° below zero. Write: ⁻15 < ⁻10.

Example 6 To compare ⁻3 and ⁻6, think of a number line. On a horizontal number line, the integer farther to the right is the greater integer.

```
◄─┼──┼──┼──┼──┼──┼──┼──┼──►
      -6      -3      0
```
⁻3 > ⁻6 and ⁻6 < ⁻3

⁻3 is to the right of ⁻6, so ⁻3 is greater than ⁻6 and ⁻6 is less than ⁻3.

FLASHBACK

= is equal to
< is less than
> is greater than

CLASS EXERCISES

Give an integer to represent each situation.

1. a profit of $250   **2.** 18° below 0   **3.** 45 s before launch

Give the integer represented by each point on the number line.

4. *A*

5. *B*

6. *C*

```
         C                 A      B
◄─┼──┼──┼──┼──┼──┼──┼──┼──┼──┼──┼──►
        -3  -1 0 1     3
```

THINK AND DISCUSS

1. Think of a number that is not an integer.

2. Explain how a thermometer is like a vertical number line.

3. Compare the set of positive integers with the set of nonnegative integers. Are they the same set? Explain.

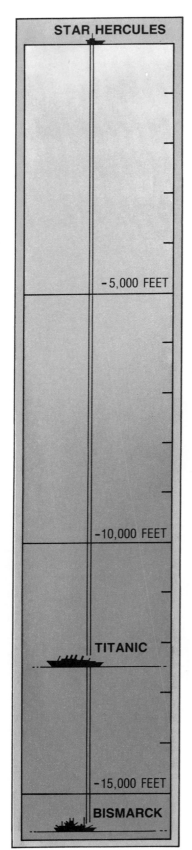

STAR HERCULES

– 5,000 FEET

–10,000 FEET

TITANIC

–15,000 FEET

BISMARCK

Give each number.

7. the opposite of 4   **8.** the opposite of ⁻9   **9.** |18| **10.** |⁻3|

Name the greater integer.

11. ⁻2, ⁻4   **12.** 8, ⁻9   **13.** ⁻12, ⁻9   **14.** 0, ⁻6

WRITTEN EXERCISES

Write an integer to represent each situation.

1. a deposit of $110   **2.** a debt of 50   **3.** 300 ft below sea level

4. win by 7 points   **5.** a loss of 8 yd   **6.** an elevation of 3,400 ft

Describe a situation that each integer could represent.

▼▼ *SAMPLE* ⁻8: 8 min before liftoff

7. ⁻5   **8.** ⁻1,000   **9.** 28   **10.** 7   **11.** 0   **12.** ⁻126

Write each integer.

13. the opposite of 6   **14.** the opposite of ⁻2   **15.** |⁻3| **16.** |13|

17. the absolute value of negative four

18. the absolute value of the opposite of sixteen

19. the opposite of the absolute value of negative nine

20. the opposite of the opposite of eight

Use the article below and the graph at the left.

21. a. Write integers that represent the positions of the *Titanic*, the *Bismarck*, and the *Star Hercules*.

b. *PROJECT* Research the *Titanic* or the *Bismarck*. Find out more about how and when each ship sank and was found.

Search Ends, Ships Found

In 1990 two historic ships were found deep in the North Atlantic Ocean. Both state-of-the-art ships survived less than one week.

The luxury passenger liner *Titanic* struck an iceberg. It came to rest 12,500 ft below sea level. The *Titanic* was 882 ft long, 92 ft wide, and displaced 66,000 t of water. The mighty warship *Bismarck* sank in battle. The *Bismarck* was 823 ft long, 118 ft wide, and displaced 50,000 t of water.

The *Star Hercules*, only 269 ft long, towed the underwater camera sled *Argo* that found the *Bismarck* under 15,617 ft of water.

Write the integer for each point on the number line,

22. A **23.** B

24. C **25.** D

(number line with points D, B, C, A marked, and 0 below)

26. 8 units to the left of ‾6   **27.** 10 units to the right of ‾2

Graph each integer and its opposite on a number line.

28. 1, ‾3   **29.** ‾2, ‾8   **30.** 5, 0   **31.** 4, ‾1

Compare. Use >, <, or =.

32. ‾8 ▮ 0   **33.** 4 ▮ ‾25   **34.** |3| ▮ |8| **35.** |‾1| ▮ |50|

36. ‾9 ▮ ‾2   **37.** |‾6| ▮ |‾12| **38.** ‾1 ▮ ‾5   **39.** |10| ▮ |‾10|

Complete with a word that makes each statement true.

40. All ▮ integers are less than zero.

41. An integer is negative, positive, or ▮.

42. The opposite of a ▮ number is negative.

43. The absolute value of an integer is never ▮.

44. *CALCULATOR*

a. Enter any positive integer on your calculator. Then enter ⊞⁄⊟. What appears in the display? What do you enter to display ‾25?

b. What integer will appear in the display after you enter these keys? 6 ⊞⁄⊟ ⊞⁄⊟ ⊞⁄⊟ ⊞⁄⊟. Check by entering the keys on your calculator.

Complete with an integer that makes each statement true.

45. ‾5 > ▮   **46.** ▮ < 6   **47.** |‾1| > ▮   **48.** |▮| < 8

Write an integer between the given integers.

49. ‾6, 2   **50.** 0, ‾4   **51.** 5, 1   **52.** ‾8, ‾12

53. *DATA FILE 1 (pp. 2–3)*

a. Find the wind chill temperature when the temperature is ‾5°F and the wind speed is 10 mi/h.

b. Starting at what wind chill temperature is there an increased danger of frostbite? a high danger of frostbite?

c. *PROJECT* Find the freezing points of two substances that are not listed.

54. *WRITE* Start a math journal. Use your journal to explain how to do an exercise you understand, to define new words in your own language, or to describe something you don't understand completely.

In 1970 Dr. Sylvia Earle Mead (b. 1935), marine biologist, lead the first United States team of female aquanauts. They lived underwater for two weeks near St. John, Virgin Islands, as part of the Tektite Underwater Research Project.

MIXED REVIEW

Find each answer.

1. 812 + 95

2. 1,061 − 247

3. 136 × 8

4. 378 ÷ 9

5. 7,920 − 48

6. How many triangles are in the figure shown?

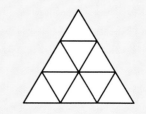

OBJECTIVE:
Use models to discover rules about integers.

MATERIALS

- Algebra tiles, checkers, or squares of paper in two different colors

- Math journal to record work

Exploring Integers

▼ You can use models, such as colored tiles, to represent integers.

Let yellow tiles represent positive integers. ▢▢▢ 3

Let red tiles represent negative integers. ◼◼ -2

1. Write the integer represented by each model.

   a. ▢▢

   b. ◼◼◼◼◼

   c. ◼

   d. ▢▢▢▢▢▢▢▢

2. Use models to represent each integer and its opposite.

   a. -3   b. 5   c. -8   d. 7

▼ You can use models to represent number sentences.

▢▢▢ + ▢ = ▢▢▢▢   and   ◼◼ + ◼◼◼ = ◼◼◼◼◼

3 + 1 = 4   -2 + (-3) = -5

3. **Model** the sum $2 + 4 = 6$. Model the sum $-2 + (-4) = -6$. How are the sums the same? How are they different?

4. **Write** a number sentence for each model.

   a. ▢▢▢▢▢ + ▢ = ▢▢▢▢▢▢

   b. ◼◼ + ◼ = ◼◼◼

   c. ◼◼ + ◼◼◼◼ = ◼◼◼◼◼◼

   d. ◼◼◼◼◼◼ + ◼◼◼ = ◼◼◼◼◼◼◼◼◼

5. Use your answers from Exercise 4. **Discuss** the following.

   a. the sum of two *positive* integers

   b. the sum of two *negative* integers

▼ Suppose you earn $5 and then spend $5. The result is a zero change in money. You can use models to represent zero. An equal number of yellow tiles and red tiles combine to make zero.

◼▢ represents zero *or* ◼ + ▢ = 0

6. a. Use models to represent a different sum of zero. How many of each color tile did you use? **Compare** with another group.

   b. If you use 12 yellow tiles, you will need ▢ red tiles to make zero.

   c. If you use 31 red tiles, you will need ▢ yellow tiles to make zero.

   d. What is the fewest number of red and yellow tiles you can combine to make zero?

   e. **Summarize** The sum of an integer and its opposite is ▢.

7. Combine tiles to make zeros. Write the integer for the remaining tiles.

a.

b.

c.

d.

8. *Explore* Use a different model to represent each integer from Exercise 7. Use both positive and negative tiles for each model. Compare your models with those of another group. In how many different ways can you represent a given integer?

9. Complete the model. Write a number sentence to show the sum.

a. ☐ + ☐

☐ + ☐ = ☐

b. ☐ + ☐

☐ + ☐ = ☐

c. ☐ + ☐

☐ + ☐ = ☐

d. ☐ + ☐

☐ + ☐ = ☐

10. Use models to find each sum.

a. $^-7 + 3$ b. $10 + (^-4)$ c. $^-5 + (^-4)$ d. $8 + (^-11)$

11. *Analyze* your answers from Exercises 9 and 10.

a. When is the sum *positive?* When is the sum *negative?*

b. ***Summarize*** Write a rule for the sign of the sum when you add two integers with different signs. *Hint:* Use absolute value.

12. Complete the model. Then write a number sentence for each sum.

a. ☐ + ☐ = ☐

b. ☐ + ☐ = ☐

1-2 Adding Integers

▼ Adding integers can be easier if you think of a familiar situation. Suppose you borrow $5 from your friend. The next day you borrow $2 more from your friend. You owe your friend $7, so you are $7 in debt. Here is your situation written as a sum of integers.

$$-5 \quad + \quad -2 \quad = \quad -7$$
borrow $5   borrow $2 more $7 in debt

▼ You can use models to add integers.

Example 1   6 + (-4)

Solution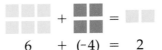

Four positive tiles and four negative tiles make a zero pair.

6   +   (-4)   =   2   Two positive tiles are left.

▼ Another useful model for adding integers is the number line.

Example 2   -8 + 9

Solution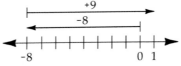

Notice that the sum falls on the same side of zero as the addend with the greater absolute value.

1. Begin at 0. Move 8 units to the *left* to *negative* eight.
2. Begin at -8. Move 9 units to the *right* to *positive* one.

-8 + 9 = 1

The early Egyptians drew pairs of legs walking in different directions to stand for addition and subtraction.

• *How is this model like the tiles and the number line?*

▼ It's not always convenient to use number lines or models. So, you can use these rules to add integers.

Adding Two Integers with the Same Sign	To add two integers with the same sign, add the absolute values of the integers. The sum has the same sign as the addends.

Adding Two Integers with Different Signs	To add two integers with different signs, find the *difference* of the absolute values of the addends. The sum has the sign of the integer with the greater absolute value.

Example 3 $-20 + 7$

Solution   **1.** Find absolute values. $|-20| = 20, |7| = 7$

   2. Subtract. $20 - 7 = 13$

   3. The sum is negative. $-20 + 7 = -13$

▼ You can use mental math or a calculator to find a sum.

Example 4   **a.** $-4 + (-1) + 4$ **Use mental math.**

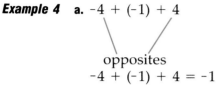

opposites
$-4 + (-1) + 4 = -1$

   b. $-865 + 77 + 240$ **Use a calculator.**
   $865 \boxed{+/-} \boxed{+} 77 \boxed{+} 240 \boxed{=} -548$

> **FLASHBACK**
>
> The sum of an integer and its opposite is zero.

▼ Sometimes you will need to add integers to solve problems.

Example 5   To win a computer game, a player must have a positive number of points after ten rounds. The points for ten rounds are shown. Did the player win the game?

Solution   Make a table to organize the data into positive and negative points. Use a calculator to add.

   The player did not win the game since the final score was negative.

Positive	Negative
6	-10
24	-55
19	-33
21	-18
12	
30	

$112 + (-116) = -4$

CLASS EXERCISES

Give a numerical expression for each situation. Find the sum.

1. Susan deposited $120, then wrote a check for $25.

2. A submarine at 35 ft below sea level moved up 10 ft.

Give a situation that describes each sum. Find the sum.

3. $235 + (-420)$ **4.** $100 + (-100)$ **5.** $-9 + (-1) + (-4)$

Give a numerical expression for the model. Find the sum.

6. ■■■■■ + ▨▨▨▨▨▨▨

7. ▨▨▨▨▨▨ + ▨■

Represent each sum on a number line. Find the sum.

8. $5 + (-7)$ **9.** $-7 + (-6)$ **10.** $4 + (-3) + 2$

> **THINK AND DISCUSS**
>
> **1.** Is the sum $6 + (-5)$ the same as $-5 + 6$? Explain.
>
> **2.** Explain how you could find each sum mentally.
> $3 + (-3) + (-2) + 5 + 2$
> $50 + 100 + 25 + (-50)$
>
> **3.** Without adding, tell whether each sum is positive, negative, or zero. Explain your reasoning.
> **a.** $-4 + (-10)$ **b.** $11 + (-3)$
> **c.** $-8 + 5$ **d.** $6 + (-6)$

Give the number sentence for the number line. In your own words, describe how each problem fits the rules.

11.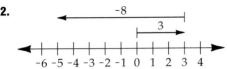

12.

WRITTEN EXERCISES

Write a sum for each situation. Explain the result.

1. borrow $20, then pay back $18   2. save $200, then spend $75

3. temperature: $-10°F$ drops 2°, rises 8°, drops 5°, drops 13°, rises 1°

Use models to represent each sum. Find the sum.

4. $-5 + 1$ 5. $-3 + (-6)$ 6. $-4 + 4 + (-5) + 0 + 8$

Represent each sum on a number line. Find the sum.

7. $-10 + 14$ 8. $5 + (-8)$ 9. $-1 + (-6) + 12 + (-7) + 8 + 3$

MENTAL MATH **Find each sum mentally.**

10. $-5 + 5 + 16$ 11. $-4 + (-2) + (-2)$

12. $-1 + (-1) + (-1) + 1 + (-1) + 1$ 13. $-120 + 100 + (-20)$

CALCULATOR **Find each sum.**

14. $145 + (-88)$ 15. $-355 + (-492)$ 16. $-192 + 825 + (-862) + 69$

Find each sum. Choose a method to use.

17. $-2 + (-3)$ 18. $-1 + 10$ 19. $-9 + 9$ 20. $8 + (-12)$
21. $14 + (-11)$ 22. $0 + (-9)$ 23. $-6 + (-7)$ 24. $-18 + 4$
25. $-5 + 20$ 26. $6 + (-6)$ 27. $-10 + (-3)$ 28. $-94 + 68$
29. $-8 + 7 + 5$ 30. $3 + (-2) + (-4)$ 31. $-1 + (-9) + 4$
32. $-3 + 2 + (-7) + 7 + 13$ 33. $-20 + (-89) + 112 + 9 + (-3)$

Use the *DATA* at the left.

34. Write the low temperatures in order from lowest to highest.

35. Compare the lowest high temperature with the highest low temperature for the week. Use > or <.

36. ***PROJECT*** Find the lowest and highest recorded temperatures in your city and state.

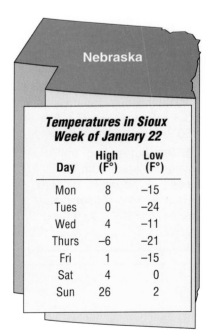

Temperatures in Sioux Week of January 22

Day	High (F°)	Low (F°)
Mon	8	−15
Tues	0	−24
Wed	4	−11
Thurs	−6	−21
Fri	1	−15
Sat	4	0
Sun	26	2

Write a numerical expression for each phrase. Find the sum.

37. negative two plus negative seven

38. twelve plus the absolute value of nine

39. positive three plus the opposite of eight

40. one hundred added to negative nineteen

Compare. Write >, <, or =.

41. -6 + 1 ▧ 5 + 1

42. 0 + 3 ▧ -2 + 0

43. -20 + (-7) ▧ -11 + (-11) ▧ 16 + 6

Solve.

44. Maria had $123. She spent $35, loaned $20 to a friend, and received her $90 paycheck. How much does she have now?

45. A football team gained 14 yd, lost 22 yd, gained 15 yd, lost 8 yd, and then lost 9 yd. Find the net gain or loss in yards.

46. *WRITE* and solve a word problem that uses the integers -10, 3, 5, -6, and -7.

Complete with integers.

47. ▧ + ▧ = 7

48. ▧ + ▧ = -8

49. ▧ + ▧ = -12

> **PROBLEM SOLVING HINT**
> Using a number line or model may be helpful.

Critical Thinking
EXPLORING CLASSIFICATION

You can organize or *classify* numbers into categories by choosing a common *attribute* or characteristic.

-7	-198	0
	-19	-47
525	-50	-78

Look at the numbers in the box.

1. Classify three integers as odd.

2. Classify three integers as less than -10.

3. Classify three integers as having a 7 as a digit.

4. Classify -7, -19, and -50 by one common attribute.

5. Classify three integers as between -49 and 0. Write three more integers that fit in this classification.

6. Now choose some classifications of your own. Design at least three more ways to classify the numbers. List your numbers, exchange with a partner, and analyze each other's lists to figure out the classification.

MIXED REVIEW
Find each number.
1. the opposite of 8
2. the opposite of -12
3. |-10| **4.** |16|
Complete with > or <.
5. -9 ▧ -6   **6.** -2 ▧ -7
7. In how many ways can you make change for a quarter?
8. Name the integer five units to the left of negative eight.

OBJECTIVE:
To subtract integers
using models,
patterns, and rules.

1-3 Subtracting Integers

▼ In one day in January 1916 the temperature change in Browning, Montana set a record. The temperature fell 100° from 44°F to -56°F. You can write the situation as subtraction of integers.

$$44 \quad - \quad 100 \quad = \quad -56$$
44° above zero ⠀⠀drop of 100° ⠀⠀new temperature

▼ You can think of a thermometer as a number line. The thermometer at the left shows the subtraction as a move along a number line.

▼ You can also use models to show subtraction situations.

Example 1⠀**a.** You have $5. You give away $1. You now have $4.
⠀⠀⠀⠀⠀**b.** You owe $3. You pay back $2. You now owe $1.

Solution⠀**a.** $5 - 1 = 4$ ⠀
⠀⠀⠀⠀⠀**b.** $-3 - (-2) = -1$ ⠀  ⠀Let 3 negative tiles stand for the money you owe. Take away 2 tiles.

Example 2⠀**a.** $4 - 5$⠀⠀**b.** $5 - (-6)$

Solution⠀**a.** You don't have 5 positive tiles. So, add a zero pair.
⠀⠀⠀⠀⠀⠀Now take away 5 positives.
⠀⠀⠀⠀⠀⠀$4 - 5 = -1$

⠀⠀⠀⠀⠀**b.** You don't have 6 negative tiles. Add some zero pairs.
⠀⠀⠀⠀⠀⠀Now take away 6 negatives.
⠀⠀⠀⠀⠀⠀$5 - (-6) = 11$

THINK How does adding zeros make it easier to subtract negative integers?

THINK What is the same for the number sentences in each pair? What is different?

▼ You know how to subtract positive integers and how to add any integers. Look at the pattern for the sums and differences you know.

$5 - 4 = 1$	$7 - 3 = 4$	$12 - 5 = 7$	$14 - 6 = 8$
$5 + (-4) = 1$	$7 + (-3) = 4$	$12 + (-5) = 7$	$14 + (-6) = 8$

You can see the same pattern when adding or subtracting any integers.

$-10 - (-6) = -4$	$7 - 8 = -1$	$2 - (-9) = 11$
$-10 + 6 = -4$	$7 + (-8) = -1$	$2 + 9 = 11$

▼ The models and patterns suggest the following rule for subtracting integers.

Subtracting Integers	To subtract an integer, add its opposite.

Example 3   **a.** $-8 - 2$ **b.** $-12 - (-4)$ **c.** $|-3| - |-7|$

Solution   **a.** $-8 - 2 = -8 + (-2)$ Add the opposite of 2.
$= -10$

b. $-12 - (-4) = -12 + 4$ Add the opposite of -4.
$= -8$

c. $|-3| - |-7| = 3 - 7$ Find absolute values.
$= 3 + (-7)$ Add the opposite of 7.
$= -4$

CLASS EXERCISES

Write each subtraction as an equivalent addition.

1. $2 - 3$ **2.** $-5 - (-6)$ **3.** $-9 - (-7)$ **4.** $1 - 8$

5. $33 - (-18)$ **6.** $0 - 75$ **7.** $-12 - (-12)$ **8.** $|-10| - |7|$

Model each situation and give the result.

9. You are $3 in debt. You get a $10 gift.

10. You pay a bill for $15. You earn $7.

11. *WRITE* In your own words, summarize the rules for adding and subtracting integers. Use examples if necessary.

▼
THINK AND DISCUSS
1. When is the absolute value of a difference the *same* as the difference of the absolute values?
2. When is the absolute value of a difference *greater* than the difference of the absolute values?
3. When is the absolute value of a difference *less* than the difference of the absolute values?

WRITTEN EXERCISES

Write a number sentence for each model or number line.

1.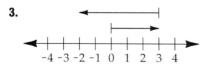

2.

3.

4.

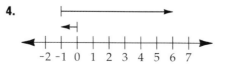

Write a numerical expression for each phrase.

5. A plane climbs 3,000 ft and then descends 600 ft.

6. The temperature increases to 15° and then drops 25°.

MENTAL MATH **Find each difference.**

7. -2 − 3   **8.** -7 − (-9)   **9.** -14 − 2

10. -6 − (-8)   **11.** -45 − 15   **12.** -7 − (-7) + (-7)

13. 100 − (-50)   **14.** 20 − (-10) − 20   **15.** -11 + 22 − (-55)

CALCULATOR **Find each difference.**

16. 88 − 97   **17.** -235 − (-39)   **18.** -49 − 75

19. 121 − (-57)   **20.** -81 − (-13)   **21.** 989 − 76

22. -59 − (-17)   **23.** -91 − (-79) − 19   **24.** 815 + 35 − (-79)

Find each sum or difference. Use any method you wish.

25. 16 − (-9)   **26.** 11 − 5   **27.** 802 + (-977)   **28.** 75 + (-25)

29. -144 − 278   **30.** 87 − (-9)   **31.** 22 + (-7)   **32.** 35 + (-15)

33. 100 − (-91)   **34.** -45 − 15   **35.** -92 + (-9)   **36.** 167 + (-3)

37. $|68| - |-12|$ **38.** $|-80| + |-28|$

39. $|-555| - |199|$ **40.** $|217| + |-317| + |0|$

41. $|-12| + |36| - |-10|$ **42.** $|-3| - |-2| - |-1|$

43. Copy and complete. The first one is done for you.

     8 − (-4) = 12
    12 − (-4) = ▨
    16 − (-4) = ▨
    20 − (-4) = ▨
    24 − (-4) = ▨

     If you begin at 8 and subtract -4 five times, the result is ▨.

In a magic square, each row, column, and diagonal has the same sum. Copy and complete each magic square.

44.

5	-9	▨
▨	-1	▨
-3	▨	-7

Sum = ▨

45.

-2	▨	▨
-9	-5	▨
-4	▨	▨

Sum = ▨

46.

▨	-5	▨	6
▨	4	3	▨
2	0	▨	5
-3	▨	▨	-6

Sum = ▨

Balloon Trip, Dress Warmly

In 1862, a meteorologist named James Glaisher set off in a hot air balloon wearing nothing warmer than a jacket.

When the balloon landed, Mr. Glaisher was unconscious and the thermometer in the balloon read -84°C.

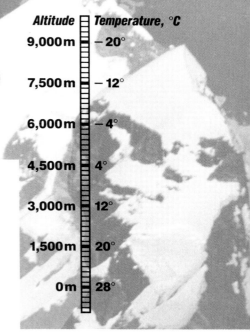

Altitude	Temperature, °C
9,000 m	-20°
7,500 m	-12°
6,000 m	-4°
4,500 m	4°
3,000 m	12°
1,500 m	20°
0 m	28°

47. DATA Use the article above and the graph at the right.

a. As the altitude increases, what happens to the temperature?

b. By how much does the temperature change from 1,500 m to 6,000 m?

c. For every 1,500 m increase in altitude there is an 8° (increase, decrease) in temperature.

d. Use the given thermometer reading to estimate the height Mr. Glaisher's balloon reached.

48. How much warmer is it when the temperature is 20° than when the temperature is -7°?

49. Suppose you had a score of 35 in a game. You then get a 50 point penalty. What is your new score?

Use positive and negative integers to write two different subtraction number sentences for each difference.

▼▼ *SAMPLE* ▨ − ▨ = -5 → -20 − (-15) = -5   17 − 22 = -5

50. ▨ − ▨ = 0   **51.** ▨ − ▨ = 10   **52.** ▨ − ▨ = -6

53. ▨ − ▨ = -15   **54.** ▨ − ▨ = |-3| **55.** ▨ − ▨ = |11|

ESTIMATION Round each number to a convenient place. Estimate each sum or difference.

▼▼ *SAMPLE* Estimate -2,216 + 488.
$$-2,200 + 500 = -1,700$$

56. -45 + (-86)   **57.** 227 − 49   **58.** 398 − 67

59. -186 + 122   **60.** 88 + 521   **61.** 3,321 − 924

62. 5,436 − (-4,725)   **63.** -864 + (-2,735) **64.** 4,599 − 3,099

MIXED REVIEW

Add or subtract.

1. -17 − 12

2. |60 − (-5)|

3. -8 + 15

4. -9 + (-4) + 7

5. Name an integer between -5 and -10.

6. 6 + ▨ = 0

Write a number sentence and solve.

7. A submarine at the surface dives 800 ft and then another 125 ft. Find the final depth.

OBJECTIVE:
To explore and describe number patterns.

Exploring Number Patterns

■ Some number patterns are familiar.

$$2, 4, 6, 8, \blacksquare, \blacksquare, \blacksquare$$
$$30, 25, 20, 15, \blacksquare, \blacksquare, \blacksquare$$
$$2, -2, 2, -2, 2, \blacksquare, \blacksquare, \blacksquare$$
$$1, 3, 4, 12, 13, 39, 40, \blacksquare, \blacksquare, \blacksquare$$

1. **a. *Write*** the next three numbers in each pattern.

   b. *Write* a rule to describe each pattern.

   c. *Discuss*—How are the patterns alike? How are they different?

2. ***Analyze*** the integer triangle.

   a. *Describe* a pattern for each row and column.

   b. Copy the triangle and add four more rows.

   c. What is the middle number in each row?

   d. How many numbers appear in each row?

   e. What is the sum of the numbers in each row?

   f. *Describe* each pattern you found.

```
          1
        1 2 1
      1 2 3 2 1
    1 2 3 4 3 2 1
  1 2 3 4 5 4 3 2 1
```

```
          0
        2   4
      6   8   10
   12  14  16  18
 20 ■  ■  ■  ■
```

3. ***Analyze*** the triangle of even numbers.

   a. Copy the pattern and add six more rows.

   b. *Describe* what happens when you alternate subtracting and adding the numbers in each row.

   Copy and complete the table. Use the table to search for patterns. ***Compare*** with another group.

Row	1	2	3	4	5	6	7	8	9	10
Result	0	-2	8	-4	■	■	■	■	■	■

4. Make up a pattern of your own. Exchange with a partner. Figure out each other's pattern.

■ You can think about some sets of numbers in more than one way. Look at the following pattern in two different ways.

$$2, \quad 6, \quad 12, \quad 20, \ldots \qquad 2, \quad 6, \quad 12, \quad 20, \ldots$$
$$\quad\searrow_{+4}\nearrow\searrow_{+6}\nearrow\searrow_{+8}\nearrow \qquad 1\cdot 2 \quad 2\cdot 3 \quad 3\cdot 4 \quad 4\cdot 5$$

5. **a.** Extend the above patterns. Do they result in the same set of numbers? Is this what you expected?

   b. Which method of extending the pattern would you use to find the 10th number in the pattern? the 100th number?

6. Make up a number pattern that you can extend in two different ways. Exchange with a partner and solve.

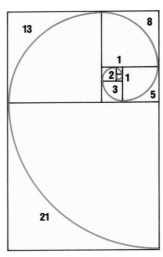

The spiral of a nautilus shell is an example of the Fibonacci numbers 1, 1, 2, 3, 5, 8, 13, . . .
- **Explain and extend the pattern.**
- **RESEARCH Find out how Fibonacci numbers occur in nature, music, and art.**

1-4 Look for a Pattern

■ You can solve many types of problems using patterns.

PROBLEM

News spreads quickly at River Dell High School. Each student who hears a story repeats that story to two other students in 15 min, and then tells no one else. A student hears some news at 8:00 A.M. How many students will know the news at 10:00 A.M.?

SOLUTION

READ ▶ Answer these questions to understand the given information.
How many students does each student tell?   2
How long does it take the news to reach
two students?   15 min

PLAN ▶ Make a table to organize the given information.
Then look for a pattern.

SOLVE ▶ Answer these questions to complete the table.
How many *new* students hear the news every
15 min?   twice as many
How many students know the news after 15 min? $1 + 2 = 3$
                                       after 30 min? $3 + 4 = 7$
                                       after 45 min? $7 + 8 = 15$
Continue the pattern until you reach 10:00 A.M.

Time	8:00	8:15	8:30	8:45	9:00	9:15	9:30	9:45	10:00
Number of new students told	1	2	4	8	16	32	64	128	256
Number of students who know	1	3	7	15	31	63	127	255	511

By 10:00 A.M., 511 students know the story.

LOOK BACK ▶ One way to check a problem is to solve it another way. A tree diagram is a visual means to solving the problem.

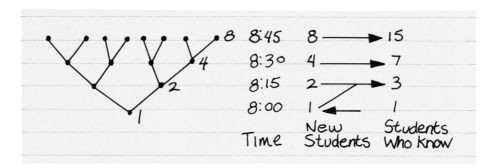

CLASS EXERCISES

Refer to the problem on page 19.

1. Describe two ways to use the pattern to tell the number of students who know at 10:15 A.M.

2. Suppose the news continues to spread through the school. There are 1,735 students at River Dell High. By what time will every student know the story?

Refer to the problem on page 19.

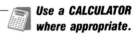
Use a CALCULATOR where appropriate.

WRITTEN EXERCISES

NOTES & QUOTES

When the German mathematician Karl Friedrich Gauss (1777–1855) was about ten years old, his teacher became annoyed with the class. As punishment, the teacher asked the class to compute the sum of the first 100 counting numbers. Gauss thought for a moment and then wrote the correct answer on his slate.

RESEARCH Find out how Gauss used patterns to solve this problem.

Solve by looking for a pattern.

1. The students in the town of Brighton are going to march in a parade. There will be one first-grader, two second-graders, three third-graders, and so on through the twelfth grade. How many students will march in the parade?

2. Caroline is training for a swim meet. The first week she swims 1 lap per day. The second week she swims 3 laps per day. The third week she swims 6 laps per day. The fourth week she swims 10 laps per day. If she keeps to this training pattern, how many laps per day will Caroline swim in the eighth week?

3. Find each product and look for a pattern.

$2 \times 2 = \blacksquare$ $3 \times 3 = \blacksquare$
$1 \times 3 = \blacksquare$ $2 \times 4 = \blacksquare$
Difference $= \blacksquare$ Difference $= \blacksquare$

$4 \times 4 = \blacksquare$ $5 \times 5 = \blacksquare$
$3 \times 5 = \blacksquare$ $4 \times 6 = \blacksquare$
Difference $= \blacksquare$ Difference $= \blacksquare$

a. Which is greater, 10×12 or 11×11? how much greater?

b. Suppose you know that $47 \times 47 = 2,209$. How can you find 46×48?

c. Suppose you know that $64 \times 66 = 4,224$. How can you find 65×65?

4. Every day Maria saves twice as many pennies as she saved the day before. She starts by saving one penny on January 1. How much money will she have by January 10?

5. **DATA FILE 8 (pp. 312–313)** Did the population grow more between 1800 and 1810 or 1810 and 1820? How much more?

Solve. Use any strategy you wish.

6. You can cut a pizza into two pieces with one straight cut. With two cuts you get four pieces. Three cuts will result in a maximum of seven pieces. What is the maximum number of pieces you can get with four cuts? with five cuts?

7. A restaurant offers special prices for groups dining together. For a buffet dinner, the restaurant charges $10 for one person, $20 for two people, $29 for three, $37 for four, and so on.

   a. How much does a buffet dinner for 8 cost? How much does the group save by eating together rather than alone?

   b. The buffet costs the restaurant $6 per person. What size group can the restaurant serve without losing money?

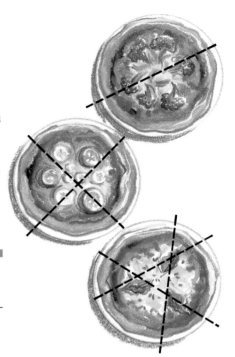

EXPLORING VENN DIAGRAMS

The principal wants to send invitations to a Science Fair to the homes of all students enrolled in biology and chemistry. Use the enrollment figures at the right to tell how many invitations are needed. A *Venn diagram* will help.

Course	Enrollment
Biology	127
Chemistry	124
Biology and Chemistry	17

- Draw intersecting circles. Label the circles with the given information.

  Biology 127 — Chemistry 124

- The *intersection* (overlap) tells the number of students enrolled in both courses. Write the number in the intersection.

  Biology 127 — 17 — Chemistry 124

- The total in the biology circle is 110 plus the 17 in the intersection. What number goes in the chemistry circle?

  Biology 127 — 110 (17) ■ — Chemistry 124

- Add the numbers in the three sections. How many invitations does the principal need?

Use a Venn diagram to solve.

A coach needs to notify soccer players and swimmers of a revised schedule. Use the data at the right and a Venn diagram to tell how many notices the coach must send.

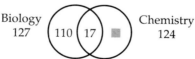

Sport	Players
Soccer	24
Swimming	19
Soccer and swimming	6

1-5 *Multiplying Integers*

▼ Suppose a football team loses 2 yd on each of 4 plays. At the end of the 4 plays the team loses 8 yd.

$$4 \quad \times \quad -2 \quad = \quad -8$$
4 plays   lose 2 yd/play   lose 8 yd

▼ You also can think of multiplication as repeated addition.

Example 1 $3 \times (-7)$

Solution $3 \times (-7) = (-7) + (-7) + (-7)$
$$= -21$$

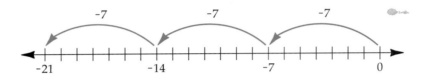

▼ Notice that the product of a negative number and a positive number is negative. You can use patterns to help find the product of two negative numbers.

Example 2   **Use patterns to find $-3(-6)$ and $-4(-5)$.**

Solution

$2(-6) = -12$	$3(-5) = -15$	**Start with products**
$1(-6) = -6$	$2(-5) = -10$	**you know.**
$0(-6) = 0$	$1(-5) = -5$	
	$0(-5) = 0$	
$-1(-6) = 6$	$-1(-5) = 5$	**Continue the pattern**
$-2(-6) = 12$	$-2(-5) = 10$	**for the product of two**
$-3(-6) = 18$	$-3(-5) = 15$	**negative integers.**
	$-4(-5) = 20$	

▼ From what you know about multiplying whole numbers and from the examples, you can write these rules for multiplying integers.

Multiplying Integers	To multiply two integers, find the product of the absolute values of the integers. Then use these rules.
	1. The product of two integers with the same sign is positive. $(+)(+) = +$ $(-)(-) = +$
	2. The product of two integers with different signs is negative. $(+)(-) = -$ $(-)(+) = -$

FLASHBACK

Symbols for multiplication

$\times$ -3×5

( ) $-3(5)$

· $-3 \cdot 5$

* $-3 * 5$

From now on, we will use · or ( ) for multiplication.

THINK Is the product increasing or decreasing? by how much?

▼ The rules are useful for finding the product of more than two integers.

Example 3   Use the rules and mental math to find the product of
-2 · 8(-5).

Solution   -2 · 8(-5)

10 · 8 = 80

-2 · 8(-5) = 80

You can multiply integers in any order. Choose factors that are easy to multiply in your head.

▼ You can use integers to solve problems.

Example 4   Your average time for a 10-km race is 54 min. You would like to take 2 min off your average time each month for 3 mo. What will be your new average time?

Solution   1. By how much do you want to reduce your average time?

2 · 3

2. Compute your new average time.

54 − (2 · 3) = 48

Your new average time will be 48 min.

CLASS EXERCISES

Without computing, tell whether the product is positive, negative, or zero.

1. -3(8)(-24)   2. 8(-83)   3. 2(-4) · 29   4. 3(-21)(-12)

Write each sum as a product. Find the product.

5. -8 + (-8) + (-8) + (-8)   6. -2 + (-2) + (-2) + (-2) + (-2)

Complete the pattern. Is the product increasing or decreasing? by how much?

7. 3(-3) = ▓
2(-3) = ▓
1(-3) = ▓
0(-3) = ▓
-1(-3) = ▓
-2(-3) = ▓
-3(-3) = ▓

8. 2(-9) = ▓
1(-9) = ▓
0(-9) = ▓
-1(-9) = ▓
-2(-9) = ▓
-3(-9) = ▓
-4(-9) = ▓

9. Write a number sentence for the product shown on the number line.

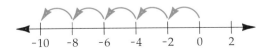

-10   -8   -6   -4   -2   0   2

▼

THINK AND DISCUSS

1. What is the product of -6 and -1? How are the product and -6 related? Complete: The product of any integer and -1 is the ▓ of the integer.

2. Will the product of three negative integers be positive or negative? what about four negative integers? five negative integers?

3. Write a rule to use in deciding the sign for the product of more than two integers.

WRITTEN EXERCISES

Use repeated addition to find each product.

1. $10(-6)$ **2.** $-12 \cdot 4$ **3.** $5(-6)$ **4.** $4(-11)$

Use patterns to find each product.

5. $-7(-3)$ **6.** $-3(-6)$ **7.** $-5(-4)$ **8.** $-9(-12)$

MENTAL MATH Find the point on the number line that shows each product.

9. $-2 \cdot 0$ **10.** $4(-2)$ **11.** $|-2| \cdot |-2|$ **12.** $2(-2)$

CALCULATOR Find each product.

13. $-59(-79)$ **14.** $243(-88)$ **15.** $-1{,}078(-43)$ **16.** $23(-54) \cdot 42(-39)$

Find each answer. Choose a method to use.

17. $-5(-3)$ **18.** $-6 \cdot 10$ **19.** $8 \cdot 3(-4)$

20. $-18(-12)$ **21.** $-11 \cdot 20$ **22.** $-8 \cdot 0$

23. $24(-16)(-32)$ **24.** $-9(-8)(-5)$ **25.** $-8 \cdot 25$

26. $|-9| + |-8|$ **27.** $|-2| \cdot (-7) \cdot 4$ **28.** $|-2| \cdot (-7)$

29. $-9 - (-2)$ **30.** $-8 + 6 + (-6)$ **31.** $0(-12) \cdot 4$

32. $14 \cdot 9$ **33.** $-20 + (-6)$ **34.** $17 - (-3)$

35. $9(-9)$ **36.** $38(-2)$ **37.** $-15 + (-4)$

Write a product for each word phrase. Then find the product.

38. negative eleven times negative five

39. eight times the opposite of five

40. the product of fourteen and negative seven

41. the product of six and negative nine

42. the absolute value of the product of negative twelve and ten

Compare. Use $>$, $<$, or $=$ to make a true statement.

43. $(-9)(-6) \ \blacksquare \ 8(-10)$ **44.** $5(-2) \ \blacksquare \ (-6)(-1)$ **45.** $|-6||-2| \ \blacksquare \ |-6(-2)|$

Solve.

46. The temperature dropped $5°$ each hour for 7 h. Use an integer to represent the total change in temperature.

---

47. The price of a stock fell $3 each day over a 12-day period.

    a. What was the total change in price?

    b. The original stock price was $76 per share. What was the price after the drop?

48. A car loan requires equal payments of $378 per month for four years.

    a. What is the total amount paid for the four years?

    b. Suppose a down payment of $2,500 was made. What was the total cost of the car?

<table>
<tr><td>PROBLEM SOLVING HINT
How many months are in four years?</td></tr>
</table>

Find two integers that fit the given description.

49. sum: -7
    product: 12

50. sum: 0
    product: -9

51. sum: 4
    product: -5

52. _DATA FILE 9 (pp. 360–361)_ Suppose your score for the first nine holes at the St. Andrew's golf course is 4 under par. What would be your score?

53. _DATA_ Use the chart below.

    a. Can a balloon carry more weight at 5,000 ft at 40° or at 4,000 ft at 50°?

    b. Suppose people who weigh 150 lb, 112 lb, 129 lb, 183 lb, 108 lb, 75 lb, and 56 lb are planning a balloon trip. The balloon weighs 620 lb. Can the group rise to 4,000 ft if the temperature is 70°?

    c. _WRITE_ Describe two patterns in the chart. Compare with a classmate. Did you find different patterns?

MAXIMUM WEIGHT A HOT AIR BALLOON CAN CARRY* (in pounds)

Altitude	Temperature (°F)						
	30°	**40°**	**50°**	**60°**	**70°**	**80°**	**90°**
2,000 ft	1,415	1,315	1,215	1,100	1,000	885	800
3,000 ft	1,370	1,270	1,170	1,070	970	850	770
4,000 ft	1,330	1,230	1,130	1,030	930	820	750
5,000 ft	1,285	1,185	1,085	985	900	800	715
10,000 ft	1,060	985	900	815	750	660	600
15,000 ft	885	815	750	670	615	550	485

*Limits include weight of the balloon

Hot air balloon trips are usually planned for early morning. Why do you think this is true?

1-6 Dividing Integers

▼ A storm system moved through Minneapolis one day and the temperature dropped 28° in 4 h. To find the average change per hour, you can divide.

$$-28 \div 4 = -7$$

You can use a related multiplication sentence to see why the quotient is negative.

$$\text{Since } -7 \cdot 4 = -28, \; -28 \div 4 = -7$$

▼ Multiplication and division are inverse operations. One *undoes* the other. Because $3 \cdot 2 = 6$, we can write $6 \div 3 = 2$ and $6 \div 2 = 3$. You can use this relationship to find quotients of integers. The table shows related multiplication and division sentences.

Multiplication Number Sentence	Division Number Sentence
8(6) = 48	48 ÷ 6 = 8
(-8)(6) = -48	-48 ÷ 6 = -8
8(-6) = -48	-48 ÷ (-6) = 8
(-8)(-6) = 48	48 ÷ (-6) = -8

▼ The examples demonstrate the following rules for dividing integers.

Dividing Integers	To divide two integers, find the quotient of the absolute values of the integers. Then use the following rules.
	1. The quotient of two integers with the same sign is positive.
	$(+) \div (+) = +$ $(-) \div (-) = +$
	2. The quotient of two integers with different signs is negative.
	$(+) \div (-) = -$ $(-) \div (+) = -$

Example 1 **a.** $27 \div 9$ **b.** $-18 \div (-3)$ **c.** $100 \div (-10)$ **d.** $-56 \div 7$

Solution **a.** $27 \div 9 = 3$ $(+) \div (+) = +$
b. $-18 \div (-3) = 6$ $(-) \div (-) = +$
c. $100 \div (-10) = -10$ $(+) \div (-) = -$
d. $-56 \div 7 = -8$ $(-) \div (+) = -$

▼ Many of the numbers you see every day are averages. The *mean* is the average you see most often. Many of the problems you encounter will ask you to compute the mean.

Finding the Mean	To find the mean of a group of numbers: 1. Find the sum of the numbers. 2. Divide the sum by the number of items.

Example 2 A student's scores on five math tests were 98, 90, 87, 95, and 90. Find the mean score.

Solution
1. Find the sum.
   98 ⊕ 90 ⊕ 87 ⊕ 95 ⊕ 90 = 460

2. Divide by 5, the number of items.
   460 ⊘ 5 ⊜ 92

The mean score is 92.

CLASS EXERCISES

Without computing, state whether the quotient is positive, negative or zero. Explain your reasoning.

1. $-25 \div 5$　　**2.** $39 \div (-3)$　　**3.** $35 \div (-7)$　　**4.** $8 \div 3$

For each product, write a related division sentence and solve.

5. $-9 \cdot 4$　　**6.** $9(-3)$　　**7.** $-11 \cdot 11$　　**8.** $8 \cdot 3$

Find the quotient.

9. $144 \div 12$　　**10.** $55 \div 11$　　**11.** $34 \div (-17)$　　**12.** $-210 \div (-30)$

Find the mean.

13. temperatures: $-9°$, $-12°$, $9°$, $4°$, $-2°$

14. feet above and below sea level: 135, -56, 92, -29, -88, -60

15. test scores: 80, 75, 90, 88, 87

16. golf scores: 3, 5, 8, 6, 4, 5, 3, 6, 5

17. bank balance: $200, $-$85, $120, $200, $280

THINK AND DISCUSS

1. Use a related multiplication sentence to explain why you can't divide by zero.

2. Compare the signs of quotients of integers with the signs of products of integers. What do you discover?

3. Must the mean of a group of a numbers be one of the numbers in the group?

WRITTEN EXERCISES

For each quotient, write a related multiplication sentence and solve.

1. $-90 \div (-9)$　　**2.** $35 \div (-7)$　　**3.** $56 \div 8$　　**4.** $88 \div 11$

MENTAL MATH Find each quotient.

5. $-63 \div 9$ **6.** $66 \div 6$ **7.** $250 \div (-50)$ **8.** $1{,}200 \div (-40)$

CALCULATOR Find each quotient.

9. $-432 \div 48$ **10.** $693 \div 21$ **11.** $-10{,}584 \div (-84)$

12. $50{,}840 \div (-328)$ **13.** $13{,}272 \div 237$ **14.** $-62{,}937 \div (-111)$

Find each answer. Choose a method to use.

15. $48 \div 12$ **16.** $1{,}000 \div (-50)$ **17.** $-38 \div (-2)$

18. $-3{,}132 \div 36$ **19.** $24 \div (-24)$ **20.** $0 \div (-56)$

21. $225 \div (-15)$ **22.** $18 \div (-1)$ **23.** $-64 \cdot 6$

24. $-33 + 11$ **25.** $5{,}959 \div (-101)$ **26.** $-58 \div (-1)$

27. $-200 - 25$ **28.** $736 \div (-23)$ **29.** $-72 + (-8)$

30. $204 \div (-12)$ **31.** $-1{,}225 \div 35$ **32.** $0 \div (-8)$

33. $128 + (-64)$ **34.** $150 - (-15)$ **35.** $225 \cdot 15$

36. $|-56 \cdot 12| \div (-24)$ **37.** $(-|-24(9)| \div |3(-8)|)$

Write a numerical expression for each word phrase. Then evaluate the expression.

38. negative twenty-four divided by negative eight

39. negative forty-two multiplied by three

40. zero divided by negative seven

41. two hundred subtracted from negative twenty-five

Find the mean.

42. temperature: $-12°, -8°, -24°, 32°, 0°, -6°$

43. weekly allowance: \$3, \$2, \$5, \$2, \$3, \$2, \$2, \$5

44. salary: \$24,000; \$18,000; \$52,000; \$27,000; \$15,000

45. score: $-203, 813, -446, -231, 466, -155, -329, -228, 312, 1$

Write $>$, $<$, or $=$ to make a true statement.

46. $-10 \div (-2)$ ■ $25 \div (-5)$ **47.** $-(-15 \div 5)$ ■ $-100 \div (-20)$

48. $|-25| \div |-5|$ ■ $|-25 \div (-5)|$ **49.** $-|-28| \div 7$ ■ $-28 \div (-7)$

Write an integer between the given integers.

50. $-2 \cdot (-2)$ and $2 \cdot 3$ **51.** $10 + (-7)$ and $10 \div (-5)$

52. $121 \div (-11)$ and $|-7| - |7|$ **53.** $50 + (-48)$ and $80 \div (-20)$

Solve.

54. An integer multiplied by -8 equals -96. What is the integer?

MIXED REVIEW

Find each answer.

1. $5(-9)$

2. $-8(-3)$

3. $|-3| \cdot 8 \cdot (-2)$

4. $|-5 \cdot (-2) \cdot 3|$

Write the next three numbers in each pattern.

5. $-7, -2, 3, 8, ■, ■, ■$

6. $1, 4, 9, 16, ■, ■, ■$

7. Make up your own pattern. Write a rule to describe it.

55. An integer multiplied by 9 equals -135. What is the integer?

56. Find two integers with a sum of -10 and a product of -75.

57. A scuba diver descended to a depth of 50 ft in 25 s. How many feet per second did she dive?

58. ***DATA FILE 9 (pp. 360–361)*** Find the average length in yards for the first 9 holes at St. Andrew's golf course.

59. ***PROJECT*** Find the shoe sizes of ten classmates who are the same gender as you. Use the information to predict the average shoe size of students of your gender and age.

60. The grade book shows students' math scores.

Name	Test 1	Test 2	Test 3	Test 4	Test 5
Abrams, Joel	88	87	74	69	92
Adams, Sam	66	72	88	81	88
Barcos, Elena	99	91	90	95	90
Cuomo, Terri	67	70	72	71	80

LETTER GRADES

A	90 - 100
B	80 - 89
C	70 - 79
D	60 - 69
F	0 - 59

a. Find each student's average grade. Use the chart at the right to assign a letter grade.

b. What would Sam Adams have needed to score on his first test to raise his grade to a B?

> ***PROBLEM SOLVING HINT***
> Try guess and test.

TEST YOURSELF

Compare. Use >, <, or =.

1. 3 ■ -8 **2.** -10 ■ -6 **3.** -4 + 3 ■ 3 + (-4)

Find each number.

4. $|-8|$ **5.** $-|-85|$ **6.** the opposite of 12

Evaluate.

7. 3 + (-11) **8.** 12 − (-8) **9.** -9 · 5 **10.** -64 ÷ (-8)

Find the mean.

11. -4, 7, 0, -3, -2, 20 **12.** 20, 40, 25, 35, 100

Practice

CAREER

Help Wanted: Airline pilot

Minimum of two years of college required. Good health and flying aptitude a must.

For more information, write to Future Aviation Professionals of America, 4959 Massachusetts Blvd., Atlanta, GA 30337.

An airline pilot makes many calculations before, during, and after a flight. The pilot studies weather conditions to determine the safest altitude, route, and speed for the trip. To calculate takeoff speed, the pilot considers temperature, wind direction, and the weight of the plane. Support staff and equipment aid the pilot and crew.

PROJECT

Interview an airline pilot or other transportation worker. Find out how math is used in the job.

Find each sum.

1. $27 + 28$
2. $12 + (-4)$
3. $-15 + (-8)$
4. $-25 + 38$
5. $0 + (-19)$
6. $59 + (-62)$
7. $-125 + 258$
8. $278 + 179$
9. $-187 + (-147)$
10. $-26 + 38 + (-28)$
11. $99 + (-127) + 268 + (-99)$
12. $-712 + 0 + (-88)$
13. $999 + (-90) + (-9) + (-1,000)$

Find each difference.

14. $36 - 17$
15. $42 - (-21)$
16. $-44 - (-35)$
17. $-57 - 32$
18. $-48 - (-44)$
19. $0 - 62$
20. $125 - 63$
21. $-167 - 71$
22. $-214 - (-158)$
23. $-89 - (-12) - 147$
24. $268 - 188 - (-12)$
25. $-439 - 0 - 255 - 11$
26. $856 - (-327) - (-144)$

Find each product.

27. $9 \cdot 7$
28. $10 \cdot (-2)$
29. $-6 \cdot 14$
30. $-15(-4)$
31. $-18(9)$
32. $21(14)$
33. $-25 \cdot (-15)$
34. $-27 \cdot 0$
35. $-32 \cdot 28$
36. $-1 \cdot (-1) \cdot (-1) \cdot (-1)$
37. $-12 \cdot 4 \cdot 2(-3)$
38. $33 \cdot 17 \cdot 0 \cdot (-199)$
39. $-248 \cdot 4 \cdot (-2) \cdot (-250)$

Find each quotient.

40. $28 \div 4$
41. $27 \div (-3)$
42. $-35 \div (-7)$
43. $-42 \div 7$
44. $-51 \div (-17)$
45. $65 \div (-13)$
46. $-1 \div (-1) \div 1 \div (-1)$
47. $-333 \div 3 \div (-3)$
48. $0 \div 23 \div (-34) \div (-13)$
49. $444 \div 2 \div 2 \div (-3)$

Find each answer.

50. $-75 + 24$
51. $132 - (-21)$
52. $-12 \cdot 13$
53. $-96 \div (-12)$
54. $-162 - 83$
55. $316 + (-174)$
56. $19(-24)$
57. $340 \div (-17)$
58. $418 - (-319)$
59. $483 \div (-161)$
60. $-163 \cdot (-83)$
61. $-512 + 512$
62. $-48 + (-13) - 12 + (-3)$
63. $127 + (-23) - (-14) - 63$
64. $-12 \cdot 3 \cdot (-8) \div 6$
65. $24 \cdot (-5) \cdot (-4) \div 48$
66. $[12 + (-3)] \cdot (14 - 2)$
67. $(-14 + 29) \div (-12 - 3)$

1-7 *Fitness and Health*

Calories (C) measure the energy provided by the food or drink you consume. You burn calories during any activity.

> When you eat a banana, you *take in* 100 C: +100.
> When you walk for 20 min, you *burn* 100 C: -100.

Food	Calories
apple	70
banana	100
wheat bread, 1 slice	55
corn cereal, 1 c	210
muffin	70
cooked oatmeal, 1 c	130
scrambled egg	110
cheese, 1 slice	45
salad dressing, 1 c	80
mayonnaise, 1T	100
carrot	20
potato chips, 10	115
grape juice, 1 c	165
skim milk, 1 c	90
lemonade, 1 c	110
hamburger, 3 oz	245
canned tuna, 3 oz	170
chicken, 3 oz	115
frankfurter	170

Example 1 Use the graph below and the chart at the left. Find the net calories if you swim for 40 min and then drink 2 c lemonade.

Solution

$$40 \cdot (-10) = -400$$ Swimming burns 10 C/min.
$$2 \cdot 110 = 220$$ Lemonade has 110 C/c.
$$-400 + 220 = -180$$ There is a net loss of 180 C.

For a weight loss or gain program, doctors recommend a change of diet combined with an exercise program.

> To *lose* a pound, *burn* 3,500 extra calories.
> To *gain* a pound, *take in* 3,500 extra calories.

Example 2 Jo wants to gain about 1 lb per week for 10 weeks. About how many extra calories should she take in each day?

Solution $3,500 \div 7 = 500$

Jo should take in about 500 extra calories per day.

Example 3 Find the net calories if you swim for 30 min and then drink 1 c grape juice.

Solution

$$30 \cdot (-10) = -300$$ Swim for 30 min at 10 C/min.
$$+165 \, C$$ Drink 1 c grape juice.
$$-300 + 165 = -135$$ net calories

Calories used during activities

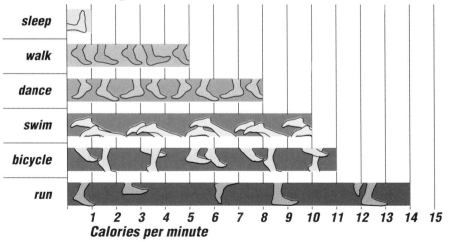

Calories per minute

CLASS EXERCISES

Use the line graph below.

1. On which days did George

    a. take in more calories than he used?

    b. use more calories than he took in?

    c. burn and take in the same number of calories?

2. Find George's net calories for the week.

    a. Did he have a net gain or a net loss of calories?

    b. If this pattern continues, how will George's weight change in a month? in a year?

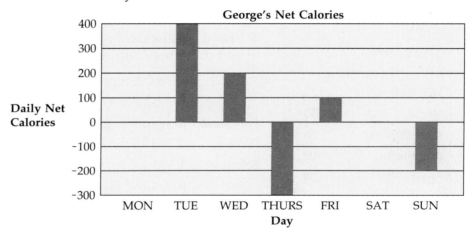

George's Net Calories

Daily Net Calories

Day

■■■■■■■ Decision Making ■ **DECISION MAKING** ■ Decision Making ■ Decision Making ■ Decision Making ■

FITNESS AND HEALTH

■ To be healthy, you must make good decisions about food and exercise. A nutritionally balanced diet and regular exercise will help you to look and feel your best.

■ **COLLECT DATA**

1. Find your normal daily intake of calories by one of the methods below.

    a. Record your daily calorie intake for a week, then find the average.

    b. Use an estimate of 16 C/lb of your weight.

    ■■ *SAMPLE* 135 lb: 135 · 16 = 2,160 C per day

2. Measure your height and weight. Look in a science book or an encyclopedia to find the ideal weight for a person your height and age.

WRITTEN EXERCISES

Use the graph and table on page 31.

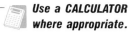

Use a CALCULATOR where appropriate.

How many calories does each food provide?

1. 2 slices of cheese
2. 2 c skim milk
3. 20 potato chips

How many calories does each activity burn?

4. bicycle 40 min
5. dance 15 min
6. sleep 8 h

Find the net calories.

7. dance 2 h, eat a tuna sandwich
8. run 20 min, eat a muffin

Solve.

9. Suppose you bicycle for an hour. About how many calories would you burn? About how many hours would it take to burn 3,500 C?

10. Juan began running 30 min each day. In order to maintain his weight, he also increased his calorie intake. How many calories should he add to his daily diet?

11. Elizabeth joined the swim team. She swims 90 min every week day. How many calories will she burn swimming each day? How many in four weeks (20 days of swimming)?

I am one of those women who has had the creative joys of a medical career. I have also had the joys of a family. I cannot think of a better way of life.

–Dr. Jane C. Wright, Associate Dean, New York Medical College

---

■ *Decision Making* ■ *Decision Making* ■ *Decision Making* ■ *Decision Making* ■ *Decision Making* ■ *Decision Making* ■

■ **ANALYZE DATA**

3. Analyze your eating habits.
   a. List the foods you eat often and the number of calories each food provides.
   b. List other healthy foods that would help balance your diet.
4. Analyze your activities.
   a. List the activities you do and the calories each activity burns.
   b. List other activities you might like to do.

■ **MAKE DECISIONS**

5. Decide on a plan to maintain or improve your health.
   a. Set a reasonable goal to gain, maintain, or lose weight.
   b. Decide how to change your eating habits and activities.

OBJECTIVE:
To assign variables
and write variable
expressions.

1-8 *Expressions and Variables*

▼ You can write a *numerical expression* to show the number of weeks in each school year if you assume a 5-day school week.

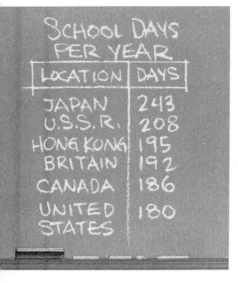

	Days Per Year		Days Per Week
Japan	243	÷	5
U.S.S.R.	208	÷	5
Hong Kong	195	÷	5
Britain	192	÷	5
Canada	186	÷	5
United States	180	÷	5

If you don't know the number of days in the school year, you can use a letter or other symbol, called a *variable,* to stand for the number. You can write a *variable expression* to show the number of weeks in the school year.

Days Per Year		Days Per Week
d	÷	5

Variable	A variable is a symbol (usually a letter) that stands for a number.

Variable Expression	A variable expression is an expression that contains at least one variable.

Example 1 Write an expression for the number of minutes in:

a. 1 hour b. 5 hours c. h hours

Solution a. $60 \cdot 1$ b. $60 \cdot 5$ c. $60h$

numerical expressions variable expression

▼ Just as we use models to stand for integers, we can use models for variable expressions. Use green rectangles for variables.

Example 2

Expression	Model
$2x$	
$3y + 3$	

▼ You can use any letter or symbol as a variable. Mathematicians often use the first letter of a word, such as *t* for time, *w* for week, or *a* for age. The most commonly used variables are x, y, z, n, a, and b.

NOTES & QUOTES
René Descartes (1596–1650) was the first to use x, y, and z as variables.

Example 3

Word Phrase	Variable Expression
a number plus nine	$y + 9$
three times a quantity decreased by four	$3z - 4$
negative one divided by a number	$-1 \div a$
the calories in two slices of toast with c calories per slice	$2c$
the cost of b books at \$5 per book	$5b$

▼ You can write variable expressions to describe situations.

Example 4   A student has several pencils in his desk. He takes out 5 pencils. Write an expression for the number of pencils left in the desk.

Solution   1. Choose a variable, say p, for the original number of pencils.

2. Then $p - 5$ is an expression for the number of pencils left in the desk.

Example 5   Suppose you study history for a different length of time each day for 3 days. Write an expression for the average amount of time you studied history each day.

Solution   1. Choose a variable, say t, for the total time spent studying for the three days.

2. Then $t \div 3$ is the average time spent each day.

THINK AND DISCUSS

1. How does the word *vary* relate to *variable*?

2. Why do you think letters of the alphabet are used as variables?

3. Describe how the expressions for each phrase differ.

• some number added to 12

• 12 equals some number

• the sum of some numbers is 12

CLASS EXERCISES

Tell whether each is a numerical expression or a variable expression. If it is a variable expression, name the variable.

1. $b + 6$ **2.** $9x$ **3.** $80 \div 8$ **4.** $14 - n$

Choose a variable and write a variable expression for each model.

5.    **6.**    **7.**

Write a variable expression for each word phrase.

8. 16 more than m **9.** y decreased by -4

10. the quotient of 6 and z **11.** the product of c and 3

Write a word phrase for each variable expression.

12. $m + 3$　　　**13.** $8 - t$　　　**14.** $-6k$　　　**15.** $t \div 12$

Write an expression for the situation.

16. The number of eggs in:

a. 1 dozen　　　**b.** 5 dozen　　　**c.** d dozen

WRITTEN EXERCISES

Choose a variable and write a variable expression for each model.

1. 　　　**2.** 　　　**3.**

Use a model to represent each variable expression.

4. $6x$　　　**5.** $y + 5$　　　**6.** $-2 + 2a$　　　**7.** $m - (-4)$

Write a numerical expression for each word phrase.

8. the quotient of fourteen and negative seven

9. the product of twenty-three and negative nine

10. four more than one thousand

11. eight less than the opposite of six

Write a variable expression for each word phrase.

12. six subtracted from k　　　**13.** m more than nineteen

14. eight less than z　　　**15.** twelve times x

16. the sum of a and b　　　**17.** n divided by negative one

18. one more than a number $3p$

19. the product of g and four times r

20. the difference of a number and three

21. the product of ten and a number

22. sixty-four decreased by a number

23. a number increased by two hundred

24. twice a number plus the absolute value of negative seven

Write two different word phrases for each variable expression.

25. $x + 2$　　　**26.** $12 - y$　　　**27.** $15 \div s$　　　**28.** $-20 + q$

29. $-5y$　　　**30.** $w - (-4)$　　　**31.** $100 + (-y)$　　　**32.** $|n| + 1$

Write an expression for each situation.

33. The number of days in:

   a. 1 week   **b.** 4 weeks   **c.** w weeks

34. The value, in cents, of:

   a. 10 pennies   **b.** 7 nickels   **c.** q quarters

35. Pam is 15 years old. Write an expression for Pam's age:

   a. 3 years ago   **b.** p years ago

   c. 10 years from now   **d.** f years from now

36. Peter has c cousins. Paul has 4 more cousins than Peter. How many cousins does Paul have?

37. Susan has $20 less than Charlotte. Charlotte has d dollars. How many dollars does Susan have?

38. There are twice as many sophomores as freshmen.

   a. If there are f freshmen, how many sophomores are there?

   b. If there are s sophomores, how many freshmen are there?

39. Richard ran b miles. Write a related situation for each expression.

   a. $b + 3$ **b.** $2b$ **c.** $10 - b$

40. A hot air balloon is at an altitude of m meters. Write a related situation for each expression.

   a. $m + 34$ **b.** $m - 2,000$ **c.** $3m$

41. Jeans sell for $25 and T-shirts sell for $12.

   a. Write a numerical expression for the selling price of 2 pairs of jeans and 4 T-shirts.

   b. Write a variable expression for the selling price of j pairs of jeans and t T-shirts.

42. *DATA* Use the calorie chart on page 31.

   a. Write a numerical expression for the number of calories in 3 eggs and a slice of wheat bread.

   b. Write a variable expression for the number of calories in e eggs and s slices of wheat bread.

Match each variable expression with a model.

43. $4x$

44. $4 + x$

45. $x \div 4$

46. $x - 4$

MIXED REVIEW

Find each answer.

1. $-10 \div 2$

2. $-120 \div (-6)$

3. $0 \div (-12)$

4. $-6 + (-17)$

5. $-20(-1)(5)$

6. $4 + (-12) + 16$

7. How much change from a five-dollar bill must the cashier give a customer who buys orange juice for $.95 and two apples for $.55 each?

Exploring Spreadsheets

■ A spreadsheet is a tool for organizing and analyzing data. The data are arranged in rows and columns. The spreadsheet below shows data for a school walkathon.

	A	B	C	D
1	Class	No. Students	Mi/Student	Tot. Distance
2	9th Grade	250	10	
3	10th Grade	234	15	
4	11th Grade	199	20	
5	12th Grade	176	20	
6			TOTAL	
7				

MATERIALS

- paper and pencil
- computer (optional)
- Math journal to record work

■ We call each section of a spreadsheet a *cell*. Cell B2 stores the value for the number of ninth-grade students who participated in the walkathon.

1. What amounts are stored in cells D2 through D5? in cell D6?

2. How are the amounts in column D found?

3. Copy the spreadsheet shown above. Use a calculator or paper and pencil to complete column D.

DATAPOINT

Cells can store numbers, letters, or a combination of letters and numbers.

■ You enter data in a spreadsheet one cell at a time. The *cursor* shows you where the next character will be entered.

4. Look at the spreadsheet above. In which cell is the cursor?

■ For a spreadsheet to perform a calculation, you need to type a formula in a cell. Look at the spreadsheet below.

	A	B	C	D
1	Type of Seat	Tickets Sold	Ticket Price	Total
2	Balcony	25	$7.50	
3	Mezzanine	34	$8.50	
4	Front row	38	$15.00	
5	Standing room	42	$4.00	
6			TOTAL	
7				

Cell D2 stores the formula B2*C2. The computer multiplies the values in cells B2 and C2 and displays the product in cell D2.

5. Write formulas for cells D3 to D5.

6. What happens if you change the value in cell B4? Which other cells will change?

■ The spreadsheet below shows test results for five students.

	A	B	C	D	E	F	G
1	Student	Test 1	Test 2	Test 3	Test 4	Test 5	Average
2	Jane C.	76	87	88	85	92	
3	Art G.	87	84	75	83	94	
4	Jose F.	95	84	78	93	92	
5	Kim C.	76	77	83	84	100	
6	Dan H.	85	91	79	78	93	
7							

One formula for G2 is (B2 + C2 + D2 + E2 + F2)/5. A shorter formula using a range of cells is Sum(B2:F2)/5.

7. Write formulas for cells G3 to G6.

8. A student wrote the formula Sum(B6:G6)/5 for G6. What is wrong with this formula? What do you think would happen if you used this formula in cell G6?

9. Suppose you drop the lowest score for each student.

   a. How will the formulas in column G change? Write the new formulas.

   b. What value should you enter in the cell that has the lowest score for each student?

   c. Use a spreadsheet to find the average when the lowest score is dropped. If you do not have a computer, use a calculator or paper and pencil.

10. *Discuss* ideas for different types of spreadsheets with the class. Make a list of your ideas.

11. *PROJECT* Create a spreadsheet using one of the ideas from Exercise 10. Use these guidelines to plan your spreadsheet.

   • Include at least five rows and four columns of data.

   • At least one row or column should involve computation using the data in the other cells.

   • The formulas in the spreadsheet should use at least two of the four basic operations.

   a. Write a list of all the formulas used in your spreadsheet. Use these operation symbols: +, −, *, /.

   b. Draw your spreadsheet on a sheet of lined paper. Show it to your class and explain how the spreadsheet is organized.

   c. Use a spreadsheet program to create your spreadsheet. Change the data for various cells to check that your formulas are correct.

DATAPOINT

Check your spreadsheet program manual to learn how to show the formula for adding across a range of cells.

OBJECTIVE:
To study order of
operations using
paper and pencil and
a calculator.

1-9 Order of Operations

▼ Suppose you spend $4 and then earn $5/h mowing lawns for 3 h. The numerical expression $-4 + 5 \cdot 3$ shows how much money you have. How do you *evaluate* this numerical expression?

$$(-4 + 5) \cdot 3 = 3 \qquad \text{or} \qquad -4 + (5 \cdot 3) = 11$$

Since you earned $15 and spent $4, you would have $11 left. The order in which you compute changes your answer.

▼ To avoid confusion and have a standard way to compute expressions with several operations, mathematicians agree on an *order of operations*.

FLASHBACK

Grouping symbols:
( ) parentheses
[ ] brackets

Order of Operations	**1.** Do all operations within grouping symbols first.
	2. Multiply or divide in order from left to right.
	3. Add or subtract in order from left to right.

▼ You can use order of operations to evaluate a numerical expression.

Example 1 Evaluate $-3 \cdot 5 - 8 \div 4 + 3$.

Solution **1.** There are no grouping symbols. So, multiply and divide from left to right.

$$-3 \cdot 5 - 8 \div 4 + 3$$

2. Add and subtract from left to right.

$$-15 - 2 + 3$$
$$-17 + 3 = -14$$

Example 2 Evaluate $3(-8 + 5) - 12$.

Solution **1.** Work in parentheses. $3(-8 + 5) - 12$

2. Multiply. $3 \ (-3) - 12$

3. Subtract. $-9 - 12 = -21$

▼ When there are two or more sets of grouping symbols, start at the inside and work out.

Example 3 Evaluate $-2[(-6 + 4) \div (3 - 5)] + 6$.

Solution **1.** Parentheses first. $-2[(-6 + 4) \div (3 - 5)] + 6$

2. Work inside brackets. $-2 \ [-2 \div (-2)] + 6$

3. Multiply. $-2 \ (1) + 6$

4. Add. $-2 + 6 = 4$

▼ Absolute value symbols are a kind of grouping symbol.

Example 4   Evaluate $-5 - |8 - (-2)|$.

Solution   **1.** Work inside the absolute $-5 - |8 - (-2)|$
value symbols.

            2. Find the absolute value. $-5 - \quad |10| \quad = -5 - 10$

            3. Subtract. $= -15$

▼ A scientific calculator follows order of operations. A standard calculator does not.

Example 5   Use a calculator to evaluate $3 \cdot 5 - 4 \div 2 + (5 + 4)$.

Solution   **Scientific calculator**

3 ⊗ 5 ⊖ 4 ÷ 2 ⊕ ((5 ⊕ 4)) ⊜ 22

Standard calculator

5 ⊕ 4 ⊜ [M+]   grouping symbols
3 ⊗ 5 ⊜ [M+]   multiplication
4 ÷ 2 ⊜ [M−]   division
[MRC] 22

THINK Why must you use the memory key with the standard calculator?

CLASS EXERCISES

Which operation would you perform first? Explain.

1. $35 \cdot 98 - 50$ **2.** $-29 - (87 + 115)$ **3.** $4(67 \div 6)$

Evaluate.

4. $2 - 6 \div 3$ **5.** $14(-6) - 12$ **6.** $|13 - 21| + 5$

7. $2(1 - 9) \cdot 9$ **8.** $7 + 3(8 \div 4)$ **9.** $[2 + (6 \cdot 8)] - 1$

THINK AND DISCUSS

Is the answer positive or negative? Explain.

1. $586 - 25 \cdot 30$

2. $(387 - 521) \cdot (-86)$

3. $-3|-5 \cdot 4|$

4. Why do we need to agree on an order of operations?

WRITTEN EXERCISES

Which operation would you perform first? Explain.

1. $14 + 15 - 10$ **2.** $-11 \div 4 + 99$ **3.** $75 \cdot 398 + |15 - 16|$

Evaluate.

4. $15 \cdot 3 - 2$ **5.** $-12 \div 4 - (-2)$ **6.** $2 + (-3) \cdot 24$

7. $|56 - 5| \div 17$ **8.** $(-21 + 15) \div (-3)$ **9.** $2 \cdot 2 + 0 \cdot (-4)$

MENTAL MATH Evaluate.

10. $12 - 8 \div 2$ **11.** $3(-8) + 4$ **12.** $6 \div (2)(-9)$

13. $3(-4) - 18$ **14.** $-21 \div 7 - (-15)$ **15.** $3(-6) + 15 \div 3$

CALCULATOR Evaluate.

16. $538 + 18 \cdot 24 - 677$ **17.** $450 \div 2 + 18$

18. $-8 - 3 \cdot 2 - (-8)$ **19.** $4 \div (-4) \cdot (-4) - (-4) + (-4)$

20. $2[8 + (3 - 5)] - 8$ **21.** $25(6 + 2)(-8) \div 4 + 6$

22. $6 \div 3 - 9 \cdot 4$ **23.** $-11 - 27 \div 9 \div (-1)$

Write an expression to match these keys on a standard calculator.

24. $5\boxed{\times}4\boxed{\div}10\boxed{+}25\boxed{\div}9\boxed{+/-}\boxed{=}\text{-}3$

25. $7\boxed{+}8\boxed{\div}5\boxed{+}5\boxed{\times}2\boxed{+/-}\boxed{=}\text{-}16$

26. How will the expressions for Exercises 24 and 25 change if you use a scientific calculator?

Compare. Use >, <, or =.

27. $8 + 12 \div (-4)$ ▨ $(8 + 12) \div (-4)$

28. $(18 - (-15)) \div (5 + 6)$ ▨ $18 - (-15) \div 5 + 6$

Insert grouping symbols to make each number sentence true.

29. $7 + 4 \cdot 6 = 66$ **30.** $7 \cdot 8 - 6 + 3 = 17$

31. $3 \cdot 8 - 2 + 5 - 12 = -3$ **32.** $2 \cdot 3 - 5 - 8 \cdot 2 + 1 = -28$

Which of the following equal 18?

33. $3 \cdot 2 + 4$ **34.** $(10 - 18) \div (-4) + (15 - (-17)) \div 2$

35. $27 - 13 \cdot 2 - 17(5 - 6)$ **36.** $16 \cdot 3 + 5 \div 5 - 18(-13)$

Solve.

37. Carmen worked 4 h on Monday and 7 h/day for the next 3 days. How many hours did she work in all?

38. Sam bought 8 CDs at $12 each and 4 tapes at $6 each. How much did he spend?

39. Alice's bowling score is 15 less than Ray's. Together, they scored 221. What did each score?

40. A cup of tomato juice has half the calories of a cup of skim milk. Together, they have 135 C. How many calories are in each?

41. Use the numbers -6, -8, 2, 4, and 6 exactly once to write a numerical expression with a value less than -100.

42. Use the digits 1–9 in order. Insert addition and subtraction signs, brackets, and parentheses to get an answer of 100.

43. Use the digits in the number of the year you were born, in order, plus operation symbols and parentheses. Write the greatest possible number and the least possible number that uses each digit exactly once.

  ▼▼ *SAMPLE* born 1966

    greatest $(1 + 9) \cdot 6 \cdot 6 = (10)(36) = 360$
    least $(1 + 9)(-6 \cdot 6) = -360$

44. *WRITE* a word problem to fit the numerical expression $3(4 + 3) + 2 \cdot 6$ and then solve.

Write and evaluate the numerical expression for each phrase.

45. five added to the product of four and nine

46. twenty-one minus the sum of fifteen and negative five

47. seventeen minus the quotient of twenty-five and five

48. one hundred divided by twenty plus the product of negative six and three

49. one hundred thirty added to the difference of one hundred sixteen and eight

50. *DATA FILE 3 (pp. 96–97)* Write a numerical expression for the value of the quarters minted each day.

Write a description of each numerical expression.

  ▼▼ *SAMPLE* The word *quantity* is a description for a grouping symbol.

The product of two and the quantity three plus four describes the numerical expression $2(3 + 4)$.

51. $2(3 + 5)$

52. $16 \div [3 - (-1)]$

53. $|4 + (-2)| \cdot (-3)$

54. $3(6 - 3) \div 9$

COMPUTER **Write using computer symbols, then evaluate.**

  ▼▼ *SAMPLE* The symbols for addition and subtraction are + and −. The multiplication symbol is an asterisk (*). The division symbol is a slash (/).

55. $74 + 5 \cdot 9 + (-7)$

56. $123 + (-5) \div (-1) + 18$

57. $70 + (8)(-9)$

58. $255 \div 5 + 117$

59. $2{,}087 \cdot 37 - 1{,}951$

60. $876 \div 12 + 13 \cdot 89$

61. *COMPUTER* Do computers follow order of operations? Use a computer to evaluate the expressions in Exercises 55–60. *Hint:* In BASIC, you use a PRINT statement such as PRINT 3*4/6 to evaluate the expression $(3 \cdot 4) \div 6$.

MIXED REVIEW

Write a variable expression.

1. the product of a number and 6

2. six less than a number

3. the sum of a number and the absolute value of -7

Complete with <, >, or =.

4. -16 ▥ -12

5. 8(-6) ▥ 48

6. 11 + (-15) ▥ -11 + 15

7. How many whole numbers between 10 and 200 have exactly two identical digits?

1-10 Evaluating Expressions

▼ Major league baseball teams use an average of 42 baseballs per game. The expression 42*g* represents the number of baseballs used in *g* games. You can *evaluate* 42*g* by replacing *g* with a number.

Suppose a team plays 50 games. Replace *g* with 50 to evaluate the expression.

$$42g = 42 \cdot 50$$
$$= 2{,}100$$

Evaluate an Expression	To evaluate an expression, replace each variable with a number. Then compute, following order of operations.

Example 1 Evaluate each expression for the given value of the variable.

    a. 12*b* for *b* = 3

    b. 4*y* − 15 for *y* = -30

Solution   **a.** $12b = 12 \cdot 3$ Use mental math.
                  $= 36$

    b. $4y - 15 = 4(-30) - 15$ Multiply first,
                $= -120 - 15$ then subtract.
                $= -135$

▼ A variable expression can have more than one variable.

Example 2 Evaluate 3*ab* − 2*c* for *a* = -2, *b* = -8, and *c* = -10.

Solution $3ab - 2c = 3(-2)(-8) - 2(-10)$ Replace each variable with
                $= 48 - (-20)$ a number.
                $= 68$ Follow order of operations.

▼ You can write and evaluate expressions to solve problems.

Example 3 Bob sells magazine subscriptions. He earns $20 per week plus $2 for each subscription he sells.

    a. Write an expression for his weekly earnings.

    b. Find Bob's weekly earnings if he sells 14 subscriptions.

Solution   **a.** Let *s* stand for the number of subscriptions. Then 20 + 2*s* is an expression for Bob's weekly earnings.

    b. $20 + 2(14) = 20 + 28$ Replace *s* with 14.
                    $= 48$

Bob earns $48 by selling 14 subscriptions in a week.

CLASS EXERCISES

Evaluate each expression for $x = 2$, $y = -3$, and $z = 10$.

1. $x + 5$ **2.** $16 - z$ **3.** $4y$ **4.** $-8 \div x$

5. $2z - 4$ **6.** $x - z$ **7.** $y + 5y$ **8.** $x \div 2 + (-9)$

9. xyz **10.** $8y \div x$ **11.** $3z - |x|$ **12.** $(z + x) \div y$

Solve.

13. A stenographer types 55 words/min. How many words does the stenographer type in m min? in 20 min?

14. An appliance repair center charges a \$25 flat fee plus a fee of \$10/h for labor. Find the cost of an oven repair that takes 3 h.

THINK AND DISCUSS

1. When is $6x$ positive? negative?

2. When is $-a + 12$ equal to zero?

3. José has 10 more books than Barbara. Barbara has 18 books. Does José have 8 books or 28 books? Explain.

4. Karen has 4 fewer tropical fish than Aaron. Aaron has 8 fish. Does Karen have 4 fish or 12 fish? Explain.

WRITTEN EXERCISES

Evaluate each expression for the given values of the variables.

1. $-12a$ for $a = 2$ **2.** $x - 6$ for $x = -16$

3. $2a + 5$ for $a = -5$ **4.** $-z$ for $z = 7$

5. $|a| + (-17)$ for $a = 5$ **6.** $|n - 10|$ for $n = -4$

7. $-6 \div a + 8$ for $a = -2$ **8.** $19 - (a - 4)$ for $a = 8$

9. $-3ab$ for $a = 1$, $b = -7$ **10.** $16 - 4mn$ for $m = 0$, $n = -3$

11. $4a - b$ for $a = 3$, $b = 5$ **12.** $3(a + b)$ for $a = 7$, $b = 9$

13. $2|a - b|$ for $a = 9$, $b = 19$ **14.** $(x - y) \div (-4)$ for $x = 52$, $y = 12$

MENTAL MATH Evaluate each expression for the given values of the variables.

15. $-7b$ for $b = 5$ **16.** $5 - b$ for $b = 4$

17. $-3b$ for $b = -7$ **18.** $x - 8$ for $x = 10$

19. $41 - 4b$ for $b = 10$ **20.** $5a + 7$ for $a = 20$

CALCULATOR Evaluate each expression for the given values of the variables.

21. $5m$ for $m = 85$ **22.** $-48 + n$ for $n = 933$

23. $-288 \div c$ for $c = -16$ **24.** $6ab$ for $a = 17$, $b = -21$

25. $7a - 13b$ for $a = 0$, $b = -9$ **26.** $5y - 5$ for $y = -178$

Find a value for each variable that makes the statement true.

27. $n > 1$ **28.** $n < -7$ **29.** $|n| = 8$ **30.** $3n = 12$

31. $n + 6 = 0$ **32.** $-4n = -4$ **33.** $3 + n = 3$ **34.** $n + 5 < 9$

35. Find a value of x for which $4x$ and $x + 9$ are equal.

36. Find values of a and b such that $a + b$ is 12 and $a - b$ is 16.

Solve.

37. Every minute about 265 babies are born in the world.

   a. Write an expression for the number of babies born in m min.

   b. CALCULATOR About how many babies are born in 6 min?

   c. CALCULATOR About how many babies are born in one day?

38. CALCULATOR The fastest speed of a sailfish is 68 mi/h.

   a. Write an expression for the number of miles a sailfish travels in h hours swimming at 68 mi/h.

   b. How many miles would a sailfish travel swimming for 3 h at 68 mi/h?

39. DATA Use the chart on page 31 to find how many calories are used per minute in running.

   a. Write an expression for the number of calories used in running m min.

   b. How many calories are used in running 25 min?

40. A carnival charges a $3 admission fee plus $1 per ride.

   a. Write an expression for the cost of riding r rides.

   b. Find the cost of riding 6 rides.

   c. How many rides can you afford if you have $10 to spend?

41. A club requires a $100 initiation fee and $25 each month. Find the cost of a one-year membership in the club.

Copy and complete.

42.

x	$x + 5$
0	5
1	▦
2	▦
5	▦
▦	20

43.

n	$6n$
1	▦
2	▦
-2	▦
6	▦
▦	24

44.

a	$10 - a$
0	▦
5	▦
10	▦
15	▦
▦	-10

45. Evaluate $1 + 2 + 3 + 4 + \ldots + n$ for $n = 10$.

46. Evaluate each number in the pattern $1n, 2n, 3n, 4n, \ldots 10n$ for $n = 2$. **WRITE** a description of the pattern.

47. Find the length of each red segment for $x = 8$.

   a.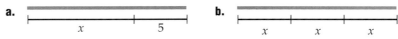
         x 5

   b.
         x x x

MIXED REVIEW

Evaluate.

1. $3(-9) - 27$

2. $3 \cdot 4 \div (-2) \cdot 8$

3. $3 \cdot (-7) + 2 \cdot 8$

4. $4[2 \cdot (3 - 6)]$

Write a word phrase for each expression.

5. $6 + x$

6. $2(n - 2)$

7. $-12y$

8. Valerie has test grades of 97, 82, 78, and 75. What is her test average?

Problem Solving Practice

READ
PLAN
SOLVE
LOOK BACK

PROBLEM SOLVING STRATEGIES

Look for a Pattern
Guess and Test
Simplify the Problem
Account for all Possibilities
Make an Organized List
Work Backwards
Make a Table
Write an Equation
Solve by Graphing
Draw a Diagram
Make a Model
Simulate the Problem

The aurora borealis, or northern lights, occurs above the thermosphere.

Solve. The list at the left shows some possible strategies you can use.

1. Marjorie opened a savings account with $100 at the beginning of January. The table shows the interest earned each month for four months.

Month	Interest	Balance
January	$1.00	$101.00
February	$1.01	$102.01
March	$1.02	$103.03
April	$1.03	$104.06

   a. Describe the pattern for the values under the interest column.

   b. Use the pattern to extend the table for the next four months.

2. Particles have a positive charge, a negative charge, or no charge at all.

   a. How much charge do these particles have?

   b. How would you show a charge of -7?

   c. Opposite charges cancel each other out. What is the total amount of charge when 12 negative charges combine with 24 positive charges?

3. The stratosphere is higher in altitude than the troposphere, but not as high as the thermosphere. The mesosphere is just below the thermosphere. Arrange these regions in order from the highest altitude to the lowest.

4. **DATA FILE 9 (pp. 360–361)** The chart below shows a golfer's score at St. Andrew's golf course. Complete the third row.

Hole	1	2	3	4	5	6	7	8	9
Score	5	5	3	3	2	3	5	5	6
Par									

   Is the total score above or below par? by how much?

5. **DATA FILE 1 (pp. 2–3)** Suppose the temperature was $-15°F$. The wind speed changed from 5 mi/h to 20 mi/h. Find the change in wind chill temperature.

6. Jeff earns $1,200 more than his brother. Together they earn $65,200. How much does each earn?

Chapter 1 Review

Complete each statement. Use the vocabulary words given.

1. Parentheses, brackets, and the absolute value symbol are ▧ that help you determine ▧.

2. The ▧ of an integer is the same distance from zero on a number line as the integer, but in the opposite direction.

3. The whole numbers, their opposites, and zero form the ▧.

4. The ▧ of an integer is its distance from zero on a number line.

5. A ▧ is an expression that contains at least one ▧.

6. The ▧ is an average.

VOCABULARY

integers
variable
opposite
variable expression
absolute value
order of operations
mean
grouping symbols

Comparing Integers 1-1

To compare integers, think of the number line. The integer farther to the right is the greater integer.

Compare. Use <, >, or =.

7. −7 ▧ −9   **8.** 0 ▧ −3   **9.** |−5| ▧ |5| **10.** −6 ▧ 2   **11.** −4 ▧ −(−5)   **12.** |−3| ▧ 1

Adding Integers and Subtracting Integers 1-2, 1-3

To add integers with the *same* sign, *add* the absolute values of the integers. The sum has the same sign as the addends. To add integers with *different* signs, *subtract* the absolute values of the integers. The sum has the sign of the integer with the greater absolute value. To subtract an integer, add its opposite.

Add or subtract.

13. 8 + (−15)   **14.** −9 + 21   **15.** −15 − (−6)   **16.** 9 − (−5)   **17.** −8 − 4

18. 32 − 48   **19.** −62 − (−59) − 24   **20.** 14 + (−9) + (−20)   **21.** −4 + 12 + (−3) + (−6)

Multiplying and Dividing Integers 1-5, 1-6

To multiply or divide integers, multiply or divide the absolute values of the integers. If the integers have the *same* sign, the product or quotient is *positive*. If the integers have *different* signs, the product or quotient is *negative*.

Multiply or divide.

22. 7(−6)   **23.** 250 ÷ (−50)   **24.** (−9)(−8)   **25.** −56 ÷ (−8)   **26.** −120 ÷ 40   **27.** −15(11)

Translating Word Phrases

To translate word phrases to algebraic expressions, look for key words that indicate operations.

addition (more than, sum)   subtraction (difference, less than)
multiplication (times, product)   division (quotient, ratio)

Write an algebraic expression for each phrase.

28. twenty-five less than x **29.** the product of n and $3r$ **30.** two more than y

Using Order of Operations

To evaluate numerical expressions:

1. Do all operations within grouping symbols first.

2. Multiply and divide from left to right.

3. Add and subtract from left to right.

Evaluate.

31. $7 + 2 \cdot 28 - 3 \cdot 9$ **32.** $9 \cdot 5 - 4(18 \div 6)$ **33.** $3 \cdot 8 - 6 + 49 \div 7$

34. $3 \cdot 7 + 6 \div 2$ **35.** $|-5 + 6| \cdot |3|$ **36.** $4 + 8 \div 2 \cdot 0$

Evaluating Algebraic Expressions

To evaluate an algebraic expression, substitute a number for the variable(s), and simplify. Follow order of operations.

Evaluate.

37. $3x + 4$ for $x = 5$ **38.** $10 - n$ for $n = 4$ **39.** $|y - 6| + 8$ for $y = -2$

40. $|m - 7|$ for $m = -7$ **41.** $15t \cdot 10$ for $t = -3$ **42.** $z + 3z$ for $z = 4$

Problem Solving

To solve a problem, use a pattern.

Use a pattern to solve.

43. To run a classified ad for 7 days costs $28 for 4 lines. Each additional line costs $10.50. What is the cost of a 12-line ad?

44. The graph at the right gives Sue's net calories for this week. If Sue continues to eat as she did this week, will she gain or lose weight in a month?

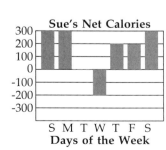

Chapter 1 Review   **49**

Write an integer.

1. opposite of 7   **2.** opposite of -9   **3.** |-5| **4.** |12|

Compare. Use <, >, or =.

5. -6 ▥ -5   **6.** 8 ▥ -10   **7.** -3 ▥ 3   **8.** 0 ▥ -7

Find each answer.

9. 15 + (-7)   **10.** -8 − (-12)   **11.** -9(-7)   **12.** 54 ÷ (-6)

13. -6 · 48   **14.** -56 ÷ (-7)   **15.** 119 − (-24)   **16.** -47 + (-21)

17. -83 + (-17) + 13   **18.** 5 · (-12) · (-3) · (-1)   **19.** 420 ÷ (-6) ÷ 7 ÷ (-2)

20. 8 · 6 ÷ (2 + 1)   **21.** 4 + 7 · 2 + 8   **22.** 4(11 + 7) − 9 · 8

23. 29 − 2 · 3(9 − 4) ÷ 6   **24.** 16 − 2 · 5 + 3 − 6   **25.** |14 − (-9)|2

Write an expression for each word phrase.

26. ten less than the absolute value of negative three

27. the product of x and negative five

28. a number increased by nineteen

29. the opposite of the quantity five more than y

Evaluate each expression for the given values of the variables.

30. $3a + 5$ for $a = -5$

31. $5m + 9 + 7n$ for $m = 8$, $n = 1$

32. $3|x − y| + x$ for $x = 1$, $y = 8$

33. $20 − 2(a − b)$ for $a = 3$, $b = 2$

Solve.

34. A submarine was at a depth of 250 m below sea level. It rose 75 m. Use an integer to describe the new depth of the submarine.

35. **DATA** Use the chart on page 31 to solve. John went swimming for $\frac{1}{2}$ h and cycling for an hour. He then ate two 3-oz hamburgers on wheat bread, and an apple, and drank 1 c of grape juice. Find his net calories.

36. You are in an elevator on the seventh floor. Go down 4 floors. Go up 8 floors. Go down 3 floors. Go up 9 floors. Following this pattern, what floor will you be on if the elevator goes down again and you get off?

37. A shirt costs $15 and jeans cost $25.

   a. Write an expression for the cost of j jeans and s shirts.

   b. Find the cost of 3 pairs of jeans and 5 shirts.

   c. How many pairs of jeans can you buy for $60?

Chapter 1   Cumulative Review

Choose the correct answer. Write A, B, C, or D.

1. What makes $-1 >$ ▓ true?

  A. -2 **B.** 1

  C. 0 **D.** not given

2. $7 + (-12)$

  A. 5 **B.** -19

  C. -5 **D.** not given

3. $|-10|$

  A. -10 **B.** $\frac{1}{10}$

  C. 10 **D.** not given

4. What is the variable expression for five less than $3n$?

  A. $5 - 3n$ **B.** $3(n - 5)$

  C. $3n - 5$ **D.** not given

5. $1, 2, 3, 5, 8, 13, \ldots$

  A. 13 **B.** 20

  C. 16 **D.** not given

6. $-9(-7)$

  A. 63 **B.** -16

  C. -63 **D.** not given

7. DATA Use the chart on page 31. How many calories are burned walking 2 h?

  A. 10 calories   **B.** 600 calories

  C. 300 calories   **D.** not given

8. Name the integer represented by the point on the number line.

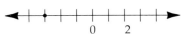

  A. 3 **B.** -3

  C. -4 **D.** not given

9. $210 \div (-3)$

  A. -7 **B.** -70

  C. -63 **D.** not given

10. $-8 - (-6)$

  A. -14 **B.** -2

  C. 2 **D.** not given

11. Evaluate $6x - 9$ for $x = 2$.

  A. -21 **B.** 3

  C. 12 **D.** not given

12. Which operation would you perform first? $12 \div 4(3 - 5)$

  A. division   **B.** subtraction

  C. multiplication   **D.** not given

13. What is the opposite of 8?

  A. -8 **B.** $\frac{1}{8}$

  C. 8 **D.** not given

14. Evaluate $-10 \div |-2 + 3|$.

  A. 8 **B.** 10

  C. -2 **D.** not given

15. $-15 + (-3)$

  A. -5 **B.** -20

  C. 5 **D.** not given

16. Give the number sentence for the number line.

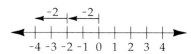

  A. $-2 + 2 = 0$ **B.** $2 - (-2) = 4$

  C. $-2 + (-2) = -4$ **D.** not given

RING THOSE BELS

The *bel*, named after Alexander Graham Bell, is a unit for measuring sound intensity. Ten bels equal one *decibel* (db).

	db	
db above 192 cause shock waves	190	
	180	
	170	some motorized toys
	160	
prolonged noise causes permanent deafness	150	rocket launch
	140	threshold of pain
sound levels above 90 are banned in factories	130	
	120	race cars, amplified rock band
	110	jet planes
	100	
	90	
	80	loud music, subway train
	70	snoring, telephone ring
	60	
safe range of sound intensity	50	loud conversation
	40	typewriter
	30	human speech
	20	whisper
	10	
	0	
below the threshold of human hearing	−10	

SONAR

(sound navigation and ranging) is a method that uses sound to locate underwater objects. A sonar device emits a sharp pulse of sound, which is reflected back when it hits an object. You can find the distance to the object by measuring the time it takes the sound to return. You can use a formula to find the distance.

Let s = the speed of sound
t = the time for the sound to strike the object and return

Then $\frac{ts}{2} = d$ is a formula to find the distance to an object.

Commercial fishing boats use sonar to detect schools of fish.

Solving Equations

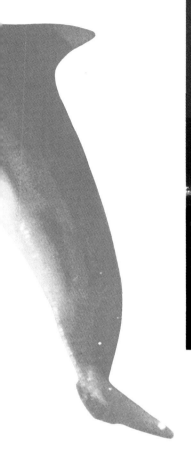

THUNDER is a shock wave produced by a lightning flash. Because light (299,460 km/s) travels faster than sound (346 m/s), you see lightning before you hear thunder. To determine how far away lightning is, you can count the seconds between the lightning flash and the thunder, then multiply by 346.

Think about it...

Look at the data about the speed of sound. What factors do you think determine the speed of sound in a given substance?

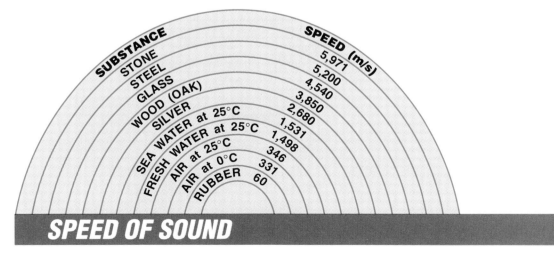

SUBSTANCE	SPEED (m/s)
STONE	5,971
STEEL	5,200
GLASS	4,540
WOOD (OAK)	3,850
SILVER	2,680
SEA WATER at 25°C	1,531
FRESH WATER at 25°C	1,498
AIR at 25°C	346
AIR at 0°C	331
RUBBER	60

SPEED OF SOUND

Variables and Equations

▼ A deep sea diver weighs 135 lb. When she puts on her diving equipment she weighs 165 lb. Let the variable w represent the weight of the equipment. You can write an *equation* to show this relationship.

$$135 + w = 165$$

Equation	An equation is a mathematical sentence with an equal sign.

THINK What is the difference between an expression and an equation?

▼ There are many types of equations.

Example 1
  a. $9 + 2 = 11$ a numerical expression equal to a numerical expression

  b. $x + 7 = 37$ a variable expression equal to a numerical expression

  c. $a + (-3) = 2a + 5$ a variable expression equal to a variable expression

▼ An equation can be true or false.

Example 2   This is a true equation.   This is a false equation.

     $6 + 12 = 18$ $6 = 4 + 3$

▼ Some equations are neither true nor false. They are called *open equations*.

Open Equation	An open equation is an equation that contains one or more variables.

Example 3   These are open equations.

    a. $c + 9 = 24$ **b.** $6x = -3 + 5x$

▼ You can replace a variable with a number to determine whether the number is a *solution* of the open equation.

Solution	A solution is a number that replaces a variable to make an open equation true.

Example 4   Is 30 a solution of the open equation $170 + x = 200$?

Solution
$$170 + x = 200$$
$$170 + 30 = 200 \quad \text{Replace } x \text{ with 30.}$$
$$200 = 200 \quad \text{True, so 30 is a solution.}$$

Example 5   Is 17 a solution of the open equation $9 = y - 10$?

Solution
$$9 = y - 10$$
$$9 = 17 - 10 \quad \text{Replace } y \text{ with 17.}$$
$$9 = 7 \quad \text{False, so 17 is not a solution.}$$

▼
THINK Find a solution to the equation $9 = y - 10$ using mental math.

▼ You can write a sentence as an equation.

Example 6   **Write an equation for the sentence. Identify the equation as true, false, or open.**

Nine times the opposite of five is forty-five.

Solution $9 \cdot (-5) = 45$ This is a false equation.

FLASHBACK

The phrases *is equal to*, *equals*, and *is* denote the equal sign.

CLASS EXERCISES

Write true or false.

1. An equation can be false.
2. An open equation is true.
3. $3w - 7$ is an open equation.
4. An open equation must contain a variable.
5. $4 + 2x = 12$ is an equation.
6. An expression contains an equal sign.

State whether each equation is true, false, or open.

7. $15 = 3 \cdot 5$
8. $4x - 8 = 25$
9. $3(-9) = -36 + 6$

Replace c with -2. State whether the equation is true or false.

10. $c + 5 = 3$
11. $24 = 2c + 29$
12. $c \div 2 - 8 = 3(-3)$

Is 7 a solution of each equation?

13. $d + 4 = 12$
14. $-12 = -2d + 2$
15. $y - 2 = y - 2$

THINK AND DISCUSS

1. Name one similarity between a sentence and an equation.
2. Can an expression be true or false? Why or why not?
3. Can zero be a solution to the equation $1 \div x = 2$? Why or why not?

NOTES & QUOTES

Robert Recorde (ca. 1510–1558) first used the equal sign as we know it in *The Whetstone of Witte*, which was published in 1557. He chose two parallel line segments of equal length because he believed that no two things could be more equal.

FLASHBACK

Order of operations:

1. Do all operations within grouping symbols.

2. Multiply and divide from left to right.

3. Add and subtract from left to right.

WRITTEN EXERCISES

State whether each is an equation.

1. $10 = 5 + x$

2. $2c + 6$

3. $3(-4) = 12$

4. $-3 + 6b$

State whether each equation is true, false, or open.

5. $4c - 12 = 20$

6. $18 = -3(-6)$

7. $36 \div 6 + 1 = 5 + 3$

8. $6[-3 - (-5)] = 2(-4 + 10)$

9. $-24(-3 + 3) = 18(4 - 2)$

10. $-9 + x = 50 \div 10 + 3$

Replace y with 5. State whether the equation is true or false.

11. $-5 + y = 0$

12. $-2y - 3 = 7$

13. $-11 = 4 - 3y$

14. $2(y - 5) = 5 - y$

Replace each variable with the given number. State whether the equation is true or false.

15. $20 - c = 12; c = 8$

16. $8 = 2a + 3; a = 0$

17. $-x - 5 = -(-6); x = 1$

18. $3 - w = 2w + 12; w = -3$

19. $3b \div 18 = 2; b = 12$

20. $2(-4g) = 10 \cdot 5 - 2; g = -6$

Is 2 a solution of each equation?

21. $4 + d = 6$

22. $12 = 26 \div x$

23. $4b - 9 = 8b - 17$

24. $4(-8 + t) = 5t - 32$

Is the given number a solution of the equation?

25. $3a = 12 + a; a = 6$

26. $-6w = -2w + 32; w = -11$

27. $2m = m + 6; m = 4$

28. $2x \div 5 = 2(10 - 5); x = 25$

29. $-4c = 6 - c; c = -2$

30. $9 - 3y = 2y + 24; y = -3$

CALCULATOR **Which of the numbers $-2, 0, 2, 4, 6$ is a solution?**

31. $253a = 0$

32. $259 = 261 - a$

33. $20 - 114z = 248$

34. $53m + 106 = 53(m + 2)$

35. $10(-2 + x) = 10x \div 2$

36. $-21x + 129 = 3(-100 + 101)$

MENTAL MATH **Is the solution greater than or less than zero?**

37. $-3x = -15$

38. $-5 + y = -35$

39. $-27 \div a = 9$

40. $-3 = y + 17$

41. $x + 25 = 50$

42. $-2 \cdot (-6) = -3a$

State which of the numbers listed are sensible replacements for the variable.

43. Let p represent the number of passengers on a fifty-passenger school bus. Can p be 30? $27\frac{1}{2}$? -5? 48?

44. Let c represent the amount of change equal to one dollar. Can c be 5 quarters? 10 dimes? 100 pennies? 17 nickels?

45. Let d represent the day of the month. Can d be 15? 56? 28? 0?

Write an equation for the sentence. Identify the equation as true, false, or open.

46. Four times the opposite of five equals negative twenty.

47. Zero times negative seven is negative seven.

48. Negative twelve divided by negative four is equal to three.

49. The sum of fifteen and a number n is fifty.

50. The product of negative twenty and nine is negative eleven.

51. The sum of negative seven and twelve equals negative five.

52. The difference of twenty-five and negative fifteen equals the sum of negative fifteen and twenty-five.

53. *DATA FILE 3 (pp. 96–97)* Three sheets of paper times the number of bills per sheet is equal to ninety-six.

54. *DATA FILE 3 (pp. 96–97)* The value of 1940 proof set in 1965 equals the value of a 1955 proof set in 1990, minus twenty.

55. *WRITE* Sentences are similar to equations.

   a. The sentence *Abraham Lincoln was an American president* is a true sentence. Write two true sentences.

   b. The sentence *Eleanor Roosevelt was an American president* is a false sentence. Write two false sentences.

   c. The sentence *He is a professional baseball player* is an open sentence. It is not clear to whom the word *he* refers. Write two open sentences.

56. Write an equation relating the number of tickets (t) to the number of dollars (d).

tickets	1	2	3	t
dollars	5	10	15	d

57. Write an equation relating the number of flowers (f) to the number of bouquets (b).

flowers	13	26	39	f
bouquets	1	2	3	b

2-2 Properties of Operations

▼ Stephanie won 6 tennis games in the first set and 4 games in the second set. Marcia won 4 games in the first set and 6 in the second set. Each won 10 games.

You can add 6 and 4 in any order and still get the same sum. This suggests the following property.

Commutative Property of Addition	You can add in any order without changing the sum.
	Arithmetic **Algebra**
	$6 + 4 = 4 + 6$ $a + b = b + a$

▼ You can also change the grouping of numbers before you add them. You may want to regroup numbers to add mentally.

FLASHBACK

We use parentheses to show which numbers to add first.

Example 1 Carlos rented golf clubs for $7 and a golf cart for $8. He paid a greens fee of $12. Here are two ways he can calculate how much money he spent.

    a. $(7 + 8) + 12 = 15 + 12$
                     $= 27$

    b. $7 + (8 + 12) = 7 + 20$
                     $= 27$

No matter how you group the numbers, the sum is 27.

▼ The mathematical name for the grouping property is the associative property.

Associative Property of Addition	You can change the grouping and then add without changing the sum.
	Arithmetic **Algebra**
	$(3 + 7) + 2 = 3 + (7 + 2)$ $(a + b) + c = a + (b + c)$

▼ You can also use the commutative and associative properties to multiply.

Commutative Property of Multiplication	You can multiply in any order without changing the product.
	Arithmetic **Algebra**
	$8 \cdot 4 = 4 \cdot 8$ $a \cdot b = b \cdot a$

Associative Property of Multiplication	You can change the grouping and then multiply without changing the product.
	Arithmetic $\quad$ **Algebra**
	$(7 \cdot 3)2 = 7(3 \cdot 2) \quad (ab)c = a(bc)$

▼ You can use the commutative and associative properties to write equivalent expressions.

Example 2
    a. $5 \cdot 7 = 7 \cdot 5$ commutative property

    b. $(5 + 4) + 9 = 5 + (4 + 9)$ associative property

    c. $7 + a = a + 7$ commutative property

    d. $5(xy) = (5x)y$ associative property

▼ Properties are helpful when adding or multiplying mentally.

Example 3   **Use mental math to evaluate 81 + 6 + 9.**

Solution
$$
\begin{aligned}
81 + 6 + 9 &= 81 + 9 + 6 \\
&= (81 + 9) + 6 \quad \text{associative property} \\
&= (90) + 6 \quad\quad\ \text{Add.} \\
&= 96
\end{aligned}
$$

THINK How do reordering and regrouping help you to add mentally?

▼ There are *identity* elements for addition and multiplication. You can compute with an identity element without changing the value of a number.

Additive Identity	The additive identity is zero.
	Arithmetic $\quad$ **Algebra**
	$12 + 0 = 12 \quad a + 0 = a$

THINK How could you model the additive identity using algebra tiles?

Multiplicative Identity	The multiplicative identity is one.
	Arithmetic $\quad$ **Algebra**
	$10 \cdot 1 = 10 \quad a \cdot 1 = a$

Example 4   **Use mental math to find the missing value.**

    a. $5 + \blacksquare = 5$ **b.** $9 \cdot \blacksquare = 9$

Solution
    a. $5 + 0 = 5$ When you add zero, the value does not change.

    b. $9 \cdot 1 = 9$ When you multiply by one, the value does not change.

THINK AND DISCUSS

1. Does the commutative property apply to subtraction? to division? Use examples to support your answers.

2. Does the associative property apply to subtraction? to division? Use examples to support your answer.

CLASS EXERCISES

State which property is shown.

1. $\square + 6 = 6 + \square$

2. $0 + 8 = 8$

3. $\triangle + s = s + \triangle$

4. $(5x)y = 5(xy)$

5. $999 \cdot 1 = 999$

6. $\blacksquare \cdot \triangle = \triangle \cdot \blacksquare$

What numbers would you combine first to evaluate mentally?

7. $5 + 36 + 95$

8. $5 \cdot 17 \cdot 2$

9. $50 \cdot 2 \cdot 43$

MENTAL MATH Evaluate.

10. $10 \cdot 13 \cdot 10$

11. $23 + 15 + 85$

12. $25 + 157 + 75$

13. $5 \cdot 20 \cdot 66$

14. $140 + 17 + 60$

15. $30 \cdot 30 \cdot 6$

MIXED REVIEW

Is each equation true, false, or open?

1. $5 = 2 - (-3)$

2. $7 = a + 4$

For $w = -5$, is each equation true?

3. $9w = 45$

4. $|w - 8| = 13$

5. $2(w + 7) = -4$

6. $w + 0 = w$

Use ( ), +, −, · to write a true equation.

7. 3 4 7 6 = -3

Solve.

8. Mrs. Laurel has two sons. The product of their ages is 36 and the sum is 13. How old is each son?

WRITTEN EXERCISES

Match each equation with the property illustrated.

1. $a \cdot 1 = 1 \cdot a$

2. $\triangle + \blacktriangle = \blacktriangle + \triangle$

3. $(6x)y = 6(xy)$

4. $(6 + 5) + x = 6 + (5 + x)$

5. $6 \cdot 1 = 6$

6. $5 + 8 = 8 + 5$

7. $(3 \cdot 4)\blacksquare = 3(4 \cdot \blacksquare)$

8. $(3 + 2)(4 + 5) = (4 + 5)(3 + 2)$

9. $ab = ba$

10. $999 + 0 = 999$

a. commutative property of addition

b. associative property of addition

c. commutative property of multiplication

d. associative property of multiplication

e. additive identity

f. multiplicative identity

Use the commutative property to write an equivalent expression.

11. $25z$

12. $n + 2$

13. $(a + b)5$

14. $(a + b)(c + d)$

Use the associative property to write an equivalent expression.

15. $(3 \cdot 25) \cdot 4$

16. $34 + (16 + 35)$

17. $(4a)b$

Use the commutative and associative properties to evaluate.

18. $725 + 563 + 275$

19. $250 \cdot 47 \cdot 4$

20. $200 + 423 + 800$

21. $5 \cdot 20 \cdot 28$

22. $5 \cdot 11 \cdot 20 \cdot 3$

23. $79 + 17 + 1 + 3$

What numbers would you combine first to evaluate mentally?

24. $5 \cdot 79 \cdot 20$ **25.** $3 + 7 + 67$ **26.** $10 \cdot 37 \cdot 10$

27. $730 + 693 + 270$ **28.** $5 \cdot 50 \cdot 20 \cdot 2$

MENTAL MATH Evaluate.

29. $35 + 15 + 8$ **30.** $25 \cdot 4 \cdot 8$ **31.** $42 + 17 - 2 + 3$

32. $125 + 18 + 75 + 162$ **33.** $4 \cdot 6 \cdot 25 \cdot 50 \cdot 2$

WRITE Explain your answer to each question below.

34. a. Can you use the commutative property of addition with $4 + 2$ to evaluate the expression $3 \cdot 4 + 2 \div (\text{-}2)$?

  b. Can you use the commutative property of multiplication?

35. a. Can you use the associative property of addition with $\text{-}4 + 20 + 30$ to evaluate $6 \cdot 5 \cdot (\text{-}4) + 20 + 30 \div 5$?

  b. Can you use the associative property of multiplication?

Use the article below to answer each question.

A Fair Fare in Alaska

Railroads are a popular means of transportation in Alaska. The *Anchorage-Fairbanks Express* is a major line that travels 356 mi from Anchorage to Fairbanks.

A one-way coach fare for the $11\frac{1}{2}$-h trip is $98. A first-class fare is $140. Because of long hours of daylight in summer, passengers are sure to get their money's worth and not miss out on any of Alaska's beautiful wilderness and wildlife.

36. a. How much would it cost a family of four to travel first class when traveling round trip from Anchorage to Fairbanks? How much money could they save if they went coach?

  b. The *Anchorage-Fairbanks Express* departed Fairbanks at 11:26 A.M. At what time will it arrive in Anchorage?

2-3 *The Distributive Property*

▼ Two rectangles, each having the same width but different lengths, are placed end to end. Find the total area.

Method 1 Placing the rectangles end to end forms one large rectangle. The length is (6 + 8) and the width is 4.

total area = 4(6 + 8)
= 4(14)
= 56

Method 2 You can find the area of each individual rectangle and then add the areas together.

6	8
4 **A**	4 **B**
Area **A** = 4·6	Area **B** = 4·8

total area = area A + area B
= 24 + 32
= 56

The total area is the same no matter how you do the calculation. Therefore, the expression 4(6 + 8) has the same value as the expression 24 + 32. This illustrates the *distributive property*.

THINK Why does $a(b + c) = (b + c)a$?

Distributive Property of Multiplication over Addition	You can distribute a factor to each term inside a set of parentheses.
	Arithmetic 3(2 + 6) = 3 · 2 + 3 · 6 (2 + 6)3 = 2 · 3 + 6 · 3
	Algebra $a(b + c) = ab + ac$ $(b + c)a = ba + ca$

Example 1 Evaluate 9(5 + 2) using the distributive property.

Solution 9(5 + 2) = 9 · 5 + 9 · 2   Distribute 9.
= 45 + 18   Multiply and add.
= 63

▼ You can also use the distributive property with subtraction.

THINK Why does $a(b - c) = (b - c)a$?

Distributive Property of Multiplication over Subtraction	You can distribute a factor to each term inside a set of parentheses.
	Arithmetic 6(7 − 4) = 6 · 7 − 6 · 4 (7 − 4)6 = 7 · 6 − 4 · 6
	Algebra $a(b - c) = ab - ac$ $(b - c)a = ba - ca$

Example 2 Evaluate $(3 - 1)6$ using the distributive property.

Solution $(3 - 1)6 = 3 \cdot 6 - 1 \cdot 6$ Distribute 6.
$\qquad\qquad\quad = 18 - 6$ Multiply and subtract.
$\qquad\qquad\quad = 12$

▼ You can use the distributive property in reverse.

Example 3 Write $5 \cdot 3 + 5 \cdot 7$ using the distributive property.

Solution $5 \cdot 3 + 5 \cdot 7$ 5 multiplies 3 and 5 multiplies 7.
$\qquad\quad 5(3 + 7)$ 5 multiplies (3 + 7).

▼ You can use the distributive property to multiply mentally and solve word problems.

Example 4 Use the distributive property to evaluate 20(102) mentally.

Solution $20(102) = 20(100 + 2)$ Think of 102 as (100 + 2)
$\qquad\qquad\quad = 20 \cdot 100 + 20 \cdot 2$ Distribute 20.
$\qquad\qquad\quad = 2{,}000 + 40$ Multiply and add.
$\qquad\qquad\quad = 2{,}040$

Example 5 The PTA sold 397 tickets for their annual pancake breakfast. Each patron will receive four pancakes. How many pancakes will the PTA members make?

Solution $4(397) = 4(400 - 3)$ Think of 397 as (400 − 3).
$\qquad\qquad\; = 4 \cdot 400 - 4 \cdot 3$ Distribute 4.
$\qquad\qquad\; = 1{,}600 - 12$ Multiply and subtract.
$\qquad\qquad\; = 1{,}588$

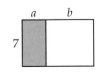

CLASS EXERCISES

Write an expression to describe the total area.

1.

2.

3.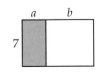

State the number or variable that can be distributed.

4. $9(5 - 3)$ **5.** $(5 + 7 + a)2$ **6.** $z(x - y)$

THINK AND DISCUSS

1. What does the word *distribute* mean? How can you relate it to the way the distributive property is used?

2. How does the distributive property affect the rules for the order of operations?

3. How would you evaluate $6(3 + 11 + 4)$ using the distributive property?

State the number or variable that has been distributed. Rewrite using the distributive property in reverse.

7. $y \cdot 4 + y \cdot 6$ **8.** $a \cdot (-3) - b \cdot (-3)$

Complete with the appropriate number or variable.

9. $9(5 + 4) = 9 \cdot \blacksquare + 9 \cdot 4$ **10.** $(y - 6)z = y \cdot z - 6 \cdot \blacksquare$

11. $12(3 + 5) = 12 \cdot 3 + \blacksquare \cdot \blacksquare$ **12.** $a(3 - b) = 3\blacksquare - \blacksquare b$

Use the distributive property to evaluate.

13. $6(4 + 8)$ **14.** $(14 - 9)2$ **15.** $-4(7 + 3 + 2)$

16. $7(3 + 5)$ **17.** $12(10 - 2)$ **18.** $3(2 + 2)$

WRITTEN EXERCISES

Write an expression to describe the total area.

1.

2.

3.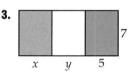

State the number or variable which can be distributed.

4. $(10 - 2)7$ **5.** $-4(6 + 7 + 9)$ **6.** $[3 + (-1)]x$

7. $(x - 4)c$ **8.** $r(s - t)$ **9.** $-w[9 + (-x)]$

State the number or variable that has been distributed. Rewrite using the distributive property in reverse.

10. $9 \cdot 3 + 9 \cdot 4$ **11.** $-9 \cdot x + (-9) \cdot y$

12. $a \cdot b + 3 \cdot b$ **13.** $(b \cdot e) - (c \cdot e) - (d \cdot e)$

14. $-6 \cdot 4 + 9 \cdot 4$ **15.** $-1 \cdot a + (-1) \cdot b$

Complete with the appropriate number or variable.

16. $6(3 + 7) = 6 \cdot 3 + \blacksquare \cdot 7$

17. $(w - x - z)y = (\blacksquare \cdot y) - (x \cdot \blacksquare) - (z \cdot y)$

18. $6 \cdot b + 12 \cdot b = (\blacksquare + 12)\blacksquare$

19. $[-2 + (-4)](-6) = \blacksquare \cdot (-6) + \blacksquare \cdot (-6)$

20. $-7 \cdot 12 - (-7) \cdot 17 = \blacksquare (\blacksquare - 17)$

21. $[10 - (-2)]5 = 10 \cdot \blacksquare - \blacksquare \cdot 5$

MENTAL MATH **Use the distributive property to evaluate.**

22. $2(122)$ **23.** $(280)4$ **24.** $2(670)$ **25.** $5(1,015)$

Use the distributive property to evaluate.

26. 4(5 + 11) **27.** (3 − 6)4 **28.** −5(6 − 7)

29. [9 − (−1)](−3) **30.** −3[2 + (−9)] **31.** −7[2 + (−3)]

32. 6(8 + 2 + 12) **33.** [26 + (−4) + 35]5

34. 2(5 + 3) − 3(4 − 2) **35.** (20 − 12)6 − 4[5 − (−3)]

Solve using the distributive property.

36. A theater was filled to capacity, 294, three nights in a row. How many people were at the show in these three nights?

37. It is 1,549 mi from Boston to Dallas. How many miles would you travel if you drove round trip?

38. *DATA FILE 3 (pp. 96–97)* Find the total number of pennies produced in 5 days by the United States Mint.

MIXED REVIEW
State the property shown.

1. 3(6 · 2) = 3(2 · 6)

2. 8 = 8 + 0

3. 4(8 · 3) = (4 · 8)3

4. 1 · 3 = 3

Compare. Use <, >, or =.

5. (−8 · 3) + 9 ▇ 8 (3 + 9)

6. 3(4 + 5) ▇ 3 · 4 + 3 · 5

7. −5 · 2 − |−9| ▇ 2 (−2)3

Solve.

8. *DATA (p. 31)* Find the total calories in a 3-oz hamburger, 20 potato chips, a carrot, and 1 c of lemonade.

Critical Thinking
EXPLORING LOGICAL THINKING

The table shows a mathematical operation, symbolized by ◆. In the table you can see that 2 ◆ 3 = 1.

◆	0	1	2	3
0	0	1	2	3
1	1	2	3	0
2	2	3	0	1
3	3	0	1	2

1. Use the table to find the following.

a. 1 ◆ 2 **b.** 1 ◆ 3 **c.** 3 ◆ 2

2. To investigate the properties, let us determine if ◆ is associative.

▼▼ *SAMPLE* 1 ◆ (3 ◆ 2) ▇ (1 ◆ 3) ◆ 2
  1 ◆ (1) ▇ (0) ◆ 2
   2 = 2

a. Compare 3 ◆ (2 ◆ 2) ▇ (3 ◆ 2) ◆ 2. Think of other combinations. Check them.

b. Is the operation associative?

3. Is ◆ commutative? Does 2 ◆ 3 = 3 ◆ 2? Check other combinations.

4. Is there an identity? If so, what is it?

5. *WRITE* a description of the operation ◆.

OBJECTIVE:
To use properties of addition and multiplication to simplify expressions.

2-4 *Simplifying Variable Expressions*

▼ The Texas state flag is made up of several rectangles and a star. You can represent the rectangles with the variable *r* and the star with the variable *s*. You can describe the parts of the flag by the following expression.

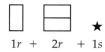

$$1r \;+\; 2r \;+\; 1s$$

This expression has three *terms*: 1*r*, 2*r*, and 1*s*. The terms are separated by addition symbols.

Term	A term is a part of an expression. Terms are separated by addition and subtraction symbols.

THINK Are the terms *r* and 1*r* equivalent? Why or why not?

▼ The term 2*r* consists of two parts. The variable is *r* and the *numerical coefficient* is 2.

Numerical Coefficient	A numerical coefficient is a number that is multiplied by a variable.

▼ 1*r* and 2*r* have the same variable. They are *like terms*.

Like Terms	Like terms have the same variable(s).

Example 1 **State the number of terms in each expression. Name the numerical coefficients and the like terms.**

　　a. $a + 5b - 3b$　　**b.** $10xy + 5y + xy - 20$

THINK Why is 10*xy* considered to be one term?

Solution **a.** three terms: *a*, 5*b*, and 3*b*
　　　numerical coefficients: 1, 5, and 3
　　　like terms: 5*b* and 3*b*

　　b. four terms: 10*xy*, 5*y*, *xy*, and 20
　　　numerical coefficients: 10, 5, and 1
　　　like terms: 10*xy* and *xy*

▼ Sometimes a term consists of a number without a variable. We call a term with no variable a *constant*.

Example 2 In the expression $5x + 2$, the constant is 2. No matter what value is substituted for *x*, the constant 2 remains the same.

▼ You can use models to represent an expression before you combine like terms to simplify the expression.

Example 3 Use algebra tiles or colored paper to simplify the expression $x + 1 + 2x$.

Solution

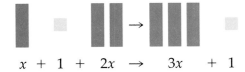

$x + 1 + 2x \rightarrow 3x + 1$

▼
THINK What is the value of the expression $3x + 1$ if $x = 3$? if $x = -2$?

▼ You can combine the numerical coefficients of like terms by using the distributive property.

Example 4 Simplify the expression $7x - 2x$ using the distributive property.

Solution
$$7x - 2x = 7 \cdot x - 2 \cdot x \quad \text{x is distributed to $7 - 2$.}$$
$$= (7 - 2)x \quad \text{Subtract coefficients.}$$
$$= 5 \cdot x \quad \text{Multiply.}$$
$$= 5x$$

▼ Combining like terms and using algebraic properties are helpful in simplifying variable expressions.

Simplify an Expression	To simplify an expression, replace it with an equivalent expression that contains no like terms or parentheses.

NOTES & QUOTES

Example 5 Simplify $4(5b)$.

Solution
$$4(5b) = (4 \cdot 5)b \quad \text{associative property}$$
$$= 20 \cdot b \quad \text{Multiply.}$$
$$= 20b$$

Francois Viète (1540–1603) introduced the use of vowels to represent unknown quantities.

▼ Sometimes you will need to use more than one property to simplify a variable expression.

Example 6 Simplify $4x + 3(3 + x)$.

Solution
$$4x + 3(3 + x) = 4x + 9 + 3x \quad \text{distributive property}$$
$$= 4x + 3x + 9 \quad \text{commutative property}$$
$$= (4x + 3x) + 9 \quad \text{associative property}$$
$$= (4 \cdot x + 3 \cdot x) + 9 \quad \text{x is distributed.}$$
$$= (4 + 3)x + 9 \quad \text{Add coefficients.}$$
$$= 7 \cdot x + 9 \quad \text{Multiply.}$$
$$= 7x + 9$$

1. What are some advantages of simplifying expressions?

2. $\square$ and $\triangle$ each stand for a different number. Which expression is equivalent to $\square + 4\triangle + 7 + 3\triangle - 2\square$?

a. $15\square\triangle$

b. $\square + 7\triangle + 7$

c. $\square + 14\triangle$

d. $\square + 7\triangle + 4 + 3$

e. $7\triangle - \square + 7$

CLASS EXERCISES

Give the number of terms in each expression. Name the numerical coefficients, the like terms, and the constants, if any.

1. $3x + 5y - 6x - 3$ **2.** $2x - 7$

3. $1a + 3b - 6c + 5a + 1$ **4.** $2r - 1s + 6r$

Combine the like terms using a model.

5. $12a + 7a$ **6.** $5 + 2b$

7. $4x - 7x + 3x$ **8.** $a + 2a + 3a - 4a$

Give the property that you can use to simplify each expression.

9. $-3(5x)$ **10.** $(n + 7) + 3$ **11.** $9x + 5x$ **12.** $(-5y)(-9)$

Simplify each expression.

13. $6(5b)$ **14.** $-6x + (9x - 3)$

15. $-4(a + 3) + 7a$ **16.** $4 + 3(a + b) - 6b$

WRITTEN EXERCISES

Give the number of terms in each expression. Name the numerical coefficients, the like terms, and the constants, if any.

1. $5a + 8a$ **2.** $6a + (-2b) + b$ **3.** $2x - (-7)$

4. $6xy - 5xy$ **5.** $-7c + 3$ **6.** $x + x + x$

7. $6ab - 4ba + 8 + ab$ **8.** $12 - 4x + 7w - 9x - w$

Combine the like terms using a model.

9. $4a + 5a$ **10.** $w - 3w + 2w$ **11.** $7b + b - 3b$

State the property that you can use to simplify each expression.

12. $6x + (-2x)$ **13.** $3(8k)$ **14.** $(4n + 3) + 8$

15. $8z + (-15z)$ **16.** $-2 + (7 + 8y)$ **17.** $-6(-5s)$

Combine the like terms using the distributive property.

18. $16z + 24z$ **19.** $52a - 47a$ **20.** $r + 6r - 3r$

Complete with the appropriate number or variable.

21. $6a + 4a + 7 = (\blacksquare a + 4a) + 7$
$= (6 + \blacksquare)a + 7$
$= \blacksquare a + 7$

Simplify each expression.

22. $5 + 2x + 8$ **23.** $5m + (-4m)$ **24.** $4(-3y) + 7 - 3$

25. $3a + 2a + a$ **26.** $9(4t) + 8$ **27.** $18 + 6(9k) - 13$

28. $8z + 8y + 3z$ **29.** $3(g + 5) + 2g$ **30.** $6(3k + 2k)$

31. $4(w + 2x) + 9(-4w)$ **32.** $-7(2f + 5e) + 8(6 + 4e)$

33. $-12(5x) + 3(-7x) - 2x$ **34.** $(2t + 4)3 + 6(-5t) - (-8)$

35. $5(4a + b - c) + 8(3a - 8b + 3c)$

Simplify. Evaluate when $x = 3$, $y = -5$, and $z = 7$.

36. $2x + x + y$ **37.** $-3(4y)$ **38.** $z(2x + 3x)$

39. $2y + 2z + y - 16$ **40.** $6(2x + y) + 2(x + 2y)$

Write an expression for each situation. Simplify.

41. Six bus loads containing x students each came to band day from one school, and 7 bus loads containing x students came from another school. Fourteen students came by car.

42. Arleen unloaded 4 boxes each containing v videotapes and 3 boxes each containing $y + 2$ videotapes.

43. Janet bought three folders costing x cents each and two report covers costing x cents each. She also purchased a binder for $1.89.

44. Mr. Unruh purchased five movie tickets for x dollars each. He also purchased a soda for $1.25 and popcorn for $2.25.

TEST YOURSELF

Is -4 a solution of each equation?

1. $2x - 6 = -14$ **2.** $16 \div 2y = 2$ **3.** $-21 = -2(3 - x)$

State which property is shown.

4. $3 \cdot (-6) = -6 \cdot 3$ **5.** $(3a)b = 3(ab)$

6. $17 \cdot 1 = 17$ **7.** $6 + 0 = 0 + 6$

8. $(3 + 2)(4 - 7) = (4 - 7)(3 + 2)$ **9.** $4(3 - 12) = 4 \cdot 3 - 4 \cdot 12$

Simplify.

10. $5(10b)$ **11.** $96 + 73 + 4$ **12.** $9y - 3y + 12y$

13. $3(a + 2a)$ **14.** $-14 + 2(9 - 3)$ **15.** $7(2w) + 2(w - 3)$

MIXED REVIEW

Complete.

1. $7(2 - 5) = 7 \cdot 2 - \blacksquare \cdot 5$

2. $3 \cdot 5 + \blacksquare \cdot 8 = 3(5 + 8)$

3. $(2 + 5) + 7 = 2 + (\blacksquare + 7)$

4. $(5 \cdot 3) = (\blacksquare \cdot 5)$

Find the mean.

5. -7, -8, 2, -3

6. 88, 93, 76, 82, 91

Use a Venn diagram to solve.

7. There are 25 students in the French class and 29 in the Spanish class. Eight students are taking both classes. What is the total number of students enrolled?

OBJECTIVE:
Use models to solve addition and subtraction equations.

Exploring Equations

▼ You can model an addition equation using algebra tiles. Use rectangles for variables and squares for positive and negative integers.

Equation 1:    Equation 2:

MATERIALS

- Algebra tiles or two different color squares of paper and rectangles of a third color

- Math journal to record work

1. **Discuss** What does the vertical bar represent?

2. **Write** an equation for each model.

3. **Model** each equation.

   a. $x + 3 = 5$ **b.** $z + 2 = -6$

   c. $y + 1 = 4$ **d.** $-3 = a - 4$

   e. $2b + 2 = 8$ **f.** $3 + 3x = -6$

▼ One way to find the solution of an equation is to *isolate* the variable. To isolate the variable, you use operations and properties to get the variable alone on one side of the equal sign.

4.

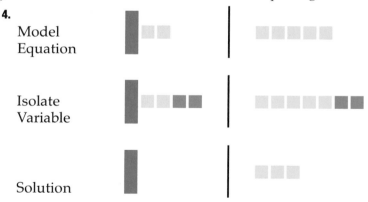

Model Equation

Isolate Variable

Solution

   a. Write What is the equation modeled in Step 1?

   b. Analyze What was done to isolate the variable?

   c. What property of integers was used to isolate the variable?

   d. What is the solution to the equation?

   e. Show mathematically what is represented in Steps 1–3.

5. **Model** and solve each equation.

   a. $x + 3 = 6$ **b.** $4 + y = -7$ **c.** $-3 = w + 2$

6. **Describe** another way you could isolate a variable in an addition equation.

▼ You can also model subtraction equations with algebra tiles.

$$y - 3 = 4$$ $$-3 = y - 2$$
WRITE $y + (-3) = 4$ **WRITE** $-3 = y + (-2)$

7. Why were the subtraction equations written as addition equations? Explain why you can write $y - 3 = 4$ as $y + (-3) = 4$.

8. **Analyze** How would you model each equation?

   a. $x - (-5) = 2$ **b.** $x - (-3) = 5$

▼ You can also solve subtraction equations using algebra tiles.

$$x - 3 = 5$$

9. How would you model this equation?

   a. What do you need to add to both sides of the equation to isolate the variable?

   b. What is the solution to the equation? Compare your solution with those of other students in the class.

10. Model and solve each equation.

    a. $x - 4 = 2$ **b.** $-5 = y - 3$

    c. $-6 = z - 3$

11. Is the equality of an equation affected when you add or subtract the same value on both sides?

2-5 Addition and Subtraction Equations

▼ In the sixteenth century, only six planets were known to exist. By the twentieth century, all nine planets had been discovered. How many planets were discovered between the sixteenth and twentieth centuries?

If we let p represent the number of planets, we can describe the situation by an equation.

$$p + 6 = 9$$

You can solve the equation $p + 6 = 9$ using a model.

THINK Is there another way to isolate the variable?

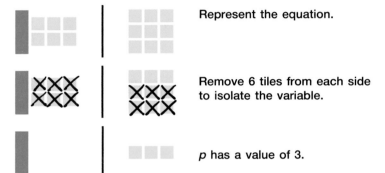

Represent the equation.

Remove 6 tiles from each side to isolate the variable.

p has a value of 3.

Three planets were discovered.

▼ Addition and subtraction are *inverse operations*. You can use subtraction to undo addition. When you subtract the same quantity from both sides of an equation, the result is an *equivalent equation*.

Subtraction Property of Equality	You can subtract the same value from both sides of an equation.
	Arithmetic　　　　**Algebra**
	$9 = 9$　　　　　If $a = b$,
	$9 - 4 = 9 - 4$　　then $a - c = b - c$.

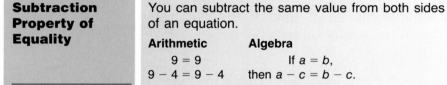

Example 1 Solve.

$$a + 22 = 28$$

Solution
$$a + 22 = 28$$
$$a + 22 - 22 = 28 - 22 \quad \text{Subtract 22 from each side.}$$
$$a + 0 = 6$$
$$a = 6$$

Check $a + 22 = 28$
$$6 + 22 = 28 \quad \text{Replace } a \text{ with 6.}$$
$$28 = 28 \checkmark \quad \text{True, so 6 is the solution.}$$

FLASHBACK
A solution makes an open equation true.

▼ To solve an equation involving subtraction, add the same value to both sides.

Addition Property of Equality	You can add the same value to both sides of an equation.	
	Arithmetic	**Algebra**
	$5 = 5$	If, $a = b$,
	$5 + 3 = 5 + 3$	then $a + c = b + c$.

Example 2 Solve.

$$b - 12 = 59$$

Solution
$$b - 12 = 59$$
$$b - 12 + 12 = 59 + 12 \quad \text{Add 12 to each side.}$$
$$b + 0 = 71$$
$$b = 71$$

Check $b - 12 = 59$
$$71 - 12 = 59 \quad \text{Replace } b \text{ with 71.}$$
$$59 = 59 \checkmark \quad \text{True, so 71 is the solution.}$$

THINK How would you graph a solution of 71 on the number line?

▼ If you remember that the sum of a number and its opposite is zero, you can solve equations in a different way.

Example 3 Solve $x - 3 = {}^-2$ using a model.

Solution

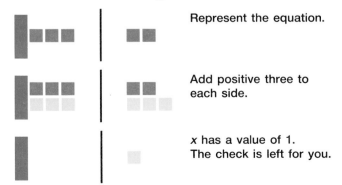

Represent the equation.

Add positive three to each side.

x has a value of 1.
The check is left for you.

FLASHBACK
$a + ({}^-a) = 0$ and
${}^-a + a = 0$.

FLASHBACK
□■ represents zero.

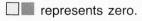

Example 4 Solve $x + 4 = -5$ using opposites.

Solution
$$x + 4 = -5$$
$$x + 4 + (-4) = -5 + (-4) \quad \text{Add -4 to each side.}$$
$$x + 0 = -9$$
$$x = -9 \quad \text{The check is left for you.}$$

THINK AND DISCUSS

1. Why is subtracting 8 from both sides of the equation $x + 8 = 17$ equivalent to adding -8 to both sides?

2. Which method do you prefer to use in solving an equation of the form $x + a = b$? Explain.

3. What properties do you need to use to show that $117 + n - 117$ is equal to n?

CLASS EXERCISES

Use a model to solve each equation. Graph each solution.

1. $6 + b = 9$ **2.** $-3 = n - 4$

State the first step in solving each equation.

3. $a + 8 = 12$ **4.** $54 + x = 98$ **5.** $34 = x - 19$ **6.** $-900 = 365 + x$

Solve each addition equation.

7. $x + 35 = 15$ **8.** $450 = x + 325$

Solve each subtraction equation.

9. $x - 34 = 20$ **10.** $-25 = b - 10$

WRITTEN EXERCISES

Use a model to solve each equation.

1. $x + 5 = 7$ **2.** $b - 4 = 3$ **3.** $-6 = w - 4$

Write and solve the equation represented by each model.

4.   **5.**

Solve each equation using the subtraction property.

6. $c + 9 = 37$ **7.** $b + 24 = 19$ **8.** $65 = n + 34$
9. $-47 = 7 + y$ **10.** $-45 = x + (-3)$ **11.** $298 + n = 924$

Solve each equation using the addition property.

12. $b - 15 = -9$ **13.** $43 = g - 39$ **14.** $x - 366 = -415$
15. $-27 = w - 14$ **16.** $-34 = c - 12$ **17.** $8{,}923 = r - 1{,}298$

Solve each equation using opposites.

18. $x - 19 = 34$ **19.** $13 + c = 54$ **20.** $432 = m - 391$

21. $48 = x + 9$ **22.** $c - 42 = 12$ **23.** $w + 3 = {}^-8$

MENTAL MATH Solve each equation.

24. $130 = 30 + s$ **25.** $x + 800 = 500$ **26.** $95 = x - 15$

27. ${}^-45 = b - 45$ **28.** $25 = x + 425$ **29.** $r - 316 = {}^-8$

CALCULATOR Solve each equation.

30. $x + 49{,}023 = 15{,}911$ **31.** $265{,}970 = b - 1{,}098{,}645$

32. $398{,}452 = x + 799{,}376$ **33.** $c - 36{,}000 = 41{,}098$

Solve each equation.

34. $v - 493 = 513$ **35.** $400 + x = 900$ **36.** $c + ({}^-90) = {}^-58$

37. $56 = c - 9$ **38.** ${}^-5 = {}^-5 + n$ **39.** ${}^-25 = {}^-5 + n$

40. $32 + a = {}^-32$ **41.** $2{,}314 = k + 716$ **42.** $e + ({}^-43) = {}^-45$

43. $34 + n + 12 = 78 - 7$ **44.** $n - 29 + ({}^-16) = {}^-24$

Complete.

45. If $x + a = b$, then $x = $ ▧.   **46.** If $x - a = b$, then $x = $ ▧.

Write an equation for each sentence. Solve for the variable.

47. A number d plus five is equal to seventeen.

48. Negative five is the same as x minus eight.

49. *DATA FILE 2 (pp. 52–53)* The number of decibels in a whisper is d decibels less than the number of decibels in a rocket launch.

50. Three hundred twenty-three is negative one hundred fifty-five plus y.

51. *DATA FILE 2 (pp. 52–53)* The speed of sound travels through steel h m/s faster than it travels through silver.

52. Thirty-three more than m is the same as negative seventeen.

53. *DATA FILE 4 (pp. 138–139)* The number of people who speak Chinese is p people more than the number who speak German.

54. Fifty-four less than a number k is equal to negative twenty-nine.

55. *PROJECT* Visit your town hall. Research the population of your town or city. Has the population increased or decreased? by how many people?

MIXED REVIEW

Find the number of terms.

1. $5w - 3z + 2w$

2. $8 + 9a + 3(2a)$

Simplify.

3. $9x - 5x + 4$

4. $5q + 8 - 3q + ({}^-2)$

5. $27 \div ({}^-3) + 4(3)$

6. $|3({}^-8) + 6 \cdot 2|$

Solve.

7. George studied math for 1 min the first week of school, 2 min the second, and 4 min the third. He continued to double his study time each week. How many minutes did he study the tenth week?

2-6 Multiplication and Division Equations

▼ Mark and Sara each have the same amount of money to spend at the basketball game. If they have a total of $6, how much does each have? Let m represent this amount. You can describe the situation by the following equation.

$$2m = 6$$

▼ You can solve a multiplication equation using a model.

Example 1 Solve the equation $2m = 6$ using a model.

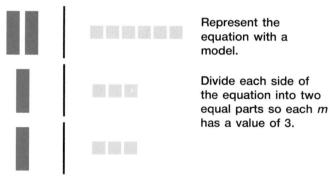

Represent the equation with a model.

Divide each side of the equation into two equal parts so each m has a value of 3.

Each person has $3 to spend.

THINK Why must you divide by a nonzero value?

▼ Division undoes multiplication. When you divide both sides of an equation by the same nonzero number, the result is an equivalent equation.

Division Property of Equality	You can divide both sides of an equation by the same nonzero value.
	Arithmetic **Algebra**
	$9 = 9$ If $a = b$,
	$9 \div 3 = 9 \div 3$ then $a \div c = b \div c$.
	$\frac{9}{3} = \frac{9}{3}$ $\frac{a}{c} = \frac{b}{c}, c \neq 0$

THINK How do you know that $\frac{5r}{5}$ is the same as $5r \div 5$?

Example 2 Solve $5r = -20$ using the division property of equality.

Solution

$$5r = -20$$

$$\frac{5r}{5} = \frac{-20}{5} \qquad \text{Divide both sides by 5.}$$

$$r = -4$$

Check $5r = -20$ Replace r with -4.

$$5 \cdot (-4) = -20 \checkmark$$

▼ To solve an equation involving division, multiply both sides by the same value.

Multiplication Property of Equality	You can multiply both sides of an equation by the same value.
	Arithmetic **Algebra**
	$12 = 12$ If $a = b$,
	$12 \cdot 2 = 12 \cdot 2$ then $ac = bc$.

Example 3   Solve $\frac{x}{-9} = -3$ using the multiplication property of equality.

Solution $\frac{x}{-9} = -3$

$$-9\left(\frac{x}{-9}\right) = -3 \cdot (-9) \quad \text{Multiply both sides by -9.}$$

$$x = 27$$

Check $\frac{x}{-9} = -3$ Replace x with 27.

$$\frac{27}{-9} = -3$$

$$-3 = -3 ✓$$

CLASS EXERCISES

State the first step in solving each equation.

1. $6x = 96$ **2.** $32 = c \div 3$ **3.** $\frac{r}{-5} = -4$

Solve each multiplication equation.

4. $8x = -48$ **5.** $-2x = 12$ **6.** $108 = 9x$

Solve each division equation.

7. $\frac{v}{3} = 14$ **8.** $-6 = n \div 4$ **9.** $\frac{m}{-2} = -20$

▼

THINK AND DISCUSS

1. Why is $1y = y$?

2. How would you solve the equation $\frac{25}{x} = 1$?

3. How are the procedures used to solve $3x = 9$ and $x + 3 = 12$ alike? How are they different?

WRITTEN EXERCISES

Use a model to solve each equation. Graph each solution.

1. $2g = 8$ **2.** $10 = 2m$ **3.** $4h = -12$

MENTAL MATH   **Is -3 a solution of each equation?**

4. $-6 = 2m$ **5.** $\frac{b}{-3} = 1$ **6.** $45p = 145$ **7.** $\frac{-18}{k} = -6$

Write and solve each equation represented by the model.

8.   **9.**

Solve each equation using the division property.

10. $4a = 28$ **11.** $-2b = 30$ **12.** $-45 = 9a$

13. $15c = 90$ **14.** $5w = 95$ **15.** $-28 = 7m$

16. $-10d = 100$ **17.** $125 = 25d$ **18.** $-35 = 5n$

Solve each equation using the multiplication property.

19. $\frac{m}{4} = 13$ **20.** $\frac{b}{-6} = 20$ **21.** $-2 = d \div 8$

22. $f \div 3 = -4$ **23.** $-50 = \frac{n}{-6}$ **24.** $9 = \frac{n}{8}$

25. $\frac{w}{12} = -2$ **26.** $13 = n \div -4$ **27.** $7 = \frac{y}{6}$

MENTAL MATH Solve each equation.

28. $20b = 2{,}000$ **29.** $\frac{v}{-50} = 300$

30. $75m = -7{,}500$ **31.** $3{,}823 = \frac{s}{100}$

CALCULATOR Solve each equation.

32. $358c = 80{,}550$ **33.** $x \div (-392) = 108$

34. $4{,}523 = \frac{n}{-921}$ **35.** $-48z = 76{,}128$

Solve each equation using any method.

36. $4c = -36$ **37.** $\frac{s}{-32} = 24$ **38.** $-84t = 0$

39. $-88 = 11w$ **40.** $6c = -96$ **41.** $56 = f \div 9$

42. $-34c = 34$ **43.** $15n = 225$ **44.** $-364 = \frac{c}{-3}$

45. $16s = 496$ **46.** $f \div 31 = 27$ **47.** $352 = 32v$

48. $25y = 500$ **49.** $0 = \frac{u}{254}$ **50.** $43x = 4{,}257$

51. A honeybee hive contains 35,000 cells. How many cells are there in 25 honeybee hives?

52. *DATA FILE 10 (pp. 404–405)* How many acres does one gray wolf require to survive?

53. Write an expression for the number of eggs in d dozen.

For what values of x is each equation true?

54. $|x| = 7$ **55.** $\frac{|x|}{3} = 2$ **56.** $2|x| = 8$

Solve each equation for x.

57. $ax = b$ **58.** $\frac{x}{a} = b$

59. $x - a = b$ **60.** $x + a = b$

Critical Thinking
EXPLORING VISUAL THINKING

Find the missing piece.

To solve this problem, you must develop a plan. What characteristics does the missing piece have?

1. What happens to the lines of the pattern as they swirl inward?

2. At some point the lines will form a dot. Where will the dot be?

3. Is all of the dot on the missing piece or is part of it on the design?

4. Based on the characteristics, which piece is the best choice?

5. Here is another puzzle. Which figure will connect with part A to form a circle? Describe how you know.

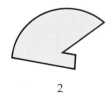

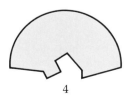

OBJECTIVE:
To write an equation
for a word problem
or model.

2-7 *Writing Equations*

▼ A group of artists is painting a large outdoor mural. The length of the mural is 410 ft. The mural has an area of 28,700 ft². How could you find the width of the painting?

To find the width, you can write an equation.

$$w \boxed{\quad A = 28{,}700 \text{ ft}^2 \quad}$$

Sketch a diagram when appropriate.

$$l = 410 \text{ ft}$$

Area $=$ *length* $\cdot$ *width*

$$\updownarrow \qquad \updownarrow$$

$$410 \quad \cdot \quad w \quad = 28{,}700$$

Let *w* equal the width.

▼ To solve a word problem, you need to translate a sentence into an equation.

Example 1 **Write an equation.**

One more than three times the number of students in the class is equal to sixty-four.

Solution In this situation, we need to find the number of students.

Let *s* = *number of students.*   Identify the variable.

$3s$ = *three times* the number of   Include the coefficient.
students.

$3s + 1$ = *one more than* three   Write the variable
times the number of students.   expression.

$3s + 1 = 64$ Write the equation.

▼ Before you write an equation decide on a variable to represent one unknown. Then write the other unknowns in terms of that variable.

▼
THINK What if you let
m = Joan's money? How
would you write the
expression for Eve's
money?

Example 2 **Write an equation.**

Joan collected twice as much money as Eve for the walkathon. Together they collected $120.

Solution In this situation, we need to find the money that each collected.

Let *m* = Eve's money   Identify the variable.
$2m$ = Joan's money   Write any like terms.
$m + 2m = 120$ Write the equation.

▼ Equations can represent real situations.

Example 3 **Write a word problem for the equation $12x = 496$.**

Solution One possible word problem is the following:

Janet makes 12 monthly payments for her automobile insurance. The yearly premium is $496. How much will she pay per month?

CLASS EXERCISES

Choose the best equation for each problem. Do not solve.

1. Kendra uses 14 C/min while running. If she burned 154 C, how many minutes (m) did she run?

   a. $m - 14 = 154$ **b.** $14m = 154$
   c. $m \div 154 = 14$ **d.** $m + 14 = 154$

2. Three less than the quantity $y - 7$ is equal to -6.

   a. $y - 7 + 3 = -6$ **b.** $3 - (y - 7) = -6$
   c. $-6 = (y - 7) - 3$ **d.** $-6 = 3(y - 7)$

Write an equation for each problem. Do not solve.

3. The product of a number and 40 is equal to 360.

4. The sum of 45 and some number is -30.

5. A number decreased by -5 is 18.

6. Three more than six times the number of books on the shelf is 63.

7. The length of a rectangle is twice the width. The perimeter is 120.

Write a word problem for each equation.

8. $500 = 10t$ 9. $120 = 150 - x$

THINK AND DISCUSS

1. Is there always just one correct equation that can be written for a given problem? Use an example to support your answer.

2. Are the equations $x + 5 = 10$ and $x = 10 - 5$ equivalent equations? Why or why not?

WRITTEN EXERCISES

Choose the best equation for each problem. Do not solve.

1. Suppose you travel 55 mi/h. How many hours (h) would it take you to go 275 mi?

   a. $55 + h = 275$ **b.** $h \div 55 = 275$
   c. $55h = 275$ **d.** $275 = h - 55$

2. The quantity $x - 9$ times -3 is equal to 21.

    a. $x - 9 \cdot (-3) = 21$ **b.** $(x - 9)(-3) = 21$

    c. $21 = 3 + (x - 9)$ **d.** $(x - 9) - 3 = 21$

Write an equation for each problem. Do not solve.

3. A number decreased by 24 is equal to -9.

4. Ten less than seven times the number of guests is sixty.

5. Sean bought 15 notebooks. Each cost the same amount. He spent a total of $30. How much was each notebook?

6. On Tuesday, 80 students were absent. The remaining 478 students were in school. How many students attend the school?

7. *PROJECT* Write an equation using one variable to represent the number of hours you study and the number of hours you watch television every week.

Write an equation for each problem. Then solve.

8. Kirsten sent out invitations for a surprise party. She then decided to invite eight more people. She sent out 52 invitations in all. How many invitations did she originally send?

9. Two sides of a triangle have lengths 46 mm and 54 mm. The perimeter is 150 mm. What is the length of the third side?

10. *DATA FILE 3 (pp. 96–97)*

    a. Jean has twice as many proof sets as Jim. They have the same type of proof sets. The 1990 value of their sets totals $10,500. What year were the proof sets made?

    b. *WRITE* a word problem using any of the data in the file. Exchange problems with a student and solve.

MIXED REVIEW

Evaluate using mental math.

1. $5(103)$ **2.** $(180)3$

State the first step in solving.

3. $5x = 35$

4. $5 + x = 35$

5. $35 = x - 5$

6. $\frac{x}{5} = 35$

Solve.

7. Badwater, California, (-282 ft alt.) is the lowest point in the Western Hemisphere. The Dead Sea ($-1,310$ ft alt.) is the lowest surface point on Earth. How much lower is the Dead Sea than Badwater?

TEST YOURSELF

Solve.

1. $a + 92 = 112$ **2.** $-17 = y \div 4$ **3.** $-46 = -12 + x$

4. $96 = 3r$ **5.** $b - 16 = -39$ **6.** $-12w = 156$

Write an equation for each problem. Solve.

7. Twelve more than some number is twenty.

8. Three less than the quantity $c - 6$ is equal to negative ten.

OBJECTIVE:
To explore the uses of a computer graphing program.

MATERIALS

- Graph paper

- Computer and graphing software (optional)

- Math journal to record work

Exploring Graphing

■ Sometimes looking at a graph is an easier way to analyze data. You can use the data from a spreadsheet to create a graph.

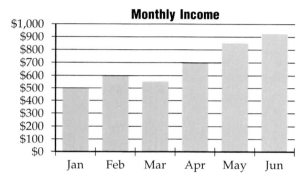

	A	B
1	Month	Income
2	Jan	$500.00
3	Feb	$600.00
4	Mar	$550.00
5	Apr	$700.00
6	May	$850.00
7	Jun	$925.00

Monthly Income

DATAPOINT

Many spreadsheet programs allow you to graph the spreadsheet data.

1. What part of the spreadsheet does the horizontal axis stand for in the bar graph? What does the vertical axis represent?

2. Does the spreadsheet or bar graph let you see exact values?

3. On a sheet of graph paper, draw a bar graph using twice the value of the spreadsheet data. How is your graph similar to the one shown above? How is it different?

■ You can also use a computer to draw a line graph.

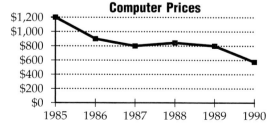

Computer Prices

4. **a.** Could you use the data in the line graph to construct a bar graph? Why or why not?

   b. *Analyze* Why would a line graph be inappropriate for the data from the spreadsheet shown earlier? Explain.

DATAPOINT

Here are some other types of graphs that you can draw with a graphing program:

- Stem and leaf plots
- Box and whisker plots
- Scattergrams
- Three-dimensional graphs

■ You can also use a computer to construct double bar graphs. The spreadsheet data below were used to construct the graph.

	A	B	C
1	Month	Income	Expenses
2	Jan	$500.00	$150.00
3	Feb	$600.00	$175.00
4	Mar	$550.00	$275.00
5	Apr	$700.00	$800.00

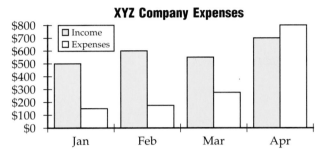

XYZ Company Expenses

□ Income
□ Expenses

5. a. Analyze Based on the graph, is this business doing well financially? Why or why not?

b. Explore How does a graph help in analyzing data?

Fund-raising Results

18.12%

9.06%

45.65%

27.17%

■ Book sale ■ Car wash
□ Food stand ■ Paper drive

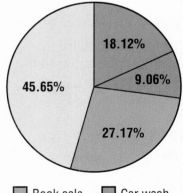

■ You can also draw a circle graph with your data. The spreadsheet below shows the results of a class fund-raising drive.

	A	B
1	Car wash	$150.00
2	Paper drive	$75.00
3	Book sale	$225.00
4	Food stand	$378.00

6. The data are shown on the circle graph at the left.

a. Which activity raised the most money? the least money? How are these two amounts shown on the graph?

b. Discuss Would a bar graph of the data be more useful? Which type of graph would you use for the data? Explain.

c. How could the circle graph be used in planning next year's fund-raiser? Which activities should the class emphasize?

7. PROJECT Draw a graph using data that you collect. Choose the two most appropriate types of graphs to display your data. If you have a computer graphing program, draw the graphs.

OBJECTIVE:
To use guess and test to solve mathematical problems.

2-8 Guess and Test

NOTES & QUOTES

Certainly, let us learn proving, but also let us learn guessing.

George Polya

■ It is sometimes useful when solving a mathematics problem to guess what the answer will be. You can use the guessing strategy to solve the following problem.

PROBLEM

Ronald Reagan is the oldest man to be elected president of the United States. John F. Kennedy was the youngest. The sum of their ages at the time of their election is 112. The difference is 26. How old was each man when elected president?

SOLUTION

READ ▶ What do you want to find?   Reagan's and Kennedy's ages when they were elected president

What is the sum of their ages when each was elected?   112
What is the difference?   26

PLAN ▶ Find two numbers with a sum of 112.
Test whether their difference is 26.
Use each incorrect guess to make a better estimate.
Keep a record of your work in a table.

SOLVE ▶

Guess	Test	Outcome
50 and 62	50 + 62 = 112 62 − 50 = 12	The difference is too small, so the numbers have to be farther apart.
40 and 72	40 + 72 = 112 72 − 40 = 32	The difference is too great, so the numbers have to be closer together.
43 and 69	43 + 69 = 112 69 − 43 = 26	Correct.

LOOK BACK ▶ Ronald Reagan was 69 years old when elected president.
John F. Kennedy was 43 years old when elected president.

CLASS EXERCISES

Make a reasonable guess for each question. Test your answer.

1. What is the length of your classroom? the width? the area?

2. How many times does your heart beat in a minute?

3. What are two whole numbers whose sum is 20 and whose difference is 2?

4. What are two whole numbers whose product is 50 and whose quotient is 2?

Which of the numbers 1, 2, 3, 4, or 5 is a solution?

5. **a.** $4y - 2 + 3y = 19$  **b.** $3 + \frac{b}{2} = 5$

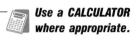
WRITTEN EXERCISES

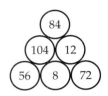

Use guess and test to solve each problem.

1. Find two pairs of numbers in the diagram whose quotient is 7.

2. The teller's drawer has some $5 bills, $10 bills, and some $20 bills. There are 15 bills worth a total of $185. How many $5 bills, $10 bills, and $20 bills are there?

3. The Smiths have two children. The sum of their ages is 23 and the product is 132. How old are the children?

4. The average of three consecutive integers is 10. Their sum is 30. What is the middle number?

FLASHBACK

Consecutive integers have a difference of 1. . . . ⁻2, ⁻1, 0, 1, 2 . . .

Use any strategy to solve each problem.

5. Three consecutive integers have a sum of ⁻9 and a product of ⁻24. What are the three integers?

6. A vegetable garden has a length of 5 ft and a width of 8 ft. Two feet are added to the length. By how much will this increase the area?

7. Trains leave New York for Boston every 40 min. The first train leaves at 5:20 A.M. What is the departure time closest to 12:55 P.M.?

8. Jean's age of 16 is the same as Rafi's age divided by three. How old is Rafi?

9. A number that when multiplied by itself and then by itself again gives ⁻1,000. What is the number?

10. In a collection of quarters and nickels, there are four more nickels than quarters. How many nickels and quarters are there if the collection is worth $2.30?

11. A triangle has sides of lengths $3x$, $4x$, and $5x$. The perimeter is 120 ft. What is the length of each side?

2-9 Ecology

OBJECTIVE:
To apply solving equations to ecology problems.

Americans throw away an average of four to five pounds of waste per person each day. As landfills across the United States fill up and the number of landfills decreases, disposing of solid waste is becoming a serious problem. One way to reduce the problem is to reduce the amount of solid waste.

FLASHBACK

1 ton (t) = 2,000 lb

Example 1 One aluminum can weighs about $\frac{1}{28}$ lb. Suppose your school starts a recycling drive. How many cans will your school need to recycle to reduce the trash by 1 t?

Solution Write an equation.

$c \div 28 = 2,000$ **Let c = number of cans.**

$c \div 28 \cdot 28 = 2,000 \cdot 28$ **Multiply both sides by 28.**

$c = 56,000$

Your school will need to recycle 56,000 cans.

Some companies pay for materials to recycle. The prices paid vary due to market conditions.

Example 2 Suppose recyclers pay $5/t for newspapers. How many tons of newspaper would your school have to recycle to earn $65?

Solution Write an equation.

$5n = 65$ **Let n = number of tons of newspaper.**

$\frac{5n}{5} = \frac{65}{5}$ **Divide both sides by 5.**

$n = 13$

Your school will have to recycle 13 t of newspaper.

CLASS EXERCISES

United States Solid Waste (lb/person/day)

Year	Generated	Recycled
1965	2.77	0.17
1970	3.16	0.21
1975	3.11	0.23
1980	3.35	0.32

Use the DATA at the left to solve.

1. In 1975, how many pounds of solid waste did the average person generate in seven days?

2. In 1980, what was the net amount of solid waste that one person generated? The net amount of waste is the difference between the waste generated and the waste recycled.

3. In 1970, the United States population was approximately 203,000,000 people. About how much solid waste did the entire population generate each day?

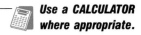
WRITTEN EXERCISES

**TYPES AND AMOUNTS
OF GARBAGE
DISCARDED PER YEAR**

60 billion cans
28 billion bottles
100 million tires
3 million cars
4 million tons of plastic
40 million tons of paper

Use the *DATA* at the left to solve each problem.

1. It costs $65/t to pick up garbage. How much will it cost per year to pick up just the paper and plastic discarded?

2. Tires weigh an average of 9 lb. It costs $72/t to dispose of tires. How much does it cost to dispose of one year's discarded tires?

3. *ESTIMATION* The weight of twenty-eight aluminum cans is approximately 1 lb.

   a. Estimate the weight of the cans discarded per year.

   b. Recycling one pound of cans saves 8 kW · h of electricity. About how many kilowatt hours of electricity would be saved if all the discarded cans were recycled?

4. A town with a population of 38,000 people discards an average of 4 lb of waste per person each day. About how many tons of waste do they discard in a week?

■■■■■■■ Decision Making ■ **DECISION MAKING** ■ Decision Making ■ Decision Making ■ Decision Making ■

ECOLOGY

■ **COLLECT DATA**

1. How much waste does your school produce each week? Keep track of what you throw away. Make a chart like the one below to tally your results.

Type of Trash	Amount of Trash (in pounds)							
	Mon	Tues	Wed	Thur	Fri	Sat	Sun	Total
Newspaper								
Other paper								
Metal								
Plastic								
Glass								
Other								

2. Find out what kinds of recycling services are available in your community.

5. Suppose a state with a population of 5 million reduces the average waste per person from 5 lb to 3 lb. How much could they save on disposal costs if the waste pickup costs $65/t?

6. A town of 63,000 collects 1,800 lb of waste per person in a year. The area of landfill (in square yards) needed for this waste is found using the formula $A = \frac{\text{weight of waste}}{1,000 \cdot \text{depth in yards}}$.

  a. Find the area in square yards of the town's landfill if the landfill's depth will be 3 yd.

  b. *ESTIMATION* There are 4,840 yd^2 in an acre. Estimate the number of acres needed per year for the town's landfill.

7. *PROJECT*

  a. Technically, solid waste, trash, and garbage are not synonyms. Find out which materials are in each category.

  b. Determine ways, other than reducing the landfill problem, in which recycling benefits the environment.

  c. Research the environmental damage that can result from an improperly managed landfill. Find out what we can do to minimize these dangers.

■ *Decision Making* ■ *Decision Making* ■ *Decision Making* ■ *Decision Making* ■ *Decision Making* ■ *Decision Making* ■

■ **ANALYZE DATA**

3. Analyze the garbage your school discards.

  a. What materials can be recycled?

  b. Could you use the garbage in other ways?

4. Other than recycling or reusing items, what ways can you think of to reduce the amount of your school's garbage?

■ **MAKE DECISIONS**

5. Plan to reduce the amount of waste your school discards.

  a. Set a reasonable goal for reducing your amount of trash.

  b. Decide on methods you can use to meet your goal.

6. Many fast-food companies use plastic wrappers or foam containers instead of coated paper to wrap their foods.

  a. Compare the ease of recycling these materials.

  b. Which wrapping do you think is better? Explain.

  c. How do you think the companies could reduce their trash?

Practice

State whether each equation is true, false, or open.

1. $-17 = x + 5$
2. $\frac{-325}{-5} = 65$
3. $29 + (-3) = 26$
4. $25 \cdot 6 = 150$
5. $2x + 5 = 3x - 7$
6. $6 = -3[4 + (-2)]$

State whether the given number is a solution of the equation.

7. $12 = 2x + (-4); x = 4$
8. $-3[2y - (-5)] = 9; y = -4$
9. $2r - 4 + r = 89; r = 31$
10. $-2 = s - (-4) + 2s; s = 6$
11. $\frac{x}{5} - (-2) = -12; x = -50$
12. $2m + 6 = 2(m + 3); m = -2$

State which property is shown.

13. $(3r)s = 3(rs)$
14. $(a - b)(r + s) = (r + s)(a - b)$
15. $653 + 0 = 0 + 653$
16. $6(t - 5) = 6 \cdot t - 6 \cdot 5$
17. $17 \cdot 1 = 17$
18. $(3 + 9) + 0 = 3 + (9 + 0)$

Evaluate.

19. $-135 + (-341)$
20. $(8 - 5)6 + 37$
21. $120 + 16 + 80$
22. $-15 - (-56)$
23. $-550 \div 50 \cdot 2$
24. $-6[4 + (-12)] + 9$
25. $4\left(\frac{-12}{-6}\right) + (-3) \cdot 5 - 3(-11)$
26. $-17 + [5 - (-7) + 2]3$
27. $-3 + (-6) - [5 - (-2)]$
28. $7 \cdot (-4) + [8 - (-5)]3$

Simplify each expression.

29. $-5(3k)$
30. $2x + 5 - x$
31. $(g + 5)3 + 2g - 7$
32. $8 + (3c + 3)4$
33. $4(x + y - z)$
34. $8(a - b) + 2b - 2a$
35. $\frac{-9}{3} + 12w - (-7) - 3(5w)$
36. $23 + 2[b + (-15) + 3b]$

Solve each equation.

37. $c + 7 = 34$
38. $-550 = 10w$
39. $\frac{k}{-4} = -3$
40. $78 = t - (-47)$
41. $6d = 54$
42. $17 = z - 3$
43. $27 + v = -12$
44. $h + (-3) = 53$
45. $-192 = \frac{w}{-16}$

46. Find the sum of the magic square. Write and solve equations to find a, b, and c.

a	3	8
5	7	b
c	11	4

Write an equation for each problem. Solve.

47. The sum of a number and 5 is equal to -123.

48. Six less than a is equal to 47.

Problem Solving Practice

PROBLEM SOLVING STRATEGIES

Look for a Pattern
Guess and Test
Simplify the Problem
Make an Organized List
Work Backwards
Account for All Possibilities
Make a Table
Write an Equation
Solve by Graphing
Draw a Diagram
Make a Model
Solve Another Way
Simulate the Problem

Solve each problem. The list at the left shows some possible strategies you can use.

1. **DATA FILE 5 (pp. 180–181)** Look at the following two equations that are expressed with musical notes.

   a. How many quarter notes are equal to a whole note?

   b. How many eighth notes are equal to a whole note?

   c. Is there a pattern? Can you use the pattern to find the number of sixteenth and half notes in a whole note?

2. The average age of five students is 15. Two of the students are 12 years old. Three students are not 12, but are the same age. How old are the other three students?

3. **COMPUTER** Look at the spreadsheet below.

	A	B	C	D
1	Employee	Hours	Wage	
2	Jones, C.	4	4.50	= B2×C2
3	Smith, G.	5	4.25	= B3×C3
4	Garcia, H.	12	5.15	= B4×C4
5				
6				
7				

   a. What values do the formulas in cells D2–D4 represent?

   b. Suppose you wanted to find the total number of hours and the total amount of wages. What formulas would you use? In which cells would you enter the formulas?

4. You are given these directions to get to a friend's house:

   Drive east on State Street. Take a right on Main. Continue on Main and take a right on Broadway. Continue on Broadway and take a left on Center Street. The house is on the corner of Center and High streets.

   Assume the streets are arranged in a grid and there are no one-way streets. Is there a shorter route? If so, describe it.

5. **DATA FILE 3 (pp. 96–97)**

   a. Tom bought a 1937 proof set in 1965 and sold it in 1968. How much did he have to add to his profit in order to purchase three 1940 proof sets the next day?

   b. How long would it take to produce $1,920,000 in $5 bills?

Chapter 2 Review

Match each word with the example that illustrates its meaning.

1. Commutative property
2. Associative property
3. Solution
4. Identity
5. Distributive property
6. Term
7. Numerical coefficient
8. Constant
9. Simplify an expression
10. Property of equality
11. False equation

a. $a \cdot (b \cdot c) = (a \cdot b) \cdot c$
b. 4 in $4x + 5 = 9$
c. 5 in $4x + 5 = 9$
d. $3x + 4 + 5 = 3x + 9$
e. $x = 2$ for $3 + x = 5$
f. $a + b = b + a$
g. $4x + 5 - 5 = 9 - 5$
h. $-4 - 7 = 3$
i. $a + 0 = a$ and $a \cdot 1 = a$
j. $4x$ in $4x + 5 = 9$
k. $a(b + c) = (a \cdot b) + (a \cdot c)$

Using the Properties of Operations   2-1, 2-2

To evaluate an expression, use the commutative property to change the order. Use the associative property to change the grouping.

Use the commutative and the associative properties to evaluate.

12. $125 + 347 + 75$
13. $58 + 16 + 2 + 4$
14. $4 \cdot 7 \cdot 25 \cdot 1$
15. $(20 \cdot 65) \cdot 5$

Using the Distributive Property   2-3

To evaluate an expression with parentheses, use the distributive property to distribute a factor to each term inside the parentheses.

Use the distributive property to evaluate.

16. $5(20 + 3)$
17. $4(50 - 2)$
18. $2(25 + 8) + 2(15 - 8)$
19. $6(40 - 21) - 6(20 - 1)$

Simplifying Variable Expressions   2-4

To simplify a variable expression, combine like terms and eliminate parentheses using the distributive property.

Simplify each expression.

20. $5x + 3y + 3x + 2y$
21. $4 + 6(a + 2) + 3a$

Addition and Subtraction Equations

2-5

To solve an addition or subtraction equation, add or subtract the same value from both sides of the equation.

Solve each equation.

22.

23.

24. $a - 7 = 28$

25. $x + 19 = 30$

26. $38 + y - 18 = 500$

27. $n + (-13) = 7$

Multiplication and Division Equations

2-6

To solve a multiplication or division equation, multiply or divide both sides of the equation by the same nonzero value.

Solve each equation.

28.

29.

30. $\frac{m}{8} = -9$

31. $8b = 96$

32. $\frac{c}{12} = 24$

33. $-3k = -54$

Writing Equations

2-7

To write an equation for a word problem, you need to recognize words that imply the variable(s), the operation(s), and the equality.

Write an equation for each problem.

34. Twice a number increased by 28 is 54.

35. Seventeen less than a number is 12.

Write a word problem to describe the equation.

36. $x + 7 = 95$

37. $4x = 17$

Problem Solving

2-8, 2-9

To solve some problems, guess at the solution. Then use each incorrect guess to make a better estimate of the correct answer.

Use guess and test to solve.

38. Paper plates come in packages of 15 or 20. Helene bought 9 packages and had 155 plates. How many packages of 15 and how many packages of 20 did she buy?

Use the data on page 88.

39. How many pounds of paper are discarded per year?

Chapter 2   Test

State whether each equation is true, false, or open.

1. $24 = 3(-8)$

2. $5x + 28 = 153$

3. $18(-7 \div 7) = (-2)(9)$

4. $-6 + 15 = (120 \div 20) - (5 - 8)$

Use the commutative and the associative properties to evaluate.

5. $250 \cdot 38 \cdot 2$

6. $675 + (-8) - (75 - 8)$

Complete with the appropriate number or variable.

7. $9(8 + 5) = 9 \cdot 8 + \blacksquare \cdot 5$

8. $(x + y)\blacksquare = xz + yz$

9. $-3 \cdot 4 + \blacksquare \cdot 11 = \blacksquare(4 + 11)$

10. $4x + 6\blacksquare = \blacksquare(4 + 6)$

Simplify each expression.

11. $6y + 4(y + 1)$

12. $5a + 2b + 3a - 7b$

13. $3(m + 2n) - 2n$

14. $3(2r - 5) + 8(r + 2)$

15. $2(x + y) - 2y$

16. $(-2c + 3d)(-5) + 3(-2c) - (-8d)$

Solve each equation.

17.

18.

19.

20. $k - 23 = 17$

21. $\frac{t}{-5} = 15$

22. $-3f = -42$

23. $120 = 38 + p$

24. $7w = -217$

25. $\frac{h}{12} = 12$

Write an equation for each problem. Do not solve.

26. Five less than 8 times the number of students is 163.

27. Three times the quantity $t + 9$ is equal to -18.

Solve.

28. The length of a room is 4 m longer than the width. The perimeter of the room is 28 m. Find the width of the room.

29. Brian bought a used bike for $25 less than its original price. He paid a total of $88 for the bike. What was the original price of the bike?

30. Write a word problem to describe the equation $4x = 2$.

Chapters 1–2   Cumulative Review

Choose the correct answer. Write A, B, C, or D.

1. 0, 1, 4, 9, 16, 25, . . .

   A. 26   **B.** 36

   C. 35   **D.** not given

2. Which property is used?

   $(ab)c = c(ab)$

   A. associative   **B.** identity

   C. commutative   **D.** not given

3. $12 - (-15)$

   A. -3   **B.** 3

   C. 27   **D.** not given

4. Simplify $(3x + 4)2 + 3(-2x)$.

   A. $-3x + 8$ **B.** $-3x + 4$

   C. $12x + 8$ **D.** not given

5. Solve $x - (-3) = 12$.

   A. 9   **B.** 4

   C. 15   **D.** not given

6. What is the variable expression for *six less than the absolute value of a number*?

   A. $|n| - 6$ **B.** $6 - |n|$

   C. $|n - 6|$ **D.** not given

7. Evaluate $3xy - 2x$ for $x = -1$, $y = 2$.

   A. -4   **B.** 8

   C. 4   **D.** not given

8. Solve $x + (-9) = 36$.

   A. 27   **B.** -4

   C. 45   **D.** not given

9. What is the opposite of $|-3|$?

   A. 3   **B.** 0

   C. -3   **D.** not given

10. Which equation has the solution -2?

   A. $x + 7 = 9$ **B.** $\frac{x}{-2} = 1$

   C. $(-3)x = -6$ **D.** not given

11. Complete $4(9 + 7) = (4 \cdot \blacksquare) + (4 \cdot 7)$.

   A. 7   **B.** 9

   C. 4   **D.** not given

12. Find two numbers whose sum is 10 and whose product is -24.

   A. -6 and 4   **B.** -12 and 2

   C. -8 and -3   **D.** not given

13. Solve $\frac{y}{4} = -12$.

   A. 3   **B.** -3

   C. -48   **D.** not given

14. Evaluate $98 + 2 \cdot 7 + 3$.

   A. 110   **B.** 118

   C. 115   **D.** not given

15. Solve $-8y = 72$.

   A. -7   **B.** -9

   C. 9   **D.** not given

16. Write an equation for the model.

   A. $x + 2 = 1$ **B.** $2x = 1$

   C. $x - 2 = 1$ **D.** $2x = -1$

A PRINTING PRESS can produce 8,000 sheets of 32 bills every hour.

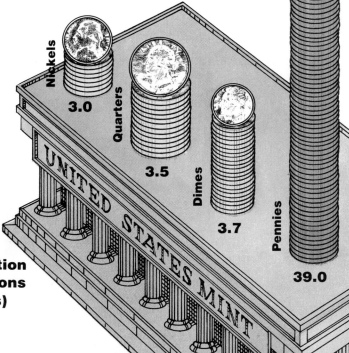

Nickels **3.0**

Quarters **3.5**

Dimes **3.7**

Pennies **39.0**

UNITED STATES MINT

Daily Coin Production (in millions of coins)

Decimals and Equations

Proof sets are special editions of a particular year's currency issued for collectors. A proof set comprises a penny, a nickel, a dime, a quarter, a half dollar, and, from 1973 to 1981, a silver dollar.

	Year	Number Produced	Value			
			At time of Issue	in 1965	in 1968	in 1990
PROOF SETS	1936	3,837	$1.81	$400.00	$5,100.00	$5,050.00
	1937	5,542	$1.81	$160.00	$3,500.00	$3,500.00
	1940	11,246	$1.81	$50.00	$1,200.00	$1,450.00
	1955	378,200	$2.10	$11.00	$60.00	$77.00
	1961	3,028,244	$2.10	$3.00	$20.00	$16.00

Think about it...

Look at the information about proof sets. What factors do you think would increase or decrease the value of a coin?

A dollar bill has a 16-mo. life expectancy

Amount of payment for a partially destroyed bill

FULL VALUE if $\frac{3}{5}$ or more is left

HALF VALUE if between $\frac{2}{5}$ and $\frac{3}{5}$ is left

NOTHING if less than $\frac{2}{5}$ is left

OBJECTIVE:
To explore decimals using decimal square models.

MATERIALS

• Decimal squares or graph paper

• Math journal to record work

Exploring Decimals

▼ You can use decimal squares to model numbers less than 1.

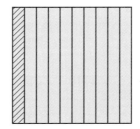

The figure above is divided into ten regions. Each region is called a *tenth*.

1. How many tenths are shaded? How many are not shaded?

2. **Model** each number using tenths' squares or graph paper.

   a. two tenths
   b. four tenths
   c. all but three tenths
   d. all but seven tenths

▼ In the figure below, each tenth has been divided into ten squares. Each small square is called a *hundredth*.

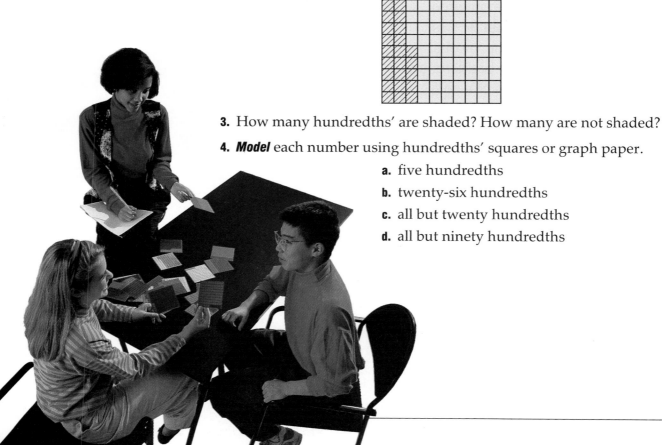

3. How many hundredths' are shaded? How many are not shaded?

4. **Model** each number using hundredths' squares or graph paper.

   a. five hundredths
   b. twenty-six hundredths
   c. all but twenty hundredths
   d. all but ninety hundredths

▼ You can use decimal squares to find equivalent decimals.

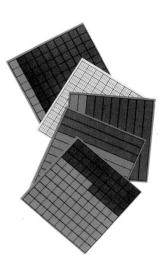

5. a. *Model* three tenths using tenths' squares.

   b. *Model* thirty hundredths using hundredths' squares.

   c. *Describe* and discuss how your models are different. How are they alike?

   d. Is three tenths equivalent to thirty hundredths? Explain.

▼ You can write each phrase as a decimal.

three tenths = 0.3   thirty hundredths = 0.30

Because three tenths and thirty hundredths are less than one, we write a zero as a place holder to the left of the *decimal point*.

6. Write each phrase as a decimal.

   a. four tenths   **b.** nine tenths   **c.** six tenths

   d. eighty-nine hundredths   **e.** fifteen hundredths

7. Determine which of the following pairs of decimals are equivalent. **Model** the decimals to justify your answer.

   a. three hundredths, three tenths

   b. seventy hundredths, seven tenths

   c. 0.5, 0.57   **d.** 0.4, 0.40

▼ You can compare decimals using models.

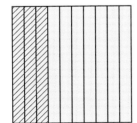   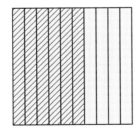

8. Write the decimals represented by the two models above.

   a. Which decimal is greater? How do you know?

   b. Write an inequality using the decimals.

9. Determine which decimal is greater. **Model** the decimals to justify your answer.

   a. 0.60 or 0.65   **b.** 0.5 or 0.47

10. How can you compare the two decimals without using a model?

OBJECTIVE:
To compare, round,
and order decimals.

3-1 Decimals

▼ The smallest flowering plant is a water plant called duckweed. Its length is 0.02 in. and its width is 0.008 in. The length is read as *two hundredths* and the width is read as *eight thousandths*. The place value chart below shows how to read and write decimals.

hundred thousands	ten thousands	thousands	hundreds	tens	ones	and	tenths	hundredths	thousandths	ten-thousandths	hundred-thousandths
				7	2	.	9				
					0	.	0	0	2		

You read and write these decimals as *seventy-two and nine tenths* and *two thousandths*.

▼ You can graph decimals on a number line.

Example 1 Give the decimal name for each point.

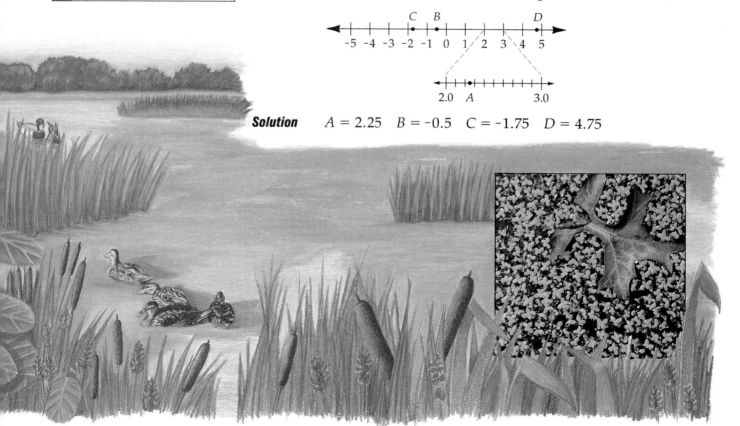

Solution $A = 2.25$ $B = -0.5$ $C = -1.75$ $D = 4.75$

▼ You can compare decimal numbers using a model.

Example 2   **Compare the decimals 0.57 and 0.69 using a model.**

Solution

0.57   0.69

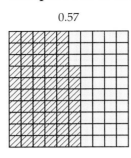

The area covered by 0.69 is greater than the area covered by 0.57. Therefore, 0.57 < 0.69.

▼ You can compare decimals using a number line.

Example 3   **Compare the decimals -0.5 and -1.25.**

Solution   On a horizontal number line, numbers are greater as you move to the right.

The decimal -0.5 is to the right of -1.25. So, -1.25 < -0.5.

THINK How could you compare the decimals 0.53 and 0.64 using the > symbol?

▼ You can compare decimals by comparing corresponding digits.

Example 4   Does Wilmington or Philadelphia receive more rain? Use the data at the right.

Solution   Compare the decimals 41.38 and 41.42.

The digits in the tens' and ones' places are the same. Compare the tenths' digits: 4 > 3. So, 41.42 > 41.38. Therefore, Philadelphia receives more rain.

▼ You can arrange decimals in order.

Example 5   **Order the cities according to their level of rainfall. Use the data at the right.**

Solution   Compare the decimals 41.84, 41.42, 41.76, and 41.38.

The digits in the tens' and ones' places are the same. Compare the tenths' digits: 8 > 7 > 4 > 3. Therefore, 41.84 > 41.76 > 41.42 > 41.38. So, the cities ranked from greatest rainfall to least rainfall are: Baltimore, Raleigh, Philadelphia, and Wilmington.

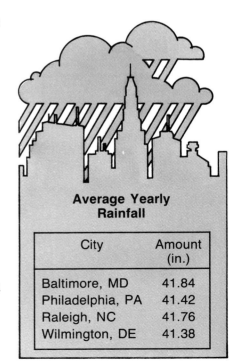

Average Yearly Rainfall

City	Amount (in.)
Baltimore, MD	41.84
Philadelphia, PA	41.42
Raleigh, NC	41.76
Wilmington, DE	41.38

THINK AND DISCUSS

1. The digit in the tenths' place of one decimal is less than the digit in the tenths' place of another decimal. Is the first decimal always less than the second? Explain.

2. Is 0.2 equivalent to 0.02? Why or why not?

3. For all nonzero decimals, is $a > -a$, where $-a$ is the opposite of a? Why or why not?

CLASS EXERCISES

Write the decimal represented by the shaded region.

1. 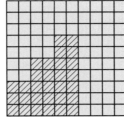   **2.**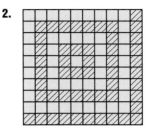

Read each decimal.

3. 0.42   **4.** 0.006   **5.** 4.801   **6.** 28.036

Write each decimal.

7. One kilometer is equivalent to *six hundred twenty-one thousandths* miles.

8. One fathom is *one and eight thousand two hundred eighty-eight ten-thousandths* meters.

Give the decimal name for each point.

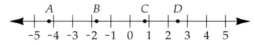

9. A **10.** B **11.** C **12.** D

Compare using >, <, or =.

13. 0.6 ▨ 0.06   **14.** 0.84 ▨ 0.840   **15.** -3.862 ▨ -3.859

WRITTEN EXERCISES

Write each decimal in words.

1. 0.83   **2.** 2.006   **3.** 392.9075   **4.** 0.00003

Write each decimal.

5. The world speed record for a motorcycle is *five hundred twelve and seventy-three hundredths* kilometers per hour.

6. The smallest book published has a length and width of *one and four tenths* millimeters.

Graph each decimal on a number line.

7. 3.6   **8.** -2.9   **9.** |-9.65| **10.** -|-2.75|

Compare. Use >, <, or =.

11. 3.8 ▨ 3.08   **12.** -5.6 ▨ -5.60   **13.** -3.9 ▨ -3.9000

14. -0.05 ▨ 0.005   **15.** -1.01 ▨ -1.101   **16.** 4.721 ▨ 4.712

17. |-0.6| ▨ |-0.09| **18.** 24.3333 ▨ 24.33333

Order from greatest to least.

19. 4.05, 4.5, 4.049   **20.** -4.98, -4.908, -4.098

21. 0.03, 0.030008, 3.003, 0.30, 0.3002

22. 27.618, 27.681, -54.091, 27.6801, 54.0900

Write a decimal between the given decimals.

23. 1.5 and 2.5   **24.** 0.6 and 0.9   **25.** 23.5 and 23.6

26. -0.5 and 0   **27.** -0.678 and -0.679   **28.** 3.57 and 3.58

MIXED REVIEW
Solve each equation.
1. $-3 + x = -8$
2. $y - 12 = -9$
3. $-9y = 81$
4. $\frac{a}{-3} = 15$
5. What are two whole numbers that when added give you 10 and when multiplied give you 21?
6. Mario had d dollars in his bank account and wrote a check for $40. He then had $182 in his account. Write an equation for this problem and solve for d.

Round each decimal to the indicated place.

▼▼   *SAMPLE*   Round 45.68 to the nearest tenth.

The number to the right of the tenths' place is eight. Since eight is greater than five, we increase the number in the tenths' place by one. So, 45.68 rounded to the nearest tenth is 45.7.

29. 0.76, nearest tenth   **30.** -9.095, nearest hundredth

31. 0.3632, nearest hundredth   **32.** 4.9677, nearest thousandth

33. 365,987.092, nearest integer   **34.** 5.9999, nearest thousandth

35. *DATA FILE 10 (pp. 404–405)* Order from least to greatest the home range in acres required by the species listed.

36. Order the data in the chart at the right from fastest winning speed to slowest winning speed of the Indianapolis 500.

37. Use the decimal 47.8364 to answer the following questions.

   a. Will interchanging the tenths' and hundredths' digits produce a greater or lesser decimal?

   b. Will interchanging the hundredths' and thousandths' digits produce a greater or lesser decimal?

   c. When will interchanging digits produce a greater decimal?

38. Which decimals make each equation true?

   a. $|x| = 0.03$ **b.** $|a| = 80.123$ **c.** $|x| = |-3.86|$

39. *WRITE* Use absolute value to describe a method for deciding when one negative number is greater than another.

Winning Speeds for Indianapolis 500

Year	Speed (mi/h)
1979	158.899
1980	142.862
1981	139.029
1982	162.029
1983	162.117
1984	162.962
1985	152.982
1986	170.722
1987	162.175
1988	144.809
1989	167.581
1990	185.984
1991	176.457
1992	134.477

OBJECTIVE:
To estimate sums,
differences, products,
and quotients of
decimals.

3-2 *Estimating with Decimals*

▼ You can estimate using decimals.

Example 1 Estimate how much of each square is shaded. Write each estimate using decimal numbers.

a. 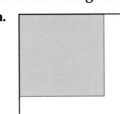   b.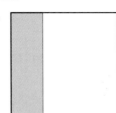

Solution   **a.** 0.7   **b.** 0.3

▼ You can use *rounding* to estimate the sum, difference, product, or quotient of decimals.

Example 2 Estimate the sum of 4.75, 2.2, and 9.86.

Solution   4.75 + 2.2 + 9.86   Round to the nearest integer.

≈ 5 + 2 + 10   Add.

≈ 17

The sum is approximately 17.

Example 3 One orange contains 1.4 g of protein. Estimate how many grams of protein 2.5 oranges contain.

Solution   1.4 · 2.5   Round to the nearest integer.

≈ 1 · 3   Multiply.

≈ 3

There are approximately 3 g of protein in 2.5 oranges.

▼ You can use *front-end estimation* when adding decimals. This method is especially helpful when estimating dollar amounts.

Front-end Estimation	To use front-end estimation:
	1. Add the front-end digits.
	2. Adjust by estimating the sum of the remaining digits.
	3. Add the two values.

Example 4   The junior class held three events to raise money for their prom. Estimate their profit.

Solution   **1.** Add front-end digits. $100 + 500 + 300$ is 900.

2. Adjust. $56.35 + 42.75 \approx 100.$
$100 + 72.70 \approx 170.$

3. Add the two values. $900 + 170 = 1{,}070$

The class earned a profit of about $1,070.

Junior Class Fund Raisers

Event	Profit
Bake Sale	$156.35
Car Wash	$542.75
Raffle	$372.70

▼ You can estimate quotients using *compatible numbers*.

Compatible Numbers	Compatible numbers are two numbers that are easy to divide mentally.

Example 5   Taylor earns $13.75 per hour. Last week he earned $385. About how many hours did he work?

Solution $385 \div 13.75$
$\approx 390 \div 13$ **Use compatible numbers 390 and 13.**
≈ 30

Taylor worked approximately 30 h.

CLASS EXERCISES

Estimate using rounding.

1. $-86.5 + 45.99 + (-91.21)$ **2.** $858.32 - 281.319$

3. $-92.81 \cdot (-48.33)$ **4.** $318.09 \div 48.33$

Estimate using front-end estimation.

5. $3.75 + $14.10 + $23.30   **6.** $88.50 - $29.60

Estimate using compatible numbers.

7. $0.8622 \div (-4)$ **8.** $-43.08 \div 5.21$

THINK AND DISCUSS

1. In what situations would an estimate be preferred over an exact amount?

2. What is the quotient of $4{,}702 \div 81$ using rounding?

3. How could you get an estimate of the range within which an answer will fall?

WRITTEN EXERCISES

Estimate the shaded region using decimal numbers.

1.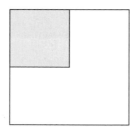

2.

Estimate using rounding.

3. $34.99 + 27.302$ 4. $416.98 - 28.301$ 5. $0.08 \cdot 400$

6. $16.092 \cdot 9.21$ 7. $329.08 \cdot (\text{-}56)$ 8. $\$378.90 \div 42$

9. $45.87 + 35.912 + 126.08 + 83.234$

10. $0.043 + 0.0591 + 0.088 + 0.0241 + 0.0473$

Estimate using front-end estimation.

11. $3.57 + 2.95 + 1.681$ 12. $\$7.25 + \$9.08 + \$6.88 + \$3.69$

13. $9.033 + 2.82 + 6.18 + 8.953$

14. $\$9.01 + \$8.94 + \$5.63 + \$6.48 + \$8.23$

Estimate using compatible numbers.

15. $9.392 \div 2.9$ 16. $\text{-}483.09 \div 72.3$

17. $\text{-}7.75 \div \text{-}1.98$ 18. $\$32.43 \div \$4.68$

19. $0.5863 \div 26.2$ 20. $\$78.92 \div \$8.55$

Estimate using the technique which seems best.

21. $\$43.92 \cdot 54$ 22. $\text{-}0.98 + (\text{-}0.34) + 0.66$

23. $0.083 + 0.149$ 24. $416.98 - 28.301$

25. $\text{-}18.9 \cdot (\text{-}12.02)$ 26. $293.7 \div 42.03$

27. $\text{-}2.843 + (\text{-}5.022) + (\text{-}8.45) + (\text{-}3.991)$

28. $21.88 + (\text{-}9.88) + 35.901 + 28.03 + (\text{-}13.99) + 26.92$

Use estimation to place the decimal point in each answer.

29. $7.008 \cdot 3.2 = 224256$ 30. $98.003 \, (\text{-}1.8) = \text{-}1764054$

31. $106.88 \div 0.5 = 21376$ 32. $14.39 + 6.132 + 0.684 = 21206$

33. $94.02 + 9.011 + 18.34 + (\text{-}11.8) = 109571$

34. $115.67 + 88.09 + (\text{-}113.6) = 9016$

35. $46.872 \cdot 0.05 + 65 = 673436$

36. $0.5 \cdot 200.8 \div 2 = 502$

ESTIMATION Use the table at the right to solve.

37. Can biscuits, puppy food, and a collar be purchased for $10?

38. Amy has $20 to buy a collar and a leash. With the remaining money, what is the greatest number of toys she can buy?

39. Todd is in the check-out line with all six items and only $17. What is the least expensive item he can put back and still pay for the other five items?

Items to Buy for the New Puppy

Item	Cost
Leash	$6.37
Biscuits	$1.79
Food	$3.29
Collar	$4.37
Toy	$2.19
Shampoo	$1.97

Use the article below to answer each question.

English, Anyone?

In 1989, the *Oxford English Dictionary* was revised for the second time. It was dedicated to Queen Elizabeth II. The dictionary consists of 20 volumes. It contains 21,728 pages and defines 616,500 words. The longest word defined is *pneumonoultramicro*-scopicsilicovolcanoconiosis, a disease of the lungs. The 20 volumes weigh almost 138 lb and take up 45 in. of shelf space. Printing the first 10,000 sets of the dictionary required 6,243 lb of ink. The *Oxford English Dictionary* can be purchased for $2,500.

40. **a.** About how many pages are contained in each volume?

 b. Estimate the weight of each volume.

 c. About how many inches of shelf would 6 volumes require?

 d. What is the approximate value of each volume?

Solve.

41. Extra-large eggs cost $1.19 per dozen. Medium eggs cost $.98 per dozen. Estimate the savings on 10 dozen eggs if you buy medium instead of extra-large.

42. Grapes cost $1.14/lb. Estimate the cost of three bunches weighing 1.3 lb, 2.6 lb, and 1.9 lb. Explain your method.

43. The cost of sending a package is $23.80. Estimate the cost of sending 156 such packages.

44. **DATA FILE 4 (pp. 138–139)** About how many children are born in a minute? an hour? a day? a week? a month? a year?

45. **DATA FILE 9 (pp. 360–361)** Estimate the total number of yards at St. Andrew's golf club for holes one through nine.

46. **WRITE** Explain how you might estimate the total cost of your purchases at the grocery store.

3-3 Expressions with Decimals

▼ The number of hours a growing child should sleep each night depends on the child's age. You can find the recommended number of hours by evaluating the expression $17 - 0.5a$, where a is the child's age.

To find the number of hours a 7-year-old child should sleep in a night, evaluate the expression $17 - 0.5a$ for $a = 7$.

$17 - 0.5a = 17 - 0.5(7)$ **Replace a with 7.**
$= 17 \boxed{-} 0.5 \boxed{\times} 7 \boxed{=} 13.5$

A 7-year-old child should sleep 13.5 h.

▼ Expressions may contain more than one variable.

Example 1   **Use a calculator to evaluate $3.7a - 4b$ for $a = -3.2$ and $b = 6.1$.**

Solution $3.7a - 4b = 3.7(-3.2) - 4(6.1)$ **Replace a with**
$3.7 \boxed{\times} 3.2 \boxed{+/-} \boxed{-} 4 \boxed{\times} 6.1 \boxed{=} -36.24$ **-3.2 and b**
                                          with 6.1.

▼ You can simplify expressions involving decimals by using properties of addition and multiplication.

Example 2   **Simplify $3.1x + 2.3y + 8.4x$.**

Solution $3.1x + 2.3y + 8.4x$
$3.1x + 8.4x + 2.3y$ commutative property
$(3.1x + 8.4x) + 2.3y$ associative property
$(3.1 + 8.4)x + 2.3y$ distributive property
$11.5x + 2.3y$ Add coefficients.

CLASS EXERCISES

Evaluate each expression for $x = -1.9$ and $y = 2.4$.

1. $2.5x$ **2.** $3 - y$ **3.** $x - y$

4. $x + y$ **5.** $-x + 2y$ **6.** $3x - 8 + 2y$

Simplify each expression.

7. $2.1x + 3.4x$ **8.** $-1.2(7.9b)$ **9.** $-2(4.3a - 2.2a)$

10. $-9.4 + 3a + 16.25$ **11.** $2.03b + 0.08a - 4.211b$

THINK AND DISCUSS

1. Would the expression given at the beginning of this lesson work for a 36-year-old person? Explain.

2. For what numbers will the expression $-3.6w$ be positive? negative?

3. What does it mean to evaluate an expression?

WRITTEN EXERCISES

Use the expression $17 - 0.5a$ to find the number of hours a child of each age should sleep each day.

1. $a = 11$ **2.** $a = 1.5$ **3.** $a = 5.25$ **4.** $a = 0.5$

Evaluate each expression for $x = 3.9$.

5. $-2x$ **6.** $28.07 - x$ **7.** $58.89 \div x$ **8.** $x + (-4.03)$

Evaluate each expression for $m = -7.06$ and $n = 13.2$.

9. $m + n$ **10.** $m - n$ **11.** $2m - 6.5$

12. $-4m + 18.234$ **13.** $-2m - 3n$ **14.** $1.5(m + n)$

15. $\dfrac{m - 4n}{4}$ **16.** $\dfrac{3m - 2n}{-118.95}$ **17.** $\dfrac{-n - m}{4 \div (3 - 1)}$

MENTAL MATH Evaluate each expression.

18. $-100x$ for $x = -3.882$ **19.** $50x$ for $x = -0.5$

20. $x + y$ for $x = -8.22$ and $y = 8.22$

21. $2x - y$ for $x = -4.22$ and $y = 12$

CALCULATOR Evaluate each expression.

22. $3.98x$ for $x = -42.91$ **23.** $\dfrac{x}{9.8}$ for $x = 29.4098$

24. $22.8x - 15.4y$ for $x = -0.092$ and $y = 21.3$.

25. $(x - a) - (y - b)$ for $a = -4.96$, $b = 12.03$, $x = -2.3$, and $y = 7$.

26. $x(2.703y - 5.6701)$ for $x = 0.051$ and $y = -3.682$.

Simplify.

27. $2.4(-16.84w)$ **28.** $-5.23x \cdot 14.1$ **29.** $8.24m \div (-10.3)$

30. $3.78(4.01m) \div 0.02$ **31.** $-5.6x + 13.2x$

MIXED REVIEW

Estimate each answer.

1. $\$35.98 + \$155.23$

2. $56{,}000.3 - 38{,}412.9$

3. $-5.33 \cdot 0.992$

4. $0.9341 \div 8.1$

Solve each equation.

5. $x + (-23) = -19$

6. $20 = a - 15$

Solve.

7. Ricky bought 9 pencils at $\$.23$ per pencil and 5 pens at $\$.37$ per pen. How much more did he spend on pencils than pens?

32. $0.007m - 0.04m$

33. $9.0578a - 4(6.057 - 2.0473a)$

34. $\dfrac{-4.79x + 1.79x}{0.003}$

35. $\dfrac{(0.2x)(4.98) - 37.2x}{20}$

ESTIMATION Estimate the value if $x = 38.953$ and $y = 127.06$.

36. $x + y$

37. $x - y$

38. $3x - 10$

39. $\dfrac{y}{x}$

40. WRITE a paragraph explaining how to find the value of $3.8 + (-7.1)x$ if x is -4.25. Tell how to find the sign as well as the numerical value of the answer.

$5.2a - 1.48$

$3a - 0.2$

$4.1a + 0.6$

Solve.

41. a. Express the perimeter of the triangle in simplest form.

 b. What is the perimeter if $a = 8.401$?

42. The interest earned on a bank account is $0.087x$, where x is the amount in the account. Find the interest earned on $10,000.

43. The selling price of a videotape is $c + 3.24$, where c is the cost of the tape. Find the selling price of a tape costing $18.43.

Critical Thinking

EXPLORING PATTERNS IN DIVISION

1. Follow the steps in the division problem below. Continue the pattern and describe what happens.

0.2 and 1.6	Begin with two numbers.
$1.6 \div 0.2 = 8$	Divide the second by the first.
$8 \div 1.6 = 5$	Divide the quotient by the number above it.
$5 \div 8 = 0.625$	Continue dividing each quotient by the number above it for four
$0.625 \div 5 = 0.125$	more divisions.

2. Follow the same pattern with the numbers 2.5 and 2. Describe your results. Did it matter that you began with a decimal number and a whole number?

3. Follow the pattern with the numbers 2 and -0.2. Describe your results. Did it matter that you began with a positive and a negative number?

4. Write a paragraph describing this pattern.

3-4 Addition and Subtraction Equations

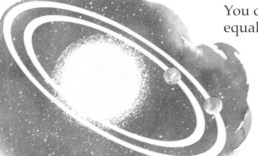

▼ Earth is 93 million miles from the sun. Mars is 141.71 million miles from the sun. What is the minimum number of miles from Earth to Mars? Let m represent the minimum number of millions of miles from Earth to Mars. You can describe the situation by the following equation.

$$93 + m = 141.71$$

You can solve this equation by using the subtraction property of equality.

$$93 + m = 141.71$$
$$93 + m - 93 = 141.71 - 93 \qquad \text{Subtract 93 from each}$$
$$m = 48.71 \qquad \text{side.}$$

Check $93 + m = 141.71$
$93 \boxed{+} 48.71 \boxed{=} 141.71 ✓$ Replace m with 48.71.

The minimum distance from Earth to Mars is 48.71 million miles.

▼ You can solve an equation involving subtraction by using the addition property of equality.

Example 1 Solve $n - 29.1 = -30.85$ and graph the solution.

Solution
$$n - 29.1 = -30.85$$
$$n - 29.1 + 29.1 = -30.85 + 29.1 \qquad \text{Add 29.1 to each side.}$$
$$n = -1.75$$

Check $n - 29.1 = -30.85$
$-1.75 \boxed{-} 29.1 \boxed{=} -30.85 ✓$ Replace n with -1.75.

Graph -1.75 on the number line.

▼ **THINK** How could you use estimation to decide if the solution is reasonable?

-2 -1 0 1

We know more about Mars
than any other planet except
Earth. Most of our infor-
mation is from Mariner 9.

RESEARCH Find out when the
Mariner 9 orbited Mars and
what some of its findings
were.

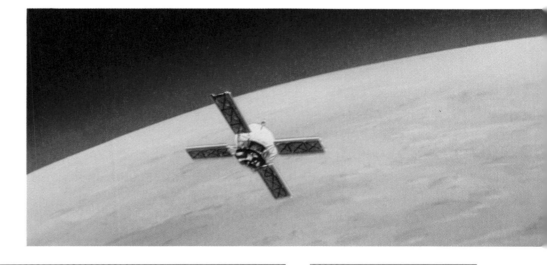

▼ You can also use opposites to solve addition and subtraction equations.

Example 2 Solve $5 = a + 2.02$ by using opposites.

Solution
$$5 = a + 2.02$$
$$5 + (-2.02) = a + 2.02 + (-2.02) \qquad \text{Add -2.02 to each side.}$$
$$2.98 = a + 0$$
$$2.98 = a \qquad \text{The check is left for you.}$$

THINK AND DISCUSS

1. Will the solution to $38.1 + x = 14.07$ be greater than or less than zero? Explain.

2. What properties would you need to use to show $a - 15.23 + 15.23$ is equivalent to a?

CLASS EXERCISES

State the first step in solving each equation.

1. $x + 4.9 = 18.8$ **2.** $a - 19.2 = 24$

3. $12.703 = n - 16.51$ **4.** $3.78 + m = 0$

Solve each addition equation.

5. $a + 0.98 = 0.24$ **6.** $-4.26 + c = 22.991$

Solve each subtraction equation.

7. $m - 43.23 = 80.9$ **8.** $-0.09 = a - 0.224$

WRITTEN EXERCISES

Solve each equation using the subtraction property.

1. $x + 4.38 = -9.011$ **2.** $0 = y + 39.4$

3. $1.77 + c = 3.4$ **4.** $-8.32 = y + 3.211$

Solve each equation using opposites.

5. $0.402 + c = 0.0322$ **6.** $s + 12.85 = 4.9$

7. $-0.021 = x + 0.0023$ **8.** $309.462 + y = 500$

Solve each equation using the addition property.

9. $11.03 = w - 1.55$ **10.** $8.9 = b - 8.88$

11. $-3.98 = m - 5.012$ **12.** $u - 400.32 = -912.268$

Solve each equation using opposites.

13. $w + (-5.07) = 8.24$ **14.** $0 = n - 29.335$

15. $-45.02 = m - 21.9$ **16.** $t + (-0.66) = 0.66$

MENTAL MATH Solve each equation.

17. $a - 2.33 = 2.33$

18. $t + 45.023 = 45.023$

19. $9.45 = w + 7.45$

20. $m - 0.003 = 18.29$

CALCULATOR Solve each equation.

21. $60,000 = w - 392.0034$

22. $-0.34264 + x = 5.920154$

23. $m + 912.87 = 920.001$

24. $t - 982.0012 = -893.20876$

Solve each equation using any method. Graph each solution.

25. $y + 0.05 = 3.95$

26. $t - 79.4 = -46.7$

27. $m - (-0.88) = 0.88$

28. $-23.9 = x + 14.1$

29. $p - 18.8 = -24.2$

30. $k + (-35.9) = 24.8$

31. $48.003 + r = 50.903$

32. $b + 6.7 = 9.90$

33. $w - (-0.34) = 0.74$

34. $t - 43.8 = 0$

35. $b + 16 = -43.9$

36. $-1.78 = v - 0.98$

Use the article below and the table at the right to answer each question.

pHase Out Acid Rain

The pH scale measures the acidity of a substance. The scale ranges from most acidic, 0, to least acidic, 14. Many plants and animals can only survive in a narrow range of acidity. Acid rain changes the acidity level of the water and soil where organisms live. As a result, many plants and animals can be severely damaged or even die. Studies have shown that industry and motor vehicle emissions are among the major sources of acid rain.

Average PH Levels

Item	PH
Unpolluted rain	5.6
Acid rain	4.6
Grapes	4.1
Grapefruit	3.2
Orange	3.5
Apple	3.1
Sea water	7.36–8.21
Milk	6.5

37. a. Order the fruits from most acidic to least acidic.

   b. Hydrangeas have blue flowers when grown in soil with a pH level less than 7. The flowers are pink when grown in soil with a pH level greater than 7. What color would the flowers be if grown in soil having the same pH level as grapes?

   c. **PROJECT** Research smog, another form of air pollution. Write a short paragraph. Be sure to include the pH level.

Solve each equation for a.

38. $a - b = c$

39. $b = a + c$

40. $-c + a = b$

41. Find values for x and y that solve both equations:
$x + y = 0.03$ and $x - y = 0.13$.

Find each value.

1. $|-4.53| + 3.099$

2. $-0.993 - |-0.6712|$

Evaluate.

3. $3x$ when $x = -0.82$

4. $x + 2y$ when $x = 3.266$ and $y = -4.01$

Simplify

5. $4.3(-9.2x)$

6. $2.9y - 4.88y + 1.7y$

Solve.

7. A large juice is $.83 and a small juice is $.57. Ann buys one juice per day. What is her weekly savings if she buys small juices instead of large ones?

42. **a.** Are the equations $1.7x + 2.4 = 1.5$ and $17x + 24 = 15$ equivalent? How do you know?

b. **WRITE** a procedure for changing a decimal equation into one with integers. Show how your method would work for any of the equations in this lesson.

Write an equation for each sentence. Solve.

43. Fifty-eight thousandths less than some number is equal to fifty-eight hundredths. Find the number.

44. Seven and three hundred thirty-nine thousandths equals five and one hundred seventy-eight thousandths more than some number. Find the number.

45. One and ninety-nine ten-thousandths equals two more than some number. Find the number.

46. Eight hundred ninety-two and thirty-two hundredths less a number is equal to one thousand, four hundred eleven and twelve thousandths. Find the number.

47. Three plus some number equals eight and sixteen hundredths. Find the number.

TEST YOURSELF

Compare. Write >, <, or =.

1. 3.088 ▨ 3.808 2. 2.3 ▨ 2.300 3. -4.23 ▨ -4.991

Round to the nearest tenth.

4. -9.65 5. 4.3088 6. 17.952

Estimate the value of each expression.

7. $0.8823 \div 3$ 8. $5.9 \cdot 3.88$ 9. $437.02 - 188.54$

Evaluate if $x = 5.8$ and $y = -2.3$.

10. xy 11. $x - 2$ 12. $-2y - x$

Simplify.

13. $2.99 + x + (-3.08)$ 14. $-3.55y - 9.01y$

Solve each equation.

15. $x - 9.09 = -15.8$ 16. $24.011 = y + 23.9$

3-5 Multiplication and Division Equations

▼ On average, an oil well produces 16.8 barrels each day. In how many days will it produce 184.8 barrels? If we represent the number of days by the variable d, we can write an equation.

$$16.8d = 184.8$$

You can solve this equation using the division property of equality.

$$16.8d = 184.8$$
$$\frac{16.8d}{16.8} = \frac{184.8}{16.8}$$ Divide both sides by 16.8, the coefficient of d.
$$d = 11$$

Check $16.8d = 184.8$
$16.8(11) = 184.8$ Replace d with 11.
$184.8 = 184.8$ ✓

It will take 11 days to produce 184.8 barrels of oil.

▼ You can solve equations involving division by using the multiplication property of equality.

Example 1   Solve $\frac{x}{2.1} = -0.9$ and graph the solution.

Solution
$$\frac{x}{2.1} = -0.9$$
$$2.1\left(\frac{x}{2.1}\right) = -0.9(2.1)$$ Multiply both sides by 2.1.
$$x = -1.89$$

Check   Use estimation to see if the solution is reasonable.

$$\frac{x}{2.1} = -0.9$$ Round each decimal to the nearest integer.

$$\approx \frac{-2}{2} = -1$$ Since -1 is close to -0.9, the solution is reasonable.

Graph -1.89 on the number line.

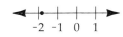

-2 -1 0 1

▼ You may need to round an answer when solving a problem.

Example 2   Use a calculator to solve $3.98x = 470$. Round to the nearest tenth.

Solution $470 \,\boxed{\div}\, 3.98 \,\boxed{=}\, 118.09045$
≈ 118.1 Round to the nearest tenth.

CLASS EXERCISES

State the first step in solving each equation.

1. $0.7x = -0.63$ **2.** $\frac{y}{0.6} = 1.2$

3. $1.5 = d \div 15$ **4.** $-1.2 = -0.4m$

Solve each multiplication equation.

5. $-0.5y = -0.73$ **6.** $0.8x = 0.448$

7. $-540 = -1.8t$ **8.** $13.133 = -2.3w$

Solve each division equation.

9. $\frac{y}{2.3} = -4.8$ **10.** $0.97 = \frac{c}{-2}$

11. $2{,}390 = z \div 0.033$ **12.** $\frac{m}{0.19} = -492.05$

WRITTEN EXERCISES

Solve using the division property of equality.

1. $2x = -4.88$ **2.** $-0.3y = 7.53$

3. $6.4x = 0.2816$ **4.** $-0.00051z = -2.026791$

5. $1.92 = 1.6s$ **6.** $0.004m = 0.12$

7. $3.17n = 135.042$ **8.** $2.21 = 1.7w$

Solve using the multiplication property of equality.

9. $\frac{n}{1.7} = 0.22$ **10.** $\frac{k}{2.01} = 0.04$ **11.** $4.5 = m \div (-3.3)$

12. $-33.04 = \frac{z}{-0.03}$ **13.** $-0.45 = x \div 12$ **14.** $\frac{m}{0.89} = 3{,}488$

15. $\frac{w}{-3.4} = -25.5$ **16.** $12{,}088.25 = \frac{v}{3.8}$ **17.** $\frac{c}{12.56} = 0.245$

MENTAL MATH Solve each equation.

18. $0.7x = 2.8$ **19.** $\frac{m}{7.08} = -100$ **20.** $6 = a \div 1.5$

21. $10{,}000r = 483.08$ **22.** $0.55t = 0.0055$

CALCULATOR Solve each equation. Round each answer to the nearest tenth.

23. $0.46x = 89.23$ **24.** $45.08t = -2{,}917.335$

25. $-0.93 = 0.0221z$ **26.** $-9.03m = 499{,}812.4$

CALCULATOR Solve each equation. Round each answer to the nearest hundredth.

27. $4.55x = 43.225$ **28.** $\frac{m}{7.08} = -35.992$

29. $y \div 84.6 = 2.79$ **30.** $90.43n = -298.0113$

Solve each equation using any method. Graph each solution.

31. $0.9 = \frac{m}{41}$ **32.** $100t = -45$

33. $\frac{z}{-0.4} = 0.5$ **34.** $3.94z = -21.67$

35. $t \div 0.4 = -15$ **36.** $-99.252 = -8.271r$

Solve each equation for x.

37. $x \div y = z$ **38.** $xz = y$ **39.** $y = \frac{x}{z}$

Write an equation for each sentence. Solve.

40. The quotient of some number t divided by -4.5 equals 200.6. Find the number.

41. Four thousandths times some number is equal to eighty-eight hundredths. Find the number.

42. The cost of an adult ticket is c. The cost of eight adult tickets is $71.60. What is the price of one ticket?

43. A number divided by -2.35 is equal to 400.9. Find the number.

44. Nineteen and five thousand five hundred twenty-five ten thousandths is the same as five and five tenths times some number. Find the number.

45. **WRITE** Write a paragraph explaining how to use estimation to place the decimal point in a multiplication or division computation.

46. Find values for x and y that satisfy both equations: $xy = 0.42$ and $x + y = 1.3$.

47. COMPUTER A school needs to buy a minimum of 2,000 pencils, 1,000 pens, 500 notebooks, and 150 reams of paper. The budget cannot exceed $3,000.

	A	B	C	D
1	Item	Quantity	Unit Price	Total
2	Pencils		0.10	=B2*C2
3	Pens		0.50	=B3*C3
4	Notebooks		2.25	=B4*C4
5	Paper (ream)		4.75	=B5*C5
6			TOTAL	=SUM(D2:D5)
7				

a. What is the least amount the school can spend?

b. Suppose the remaining money is spent on notebooks. How many more notebooks can be bought?

c. Suppose the price of pencils increases to $.15 and the price of a ream of paper drops to $4.55. Can the school afford its minimum amount of supplies?

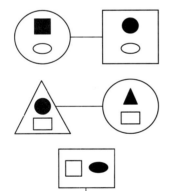

Critical Thinking

EXPLORING LOGICAL FAMILIES

The figures at the left are called Quipps.

1. What are the distinguishing characteristics of a Quipp?

2. Which of the following are Quipps?

a. 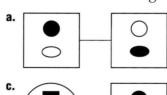   b.

c. 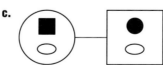   d.

3. Create two of your own Quipps.

4. Create a logical family consisting of three members. Trade with a classmate to see if they can determine the distinguishing characteristic.

Practice

Write each decimal in words.

1. 0.67   **2.** 2.90   **3.** 637.0004   **4.** 0.00007

Write each decimal.

5. two hundred fifteen and seventy-four hundredths

6. six and eight tenths

7. forty-two and seven hundredths

8. five hundred four thousandths

Compare using >, <, or =.

9. 9.9 ▓ 9.09   **10.** -4.2 ▓ -4.20   **11.** -8.600 ▓ 8.6

12. -0.06 ▓ 0.006   **13.** -3.47 ▓ -3.547   **14.** 85.706 ▓ 85.7

15. $|-0.2|$ ▓ $|0.2|$ **16.** $|8.9|$ ▓ $|-10.7|$ **17.** 0.36 ▓ 0.3600

Estimate using rounding, front-end estimation, or compatible numbers.

18. $57.96 · 45   **19.** 95.27 ÷ 5.2

20. 0.029 + 0.999   **21.** 0.98 ÷ 1.03

22. -490.6 − 25.302   **23.** $10.25 + $36.32 + $9.05

Evaluate each expression for $x = -2.3$ and $y = 8.92$.

24. $-x - y$ **25.** $y - (-x)$ **26.** $4x + 7.39$

27. $-10y - 4.8$ **28.** $x - 4y$ **29.** $-6.3(x + y)$

30. $\dfrac{x - y + y}{-x}$ **31.** $\dfrac{-x - y}{x + y}$ **32.** $-x + y$

Solve each equation.

33. $x + 0.25 = 8$ **34.** $\dfrac{w}{18} = -2.7$ **35.** $a - (-42.4) = 42.4$

36. $n \div 8 = 3.02$ **37.** $0.008z = 0.24$ **38.** $m - (-9.4) = 0$

39. $-0.96 = 0.8t$ **40.** $0.59 + s = -1.0$ **41.** $y - 42.76 = -0.05$

42. $-132 = 66i$ **43.** $25j = -100.9$ **44.** $d - (-0.04) = 0.74$

45. $8x = -15.52$ **46.** $-100.05 = c + 5$ **47.** $-18.07 - r = 0.5$

Solve each equation for m.

48. $m + n = p$ **49.** $n = \dfrac{m}{p}$ **50.** $p + m = n$

51. $p = \dfrac{n}{m}$ **52.** $n - m = p$ **53.** $mn = p$

OBJECTIVE:
To explore using data in tables.

Exploring Data in Tables

■ A sports camp holds track and field trials on the first day of camp. The table below shows the performance of the campers on several different measures.

Name	Running 50 m	Running 1,500 m	Jumping (cm) high jump	Jumping (cm) long jump	Shooting basketball throw (out of 20 shots)
Aimee	8.6 s	12 min 25 s	127.0	325.1	10
Barbara	10.3 s	15 min 49 s	106.7	299.7	8
Dwayne	8.5 s	12 min 4 s	139.7	365.8	15
Floyd	8.7 s	10 min 54 s	124.5	327.7	14
Hannah	7.9 s	11 min 0 s	129.6	294.6	17
Isaiah	8.1 s	10 min 37 s	116.8	342.9	15
Jane	8.4 s	10 min 37 s	132.1	332.7	15
Manuel	8.7 s	13 min 9 s	121.9	309.9	13
Nancy	7.4 s	9 min 4 s	139.2	364.8	18
Sydney	8.6 s	12 min 2 s	127.1	327.7	11
Tran	8.4 s	12 min 46 s	137.1	340.4	16
Warren	7.7 s	8 min 18 s	134.6	368.4	18

MATERIALS

• Math journal to record work

1. a. Which event best demonstrates the campers' endurance?

   b. Which best demonstrates the campers' speed? Which best demonstrates accuracy?

   c. Does the camper who runs the 50 m fastest also run the 1,500 m fastest? Is this true for the second-fastest runner? the third fastest? Is there a relationship between the time run in the 50 m and the time run in the 1,500 m? Explain.

   d. Who would you consider a better runner, the camper who runs the 50 m faster or the 1,500 m faster? Why?

2. a. Who is the highest jumper? Who is the longest jumper?

   b. Is the highest jumper the same person as the longest jumper? Is this always true? Explain.

   c. Is there a relationship between the best runners and the best jumpers? Explain.

3. Who is the best shooter? Is there a relationship between the campers' running, jumping, and shooting skills?

4. Who is the fastest runner in the 50-m run?

   a. List the campers in order from fastest to slowest.

   b. Could you list the campers in order from slowest to fastest? Explain.

c. Tran and Jane both ran the 50 m in 8.4 s. In what order will you list them? Explain.

d. In what order will you list Aimee, Sydney, Floyd, and Manuel?

5. Continue to list the campers in order in the 1,500-m run, the high jump, the long jump, and the basketball throw.

6. In the jumping events, could you order the campers from shortest distance jumped to longest distance jumped? Explain.

■ The camp uses the results to assign campers to teams. The first event is a 2,000-m relay race between three evenly matched teams.

7. How far must each camper run in the relay race?

8. Who do you think would run best in the relay race: the campers who ran the fastest in the 50 m or the 1,500 m? Why?

a. Would you take the campers' jumping and basketball throw scores into consideration? Explain.

b. What other factors will help you decide who should be on the three evenly matched teams?

9. Make a list of the three teams. **Compare** with another group.

■ The second sporting event is a basketball game. There will be two evenly matched teams, with five on a team. The two extra campers will rotate positions in the game.

10. The two guards need to be the fastest runners, and they also must have good endurance and shooting skills. Who would you pick? Why?

11. The center doesn't need to be as fast as the guards. It's important for the center to be a good shooter and jumper, and have good endurance. Who would you pick? Why?

12. The two forwards need to have excellent endurance and strength. They need to be good jumpers and they must be fast. Who would you pick? Why?

13. Make a list of the two teams. **Compare** with another group.

14. Did you choose the same teams the other groups chose? **Describe** and discuss why you made your choices. Is there one right answer?

15. **Summarize** For which event was it easiest to pick the teams? Why?

Exploring Data Bases

MATERIALS

- Paper
- Computer and data base software (optional)
- Math journal to record work

■ A *data base* is a collection of information. The data is usually arranged in rows and columns and can be rearranged in any order. Below is a data base of names and addresses.

Name	Street	City	State	Zip Code
Smith, Greg	123 Main St.	Tucson	Arizona	85726
Cruz, Maria	97 South St.	Burbank	California	91505
Chien, Janice	876 Water St.	Honolulu	Hawaii	96820
Jones, Carl	8 Division St.	Albany	New York	12266

1. In what order are the data arranged? How else can they be arranged?

2. Suppose you wanted to arrange the data in alphabetical order. Show the results on a sheet of paper (by last name).

3. Suppose you need to update the data base with this information.

Name	Street	City	State	Zip Code
Ales, George	24 Broadway	Dallas	Texas	74356
Costa, Anna	568 Beach St.	Miami	Florida	48576

Write the new data base in alphabetical order by name.

■ In a data base, each column is known as a *field*. Each row is known as a *record*.

DATAPOINT

Notice that the first field contains words and the other two contain numbers.

4. Look at the data base shown below.

Student	Grade	Grade Point Average
Adams, Karen	8	3.2
Eng, Charles	9	3.5
Garcia, Fran	8	3.4
Mitchell, Dennis	9	3.2

a. How many fields are there? What are they?

b. How many records are there?

5. The first field showing the student names could have been made up of two separate fields. What are they?

6. Arrange the data base by grade point average. Show the results of the new data base on a sheet of paper.

DATAPOINT

When you sort a data base, you rearrange the data in a particular order.

7. How did you sort the two records with the same grade point average in Question 6? In what other way could you have sorted them?

■ You enter data in a data base one record at a time. For example, the record below is from a data base that is used to keep track of inventory at a shoe store.

```
ITEM : Boots
QUANTITY (PAIRS) : 150
NEXT SHIPMENT DUE : Dec 10
```

8. How many field names are there? What are they?

■ After entering several records, you can view the data in rows and columns. This is part of the shoe store data base in column form.

Item	Quantity (on hand)	Next Shipment Due
Boots	150	Dec 10
Running shoes	34	Dec 5
Sandals	25	Dec 17
Loafers	16	Dec 28

9. Suppose it is the morning of December 1. On average, the store sells nine pairs of running shoes per day. Will there be enough before the next shipment arrives, which is scheduled for an evening delivery?

10. *Explore* What other fields could you add to this data base to keep an accurate count of the inventory? Share your results with your classmates.

■ A data base can help you keep track of information.

11. *PROJECT* Make up your own data base. Choose any data that you like. Use the following questions as a guide.

   a. What kind of information will your data base contain?

   b. How many fields will the data base have? Have you included every field needed to make a useful data base?

   c. How will you gather the data? Is the data simple to obtain?

   d. How many records will your data base have? Is there a limit to the number of records it can have?

   e. How often do you need to update the data? How will you know when you need to change the data for a particular field?

   f. How will you arrange the data?

   g. If you have a computer and data base software, create a data base.

Problem Solving Practice

PROBLEM SOLVING STRATEGIES

Look for a Pattern
Guess and Test
Simplify the Problem
Make an Organized List
Work Backwards
Account for All Possibilities
Make a Table
Write an Equation
Solve by Graphing
Draw a Diagram
Make a Model
Solve Another Way
Simulate the Problem

Solve each problem. The list at the left shows some possible strategies you can use.

1. Lisa is slower than Christine, but faster than Nicole. Nicole is slower than Lisa, but faster than Jo Ann. Order the girls from fastest to slowest.

2. The convenience store sells pens for $0.05, $0.10, and $0.15. List all the ways that Joseph can spend exactly $0.45 on pens.

3. Miguel lives 2.75 mi from school. His friend lives 1.35 mi from school in the opposite direction. If Miguel rode his bicycle to school, visited his friend, and then returned home, how many miles would he ride in all?

4. Janet purchased three spools of thread at $.89 each, five yards of material at $2.29 per yard, one sewing pattern at $1.89, and five yards of ribbon at $.45 per yard. She gave the cashier a $20 bill. How much change should she receive? How many more spools of thread can she buy with her change?

5. *DATA FILE 2 (pp. 52–53)* Maria hears thunder 1.4 s after she sees a flash of lightning. Paul hears thunder 2.2 s after he sees a flash of lightning. How many meters farther from the lightning is Paul than Maria?

6. An art teacher is purchasing sketch paper for her students. She can buy a 12-package box with 300 sheets per package for $72.00, or a 6-package box with 200 sheets of paper per package for $30.00. Which is the better purchase?

7. The alarm on a clock rang at 6:00 A.M. It continued ringing at regular intervals. At 6:08 the buzzer was on, at 6:10 the buzzer was off, at 6:16 it was on, and at 6:48 it was on. Will the buzzer be on or off at 7:52? at 9:18?

8. Five women ran the 100-m dash. Their times were 11.6 s, 10.2 s, 9.9 s, 10.6 s, and 11.9 s. What was the average time? Is 10.787 s above or below this average?

9. It is 398 mi from Buffalo to Boston. Nan leaves in her car and drives at an average of 47 mi/h. Barb leaves in her car and drives at an average rate of 55 mi/h. If they both drive straight through, how many hours to the nearest tenth will Barb have to wait for Nan to arrive?

10. June earns d dollars per hour for the first 40 h of work each week and $1.5d$ for each hour over 40. June worked 46 hours and 15 minutes last week. How much did she earn if d equals 5?

3-6 *Using the Metric System*

■ The units of length, mass, and capacity in the metric system are related by water. A cube measuring 1 cm on each side has a volume of 1 cm^3. This is equivalent to 1 mL. A centimeter cube filled with water has a mass of 1 g.

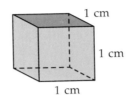

1 cm
1 cm
1 cm

The *density* of a substance is its mass per cubic centimeter. The density of water is 1 g/cm^3. Substances with densities greater than 1 g/cm^3 sink in water. Substances with densities less than 1 g/cm^3 float in water.

■ You can use the following formula to find density.

$$\text{density } (d) = \frac{\text{mass}}{\text{volume}}$$

FLASHBACK

Prefix	Meaning
milli-	0.001
centi-	0.01
deci-	0.10
kilo-	1,000

Symbol	
cm	centimeter
cm^3	cubic centimeter
g	gram
L	liter
mL	milliliter

Example 1   A block of wood has a volume of 20.52 cm^3. Its mass is 17 g. Find the density of the block in grams per cubic centimeter. Tell whether the block will float or sink in water.

Solution   density $= \dfrac{\text{mass}}{\text{volume}}$ Use the formula for density.

$\qquad\qquad d = 17 \div 20.52$ Substitute values.

$\qquad\qquad \approx 0.83$ g/cm^3

Since the density of the block is less than that of water, the block will float in water.

■ You can use the formula to find mass when density and volume are known or volume when density and mass are known.

Example 2   A diamond has a density of 3.5 g/cm^3 and a volume of 0.5 cm^3. Find the mass of the diamond.

Solution   density $= \dfrac{\text{mass}}{\text{volume}}$ Use the formula for density.

$\qquad\qquad 3.5 = \dfrac{m}{0.5}$ Substitute values.

$\qquad\qquad 0.5 \cdot 3.5 = \dfrac{m}{0.5} \cdot 0.5$ Multiply each side by 0.5.

$\qquad\qquad m = 1.75$ g

CLASS EXERCISES

Masses of Metal Blocks (V = 8 cm³)

aluminum	22 g
gold	154.4 g
silver	84 g

Use the **DATA** at the left. Round to the nearest tenth.

1. Find the density of aluminum, gold, and silver.

2. How much greater is the mass of a cubic centimeter of gold than a cubic centimeter of silver?

3. How many milliliters of water equal the mass of a block of gold having a volume of 125 cm³?

WRITTEN EXERCISES

Use a CALCULATOR where appropriate.

Densities of Selected Substances (g/cm³)

gasoline	0.68
ethyl alcohol	0.79
rubber	1.34
iron	7.9
copper	8.9
mercury	13.5

Use the **DATA** at the left to solve each problem. Express answers to the nearest tenth.

1. What is the mass in grams of a lump of copper that has a volume of 7.5 cm³?

2. What is the volume in cubic centimeters of a block of iron that has a mass of 100 g?

3. Which of the substances listed will float in water? in mercury?

■■■■■■ Decision Making ■ **DECISION MAKING** ■ Decision Making ■ Decision Making ■ Decision Making ■

USING THE METRIC SYSTEM

■ **COLLECT DATA**

1. Test various objects in the classroom to find out which ones sink and which float in water. First guess, then check your guess by putting the object in water to see whether it sinks or floats. Keep a record of your results.

Object	Substance	Sink	Float

2. Why would it not be good to have objects such as pencils or sponges on your list to use for Exercise 1?

■ **ANALYZE DATA**

Suppose you have a ruler, a clear drinking glass with vertical sides and flat bottom, a scale that measures in grams, and several marbles of the same size.

4. Will copper float in mercury? in ethyl alcohol?

5. How much greater is the mass of 1,000 mL of ethyl alcohol than 1,000 mL of gasoline?

6. What is the mass in kilograms of 20.75 L of gasoline?

Solve.

7. Water expands when it freezes. If you freeze 11 cm³ of water, you will get about 12 cm³ of ice. Use this fact to find the density of ice.

8. **ESTIMATION** A gasoline truck is going to take on 1,289 L more gasoline. The density of gasoline is 0.68 g/cm³. About how many kilograms more is the truck going to take on?

9. A silver necklace has a volume of 100 cm³. Use the chart on page 126 to find the density. Then find the mass of the necklace.

10. **PROJECT** Find out what the relationship is between density and buoyancy. Explain why a steel ocean liner floats in water.

Ice floats since it is less dense than water. How does this relate to the fact that 0.9 of an iceberg is below the surface of the water?

■ *Decision Making* ■ *Decision Making* ■ *Decision Making* ■ *Decision Making* ■ *Decision Making* ■ *Decision Making* ■

3. If you pour some water in the glass, how can you use the materials to find out how many cubic centimeters of space the water occupies?

4. If you take several marbles, how can you use the materials to find how many cubic centimeters of space they occupy?

■ **MAKE DECISIONS**

5. Decide how you could use the materials listed in the *Analyze Data* section to find the density of the glass from which the marbles are made. Describe your plan in a paragraph. Use diagrams as needed to explain your plan.

6. Decide how you could use the materials to find the density of something that will not sink in water. Describe your plan in a paragraph.

3-7 Using Formulas

▼ You can use the number of chirps a cricket makes in a minute to estimate the temperature in degrees Fahrenheit.

Chirps per min (n)	Temperature (°F)
12	40°
16	41°
20	42°
24	43°
28	44°

▼ A science class conducted an experiment. For five weekdays the class counted the number of chirps their pet cricket made in a minute. They recorded this information in a table, along with the actual temperature. The class observed that if they divided the number of chirps per minute (n) by 4, and added 37, the result was the temperature in degrees Fahrenheit (F). A student wrote the following *formula* on the board.

$$F = \frac{n}{4} + 37$$

Formula	A formula is an equation that shows the relationship between two or more variables.

THINK Will the formula $F = \frac{n}{4} + 37$ ever produce negative temperatures? Why or why not?

Example 1 If the class counted 32 cricket chirps in 1 min, what is the Fahrenheit temperature?

Solution 1. Write the formula. $F = \frac{n}{4} + 37$

2. Substitute values. $F = \frac{32}{4} + 37$

$= 45$

The Fahrenheit temperature is 45°.

▼ The *distance formula* is an important and useful formula. The distance formula is $d = rt$, where d is the distance, r is the rate at which you travel, and t is the time you spend traveling.

Example 2 **Find the distance Sara traveled if she drove 8.5 h at an average speed (rate) of 49.7 mi/h.**

Solution 1. Write the formula. $d = rt$

2. Substitute values. $d = (49.7)(8.5)$
$d = 422.45$

Sara traveled 422.45 mi.

▼ You can write a formula in more than one way.

Example 3 State whether each formula is equivalent to $d = rt$. If so, state what was done to each side of the equation.

   a. $\frac{d}{r} = t$ b. $d + r = t$

Solution a. yes; both sides divided by r b. no

▼ Batting average is determined by the formula $a = \frac{h}{n}$, where a is the batting average, h is the number of hits made, and n is the number of times up at bat.

Example 4 Use a calculator to solve. How many hits did Babe Ruth make if he was up at bat 8,399 times and had a batting average of 0.342?

Solution

1. Write the formula. $a = \frac{h}{n}$

2. Substitute values. $0.342 = \frac{h}{8,399}$

3. Multiply. $0.342 \, \boxed{\times} \, 8,399 \, \boxed{=} \, 2,872.458$

4. Round to nearest integer. $2,872$

Babe Ruth made 2,872 hits.

CLASS EXERCISES

Solve. Use the appropriate formula.

1. Find the temperature if a cricket chirps 44 times per minute.

2. A snail travels about 0.14 cm/s. To find how far the snail travels, in what unit should time be given? How far will the snail travel in one hour?

3. The spine-tailed swift is the fastest creature alive. It has been clocked traveling at 106.25 mi/h. At that speed, how far could the swift travel in 2.5 h?

4. Florence Griffith-Joyner holds the American record in the 100-m run. She ran in 10.49 s. If she could continue at this rate, how long would it take her to run 1,000 m?

THINK AND DISCUSS

1. What would you expect to happen to the number of times a cricket would chirp in 1 min if the temperature increased?

2. How many variables are there in the distance formula? To use the formula, how many variables must equal a number?

3. How are formulas and equations alike? How are they different?

WRITTEN EXERCISES

Use the formula $F = \frac{n}{4} + 37$, where n is the number of cricket chirps per minute, to find the temperature in degrees Fahrenheit.

1. $n = 200$ 2. $n = 288$ 3. $n = 60$ 4. $n = 104$

Use the formula $d = rt$ to find the distance traveled.

5. $r = 38.5$ mi/h, $t = 12.1$ h 6. $r = 280$ mi/h, $t = 9.75$ h

7. $r = 213$ cm/s, $t = 8$ s 8. $r = 0.08$ ft/s, $t = 2.5$ h

9. **ESTIMATE** The first plane to fly faster than the speed of sound was piloted by Chuck Yeager. He flew at 670 mi/h. About how far could he fly in 9.8 h? Is this estimate high or low?

10. The solar probe *Helios B* reached a speed of 149,125 mi/h. Suppose the probe traveled at this speed for its entire journey. About how long would it take to reach the sun, which is 93,000,000 mi away? Round to the nearest hundredth.

Major League Lifetime Leading Batters

Player	At bats *(n)*	Hits *(h)*
Browning	4,795	1,664
Hornsby	8,173	2,930
Cobb	11,436	4,190
Delahanty	7,493	2,593
Keeler	8,570	2,955
Jackson	4,981	1,774

Use the formula $a = \dfrac{h}{n}$ and the table at the left to determine each batting average. Round answers to the nearest thousandth.

11. Browning
12. Hornsby
13. Cobb
14. Delahanty
15. Keeler
16. Jackson

17. Order each player from highest batting average to lowest.

Use the formula $w = rt + 1.5r \cdot o$ to find a person's wage. Let w be the wage, r the hourly rate of pay, t the number of hours worked at the hourly rate, and o the number of hours worked overtime. Round to the nearest cent where necessary.

	Worker	*r*	*t*	*o*
18.	Jeremy	6.20	40	8
19.	Elaine	9.75	40	10
20.	Eric	4.35	38	3
21.	Serena	12.55	41	9

CALCULATOR Use the formula $F = 1.8C + 32$ to find the temperature in degrees Fahrenheit, where C is the temperature in degrees Celsius.

22. Find the Fahrenheit temperature corresponding to 58°C, the highest recorded temperature in the world.

23. Find the Fahrenheit temperature corresponding to -89°C, the lowest recorded temperature in the world.

Bread and Milk

Years	Loaf of bread	Half gal of milk
1890s	$.03	$.14
1930s	$.09	$.28
1950s	$.18	$.48
1970s	$.24	$.66
1980s	$1.39	$1.09

Use the formula $I = N - O$ to find the price increase. Let I be the price increase, N the new price, and O the old price. Use the chart at the left to answer the following questions.

24. What was the price increase of a half gallon of milk from the 1930s to the 1970s?

25. What was the price increase of a half gallon of milk from the 1970s to the 1980s?

26. How much more was spent in the 1970s than in the 1890s for 5 loaves of bread and 6 half gallons of milk?

Use the formula $k = \frac{t \cdot w}{1,000}$ to find the number of kilowatt hours used. Let k = kilowatt hours, t = hours, and w = watts. Refer to the data at the right.

27. a. How many kilowatt hours are used by cooking in the microwave for 0.75 h per evening for one week? How many are used by cooking in a conventional oven?

   b. How much would each cost if the electric company charges $.04 per kilowatt hour?

   c. What is the savings over a year by using a microwave instead of a conventional oven?

28. Are more kilowatt hours used by working on the computer for 2.25 h or by drying your hair for 0.25 h?

29. PROJECT Find the local rate for electricity. Develop a plan for cutting back on your use of electricity. Determine how much money you would save in a year.

30. Gross earnings g is equal to net pay p, plus deductions d. Write a formula to find gross earnings. Solve the formula for d.

31. The voltage, V, across any part of a circuit is the product of the current I and the resistance R. Write a formula to find the voltage. Solve the formula for R.

Appliance	Watts of electricity used by appliance
Television	145
Computer	155
Hair dryer	1,000
Microwave	1,500
Conventional oven	12,200
Stereo	109
VCR	45

TEST YOURSELF

CALCULATOR Solve each equation.

1. $16.9376 = 6.32s$ **2.** $-8.125 = \frac{b}{0.023}$ **3.** $n \div (-7.34) = -2.758$

4. $\frac{w}{105.1} = 0.7352$ **5.** $0.0812g = 3.248$ **6.** $10.20807 = 3.369c$

Solve for variable a.

7. $c = ab$ **8.** $a + c = b$ **9.** $c = \frac{a}{b}$

Use the formula $d = rt$.

10. a. Find d when $r = 48$ and $t = 3.5$.

   b. Find t when $d = 693$ and $r = 63$.

   c. Hal drove a distance of 562 mi at an average rate of 58 mi/h. How many hours, to the nearest tenth, did Hal drive?

MIXED REVIEW

Solve each equation.

1. $-3n = 92.01$

2. $\frac{x}{0.43} = -5.2$

3. $10,000 \cdot 0.0034 = k$

Evaluate when $x = -3.1$ and $y = 10.7$.

4. $4x - 2y$

5. $x(-12 + y)$

Solve.

6. A stockholder owns 1,000 shares of stock. She receives a dividend of $.65 per share four times per year. How much is the yearly dividend?

3-8 *Simplify the Problem*

OBJECTIVE:
To solve problems by using a simpler problem.

■ Sometimes when you solve a problem, it helps to first solve one or more simpler problems that have similar conditions.

PROBLEM

A typesetter needs one piece of type for each digit in the page numbers of the book. How many pieces of type will the printer need to number pages 1–476?

SOLUTION

READER ▶ What do you want to find?

number of pieces of type required to number pages 1–476

PLAN ▶ Simplify the problem.

How many one-digit page numbers are there?	pages 1–9 9 pieces of type
How many two-digit page numbers are there?	pages 10–99 90 two-digit page numbers $90 \cdot 2 = 180$ pieces of type
How many three-digit page numbers are there?	pages 100–476 377 three-digit pages $377 \cdot 3 = 1{,}131$ pieces of type

SOLVE ▶ Add the numbers for the pieces of type required for the one-, two-, and three-digit numbers.

$$9 + 180 + 1{,}131 = 1{,}320$$

LOOK BACK ▶ Interpret your answer.
The printer will need 1,320 pieces of type to number pages 1–476.

CLASS EXERCISES

1. Janetta numbered the pages in her diary from 1 to 58. How many digits did she write?

2. A printer used 330 pieces of type to number the pages of a book. The first page is numbered one. How many numbered pages are in the book?

3. A book is opened. The product of the two page numbers that appear is 272. What are the two page numbers?

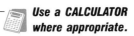
WRITTEN EXERCISES

Solve by using simpler problems.

1. A printer is typesetting a book. He needs one piece of type for each digit in the page numbers of the book. How many twos will he need to number pages 1–232?

2. One pastry chef can decorate 12 cupcakes in 14 min. The bakery receives an order for 672 cupcakes. To the nearest hour, how long will it take four pastry chefs to decorate the cupcakes?

Solve using any strategy.

3. A city has a population of 586,785. The area is 25 mi². Find the population per square mile.

4. To accommodate a wheelchair, Tom installed counter tops that were 0.72 ft lower than the original ones in his house. The new counter tops are 2.5 ft high. How high were the original counter tops?

5. The houses on Wheeler Avenue are numbered 1 to 138. How many house numbers contain at least one digit 6?

6. On their way to a concert, Betsy, Meg, and Mary each took turns driving. Mary drove seven miles more than Meg. Meg drove three times as far as Betsy. Betsy drove nine miles. How many total miles did they drive?

7. The carnival has two types of rides for children. Each airplane seats 4 children and each spaceship seats 6 children. Altogether there are 24 airplanes and spaceships that seat a total of 128 children. How many of each are there?

8. Jim has $8 in his savings account. Jo has $12 in her savings account. Jim will add $1 to his account each week and Jo will add $3 to her account each week. After how many weeks will Jo's account have twice as much money as Jim's?

9. Julie had to number 275 dance tickets by hand. How many digits did she have to write?

10. Aaron can work 21.5 h per week at the gas station for $5.75/h. He could also work 27.75 h per week at the convenience store for $4.80/h. At which job will he earn more per week?

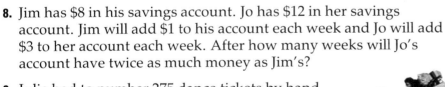
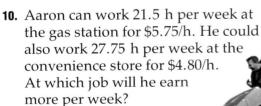
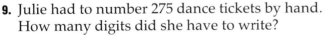

Chapter 3 Review

True or false? If false, change the underlined word(s) to make the statement true.

1. You read and write the decimal 0.05 as five <u>tenths</u>.
2. The steps for front-end estimation are:
   - Add the front-end digits.
   - Adjust by <u>finding</u> the sum of the remaining digits.
   - Add these two values.
3. <u>Compatible numbers</u> are used to make estimation easier.
4. To rank a set of data, write the data <u>in order</u>.
5. A formula is an equation that shows the relationship between two or more <u>numbers</u>.

Comparing Decimals 3-1

To compare decimals, think of a number line. The decimal farther to the right is the greater decimal.

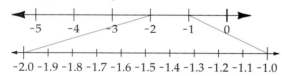

Compare using <, >, or =.

6. −1.9 ▨ −1.3   7. −1.0 ▨ −1   8. −2.0 ▨ −2.3   9. −1.25 ▨ −1.2   10. −1.4 ▨ 1.4

Estimating Decimals 3-2

To estimate decimals, use rounding, front-end estimation, or compatible numbers.

ESTIMATION **Estimate each shaded region using decimals.**

11.    12. 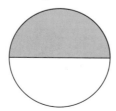   13.

ESTIMATION **Write the technique that seems best. Then estimate.**

14. 9.21 + 28.301 + 16.092   15. 2.531 ÷ 3.915   16. $6.15 + $9.28 + $3.69 + $5.90

17. 0.7845 ÷ 4.3   18. 12,909.3 − 3.899   19. $48.75 + $22.95 + $7.50

Evaluating Expressions with Decimals 3-3

To evaluate an algebraic expression, substitute a number for the variable(s), and simplify. Follow order of operations.

Evaluate each expression for $x = -0.5$ and $y = 0.3$.

20. $2x + 3y - 1$ **21.** $4(x + 2y)$ **22.** $|2x| - 3y + 4$ **23.** $5x - 5y + |-15|$

Simplifying Expressions with Decimals 3-3

To simplify a variable expression, combine like terms and eliminate parentheses using the distributive property.

Simplify each expression.

24. $7.5a - 3(a - 0.2) + 2.5$ **25.** $\dfrac{(0.8x)(2.5) + 3x}{10}$ **26.** $5a + a(3 + b) + 12ab$

Solving Equations 3-4, 3-5

To solve an equation, use the properties of equality.

Solve.

27. $-3.8x = 19$ **28.** $m + 2.45 = 3$ **29.** $\dfrac{k}{3.5} = 2.1$ **30.** $y - 2.9 = 8.1$

31. $5.3t = 53$ **32.** $a - (-5.6) = 12.9$ **33.** $14w = 42$ **34.** $r + 7 = 10.8$

Using Formulas 3-7

To use a formula, substitute the known value(s) of the variable(s), and solve for the unknown value.

Use the formula $d = rt$. Solve.

35. $r = 55$ mi/h, $t = 3.5$ h   **36.** $r = 30$ ft/s, $t = 1.2$ s   **37.** $d = 365$ km, $r = 40$ km/h

Problem Solving 3-6, 3-8

To solve a problem that has difficult numbers, use simpler numbers to see *how* to solve the problem. Then use the real data.

Solve.

38. An auditorium was filled to capacity with 3,500 people. An usher estimated there were 3 adults for every 2 children. How many children were in the auditorium?

39. Use the table on page 126. Find the density of silver. Use the formula density $= \dfrac{\text{mass}}{\text{volume}}$.

Write each decimal.

1. four hundred fifty-three and fifty-nine hundredths

2. three and seven thousand eight hundred fifty-three ten thousandths

Compare using >, <, or =.

3. 0.125 ▨ 0.333

4. -7.656 ▨ -0.777

5. 0.1001 ▨ 0.10010

6. 0.05 ▨ -0.05

Round each decimal to the indicated place.

7. 2.547 nearest tenth

8. 8.029 nearest hundredth

9. 159.809 nearest unit

10. -0.352 nearest tenth

11. 0.295 nearest tenth

12. 14.953 nearest tenth

ESTIMATION **Estimate the shaded region using decimal numbers.**

13.

14.

15.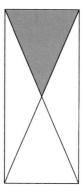

ESTIMATION **Use the technique that seems best.**

16. $24.79 ÷ 62

17. -45.167 ÷ 13.92

18. 9.057 − 4.01

19. 31.597 ÷ 19

20. 300.5 + 98.2

21. 17.63 − 3.58

22. 1.78 + 2.12 + 18.49 + 7.23 + (-5.54)

Solve each equation.

23. $m + 7.8 = 5.2$

24. $z − (-8.9) = -2.1$

25. $-4r = -2.8$

26. $\frac{h}{11} = -0.3$

27. $a + (-3.24) = 5.8$

28. $\frac{x}{-0.2} = 0.6$

29. $0.9k = 2.7$

30. $b − 9.4 = 0.6$

Use the formula $C = \frac{(F − 32)}{1.8}$ to find the Celsius temperature where F is the temperature in degrees Fahrenheit. Round to the nearest tenth.

31. 86°F

32. 50°F

33. 4°F

34. 65°F

35. -10°F

Solve.

36. A city has a population of 8,276,386 people. The area is 359 mi². What is the population per square mile?

37. ***DATA*** Use the table on page 120. Dwayne is the top high jumper. How does Dwayne rank in the long jump? Who ranks second in the high jump?

Chapters 1–3   Cumulative Review

Choose the correct answer. Write A, B, C, or D.

1. Name the decimal represented by the point on the number line.

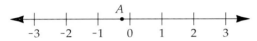

   A. 0.25   **B.** -0.25

   C. -1.75   **D.** not given

2. two hundred five and six hundredths
   A. 205.600   **B.** 200.56
   C. 205.06   **D.** not given

3. What integer represents 15 s before launch?
   A. -15   **B.** +15
   C. |15| **D.** not given

4. $|-3| \cdot (-6) \cdot 2$
   A. 36   **B.** -36
   C. -18   **D.** not given

5. Find the mean temperature:
   6°, -5°, 2°, 0°, -8°.
   A. -5°   **B.** 1°
   C. -1°   **D.** not given

6. What replacement for a will make the equation $4a - 7 = 25$ true?
   A. 5   **B.** 7
   C. -8   **D.** not given

7. $3 \cdot [2 \cdot (-4)] = (3 \cdot 2) \cdot (\blacksquare)$.
   A. -4   **B.** 2
   C. 3   **D.** not given

8. Write an expression for the total area of the figure.

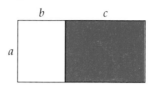

   A. $a \cdot (b \cdot c)$ **B.** $a + (b + c)$
   C. $a(b + c)$ **D.** not given

9. Round 6.54901 to the nearest tenth.
   A. 6.5   **B.** 6.55
   C. 7   **D.** not given

10. Solve $x - 2.5 = -5$.
    A. -2.5   **B.** 7.5
    C. -7.5   **D.** not given

11. Simplify $3x + (5 - 2x)0.5$.
    A. $2x + 2.5$ **B.** $x + 2.5$
    C. $x - 2.5$ **D.** not given

12. Solve $\frac{y}{1.2} = -3.6$.
    A. -0.3   **B.** -4.32
    C. 0.3   **D.** not given

13. Find the distance for $r = 50.5$ mi/h, and $t = 3$ h. Use $d = rt$.
    A. 16.5 mi   **B.** 350 mi
    C. 151.5 mi   **D.** not given

14. Solve $5.6 = x + 3.5$.
    A. 9.1   **B.** 2.1
    C. 8.5   **D.** not given

TOP 10 MOST SPOKEN LANGUAGES
(millions of speakers)

Language	Millions
CHINESE	700
ENGLISH	400
RUSSIAN	265
SPANISH	240
HINDI	230
ARABIC	146
PORTUGUESE	145
BENGALI	144
GERMAN	119
JAPANESE	116

Population Facts

Most crowded:

Monaco with 15,000 people/km^2

Least crowded:

Western Sahara with 0.5 people/km^2

Fraction of population under 15 years of age:

Africa: about $\frac{1}{2}$ Europe: about $\frac{1}{5}$

DEMOGRAPHERS look for patterns in the size, movement, density, and other characteristics of human populations. Demographers use graphs, like the population pyramid, to look for trends and determine future growth patterns.

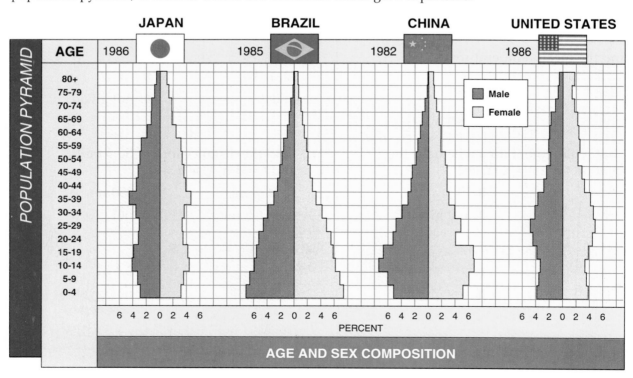

POPULATION PYRAMID	JAPAN 1986	BRAZIL 1985	CHINA 1982	UNITED STATES 1986

Male ■ Female □

AGE: 80+, 75-79, 70-74, 65-69, 60-64, 55-59, 50-54, 45-49, 40-44, 35-39, 30-34, 25-29, 20-24, 15-19, 10-14, 5-9, 0-4

PERCENT: 6 4 2 0 2 4 6

AGE AND SEX COMPOSITION

Number Theory

WORLD POPULATION GROWTH ■ From 1450 to 1750 the world population doubled. It doubled again from 1750 to 1855, from 1855 to 1950, and from 1950 to 1989.

Each square stands for five years

Each square stands for 100 million people

1450 1500 1550 1600 1650 1700 1750 1800 1850 1900 1950 1990

—5
—4
—3
—2
—1
—0

Think about it...

Look at the population growth graph. In 1989 the world population was about 5 billion. When do you think the population will double again?

A baby is born every 0.22 s.

A person dies every 0.67 s.

| BIRTHS | – | DEATHS | + | IMMIGRANTS | – | EMIGRANTS | = | POPULATION CHANGE |

Exploring Square Numbers

OBJECTIVE:
To explore square numbers using patterns.

MATERIALS

- Graph paper or algebra tiles

- Math journal to record work

▼ Each year the aviation club sponsors an air show. As part of the routine, the planes fly in formation. First one plane flies up, then three planes, then five, then seven.

1. Look at the table below. What was the total number of planes in the air after the third takeoff? after the fourth?

Group	Number of New Planes	Total Number in Air
1	1	1
2	3	4
3	5	9
4	7	16

2. If the flight pattern continued, how many planes would be in the fifth group? in the sixth group? Extend the table to organize your data.

3. What is the total number of planes in the air after the fifth group? after the sixth group?

4. ***Describe*** and discuss the relationship between the group number and the total number of planes in the air.

5. How do the models at the left show the relationship between the group number and the total number of planes in the air?

1   4   9

▼ The numbers in the last column of the table are called *square numbers* or *squares*.

6. ***Write*** two characteristics that describe square numbers.

7. Without using the table, figure out how many planes would be in the air if there could be a group 20.

▼ The models below show the relationship between the number of new planes and square numbers.

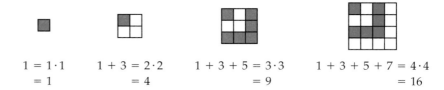

$1 = 1 \cdot 1$ $1 + 3 = 2 \cdot 2$ $1 + 3 + 5 = 3 \cdot 3$ $1 + 3 + 5 + 7 = 4 \cdot 4$
$\quad = 1$ $\qquad = 4$ $\qquad\qquad = 9$ $\qquad\qquad\qquad = 16$

8. Use tiles or graph paper to model this relationship for the next three square numbers. ***Compare*** with another group.

9. ***Summarize***—How can you use an odd number of tiles to form a square number?

4-1 **Exponents**

▼ Suppose a cell splits into two cells every hour. How many cells will there be after 12 hours?

The number of cells doubles every hour. You find the total by multiplying 2 twelve times.

$$2 \cdot 2 \cdot 2 \cdot 2 \cdot 2 \cdot 2 \cdot 2 \cdot 2 \cdot 2 \cdot 2 \cdot 2 \cdot 2 = 4{,}096$$

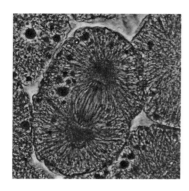

You can also express the product using an *exponent*.

$$\text{base} \rightarrow 2^{12} \leftarrow \text{exponent}$$

READ 2^{12} as *2 to the twelfth power*.

Base	The base is the number used as a factor.

Exponent	The exponent shows the number of times the base is used as a factor.

THINK Why does a^1 equal a?

▼ You can refer to expressions with exponents as *powers*.

Write	Read	Evaluate
2^0	*two to the zero power*	1
12^1	*twelve to the first power*	12
5^2	*five to the second power, or five squared*	$5 \cdot 5 = 25$
6^3	*six to the third power, or six cubed*	$6 \cdot 6 \cdot 6 = 216$
-3^4	*the opposite of the fourth power of three*	$-(3 \cdot 3 \cdot 3 \cdot 3) = -81$

THINK What is the base in -3^4? in $(-3)^4$?

Example 1 **Write using exponents.**

  a. $5 \cdot 5 \cdot 5$ **b.** $-2 \cdot a \cdot 7 \cdot b \cdot b$

Solution   **a.** 5^3

  b. $-2 \cdot 7 \cdot a \cdot b \cdot b = -14ab^2$ Use the commutative and associative properties of multiplication.

FLASHBACK
Grouping symbols include parentheses ( ), brackets [ ], and absolute value | | symbols.

▼ You can extend the order of operations to include powers.

1. Do all operations within grouping symbols first.

2. Evaluate powers.

3. Multiply and divide from left to right.

4. Add and subtract from left to right.

NOTES & QUOTES

Edward Kasner (1878–1955), an American mathematician, asked his nine-year-old nephew what he would call the number 1 followed by 100 zeros or 10^{100}. The child responded with the word *googol*.

Example 2   Evaluate.

   a. $5(3 + 2)^2$ **b.** $-2x^3 + 4y$ for $x = 2$, $y = -3$

Solution   **a.** $5(5)^2 = 5 \cdot 25$ **b.** $-2(2)^3 + 4(-3) = -2 \cdot 8 + (-12)$
$= 125$ $= -16 + (-12)$
$= -28$

▼   A calculator is useful for evaluating expressions with exponents.

Example 3   Evaluate 8^5 using a calculator.

Solution   Use the $\boxed{x^y}$ key.
$8 \boxed{x^y} 5 \boxed{=} 32{,}768$

THINK AND DISCUSS

1. How and when are exponents useful?

2. Compare the values of -6^2 and $(-6)^2$. Why are they different?

3. Let n be any positive integer. Find the value of 1^n, -1^n.

4. In the expression a^0, how many times is a used as a factor? What is the value of a^0?

CLASS EXERCISES

Name the base and the exponent.

1. 7^4 **2.** $(-10)^2$ **3.** x^y **4.** -2^5

Read aloud and evaluate.

5. 4^4 **6.** $(-9)^0$ **7.** -4^3 **8.** -2^1

Write using exponents.

9. $6 \cdot 6 \cdot 6 \cdot 6 \cdot 6$ **10.** $4 \cdot y \cdot y \cdot y \cdot 3 \cdot x$

Evaluate.

11. $10(5 + 4)^2$ **12.** $[15 + (-18)]^2 + (-2)^3$

13. $x^2 + y^3$; $x = 3$ and $y = -1$ **14.** $-x^2 - 3 \cdot 2x$; $x = 3$

WRITTEN EXERCISES

Write using exponents.

1. $8 \cdot 8 \cdot 8$ **2.** $p \cdot p \cdot p \cdot p$ **3.** $2 \cdot r \cdot r \cdot r \cdot r \cdot s \cdot s$

4. $5 \cdot 5 \cdot y \cdot y$ **5.** $x \cdot x \cdot y \cdot y \cdot z$ **6.** $-9 \cdot m \cdot m \cdot (-4) \cdot n$

7. $\underbrace{n \cdot n \cdot n \ldots \cdot n}_{30 \text{ factors}}$ **8.** $\underbrace{m \cdot m \cdot m \ldots \cdot m}_{y \text{ factors}}$ **9.** $\underbrace{a \cdot a \cdot a \ldots \cdot a}_{a \text{ factors}}$

10. $(-4n)(-4n)(-4n)(-4n)(-4n)$ **11.** $(a + 1)(a + 1)(a + 1)$

Evaluate.

12. a. 5^3 **13. a.** 10^0 **14. a.** -1^8 **15. a.** -2^4
   b. 3^5 **b.** 10^6 **b.** $(-1)^9$ **b.** $(-2)^0$

16. x^5 for $x = 2$ **17.** $(3a)^2$ for $a = -2$ **18.** $-(4y)^2$ for $y = 3$
19. $-(x)^2$ for $x = -2$ **20.** $-2x^5$ for $x = -1$ **21.** $(-x)^5$ for $x = -1$

CALCULATOR You can use a calculator to find the positive *square root* of a number.

▼▼   *SAMPLE* $25 \boxed{\sqrt{}} \boxed{=} 5$. So, $\sqrt{25} = 5$ since $5^2 = 25$

Find the square root.

22. $\sqrt{36}$ **23.** $\sqrt{49}$ **24.** $\sqrt{64}$ **25.** $\sqrt{81}$ **26.** $\sqrt{100}$

Compare. Use <, >, or =.

27. $3^3 \blacksquare 5^2$ **28.** $4^3 \blacksquare 8^2$ **29.** $64 \div 8 \blacksquare 2^3$ **30.** $4 \cdot 10 \blacksquare 10^4$
31. $-5^3 \blacksquare -3^0$ **32.** $10^2 \blacksquare 2^{10}$ **33.** $3^4 \blacksquare 4^3$ **34.** $-10^3 \blacksquare (-10)^3$

Solve.

35. Which of the following is equal to 1?

   a. -1^2 **b.** $(-1)^3$ **c.** $-(-1)^2$ **d.** $|-1|^3$

36. MENTAL MATH Given that $2^{10} = 1{,}024$, find 2^{11} mentally.

37. MENTAL MATH Explain how to find $(-1)^{100}$ mentally.

38. WRITE a sentence that explains the roles of the base and the exponent of 8^4.

39. Make a table of the powers of 10: 10^0, 10^1, 10^2, 10^3, 10^4. Describe the pattern you see. Use the pattern to find 10^6 and 10^{10}.

40. The formula for the area of a square is $A = s^2$, where A is area and s is the length of a side.

   a. Find the area of a square with a side of length 3.5 cm.

   b. Find the length of a side of a square with area 144 m^2.

41. CALCULATOR

   a. Copy and complete the table.

n	$4n$	4^n	n^4
0			
1			
2			
3			
4			

   b. For what value(s) of n is each true?

   $4^n = n^4$
   $4^n < n^4$
   $4^n > n^4$

MIXED REVIEW

Solve.

1. $m - 7.5 = 12$

2. $2.8h = -53.2$

Use the formula $d = rt$ to find distance traveled.

3. $r = 55$ mi/h, $t = 2.25$ h

4. $r = 80$ km/h, $t = 3.5$ h

5. $r = 635$ mi/h, $t = 0.45$ h

Simplify.

6. $3x - 2y + x$

7. $w + 8 - 4w - 15$

8. Sara wished to average her grades which were 79, 83, 74, 86, and 93. What is the average?

PROBLEM SOLVING HINT
Draw a diagram.

PROBLEM SOLVING HINT
Try guess and test.

Find the value of n.

42. $5^n = 125$ **43.** $3^n = 1$ **44.** $n^3 = 8$

For what positive value(s) of x is each true?

45. $1x = x^1$ **46.** $2x = x^2$ **47.** $9x = x^3$

48. Evaluate $(-1)^m$ for $m = 2, 4,$ and 6. Now let $m = 1, 3,$ and 5. ***WRITE*** a rule for raising a negative number to an even power or an odd power.

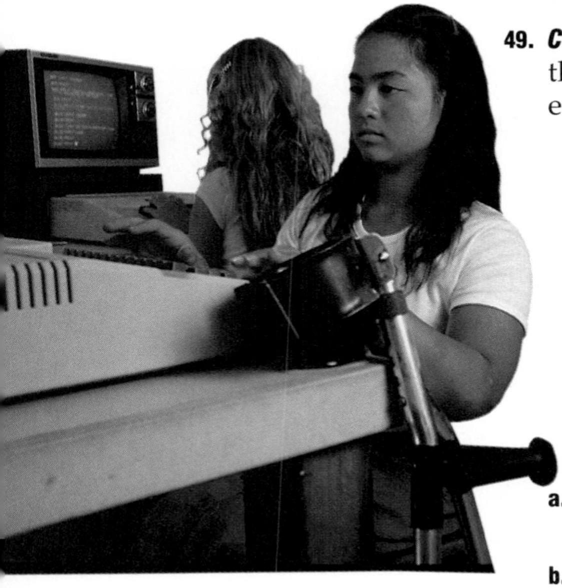

49. ***COMPUTER*** You can use a spreadsheet to construct a bar graph for the powers of 2. Note that the caret (^) is used to indicate exponentiation. Use the spreadsheet data to construct a graph.

	A	B	
1	Number	Power	
2	2	=A2^2	
3	2	=A3^3	
4	2	=A4^4	
5	2	=A5^5	
6	2	=A6^6	
7			

a. What do you notice about the bar for cell B2 compared to the bar for cell B3? Is the same true for cells B3 and B4?

b. ***WRITE*** a description for the bar graph of the powers of 2.

50. ***PROJECT*** Use a spreadsheet format similar to Exercise 49 to construct a bar graph for the powers of 3. Answer Exercise 49 (a) and (b) for this bar graph.

Critical Thinking

EXPLORING NUMBER PATTERNS

1
3 5
7 9 11

You know that the sum of consecutive odd integers is a square number. Now consider the odd numbers shown at the left.

1. Copy the odd number formation and add two more rows.

2. The sum of the first row is 1. What is the sum of the second row? the third row? the fourth row?

3. What is 1^3? 2^3? 3^3? 4^3?

4. Predict the sum of the tenth row.

4-2 Rules About Exponents

72

▼ Without evaluating the expressions, compare $7^2 \cdot 7^3$ and $7^4 \cdot 7^1$. Use what you've learned about exponents.

$$7^2 \cdot 7^3 = (7 \cdot 7) \cdot (7 \cdot 7 \cdot 7) = 7^5$$
$$7^4 \cdot 7^1 = (7 \cdot 7 \cdot 7 \cdot 7) \cdot (7) = 7^5$$
$$7^2 \cdot 7^3 = 7^4 \cdot 7^1 \text{ since } 7^5 = 7^5$$

7^1

Notice that $7^2 \cdot 7^3 = 7^{2+3} = 7^5$. This suggests the following rule.

Rule of Exponents for Multiplication	To multiply numbers or variables with the *same* base, add exponents.
	Arithmetic **Algebra**
	$2^3 \cdot 2^4 = 2^{3+4} = 2^7$ $a^m \cdot a^n = a^{m+n}$

7^3

How do the blocks show 7^1, 7^2, and 7^3?

Example 1   Simplify using exponents.

      a. $a \cdot a^3 \cdot a^4$ **b.** $xy^2 \cdot x^3$

Solution   **a.** $a \cdot a^3 \cdot a^4 = a^{1+3+4}$ **b.** $xy^2 \cdot x^3 = x \cdot x^3 \cdot y^2$
                       $= a^8$ $= x^{1+3} \cdot y^2$
                                                    $= x^4y^2$

THINK How would you simplify $(5^0)^3$? What is the result?

▼ You can raise a power to a power.

Example 2   Simplify $(5^2)^3$.

Solution   **a.** Use the meaning   **b.** Use the rule for
              of exponents.   multiplication.
              $(5^2)^3 = 5^2 \cdot 5^2 \cdot 5^2$ $(5^2)^3 = 5^2 \cdot 5^2 \cdot 5^2$
                      $= (5 \cdot 5)(5 \cdot 5)(5 \cdot 5)$ $= 5^{2+2+2}$
                      $= 5^6$ $= 5^6$

▼ Notice that $(5^2)^3 = 5^6$. This suggests the following rule.

Rule of a Power Raised to a Power	To raise a power to a power, multiply the exponents.
	Arithmetic **Algebra**
	$(2^3)^4 = 2^{3 \cdot 4} = 2^{12}$ $(a^m)^n = a^{m \cdot n}$

Example 3   Simplify.

      a. $(3^2)^3$ **b.** $(a^6)^2$

Solution   **a.** $(3^2)^3 = 3^{2 \cdot 3}$ **b.** $(a^6)^2 = a^{6 \cdot 2}$
                     $= 3^6$ $= a^{12}$
                     $= 729$

▼ You can also raise a product to a power.

Example 4 Simplify $(xy^2)^3$.

Solution Use the meaning of exponents.

$$(xy^2)^3 = xy \cdot y \cdot xy \cdot y \cdot xy \cdot y$$
$$= (x \cdot x \cdot x) \cdot (y \cdot y \cdot y \cdot y \cdot y \cdot y)$$
$$= x^3y^6$$

▼ Notice that $(xy^2)^3 = x^3y^6$. This suggests the following rule.

Rule of a Product Raised to a Power	To raise a product to a power, raise each factor to the power and then use the rule of exponents for multiplication.
	Arithmetic $(10^3 \cdot 10^2)^4 = 10^{12} \cdot 10^8$ $= 10^{20}$ **Algebra** $(ab)^m = a^m b^m$

Example 5 Simplify $(6x^4)^3$.

Solution
$$(6x^4)^3 = 6^3 \cdot (x^4)^3$$
$$= 216x^{12}$$

THINK AND DISCUSS

1. Can you simplify $x^6 \cdot y^7$? Explain.

2. Evaluate $-(2^3)^2$ and $(-2^3)^2$. Compare your answers.

3. How many times is the expression xy^2 used as a factor in $(xy^2)^0$? What is the value of $(xy^2)^0$?

CLASS EXERCISES

Evaluate or simplify. No variable has a value of zero.

1. $(-4)^3$ **2.** -4^2 **3.** $(-2 + 3)^7$ **4.** $2^3 \cdot 2^0$ **5.** $4 \cdot 4^3$

6. $x \cdot x^2 \cdot x^5$ **7.** $4^7 \cdot 4^{10}$ **8.** $w^2(w^6)$ **9.** $(y^3)^5$ **10.** $(4x^5)^0$

Evaluate for $a = -1$, $b = -3$, $c = 2$.

11. a^3b **12.** abc^0 **13.** $(abc)^0$ **14.** $2a^5c^1$

15. $(a^3)^6$ **16.** $(a^2b^3)^5$ **17.** $(c^2 \cdot c)^8$ **18.** $(4c^2 \cdot 4c^3)^2$

WRITTEN EXERCISES

Evaluate. No variable has a value of zero.

1. $(-2)^3$ **2.** $(2)^3$ **3.** $-(-2)^3$ **4.** $10^2 \cdot 10^5$

5. $(x^6)(x^3)$ **6.** $(x^2)(y^5)(x)$ **7.** $5x^3 \cdot 2x^6$ **8.** $a^{10} \cdot a^2$

9. $(2^3)(3^2)$ **10.** $(4^5)(4^3)$ **11.** $(-x^4)(-x)^4$ **12.** $(z^6)(-z^3)(z^2)$

13. $(-2a)^3 \cdot (-2a^3)$ **14.** $(a^4b^4)^4$ **15.** $(6y^3)^4$

16. $-(3xy)^2$ **17.** $(-3y^4)^3$ **18.** $(x^5)^7$

Evaluate each expression for $a = -3$, $b = 2$, $c = -1$.

19. $(2c)^3$ **20.** $5abc^0$ **21.** $(a^2)^3 \cdot (a^3)^2$

22. bc **23.** $(ac)^b$ **24.** ab^3c^{100}

25. $a^2 + b^3$ **26.** $(a + b)^3$ **27.** $(ab)^3$

True or False? Explain your answer. No variable has a value of zero.

28. $x^8 \cdot x^2 = x^5 \cdot x^5$ **29.** $x^5 \cdot x^3 = x^{15}$

30. $x^3 \cdot y^4 = (xy)^7$ **31.** $5^0 = 7^0$

32. $(-r^3)^2 > 0$ **33.** $-(r^2)^3 < 0$ **34.** $1^8 = 1^{23}$

Which of the following is equal to 2^{13}?

35. $(2^3)^{10}$ **36.** $2^5 \cdot 2^8$ **37.** $2^1 \cdot 2^0 \cdot 2^{13}$ **38.** $8{,}190$

Which of the following is twice the value of 2^{15}?

39. 2^{30} **40.** 2^{16} **41.** $2 \cdot 2^{15}$ **42.** $65{,}536$

Compare. Use $>$, $<$, or $=$.

43. $5^2 \ \blacksquare\ (5^3)^2$ **44.** $7^2 \cdot 7^5 \ \blacksquare\ (7^6)^2$ **45.** $(-2^2)^3 \ \blacksquare\ 2^5$

46. $25^2 \ \blacksquare\ (5^2)^2$ **47.** $(2^7)^7 \ \blacksquare\ (2^{25})^2$ **48.** $(4^5 \cdot 4^2)^3 \ \blacksquare\ (4^4)^0$

49. Without computing, determine which is greater: 2^{75} or 3^{50}. *Hint:* write each as an expression with the same exponent.

Solve.

50. Is $(a^3)^4 = (a^4)^3$ a true equation? Explain your answer.

51. If $(3^2 + 3^2 + 3^2) \cdot 3^x = 243$ is a true equation, find x.

52. *CALCULATOR* Find a pattern in the last digits of the powers of 7.

  a. What is the last digit of 7^{10}? What is the last digit of 7^{11}?

  b. Predict the last digit of 7^{21}. What method did you use to find the answer?

53. *COMPUTER* In computer science, information is measured and stored in *bits*. Eight bits are equal to one *byte*.

  a. One *kilobyte* is defined as 2^{10} bytes. How many bytes are in a kilobyte?

  b. *ESTIMATION* What is an approximate value for a kilobyte using a power of ten?

  c. Write the number of bits in one byte as a power of 2.

  d. A *megabyte* is 2^{20} bytes. Write the number of bytes in a megabyte as the product of exponents.

  e. Write the number of bits there are in one megabyte as the product of exponents.

MIXED REVIEW

Estimate.

1. $3.8 + 4.62 - 5.3$

2. $42.7 \cdot 8.5$

Write using exponents.

3. $-5 \cdot a \cdot a \cdot a \cdot b \cdot b$

4. $2 \cdot c \cdot c \cdot (-7) \cdot d \cdot d \cdot d$

Evaluate for $x = 3$, $y = -2$.

5. $4(x + 3y)$

6. $\sqrt{x^3 + 3x}$

7. $(1 + y)^x$

8. *DATA FILE 3 (pp. 96–97)* Approximately how many times did the value of a 1961 proof set increase by 1990?

54. Aunt Helen will open a savings account for you. You have a choice of two savings plans.

Plan A. Aunt Helen will deposit $20 each month for the next 15 months.

Plan B. Aunt Helen will deposit one cent the first month, two cents the second month, four cents the third month, and so on, doubling each month, for the next fifteen months.

a. For how many months is Plan A the better choice?

b. At what amount of money is Plan B the better choice?

Critical Thinking

EXPLORING PASCAL'S TRIANGLE

The number triangle below was published in China about 1300 A.D. It is usually called *Pascal's triangle,* after the French mathematician Blaise Pascal, who wrote about many of its patterns in a 1653 paper.

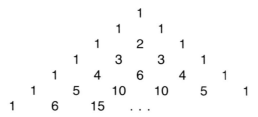

```
            1
          1   1
        1   2   1
      1   3   3   1
    1   4   6   4   1
  1   5   10  10   5   1
1   6   15    . . .
```

1. Analyze the pattern.
Complete: Each entry in a row is the sum of ▦.

If we call the row in which the number 2 first appears Row 2, the top row is Row 0.

2. What numbers appear in Row 6?

3. What is the sum of the numbers in Row 3?

4. Find the sum of the numbers in the twentieth row of Pascal's triangle. You may wish to use a calculator. *Hint:* Starting with Row 0, make a table that shows each row number and the sum of the numbers in that row. Look for a pattern.

OBJECTIVE:
To write and compute
with numbers using
scientific notation.

4-3 Scientific Notation

▼ You can write a number in different ways without changing its value. Here are some ways to write 75.

$$60 + 15 \qquad 2(37.5) \qquad 150 \div 2 \qquad 100 - 25$$

▼ You can also write numbers using powers of 10. Here are some ways you can write 4,000 using powers of 10.

$$4 \cdot 1{,}000 = 4 \cdot 10^3$$
$$40 \cdot 100 = 40 \cdot 10^2$$
$$400 \cdot 10 = 400 \cdot 10^1$$

FLASHBACK

The powers of 10:
$10^0 = 1$
$10^1 = 10$
$10^2 = 100$
⋮ ⋮

▼ *Scientific notation* is a way to write numbers using powers of 10.

Example 1 The numbers below on the left are written in scientific notation. The numbers below on the right are not.

3.45×10^3	34.5×10^2
9.5×10^2	0.95×10^1
2.0×10^4	200×10^2

Scientific Notation	A number is in scientific notation when it is written as the product of a number greater than or equal to 1 and less than 10, and a power of 10.

THINK How can you use mental math to find the exponent when writing a number in scientific notation?

▼ You can write large numbers in scientific notation.

Example 2 Write 5,460,000 in scientific notation.

Solution
1. Express as a number between 1 and 10.   5.460000
2. To keep the value the same, multiply by a power of 10. $5.46 \cdot 1{,}000{,}000$
3. Write the power of 10 with exponents. 5.46×10^6

THINK How can you use mental math to multiply by a power of 10?

▼ By multiplying, you can write any number that is in scientific notation in *standard notation*.

Example 3 Write each number in standard notation.

a. 9.3×10^7 b. 4.235×10^2

Solution a. $9.3 \cdot 10{,}000{,}000 = 93{,}000{,}000$ b. $4.235 \cdot 100 = 423.5$

▼ You can multiply numbers in scientific notation.

Example 4 **Write the product in scientific notation.**

$(3.46 \times 10^5)(9.2 \times 10^3)$

Solution
1. Multiply the decimals. $3.46 \times 9.2 = 31.832$
2. Multiply the powers of 10. $10^5 \cdot 10^3 = 10^8$
3. Write the product. 31.832×10^8
4. Write the first factor in scientific $(3.1832 \times 10) \times 10^8$
   notation.
5. Simplify. 3.1832×10^9

THINK AND DISCUSS

1. How does scientific notation prevent careless error when working with very large numbers?

2. How would you add 1×10^5 and 1×10^4?

CLASS EXERCISES

Write each number in standard notation.

1. 10^6 **2.** 10^7 **3.** 0.93×10^4

Is each number written in scientific notation? Explain.

4. 10^4 **5.** 0.12×10^1 **6.** 5.24×10^1 **7.** 7.2×3^4

Write each number in scientific notation.

8. Some computers can process 3.5 million instructions per second.

9. Light travels 299,790,000 m/s.

Write each number in standard notation.

10. The radius of the earth is 5×10^6 m.

11. The estimated age of Earth is 4.7×10^9 years.

Write the result in scientific notation.

12. $(3.45 \times 10^6)(1.84 \times 10^2)$ **13.** $(4.32 \times 10^3) \cdot (2.4 \times 10^1)$

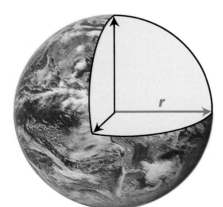

WRITTEN EXERCISES

1. Write 625,000,000 three different ways using powers of 10.

2. Write 4.97×10^7 three different ways using powers of 10.

Write each number in scientific notation.

3. The average adult human male, weighing about 160 lb, consists of about 60,000,000,000,000 cells.

4. The temperature inside the sun is greater than 16,000,000°C.

5. *DATA FILE 10 (pp. 404–405)* Write the area of the Pacific Ocean in scientific notation.

Write each number in standard notation.

6. 10^8

7. 10^5

8. 59×10

9. 7.654×10^3

10. 1.45×10^{10}

11. 6.0032×10^2

12. 9.84×10^5

13. 4.06×10^3

14. 1.7×10^2

Simplify. Write each answer in scientific and standard notation. Round to the nearest tenth.

15. $(3 \times 10^2)(5 \times 10^2)$

16. $(4.2 \times 10^3)(3.84 \times 10^1)$

17. $389,000 \cdot 25,475,000$

18. $0.00125 \times 50,000$

19. $(9.087 \times 10^6)0.52$

20. $4(2.3 \times 10^5)$

Complete.

21. $8,450 = 8.45 \times 10^{\blacksquare}$

22. $\blacksquare \times 10^2 = 8.45 \times 10^3$

23. $84.5 = \blacksquare \times 10^1$

24. $8.45 = 8.45 \times 10^{\blacksquare}$

25. $0.845 = \blacksquare \times 10^3$

26. $\blacksquare \times 10^4 = 8.45 \times 10^3$

CALCULATOR Solve using a scientific calculator. Round each answer to the nearest hundredth.

▼▼ *SAMPLE* $(6.28 \times 10^{24}) \times (5.3 \times 10^7)$

Enter: 6.28 (EXP) 24 (×) 5.3 (EXP) 7 (=)

Display: 3.3284 E 32

27. $(7.892 \times 10^{17})(3.16 \times 10^3)$

28. $(7.892 \times 10^{17})^2$

29. $(7.892 \times 10^{17}) \cdot 10^3$

30. $(4.32 \times 10^5) \cdot 673$

31. $905,200,000,000,000,000 \cdot 3,560,090,000,000$

32. How many seconds are there in 1,000 years?

DATA FILE 4 (pp. 138–139) **Solve.**

33. Write the number of speakers of Chinese in scientific notation.

34. Find the increase in population from 1900 to 1980. Express the number in scientific notation.

35. *PROJECT* Use an encyclopedia, almanac, or other reference book. Find the answers to the following questions and write in scientific notation.

  a. What is the diameter of a water molecule?

  b. How far from Earth is Mars?

  c. What is the shutter speed of the fastest still camera?

The Average Distance to the Sun (km)	
Planet	**Distance**
Neptune	4.497×10^9
Mercury	5.79×10^7
Jupiter	7.783×10^8
Venus	1.082×10^8
Saturn	1.427×10^9
Earth	1.496×10^8
Uranus	2.869×10^9
Mars	2.279×10^8
Pluto	5.9×10^9

Our Nearest Neighbor

The moon is Earth's only satellite. Although it is not a planet, the moon is the closest object to Earth in our solar system. The moon is about 380,000 km from Earth.

On July 20, 1969, American astronauts from the *Apollo* mission were the first men to set foot on the moon. They returned to Earth with 382 kg of moon rocks and dust. The footsteps the astronauts left on the moon will probably be visible for at least 10 million years.

Use the table at the left to solve.

36. Which is closer to the sun, Saturn or Jupiter? Earth or Venus?

37. Order the distances from the least to greatest.

38. *WRITE* a procedure for ordering numbers in scientific notation.

39. Alpha Centauri, the star closest to the sun, is about 40,600,000,000,000 km away. Write this in scientific notation.

40. Why do you think astronomers prefer scientific notation?

41. *PROJECT* Astronomers measure very great distances in *light years*. Find out what a light year is and the distance in light years from one side of our galaxy to the other.

Use the article at the left to solve.

42. How would you express the distance from Earth to the moon in meters? Express this distance using scientific notation.

43. How many 0.5-meter footsteps are there from here to the moon? Express using scientific notation.

44. *PROJECT* Find out why the footprints on the moon will be visible for 10 million years.

TEST YOURSELF

Write using exponents.

1. $a \cdot b \cdot a \cdot b \cdot b$

2. $-2 \cdot x \cdot (-2) \cdot y \cdot x \cdot x$

Evaluate.

3. 4^3

4. 12^2

5. $(-3)^5$

6. $(3^2)^0$

7. -5^4

8. $2^2 \cdot 2^3 \cdot 2^4$

Write each number in scientific notation.

9. 10,000

10. 100,000

11. 10,000,000

12. 75,000

13. 854,000

14. 1,645,123

OBJECTIVE:
To apply scientific notation to solve problems concerning water resources and usage.

4-4 Water Resources

■ Water is critical for life. Our bodies are 0.65 water. About 0.95 of the total weight of a tomato plant is water. We need water to grow the food we eat and to manufacture the goods we use. Without water, we could not exist.

Example 1 The total amount of water on Earth is about 3.26×10^8 mi^3. A cubic mile of water contains about 1.1×10^{12} gal of water. In gallons, what is the total amount of water on Earth?

Solution Multiply the number of cubic miles of water by the number of gallons in each cubic mile.

$$(3.26 \times 10^8) \times (1.1 \times 10^{12}) = (3.26 \times 1.1) \times (10^8 \times 10^{12})$$
$$= 3.586 \times 10^{20}$$

There are about 3.586×10^{20} gal of water on Earth.

Example 2 Find the total number of gallons of ocean water.

Solution Multiply 0.97 by the result from Example 1.

$$(0.97)(3.586 \times 10^{20}) = (0.97 \times 3.586) \times (10^{20})$$
$$= 3.47842 \times 10^{20}$$

There are 3.47842×10^{20} gal of ocean water.

■ You can find the portion of water given an amount.

Example 3 For every 50,000 gal of Earth's water supply, how much is found in icecaps and glaciers?

Solution Multiply the amount by 0.023 and express the product in scientific notation.

$$(0.023)(50,000) = 1,150$$
$$= 1.15 \times 10^3$$

The amount of water is 1.15×10^3 gal.

Earth's Water Supply
(for every gallon)

Source	Amount
ocean	0.97
icecaps and glaciers	0.023
lakes and rivers	0.0001
underground	0.0059
atmosphere	0.001

CLASS EXERCISES

Use the DATA at the left to solve each problem. Give your answers in scientific notation.

1. There are 358,600,000,000,000,000,000 gal of water on Earth. What is the total amount from underground sources?

2. For every 75,000 gal of water, how much comes from lakes and rivers?

WRITTEN EXERCISES

■ Use a **CALCULATOR** where appropriate.

Use the **DATA** at the left to solve each problem. Express answers in scientific notation.

Average Water Usage in United States Cities (per person/day)

home	70 gal
factories and businesses	70 gal
city services	10 gal

1. There are about 187,500,000 people that live in cities in the United States. About how many gallons of water will these people use each day in their homes?

2. In all, about how many gallons of water do the 187,500,000 people in cities use in a day for all purposes?

3. The population of the city of Chicago is about 4,000,000 people.

   a. About how many gallons of water do the people in Chicago use each day in their homes?

   b. Chicago gets its drinking water from Lake Michigan, the largest body of fresh water in the United States. If you took the top inch of water from Lake Michigan, you would get about 3.9×10^{11} gal of water. Suppose this water is used exclusively by Chicago's homes. About how many days of water would it supply?

■ ■ ■ ■ ■ ■ Decision Making ■ **DECISION MAKING** ■ Decision Making ■ Decision Making ■ Decision Making ■

WATER RESOURCES

■ COLLECT DATA

1. Survey how much water your family uses in one week. You can estimate the amounts. For example, to measure the amount of water it takes to fill a bathtub, estimate how many quart or one-gallon milk cartons of water it would take to cover the bottom of the bathtub. Record your estimates in a chart like the one below.

Amount of Water Used Each Day (gal)							
Type of Use	Mon	Tues	Wed	Thur	Fri	Sat	Sun
bath/shower							
dish washing							
drinking							
brushing teeth							
washing hands/ laundry							

4. Chicago's main water purification plant can produce nearly 1.75 billion gal of water each day. The plant serves about 4.5 million people in the city and suburbs. About how many times greater is the plant capacity than the daily water needed for homes, factories, businesses, and city services?

Solve.

5. Many places in the world do not have access to fresh water from lakes and rivers. They must purify ocean water. A desalting plant in Key West, Florida, can produce about 2 million gal of fresh water per day. Assume the plant operates every day. About how many gallons of pure water can the plant produce in a year?

6. The Great Salt Lake in Utah holds about 5.7 mi³ of water and about 4.0×10^9 t of salt. About how many tons of salt is this per cubic mile?

7. The total amount of water on the planet is about 326,000,000 mi³. About how many cubic miles are in glaciers and icecaps?

8. *PROJECT* Water is naturally recycled by the processes of *evaporation* and *condensation*. Research how ocean water and fresh water are recycled through these processes.

■ *Decision Making* ■ *Decision Making* ■ *Decision Making* ■ *Decision Making* ■ *Decision Making* ■ *Decision Making* ■

■ **ANALYZE DATA**

2. What is the total amount of water your family uses in one week? Which activities use more water?

3. Estimate the amount of water used for brushing your teeth if the water is left running. How much water would be used in a year?

4. What ways can you think of to reduce the amount of water you and your family use?

■ **MAKE DECISIONS**

5. Discuss ways your classmates and families can conserve water. Make a list of ideas that you can use at home.

6. Try several water-saving ideas. Keep track of your family's water consumption for another week. Record your data.

7. How much water did you save in one week? Compare your results with those of your classmates.

8. Make a poster with at least three suggestions and the amount of water they would save in a year.

OBJECTIVE:
To explore factors
and multiples.

MATERIALS

- Graph paper or lined
  paper
- Math journal to record
  work

Exploring Factors and Multiples

▼   A high school has 1,000 lockers, numbered 1 to 1,000, and 1,000
students. The students enter the building one at a time.

- The first student opens all the lockers.
- The second student starts with locker 2 and closes every second
  locker.
- The third student starts with locker 3 and moves to every third
  locker. The student opens the closed lockers and closes the open
  ones.
- The fourth student changes every fourth locker starting with
  locker 4, and so on for the remaining students.

**Answer the questions below to find out which lockers are open and
which lockers are closed after all the students enter.**

1. Which of the first nine lockers will be open after the first student
   passes through? the second student?

2. Using a table like the one below, find out which lockers will be
   open after the third student passes through.

Student Number	Locker Number								
	1	2	3	4	5	6	7	8	9
1	O	O	O	O	O	O	O	O	O
2	O	C	O	C	O	C	O	C	O
3	O	C	C	C	O	O	O	C	C
4	O	C	C	O	O	O	O	O	C

KEY
O   Open
C   Closed

3. Which students change the condition of locker 1? 2? 3?

4. ***Extend*** and complete the table for 12 students and 12 lockers.

5. Which students changed the condition of locker 12? Will any
   of the other 1,000 students change locker 12? Explain.

6. ***Describe*** and discuss the relationship between the numbers of the
   students who changed locker 12 and the number 12.

▼ The numbers that correspond to the students who changed locker 12 are *factors* of the number 12.

7. Use the relationship between the student number and the locker number to predict which students will change locker 20.

8. **Test** your prediction by extending and completing the table for 20 students and 20 lockers.

9. List all the factors of each number.

   a. 1   **b.** 4   **c.** 6   **d.** 9

▼ Student 3 changed six of the first 20 lockers. List them.

10. Will student 3 change any other of the 1,000 lockers? Explain.

11. **Describe** and discuss the relationship between the student number and the number of lockers the student changes.

▼ The numbers of the lockers that student 3 changed are *multiples* of the number 3.

12. Use the relationship between the student and the locker number to predict which lockers student 25 will change.

13. List the multiples found in your table for each number.

   a. 1   **b.** 4   **c.** 5   **d.** 6

14. Refer to your table.

   a. Which of the 20 lockers will be open after 20 students pass through?

   b. **Predict** the next two lockers that will be open.

   c. What do you call these numbers? Do they have an odd or even number of factors? Is this true for all numbers of this type?

▼ After the 1,000 students pass through, each locker with an open door corresponds to a number with an odd number of factors.

15. Why do you think an odd number of factors would correspond to a locker with an open door?

16. Does an even number of factors correspond to a locker with a closed door? Explain.

17. **Write** a rule that explains which lockers are open and which are closed after the 1,000 students pass through.

18. **Calculator** Make a list of the numbers that correspond to an open locker once all the students have passed through.

Exploring Factors and Multiples

Practice

CAREER

Help Wanted:
Demographer

Bachelor's degree in sociology required. A masters degree is suggested. For more information, write to Population Association of America, 1722 N Street, NW, Washington, DC 20036.

Demographers study size, characteristics, and movement of populations to forecast future trends. Lawmakers, administrators, and marketers use demographers' findings to help improve intergroup relations, to solve social problems, and formulate better public policy.

PROJECT

Find out how the population in your town or city changed in the past ten years. Make a graph to show the change in population.

Write using exponents.

1. $5 \cdot 3 \cdot 3 \cdot 5 \cdot 5$

2. $-3 \cdot t \cdot s \cdot s \cdot 4 \cdot s$

3. $(-3a)(-3a)(-3a)(-3a)(-3a)$

4. $(2n - 1)(2n - 1)(2n - 1)$

Evaluate.

5. 8^3

6. $(-1)^{17}$

7. $(-3)^5$

8. -4^3

9. 4^3

10. -2^5

11. $(-4)^2$

12. $\sqrt{36}$

13. $7^3 \cdot 7^6$

14. $6^5 \cdot 6^3$

15. $16 \cdot 4^2$

16. $(4^5 \cdot 4^9)^0$

17. $-3[5 - (-2)]^2$

18. $[7 + (-2)]^4$

19. $(3^2)(3^6)$

20. $(2^4)(4^2) \div 4$

21. $4^4 \cdot 4^6 \cdot 2^3$

22. $5^3 - 2^3 \cdot 2^1$

Simplify.

23. $b \cdot b^2$

24. $g^{12} \cdot g^{10}$

25. $k^5 \cdot k^8$

26. $6x^4y^3$

27. $c \cdot c^6 \cdot c^4$

28. $a^3b^2c^6 \cdot a^0b^4c^5$

29. $(-y^3)(-y)^3$

30. $ab^6c^3 \cdot a^5bc^8$

31. $(3r^3)^5$

32. $(-3s)^4 \cdot 9^1$

33. $(3m^2)^4 \cdot 5m^2$

34. $(-4m^3y^7)^2$

Evaluate for $a = 4$, $b = -1$, and $c = -5$.

35. $-4b^3 + ac^2$

36. $a^3 + 6cb^0$

37. $abc \cdot \sqrt{100}$

38. $(c^2 - a^2) \cdot (-3b^8c^0)$

39. $a^2c + b$

40. $-(c)^2 - (b)^2 \cdot (a^2 + 3b)$

41. $(ab^2)^4 \cdot (4a^2b)$

Write each number in standard notation.

42. 5×10^5

43. 24×10^7

44. 35.6×10^6

45. 10^7

46. 63.57×10^5

47. 9.83675×10^4

Write each number in scientific notation.

48. The height of Mt. Everest is 10,000 m.

49. The sun's diameter is 3,392,000 km.

50. In an average lifetime a heart beats about 2,500,000,000,000 times.

51. The approximate weight of Earth is 5,880,000,000,000,000,000,000 t.

52. The radius of our solar system is 100,000,000,000 m.

53. The radius of the Milky Way galaxy is 10,000,000,000,000,000,000,000 m.

54. In the 1864 presidential election, 2,218,388 votes were cast for Abraham Lincoln.

OBJECTIVE:
To identify whole
number factors and
multiples of a number
and to determine
divisibility by 2, 3, 4,
5, 6, 9, or 10.

4-5 *Factors, Multiples, and Divisibility*

▼ The diagram at the right shows all the
different rectangles that you can make with
12 squares. The dimensions are 1 by 12,
2 by 6, and 3 by 4. The numbers 1, 2, 3, 4,
6, and 12 are the *factors* of 12. The number
12 is *divisible* by its factors.

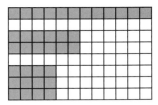

Divisible	A number is divisible by a second number if the second number divides the first with no remainder.

Factor	One number is a factor of another if it divides that number with no remainder.

Example 1 **Find the factors of 15.**

Solution   1 · 15   3 · 5

The factors of 15 are 1, 3, 5, and 15.

Example 2 Are 5 and 8 factors of 45?

THINK Why is 8 not a factor
of 45?

Solution   45 ÷ 5 = 9 ✓   Yes, 5 is a factor of 45.

45 ÷ 8 = 5.625 ✗   No, 8 is not a factor of 45.

▼ You can find the *multiples* of any number. The multiples of 12 are
12, 24, 36, 48, . . .

Multiple	A multiple of a number is the product of that number and any other non-zero whole number.

Example 3 **Find the first three multiples of each number.**

a. 2   **b.** 10

Solution   **a.** 2 · 1 = 2   **b.** 10 · 1 = 10
               2 · 2 = 4   10 · 2 = 20
               2 · 3 = 6   10 · 3 = 30

Example 4 Is 45 a multiple of 15?

Solution   The multiples of 15 are 15, 30, 45, 60, . . .

Yes, 45 is a multiple of 15 because 3 · 15 = 45.

▼ You can use divisibility tests to find out if one number is divisible by another.

FLASHBACK

Even numbers are divisible by 2.
Odd numbers are not divisible by 2.

Divisibility Tests

A number is divisible by 2 if the ones' digit is 0, 2, 4, 6, or 8.

A number is divisible by 5 if the ones' digit is 0 or 5.

A number is divisible by 10 if the ones' digit is 0.

▼ To discover a divisibility test for 3, analyze the following table.

Number	Sum of digits	Is the sum divisible by 3?	Is the number divisible by 3?
136	1 + 3 + 6 = 10	no	no
462	4 + 6 + 2 = 12	yes	yes
216	2 + 1 + 6 = 9	yes	yes
1,017	1 + 0 + 1 + 7 = 9	yes	yes

Divisible by 3

A number is divisible by 3 if the sum of its digits is divisible by 3.

▼ To discover a divisibility test for 9, analyze the following table.

Number	Sum of digits	Is the sum divisible by 9?	Is the number divisible by 9?
136	1 + 3 + 6 = 10	no	no
462	4 + 6 + 2 = 12	no	no
216	2 + 1 + 6 = 9	yes	yes
1,017	1 + 0 + 1 + 7 = 9	yes	yes

THINK If a number is divisible by 3, is it also divisible by 9? Is the reverse true? Explain.

Divisible by 9

A number is divisible by 9 if the sum of its digits is divisible by 9.

Example 5 **Is the first number divisible by the second?**

    a. 567; 2   **b.** 567; 3   **c.** 567; 5   **d.** 567; 9

Solution **a.** No, the ones' digit is not 0, 2, 4, 6, or 8.

    b. Yes, the sum of the digits is 18, which is divisible by 3. Write: 3|567 (3 divides 567 with no remainder).

    c. No, the ones' digit is not 0 or 5.

    d. Yes, the sum of the digits is divisible by 9. Write: 9|567.

CLASS EXERCISES

True or *false*? Explain your answer.

1. 3|555

2. 981 is divisible by 9.

3. 9 is a multiple of 18.

4. 5 is a factor of 435.

5. 6 divides 56.

6. 2 divides every even number.

7. If a number is divisible by both 2 and 5, it is divisible by 10.

8. If a number is divisible by 6, then it is divisible by 2.

9. If a number is divisible by 2, then it is divisible by 6.

10. List the first ten multiples of 11.

11. Write a missing digit so that the resulting number is divisible by 3.   4,826,▮51

12. Write a missing digit so that the resulting number is divisible by 9.   4,826,▮51

13. State a rule for divisibility by 100.

THINK AND DISCUSS

1. What number is a factor of all numbers?

2. How many multiples does any number have?

3. What number can never be a factor of a number?

WRITTEN EXERCISES

Decide whether the first number is a factor of the second.

1. 8; 72

2. 12; 54

3. 7; 91

4. 6; 68

5. 9; 621

6. 3; 101

7. 5; 46,582

8. 4; 128

9. 10; 75,020

10. 9; 74,520

11. 3; 876

12. 15; 120

List all the factors of each number.

13. 30

14. 1

15. 55

16. 126

17. 29

List the first five multiples of each number.

18. 1

19. 12

20. 16

21. 25

State whether each number is divisible by 2, 3, 5, or 9.

22. 213

23. 630

24. 138

25. 204

26. 131

27. 4,805

28. 288

29. 4,719

30. Which numbers are divisible by both 2 and 3?

  a. 10   **b.** 66   **c.** 898   **d.** 47,820   **e.** 975

  f. *WRITE* a divisibility rule for 6.

NOTES & QUOTES

A perfect number is a number that is the sum of all its possible factors, excluding itself. Six is the first perfect number (1 + 2 + 3 = 6). At present, only 30 perfect numbers have been calculated.

RESEARCH Can you find the second perfect number?

31. a. Copy and complete the table.

Number	Last two digits	Last 2 digits divisible by 4?	Is the number divisible by 4?
136	36	yes	yes
1,268	68	yes	yes
314	14	no	no
1,078	▨	▨	▨
696	▨	▨	▨

b. *WRITE* a divisibility rule for 4.

Write the missing digit to make each number divisible by 9.

32. 29▨,634 **33.** 4▨,817 **34.** 8,03▨,373

Solve.

35. If a is divisible by 2, is $a + 1$ even or odd?

36. If a is divisible by 9, is $2a$ divisible by 9?

37. If a^2 is divisible by both 2 and 5, can $a = 10$?

38. Find a number less than 100 that is divisible by the first six positive integers.

TEST YOURSELF

Write in standard notation.

1. 9.604×10^3 **2.** 1.23×10^4 **3.** $(42 \times 10^9)(0.68 \times 10^6)$

Write in scientific notation.

4. 9,650,000 **5.** 548 **6.** 30×10^5

List all the factors of each number.

7. 27 **8.** 45 **9.** 60

State whether each number is divisible by 2, 3, 5, or 9.

10. 45 **11.** 300 **12.** 369

Write using exponents.

13. $4 \cdot 4 \cdot 4 \cdot 4$ **14.** $17 \cdot 17 \cdot 17$ **15.** $z \cdot z \cdot z \cdot z$

Evaluate for $x = 2$ and $y = 5$.

16. x^2y **17.** y^2x **18.** $x^2 + y^2$ **19.** $x^4 - y^2$

OBJECTIVE:
To determine whether
a number is prime or
composite and to find
its prime
factorization.

4-6 Prime Factorization

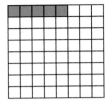

▼ The graph paper diagram shows all the possible factors of 5. Notice there is only one rectangle. The factors of 5 are 1 and 5. We call the number 5 a *prime number*.

Prime Number	A prime number is a whole number greater than one with exactly two factors, 1 and the number itself.

▼ Numbers greater than 1 that are not prime are *composite numbers*.

Example 1 **Prime numbers**   **Composite numbers**

   2, 3, 5, 7, 11, 13 . . .   4, 6, 8, 9, 10, 12, 14, 15 . . .

THINK Why is 2 the only even prime number?

Composite Number	A composite number is a whole number greater than one with more than two factors.

▼ A composite number is divisible by prime factors.

Example 2 **Tell whether each number is prime or composite.**

   a. 129   **b.** 23

Solution To test for divisibility, start with the smallest prime. Stop when you reach a prime whose square is greater than the number you are testing.

a. Is 129 divisible by 2? No, it is odd.

Is 129 divisible by 3? Yes, the sum of the digits is 12, a multiple of 3.

129 is composite.

b. Is 23 divisible by 2? No, it is odd.

Is 23 divisible by 3? No, the sum of the digits is 5.

Is 23 divisible by 5? No, the ones' digit is not 0 or 5.

Since $5^2 > 23$, 23 is prime.

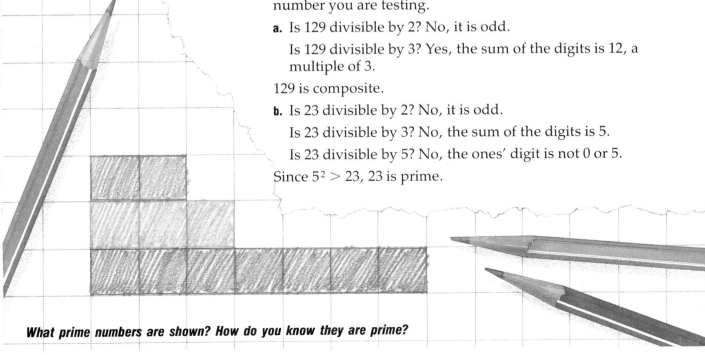

What prime numbers are shown? How do you know they are prime?

▼ You can write a composite number as a product of its prime factors, called the *prime factorization*.

Example 3 **Write the prime factorization of 60 using division.**

Solution Divide by prime numbers until the quotient is 1.

1. Is 60 divisible by 2? Yes. $60 \div 2 = 30$
2. Is 30 divisible by 2? Yes. $30 \div 2 = 15$
3. Is 15 divisible by 2? No.
4. Is 15 divisible by 3? Yes. $15 \div 3 = 5$
5. Is 5 divisible by 3? No.
6. Since $5 \div 5 = 1$, you are done. $5 \div 5 = 1$

$60 = 2 \cdot 2 \cdot 3 \cdot 5$, or $2^2 \cdot 3 \cdot 5$

THINK What other ways can you write the prime factorization of 825 using a factor tree?

Example 4 **Write the prime factorization of 825 using a factor tree.**

Solution
1. Write the composite number as the product of two factors.
2. Continue Step 1 with any remaining composite factors.
3. Stop when all factors are prime.
4. Write the prime factorization.

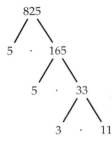

$5 \cdot 5 \cdot 3 \cdot 11 = 5^2 \cdot 3 \cdot 11$

CLASS EXERCISES

Tell whether each number is prime or composite.

1. 102   **2.** 197   **3.** 253

4. 367   **5.** 221   **6.** 209

Write the prime factorization using division.

7. 150   **8.** 280   **9.** 225

Write the prime factorization using a factor tree.

10. 236   **11.** 294   **12.** 275

Find the number with the given prime factorization.

13. $2 \cdot 3^2 \cdot 5^2$ **14.** $3 \cdot 5 \cdot 7^2$

THINK AND DISCUSS

1. Why is the number 1 neither prime nor composite?

2. Why is zero neither prime nor composite?

3. Do you think there is a largest prime number? Explain.

WRITTEN EXERCISES

Tell whether each number is prime or composite.

1. 45   **2.** 87   **3.** 97

4. 109   **5.** 301   **6.** 1,001

Write the prime factorization using division.

7. 425   **8.** 240   **9.** 186

Write the prime factorization using a factor tree.

10. 650   **11.** 1,575   **12.** 1,617

CALCULATOR Find the number with the given prime factorization.

13. $2^5 \cdot 3 \cdot 11$ **14.** $2 \cdot 5 \cdot 17^2$ **15.** $2^5 \cdot 5 \cdot 7^3 \cdot 13^2$

Use 5, 11, and 23 to find the prime factors of each number.

16. 115   **17.** 621   **18.** 3,105   **19.** 253

Will each integer expression be even or odd?

20. $2ab^2$ **21.** $2(a + b)^2$ **22.** $2a^2b + 1$

Solve.

23. The numbers 2, 3, and 7 are factors of x. Find four other factors of x.

24. Find a number between 50 and 100 whose prime factorization has two factors.

25. Ms. Schwartz wrote a number on the chalkboard and said, "I know that to be sure this number is prime, I must check each prime divisor from 2 to 29." What is the least number Ms. Schwartz could have written? What is the greatest number she could have written?

26. Kim and her grandmother have the same birthday and they have a family party together every year. Kim's age was a divisor of her grandmother's age for six birthdays in a row. What were their ages at each of those birthdays?

27. DATA FILE 4 (pp. 138–139)

     a. Which country has the greatest percent of its population between the ages of 10 and 14?

     b. Which country has the greatest percent of its population between the ages of 0 and 4?

NOTES & QUOTES

The largest prime number yet calculated (on a CRAY supercomputer in Houston, Texas, in 1985) has 65,050 digits. It is mathematically written as $2^{216091} - 1$. The computer worked at a rate of 400 million calculations per second for 3 h to insure that this number was in fact prime.

MIXED REVIEW

1. List the factors of 8.

2. List the first four multiples of 8.

3. List the factors of 36.

Evaluate.

4. $54 \div (9 - 15)$

5. $5(-4 + 7)^2$

6. $36 \div [2 - (-1)]^2$

7. DATA FILE 1 (pp. 2–3) Predict the equivalent wind chill temperature for air temperature $-30°F$ and wind speed 10 mi/h.

PROBLEM SOLVING HINT
Use guess and test.

Eratosthenes of Cyrene (c. 276–195 B.C.) was a Greek mathematician. He established a procedure for determining all prime numbers less than a given value. This procedure is called the *Sieve of Eratosthenes.*

RESEARCH Find out how Eratosthenes used his sieve to determine prime numbers. Use his method to determine all prime numbers less than 150.

28. Find two prime numbers whose product is 221.

29. Twin primes are prime numbers whose difference is 2. For example, 11 and 13 are twin primes.

   a. List the first seven pairs of twin primes.

   b. What do these numbers have in common?

   c. Predict whether this will be true for all twin primes.

   d. Use a computer or sieve (see below) to generate primes less than 100.

   e. Test your prediction.

30. Find a pattern in the chart. Write an equation relating c and t.

chairs	5	10	15	c
tables	1	2	3	t

Critical Thinking

EXPLORING CLASSIFICATION

▼ You can use a *sieve* to find prime numbers. The first step is to list the numbers from 1 to 100 in rows of six on paper.

Mark out 1, since it's not prime. Circle 2, since it is prime. Mark out every multiple of 2.

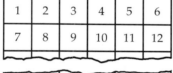

1. What pattern do you notice for the multiples of 2?

2. Circle the first number after 2 that is unmarked. This is the next prime number. Mark out all of its multiples. What pattern do you notice for these multiples?

3. The next prime is 5. Circle it and mark out all of its multiples. Describe the pattern formed by the multiples of 5.

4. What is the next prime number? Mark out its multiples.

5. Eleven is prime. Circle it. Why have you already marked out all of the multiples of 11?

6. What do you notice about the rest of the unmarked numbers? Why is this true?

7. Find all the primes less than 200. When is it no longer necessary to mark out multiples?

OBJECTIVE:
To find the GCF or
LCM by listing or
using prime
factorization.

4-7 GCF and LCM

▼ At a school fund raiser, the math class raised $150 and the science class raised $120. Each class will divide the money it raised equally, in whole dollar amounts, and give to the same number of charities. What method could you use to find the possible number of charities? the greatest possible number of charities?

List the factors of 150 and 120. Find the factors that are the same.

150: **1, 2, 3, 5, 6, 10, 15,** 25, **30,** 50, 75, 150

120: **1, 2, 3,** 4, **5, 6,** 8, **10,** 12, **15,** 20, 24, **30,** 40, 60, 120

The *common factors* are 1, 2, 3, 5, 6, 10, 15, and 30. The *greatest common factor (GCF)* is 30. The classes can distribute whole dollar amounts of money to 1, 2, 3, 5, 6, 10, 15, or, at most, 30 charities.

Common Factor	The factors that are the same for a given set of numbers are their common factors.

Greatest Common Factor (GCF)	The greatest common factor of a set of numbers is the greatest number that is a factor of the given numbers.

▼ Another way to find the GCF is to use prime factorization.

Example 1 **Find the GCF of 40 and 140.**

Solution 1. Write the prime factorization for each number.

2. Circle each pair of common factors.

3. Multiply common factors.

The GCF is 20.

$40 = 2 \cdot 2 \cdot 2 \cdot 5$
$140 = 2 \cdot 2 \cdot 5 \cdot 7$

$2 \cdot 2 \cdot 5$

▼ When the GCF of two numbers is 1, the numbers are *relatively prime*.

Example 2 **Find the GCF of 28 and 33.**

Solution 1. Write the prime factorization.

2. Circle common factors.

There are no common prime factors. The GCF is 1.

$28 = 2 \cdot 2 \cdot 7$
$33 = 3 \cdot 11$

▲
THINK Do relatively prime numbers have any common factors besides 1?

▼ You can find the GCF of variable expressions by writing each expression as the product of its factors. This is called *algebraic factorization*.

Example 3 Find the GCF of $12a^3b$ and $15a^2b^2$.

Solution
1. Write the algebraic factorizations.
2. Circle the common factors.

$$12a^3b = 2 \cdot 2 \cdot 3 \cdot a \cdot a \cdot a \cdot b$$
$$15a^2b^2 = 3 \cdot 5 \cdot a \cdot a \cdot b \cdot b$$

3. Multiply.

$$3 \cdot a \cdot a \cdot b$$

The GCF is $3a^2b$.

▼ Some problems require that you work with *common multiples* and the *least common multiple (LCM)*.

THINK How many common multiples do any two numbers have?

Common Multiples	The multiples that are the same for a given set of whole numbers are the common multiples.

Least Common Multiple	The least common multiple is the least number that is a common multiple of two or more given numbers.

Example 4 Aisha and Tom visited their aunt today. Aisha visits every 4 days; Tom visits every 3 days. When will Aisha and Tom visit their aunt again on the same day?

Solution
1. List the multiples of each number.
2. Circle common multiples.

4: 4, 8, 12, 16, 20, 24 . . .
3: 3, 6, 9, 12, 15, 18, 21, 24 . . .

3. Write the least common multiple.   LCM = 12

Aisha and Tom will visit their aunt together in 12 days.

▼ You can find the LCM using prime factorization.

Example 5 Find the LCM of 72 and 60.

Solution
1. Write the prime factorizations.
2. Circle each factor the greatest number of times it appears.

$$72 = 2 \cdot 2 \cdot 2 \cdot 3 \cdot 3$$
$$60 = 2 \cdot 2 \cdot 3 \cdot 5$$

3. Multiply.

$$2 \cdot 2 \cdot 2 \cdot 3 \cdot 3 \cdot 5$$

The LCM is 360.

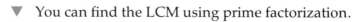

▼ You can find the LCM of variable expressions using algebraic factorization.

Example 6 Find the LCM of $4a^2$ and $6ab$.

Solution
1. Write the algebraic factorizations.
2. Circle each factor the greatest number of times it appears.
3. Multiply.

$$4a^2 = \boxed{2 \cdot 2} \cdot \boxed{a \cdot a}$$
$$6ab = 2 \cdot \boxed{3} \cdot a \cdot \boxed{b}$$

$$2 \cdot 2 \cdot 3 \cdot a \cdot a \cdot b$$

The LCM is $12a^2b$.

CLASS EXERCISES

Find the GCF of each set of numbers or expressions.

1. 10, 45   **2.** 6, 8, 12   **3.** $12r^3$, $8r$

Find the LCM of each set of numbers or expressions.

4. 10, 45   **5.** 6, 8, 12   **6.** $12r^3$, $8r$

Is the pair of numbers relatively prime? Write *yes* or *no*.

7. 51, 17   **8.** 9, 10   **9.** 13, 23

10. Find the GCF and the LCM for each pair of numbers. Find the product of the GCF and the LCM. Find the product of the two original numbers. What do you notice? Will this always be true? Is it true that the LCM of two numbers is a multiple of their GCF?

  a. 6, 8   **b.** 15, 18   **c.** 20, 30

  d. 20, 25   **e.** 12, 30   **f.** 84, 120

11. Name four numbers that have both 6 and 10 as factors. What is the least number that has 6 and 10 as factors?

12. *True* or *false*? Explain.

  a. If a and b are positive integers and $a|b$, then the LCM of a and b is b.

  b. The set of all common factors of two given positive integers is finite.

THINK AND DISCUSS

1. Can any two numbers have a common multiple? Explain.

2. Can two consecutive positive integers be relatively prime?

3. Is the LCM of two different prime numbers equal to their product?

WRITTEN EXERCISES

Find the GCF of each set of numbers or expressions.

1. 14, 21   **2.** 54, 144   **3.** 52, 65

4. 18, 30   **5.** $27x^2y^4$, $46x^2yz$ **6.** 8, 15, 20

7. $180a^2$, $210ab$ **8.** $6a^3b$, $8ab^2$ **9.** 12, 15, 18

Find the LCM of each set of numbers or expressions.

10. 10, 55   **11.** 12, 20   **12.** 54, 36

13. 180, 210   **14.** $8x$, $25y$ **15.** $6a^3b$, $8ab^2$

16. $6cd^3$, $8c$, $12d^2$ **17.** 12, 15, 18   **18.** 14, 18, 21

CALCULATOR Find the GCF and LCM for each set of numbers.

19. 32, 12   **20.** 119, 391   **21.** 135; 280; 300

22. The GCF of 30 and x is 6. Could x be each of the following?

  a. 15   **b.** 24   **c.** 60   **d.** 84

23. The LCM of 8 and x is a. Explain why a is divisible by 2^3.

Solve.

24. When Jim sorts his stamps into piles of 2, 3, 4, or 5, there is always one stamp left over. What is the smallest number of stamps Jim can have?

25. Two neon signs turn on at the same time. One blinks on every 10 s, the other blinks on every 6 s. How many times per minute do the signs blink on together?

26. The numbers of students attending a conference from three schools are 42, 48, and 60. The students will form discussion groups with an equal number of students from each school in each group. What is the greatest number of discussion groups that can be formed?

27. There are two sizes of tables in a banquet hall. One size seats exactly 5 people and the other size seats exactly 8 people. Last night, 66 people were seated at fewer than 10 tables with no empty seats. How many tables of each size were there?

28. A band of pirates shared 187 pieces of silver and 136 gold coins. Each pirate received a fair share. How many pirates were in the band?

29. A farmer has three pieces of timber with lengths of 63 ft, 84 ft, and 105 ft. What is the length of the longest logs of equal length the farmer can cut from the timber?

DATA FILE 10 (pp. 404–405) Solve.

30. About how many acres should 22 grizzly bears have for a home range?

31. About how many striped skunks can live within 15,000 acres?

MIXED REVIEW

Write the prime factorization using a factor tree.

1. 12

2. 123

3. What are all the factors of 12?

4. State the first four multiples of 12.

Solve.

5. $3.5n = 14$

6. $-7.3 = p + 4.1$

7. $\frac{n}{3.2} = -5$

Use guess and test.

8. Find two numbers that have a sum of 11 and product of 24.

Exploring Counting Problems

OBJECTIVE:
To explore a problem using a systematic approach.

■ Counting figures can be confusing.

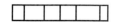

1. Count the rectangles. Are there more than six? Did you count the large rectangle bordering the figure?

MATERIALS

- Graph paper
- Math journal to record work

---

2. Can a rectangle be made up of smaller rectangles? Can the rectangles overlap? How would this affect your total count?

3. How can you count the rectangles *systematically*, so you are sure you counted them all? ***Discuss*** with a partner.

■ One way to count the rectangles is to trace around the different rectangles, starting at the left and working across.

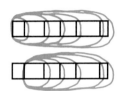

4. Start at the left vertical segment and count all the rectangles that use that segment as a left side. How many are there?

5. Continue with the next vertical segment.

6. Continue counting. When do you know you are done?

Number of Small Rectangles	Labeled Rectangles
1	A, B, C, D, E, F, G, H
2	AB, BC, CD, DE, EF, FG, GH

■ Another systematic way to count the rectangles is to account for the different combinations of smaller rectangles. To keep track, label the smaller rectangles. Refer to the figure at the left.

7. How many rectangles include only one small rectangle? two small rectangles? Continue until you have counted all the combinations of small rectangles. Make a table to organize your data.

8. What is the total number of rectangles? How can you be sure you counted them all?

9. ***Describe*** the pattern in the table. Did you see this pattern when you used the tracing method?

10. Use the pattern to find the number of different rectangles in a figure with 5 regions; 15 regions.

11. ***Compare*** the two methods for counting. How are they the same? How are they different?

■ Now look at the squares in the figure at the left.

12. ***Explore*** a method of your own or use one of the counting methods above. Which method would you use? Why?

13. What is the total number of squares?

4-8 Account for All Possibilities

OBJECTIVE:
To solve problems by accounting for all possibilities.

■ To account systematically for all possibilities, you can make an organized list, a table, or a diagram.

PROBLEM

Mandy invited Rachel, Sue, Jenny, Pam, Erica, and Latosha for lunch. They decided to take pictures of all seven girls with two in each picture. How many pictures did they take?

SOLUTION

READf Answer these questions to understand the given information.

What do you want to find?	the total number of pictures
How many girls are at the party?	seven
How many girls are in each picture?	two

PLAN One way to account for all the possibilities is to make an organized list of all the pairs of girls.

SOLVE Begin by pairing Mandy with her six friends. Next, pair Latosha with each of the five friends. Since Latosha and Mandy have already been paired, you don't need to count them again.

Mandy—Latosha

Mandy—Pam	Latosha—Pam	
Mandy—Rachel	Latosha—Rachel	Pam—
Mandy—Sue	Latosha—Sue	
Mandy—Jenny	Latosha—Jenny	
Mandy—Erica	Latosha—Erica	

Continue the list to find the total number of pairings. Altogether, there are 21 pairs of girls, so there will be 21 pictures.

LOOK BACK Another way to account systematically for all the possibilities is to use a diagram. Draw line segments to connect all the pairs of girls. If you count the segments as you draw them, you will count 21.

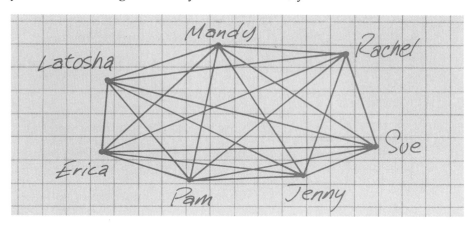

CLASS EXERCISES

Refer to the problem on page 172.

1. Complete the list of paired girls. Count how many pairs are in each group. What pattern do you see?

2. Suppose there were a total of ten girls at Mandy's party. Using the pattern you found, determine how many pictures there would be if there were two girls in each picture.

3. How many pictures would there be if there were a total of 20 girls at Mandy's party, with two girls in each picture? Use the pattern.

Solve.

4. André has a job making yogurt sundaes. The yogurt flavors are chocolate and vanilla. The toppings are granola, raisin, cherry, and coconut. How many *different* sundaes consisting of one scoop of yogurt and one topping can André make?

5. This year there are seven softball teams in the play-offs. Each team competes against each of the other teams twice. What is the total number of games played?

WRITTEN EXERCISES

 Use a CALCULATOR where appropriate.

Solve by accounting systematically for all possibilities.

1. Three darts are thrown at the target shown at the right. If each dart lands on the dart board, how many different point totals are possible?

2. You have four 25-cent stamps and three 30-cent stamps. How many different amounts of postage can you have?

3. Each of the small boxes in the figure at the right is a square. What is the total number of different squares shown in the figure?

4. You have a collection of coins consisting of one penny, one nickel, one dime, and one quarter. How many different amounts of money can be made using one or more of these coins?

Solve. Use any strategy you wish.

5. Fred has a coordinated wardrobe consisting of three pairs of pants, four shirts, and two sweaters. How many different three-piece outfits can he make?

6. You have mushrooms, onions, green peppers, and olives. How many different pizzas can you make by adding any combinations of the ingredients to a plain pizza?

7. Without evaluating, what is the final digit of 8^{66}? How did you find the answer?

8. A collector sorted stamps into 2 piles and had 1 stamp left over. When she sorted them into piles of 3, there were 2 left over. For piles of 4, there were 3 left over. What is the least number of stamps the collector could have?

9. The Valley High chorus has 28 members. The band has 52 members. A total of 17 students are in both the band and the chorus. The music teacher wants to distribute the fewest possible tickets to the spring concert. How many tickets must the teacher distribute for each student in band or chorus to get at least one ticket?

10. This is a list of consecutive odd integers from 1 to n: {1, 3, 5, . . . n}. The square root of the sum of the numbers is 10. What is the value of n? How did you find the answer?

11. Make a list of the two-digit square numbers. Find the difference between the digits of each number. What do you discover?

12. A runner averages 10 km/h. The runner takes a 10 min rest every 5 km. How long will it take to complete a course of 25 km?

13. Pete and Jack earned $12.50 babysitting. Edward earned half as much as Jack. Pete earned $2.50 less than Jack. How much money does Pete have?

14. A chime clock strikes once at one o'clock, twice at two o'clock, and so on. What is the total number of chimes the clock strikes in a twelve-hour period?

Problem Solving Practice

READ PLAN LOOK BACK SOLVE

PROBLEM SOLVING STRATEGIES

Look for a Pattern
Guess and Test
Simplify the Problem
Make an Organized List
Work Backwards
Account for All Possibilities
Make a Table
Write an Equation
Solve by Graphing
Draw a Diagram
Make a Model
Solve Another Way
Simulate the Problem

Solve. The list at the left shows some strategies you can use.

1. A car dealer recommends an oil change every 3,000 mi and a tire rotation every 7,000 mi. When will the oil be changed and the tires rotated at the same time?

2. Thomas was training for a race for six weeks. Every week he ran one more mile than he ran the week before. Thomas ran a total of 51 miles while in training. How many miles did he run each week?

3. Bonnie had 16 coins in her pocket totaling $1.50. What are two combinations of coins she could have had in her pocket?

4. At 5 P.M., the temperature was 65°F. At 5:30 P.M., the temperature was 62°F. At 6 P.M., it was 59°F, at 6:30 P.M., it was 56°F. If the pattern continued, at what time would the temperature go below freezing?

5. How many different pizzas can be made if meatballs, anchovies, green peppers, or olives can be added to a plain pizza?

6. The florist orders carnations, roses, and tulips. Carnations can be bought only in bunches of sixteen. Roses come in bunches of four, and tulips in bunches of eight. The florist wants the same number of each flower. What is the least number of flowers the florist can order?

7. Copy the diagrams at the left.

   a. Using the paths shown, Jillian can walk directly to Trisha's house six different ways. Each route is four blocks long. Draw each route.

   b. There are 20 different routes Courtney can use to walk directly to Justin's house. Each route is six blocks long. How many can you find?

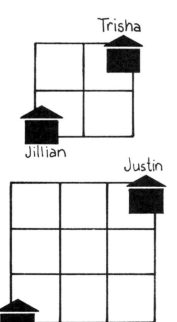

8. In a swim meet, Helen places 7.5 m behind Laney. Laney is 16.5 m ahead of Kay. Kay places 3.75 m behind Julia. How far is Julia behind Laney?

9. **DATA FILE 4 (pp. 138–139)**

   a. In what year was the world population five times the population in 1600?

   b. In what span of years was the world population one sixth of the population in 1975?

10. Five pears weigh the same as 3 apples and 2 strawberries. An apple weighs the same as 21 strawberries. How many strawberries equal the weight of a pear?

Chapter 4 Review

Match each word with the example that illustrates its meaning.

1. rules of exponents for multiplication
2. base
3. greatest common factor
4. rule of a power raised to a power
5. exponent
6. prime number
7. least common multiple
8. rule of a product raised to a power

a. 3 in 2^3
b. $3^2 \cdot 3^5 = 3^7$
c. 5
d. 2 in 2^3
e. 35 for 5 and 7
f. $(2^3)^2 = 2^6$
g. $(3 \cdot 5)^3 = 3^3 \cdot 5^3$
h. 3 for 12 and 15

Using Exponents 4-1

To evaluate a number that has exponents, remember the base is the number used as a factor and the exponent shows the number of times the base is used as a factor.

$$\text{base} \longrightarrow 3^5 \overset{\text{exponent}}{=} 3 \cdot 3 \cdot 3 \cdot 3 \cdot 3 = 243$$

Evaluate

9. 2^3
10. 5^0
11. 3^3
12. 25^1
13. $(3 + 1)^2$

Multiplication and Exponents 4-2

To simplify or evaluate multiplication expressions with exponents, use the following rules.

$3^2 \cdot 3^5 = 3^{2+5} = 3^7$ $(3^2)^5 = 3^{2 \cdot 5} = 3^{10}$ $(2 \cdot 3)^3 = 2^3 \cdot 3^3$

14. $a^2 \cdot a^3$
15. $(2a^2)^3$
16. $a(b^3 + b^2)$
17. $(a^2b)^2$
18. $ab^3a^2b^4$

Scientific Notation 4-3

To write a number in scientific notation, express it as a number between 1 and 10 times a power of 10 with exponents.

Write each number in scientific notation.

19. 465,000,000
20. 13,600,000
21. 1,280
22. 5,090,000

Write each number in standard form.

23. 2.1×10^5
24. 6.13×10^7
25. 1.05×10^3
26. 8.35×10^2

Factors, Multiples, and Divisibility

To help you to remember the meanings of these words, take a look at the number 15.

3 and 5 are factors of 15.

15 is a multiple of 3: 3, 6, 9, 12, 15.   15 is divisible by 3.
15 is a multiple of 5: 5, 10, 15.   15 is divisible by 5.

True or false. Explain your answer.

27. -378 is divisible by 9.

28. 800 is a multiple of 5.

29. 12 is a factor of 144.

30. 9 is a factor of 93.

31. 93 is divisible by 12.

32. 95 is a multiple of 19.

Prime Factorization

To write a composite number as the product of its prime factors, divide by prime numbers until the quotient is 1, or use a factor tree.

Write the prime factorization using division or a factor tree.

33. 75   **34.** 420   **35.** 108   **36.** 765   **37.** 228   **38.** 595

Finding the Greatest Common Factor, the Least Common Multiple

To find the GCF or LCM, use the prime factorization.

the GCF of 35 and 42   the LCM of 35 and 42
$35 = 5 \cdot 7$ $35 = 5 \cdot 7$
$42 = 2 \cdot 3 \cdot 7$ $42 = 2 \cdot 3 \cdot 7$
$\text{GCF} = 7$ $\text{LCM} = 2 \cdot 3 \cdot 5 \cdot 7 = 210$

Find the GCF of each set of numbers.

39. 16, 60   **40.** 24, 56   **41.** 36, 81, 27   **42.** $3x^2y, 6x^2$

Find the LCM of each set of numbers.

43. 12, 18   **44.** 8, 14   **45.** 3, 5, 7   **46.** $12x^2y, 15x^2y^3$ **47.** $18abc^2, 22ab^3$

Problem Solving

To account for all possibilities in a word problem, make an organized list, a table, or a diagram.

Solve.

48. There are 10 students competing for the tennis trophy. Each student plays another student once. How many games must be played?

Evaluate.

1. 5^3
2. $2^0 \cdot 2^3$
3. $3^2 + 3^3$
4. $4^2 \cdot 1^3$
5. $1{,}250^1$

Evaluate for $a = -2$, $b = 3$.

6. a^2b
7. $(a \cdot b)^2$
8. $b^3 \cdot b^0$
9. $(a + b)^5$
10. $2(a^2 + b^3)$

Write each number in scientific notation.

11. Every hour 2,500,000 plastic bottles are thrown away in the United States.

12. The estimated population of the U.S.S.R. is 287,000,000.

Write each number in standard notation.

13. 3.51×10^5
14. 1.9×10^7
15. 2.659×10^8
16. 4.2×10^3

List all the factors of each number.

17. 24
18. 56
19. 63
20. 105
21. 19

Tell whether each number is prime or composite.

22. 61
23. 57
24. 83
25. 4,563
26. 954
27. 771

Write the prime factorization.

28. 245
29. 378
30. 242
31. 525
32. 333
33. 848

Find the GCF of each set of numbers.

34. 15, 24
35. 36, 60
36. 56, 96
37. $14a^2b^3$, $21ab^2$

Find the LCM of each set of numbers.

38. 6, 8
39. 18, 36
40. 12, 15
41. $10x$, $15y$

Solve.

42. Vince has a job making pizzas. There is regular pizza and pan pizza. The choice of toppings is extra cheese, meatballs, or pepperoni. How many different pizzas can he make?

43. What is the total number of squares in the figure?

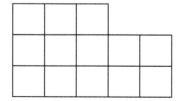

Chapters 1–4   *Cumulative Review*

Choose the correct answer. Write A, B, C, or D.

1. What relationship does this diagram represent?

A. $5 - 1 = 7 - 3 = 2^2$

B. $9 + 16 = 5^2$

C. $1 + 3 + 5 + 7 = 4^2$

D. not given

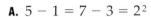

2. Simplify $x^2y \cdot xy^3$.

A. $2x^2y^3$ **B.** x^3y^4

C. x^2y^3 **D.** not given

3. Find a decimal between -1.5 and -1.3.

A. 1.4 **B.** -1.4

C. -1.2 **D.** not given

4. Solve $y + 0.5 = 3$.

A. 2.5 **B.** 1.5

C. 3.5 **D.** not given

5. -4 is a solution of which of the following?

A. $9x = 36$ **B.** $x - 9 = -5$

C. $x + 9 = 5$ **D.** not given

6. $56{,}600{,}000{,}000$

A. 5.65×10^8 **B.** 56.5×10^9

C. 5.6×10^{10} **D.** not given

7. Compare $|-1|^3$ $-(-1)^3$.

A. $<$ **B.** $>$

C. $=$ **D.** not given

8. Which number is prime?

A. 57 **B.** 23

C. 49 **D.** not given

9. Solve.

A. -7 **B.** 4

C. 1 **D.** not given

10. Which of the following is equal to x^{12}?

A. $x^6 \cdot x^6$ **B.** $(x^4)^8$

C. $x^6 + x^6$ **D.** not given

11. What is the expression for *the square of the quantity 3 times the absolute value of negative 3*?

A. $3|(-3)^2|$ **B.** $3|-3|^2$

C. $(3|-3|)^2$ **D.** not given

12. Simplify $3(a + 2b) - 3a$.

A. $-6a + 6b$ **B.** $3a + 6b$

C. $2b$ **D.** not given

13. Evaluate $(-1)^7 \cdot (-2)^0$.

A. 2 **B.** -1

C. 1 **D.** not given

14. Which number is divisible by 9?

A. $1{,}578$ **B.** $5{,}381$

C. $8{,}622$ **D.** not given

15. What is the prime factorization of 90?

A. $2 \cdot 45$ **B.** $2 \cdot 5 \cdot 9$

C. $2 \cdot 3^2 \cdot 5$ **D.** not given

16. Find the GCF of $4a^3b^2$ and $12ab^3$.

A. $4ab^2$ **B.** $12a^3b^3$

C. $3a^2b$ **D.** not given

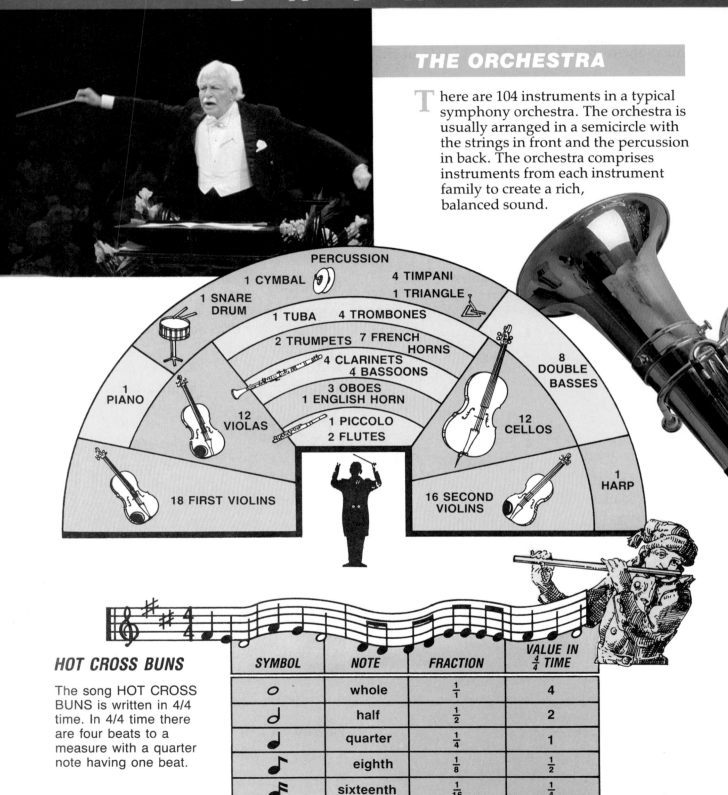

THE ORCHESTRA

There are 104 instruments in a typical symphony orchestra. The orchestra is usually arranged in a semicircle with the strings in front and the percussion in back. The orchestra comprises instruments from each instrument family to create a rich, balanced sound.

PERCUSSION

1 CYMBAL   4 TIMPANI
1 SNARE DRUM   1 TRIANGLE
1 TUBA   4 TROMBONES
2 TRUMPETS   7 FRENCH HORNS
4 CLARINETS   4 BASSOONS
3 OBOES   1 ENGLISH HORN
1 PICCOLO   2 FLUTES
1 PIANO
12 VIOLAS
8 DOUBLE BASSES
12 CELLOS
1 HARP
18 FIRST VIOLINS   16 SECOND VIOLINS

HOT CROSS BUNS

The song HOT CROSS BUNS is written in 4/4 time. In 4/4 time there are four beats to a measure with a quarter note having one beat.

SYMBOL	NOTE	FRACTION	VALUE IN $\frac{4}{4}$ TIME
𝅝	whole	$\frac{1}{1}$	4
𝅗𝅥	half	$\frac{1}{2}$	2
𝅘𝅥	quarter	$\frac{1}{4}$	1
𝅘𝅥𝅮	eighth	$\frac{1}{8}$	$\frac{1}{2}$
𝅘𝅥𝅯	sixteenth	$\frac{1}{16}$	$\frac{1}{4}$

Rational Numbers and Expressions

A portion of the price you pay for a CD is paid to the artist who made the recording. Artists usually receive $\frac{1}{4}$ of the list price of the CD in the form of a royalty.

Think about it...

Look at the triple line graph. Do you think CDs will ever completely replace records and tapes?

Bessie Smith (1894–1937) was a famous blues singer known for her beautiful singing voice. She recorded almost 200 songs.

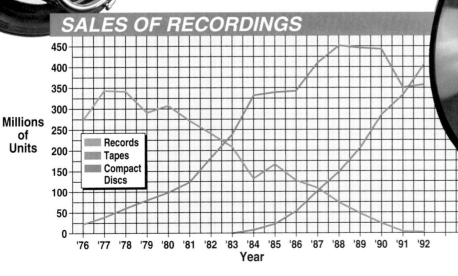

SALES OF RECORDINGS

Millions of Units

Records
Tapes
Compact Discs

450
400
350
300
250
200
150
100
50
0

'76 '77 '78 '79 '80 '81 '82 '83 '84 '85 '86 '87 '88 '89 '90 '91 '92
Year

OBJECTIVE:
To explore fractions
using models.

Exploring Fractions

▼   You can use a variety of models to represent fractions. *Fraction bars* represent fractions as a shaded part of a region.

MATERIALS

• Fraction bars

• Pattern blocks

• Graph paper

• Math journal to record work

1. **Explain** how the numerator (3) and denominator (6) describe the model. $\frac{3}{6}$

▼   Each fraction bar represents the same amount. The fraction bars show *equivalent fractions*. $\frac{2}{4}$

2. **a.** Find or draw two other fraction bars that show the same fraction. $\frac{1}{2}$

   b. **Discuss** Can you find a thirds' bar that shows a fraction equivalent to $\frac{1}{2}$? Why or why not?

3. **Model** each pair of equivalent fractions.

   a. $\frac{2}{3} = \frac{4}{6}$ **b.** $\frac{4}{12} = \frac{2}{6}$ **c.** $\frac{6}{6} = \frac{12}{12}$ **d.** $\frac{8}{6} = \frac{4}{3}$

▼   You can use *pattern blocks* to represent fractions as a part of a whole or part of a set.

4. Suppose one yellow stands for a whole.

   a. Write the fraction for each piece.

   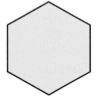

   b. How many greens equal one blue? Write as equivalent fractions.

   c. How many greens equal one red? Write as equivalent fractions.

5. Now let one *red* stand for a whole. **Discuss** and model.

   a. What pattern block represents $\frac{1}{3}$? What does one blue block represent?

   b. How many greens equal one red? Write as equivalent fractions.

   c. **Discuss** Why is one green $\frac{1}{6}$ when the whole is yellow and $\frac{1}{3}$ when the whole is red?

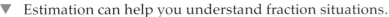

6. a. Suppose one green represents $\frac{1}{2}$. What piece represents a whole?

   b. Suppose one yellow represents $\frac{1}{2}$. What represents a whole?

▼ Estimation can help you understand fraction situations.

7. a. Take a sheet of paper and tear off a piece that you think is about $\frac{1}{3}$. Now fold another piece of paper in thirds and compare. How close were you? Compare with another member of your group.

   b. Repeat the tearing and comparing for the following fractions.

   $$\frac{1}{2} \qquad \frac{3}{4} \qquad \frac{2}{3}$$

▼ You can estimate fractions by comparing the numerator to the denominator.

8. a. These fractions are close to zero. **Write** a rule to tell when a fraction is close to zero.

   $$\frac{1}{14} \qquad \frac{3}{17} \qquad \frac{2}{25} \qquad \frac{7}{125}$$

   b. These fractions are close to $\frac{1}{2}$. **Write** a rule to tell when a fraction is close to $\frac{1}{2}$.

   $$\frac{3}{8} \qquad \frac{6}{14} \qquad \frac{11}{23} \qquad \frac{51}{100}$$

   c. These fractions are close to 1. **Write** a rule to tell when a fraction is close to 1.

   $$\frac{99}{100} \qquad \frac{3}{4} \qquad \frac{45}{50} \qquad \frac{79}{91}$$

▼ You can also compare the numerator and the denominator to decide if fractions are greater than, less than, or equal to one.

$\frac{5}{6}$	$\frac{25}{25}$	$\frac{17}{3}$	$\frac{100}{100}$
$\frac{7}{6}$	$\frac{2}{3}$	$\frac{9}{11}$	$\frac{7}{10}$
$\frac{81}{79}$	$\frac{4}{4}$	$\frac{7}{7}$	$\frac{10}{8}$

9. Use the fractions in the box at the right to complete.

   a. fractions less than one ▦ , ▦ , ▦ , ▦

   b. fractions greater than one ▦ , ▦ , ▦ , ▦

   c. fractions equal to one ▦ , ▦ , ▦ , ▦

10. a. Complete to show fractions close to 0. $\frac{▦}{7}$, $\frac{▦}{3}$, $\frac{5}{▦}$, $\frac{17}{▦}$

   b. Complete to show fractions close to $\frac{1}{2}$. $\frac{▦}{7}$, $\frac{▦}{9}$, $\frac{13}{▦}$, $\frac{5}{▦}$

   c. Complete to show fractions close to 1. $\frac{▦}{22}$, $\frac{▦}{11}$, $\frac{4}{▦}$, $\frac{20}{▦}$

   d. Complete to show fractions greater than 1. $\frac{▦}{2}$, $\frac{▦}{7}$, $\frac{9}{▦}$, $\frac{15}{▦}$

OBJECTIVE:
*To write equivalent
fractions and
fractions in lowest
terms.*

5-1 *Equivalent Fractions and Lowest Terms*

▼ Suppose you divide a pizza into eight equal size pieces and eat four of the pieces. You can draw a model and write a fraction to represent the amount eaten.

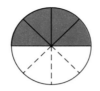

$$\frac{\text{numerator} \rightarrow 4 \leftarrow \text{pieces eaten}}{\text{denominator} \rightarrow 8 \leftarrow \text{pieces in all}}$$

The model shows that the fractions $\frac{4}{8}$ and $\frac{1}{2}$ describe the same part of the pizza. They are *equivalent fractions*.

Equivalent Fractions	You can form equivalent fractions by multiplying or dividing the numerator and denominator by the same nonzero factor.

▼ You can write equivalent fractions using numbers, numbers and variables, or just variables.

THINK Why can you multiply the numerator and denominator by $\frac{2}{2}$, $\frac{3}{3}$, or $\frac{n}{n}$?

Arithmetic   **Algebra**

$\frac{1}{2} = \frac{1 \cdot 2}{2 \cdot 2} = \frac{2}{4}$ $\frac{a}{b} = \frac{ac}{bc}$ $(b \neq 0, c \neq 0)$

$\frac{3}{6} = \frac{3 \div 3}{6 \div 3} = \frac{1}{2}$ $\frac{a}{b} = \frac{a \div c}{b \div c}$ $(b \neq 0, c \neq 0)$

Example 1   **Write a fraction equivalent to each fraction.**

       a. $\frac{4}{6}$ **b.** $\frac{3x}{5y}$

THINK Are there other possible solutions?

Solution   **a.** We can divide by $1 = \frac{2}{2}$.   **b.** We can multiply by $1 = \frac{2}{2}$.

$$\frac{4}{6} = \frac{4 \div 2}{6 \div 2} \qquad\qquad \frac{3x}{5y} = \frac{3x \cdot 2}{5y \cdot 2}$$

$$= \frac{2}{3} \qquad\qquad\qquad\quad = \frac{6x}{10y}$$

Example 2   **Replace the variable to form equivalent fractions.**

$$\frac{5}{8} = \frac{n}{24}$$

Solution $\frac{5 \cdot 3}{8 \cdot 3} = \frac{n}{24}$ Since $8 \cdot 3 = 24$, multiply both numerator and denominator by 3.

$$\frac{5}{8} = \frac{15}{24}$$

So, $n = 15$.

▼ When two fractions are equivalent, their *cross products* are equal. You can use this idea to test for equivalence.

Example 3

a. Is $\frac{6}{18} = \frac{7}{21}$?

b. Is $\frac{3}{15} = \frac{12}{45}$?

$$\frac{6}{18} \overset{?}{=} \frac{7}{21}$$

$$\frac{3}{15} \overset{?}{=} \frac{12}{45}$$

Solution

a. $6 \cdot 21 \overset{?}{=} 18 \cdot 7$

$6 \;\boxed{\times}\; 21 \;\boxed{=}\; 126$

$18 \;\boxed{\times}\; 7 \;\boxed{=}\; 126$

The cross products are equal, so the fractions are equivalent.

b. $3 \cdot 45 \overset{?}{=} 15 \cdot 12$

$3 \;\boxed{\times}\; 45 \;\boxed{=}\; 135$

$15 \;\boxed{\times}\; 12 \;\boxed{=}\; 180$

The cross products are not equal, so the fractions are not equivalent.

▼ You can divide both terms of a fraction by the *greatest common factor (GCF)* to write the fraction in *lowest terms*.

Lowest Terms	When a fraction is in lowest terms, the only common factor of the numerator and denominator is 1.

Example 4 Write $\frac{18}{24}$ in lowest terms.

Solution $\frac{18}{24} = \frac{18 \div 6}{24 \div 6} = \frac{3}{4}$ Divide by 6, the GCF of 18 and 24.

▼ You also can write the numerator and denominator as a product of prime factors. Then divide by common factors to write in lowest terms.

Example 5 $\frac{18}{24} = \dfrac{\overset{1}{2} \cdot \overset{1}{3} \cdot 3}{\underset{1}{2} \cdot 2 \cdot 2 \cdot \underset{1}{3}} = \frac{3}{4}$ Divide common factors. Multiply the remaining factors.

▼ When a fraction includes variables you can divide common variable factors to write the fraction in lowest terms.

Example 6 Write $\frac{2a^2b}{6ac}$ in lowest terms.

Solution $\frac{2a^2b}{6ac} = \frac{2 \cdot a \cdot a \cdot b}{2 \cdot 3 \cdot a \cdot c}$ Write as a product of prime factors.

$= \dfrac{\overset{1}{2} \cdot \overset{1}{a} \cdot a \cdot b}{\underset{1}{2} \cdot 3 \cdot \underset{1}{a} \cdot c} = \frac{ab}{3c}$ Divide common factors. Multiply the remaining factors.

THINK AND DISCUSS

1. How are $\frac{1}{2}$ pizza and $\frac{1}{2}$ mi the same? How are they different?

2. Can you write a fraction in lowest terms if you divide by a factor other than the GCF? Explain.

CLASS EXERCISES

1. During a 30-min radio broadcast there were 7 min of commercials.

    a. Write a fraction for the commercial time.

    b. Write a fraction for the noncommercial time.

Use or draw a model to represent each pair of equivalent fractions.

2. $\frac{2}{4} = \frac{3}{6}$ **3.** $\frac{6}{8} = \frac{9}{12}$ **4.** $\frac{3}{5} = \frac{6}{10}$

Write a fraction equivalent to each fraction.

5. $\frac{2}{3}$ **6.** $\frac{5w}{7x}$ **7.** $\frac{9}{10x}$ **8.** $\frac{13c}{26}$ **9.** $\frac{5a}{7a}$

Write in lowest terms.

10. $\frac{3}{9}$ **11.** $\frac{4}{10}$ **12.** $\frac{2}{8}$ **13.** $\frac{2a}{3a}$ **14.** $\frac{4ab^2}{12b}$

WRITTEN EXERCISES

Write a fraction for each sentence.

1. Three out of thirteen students are in the band.

2. A student grew five-eighths inches.

3. Copy and complete the chart.

Model	Word Name	Fraction
▲ ▲ ▲ △ △ △	one-half	▨
⬤⬤○○○○	▨	$\frac{1}{4}$
▨	seven-eighths	$\frac{7}{8}$
★ ★ ★ ★ ★ ☆ ☆	▨	▨

Write a fraction for each shaded region.

4.   **5.**   **6.**

Write three fractions equivalent to each fraction.

7. $\dfrac{5}{6}$ **8.** $\dfrac{12}{20}$ **9.** $\dfrac{12}{36}$ **10.** $\dfrac{1}{3}$ **11.** $\dfrac{2}{5}$

12. $\dfrac{7b}{14c}$ **13.** $\dfrac{8k}{9j}$ **14.** $\dfrac{4t}{100w}$ **15.** $\dfrac{25x}{75x}$ **16.** $\dfrac{8p}{24p^2}$

MENTAL MATH Find the value of the variable to form equivalent fractions.

17. $\dfrac{1}{3} = \dfrac{n}{6}$ **18.** $\dfrac{2}{5} = \dfrac{10}{y}$ **19.** $\dfrac{3}{8} = \dfrac{a}{16}$ **20.** $\dfrac{5}{10} = \dfrac{1}{b}$

21. $\dfrac{12}{36} = \dfrac{x}{3}$ **22.** $\dfrac{a}{12} = \dfrac{1}{4}$ **23.** $\dfrac{2}{7} = \dfrac{w}{14}$ **24.** $\dfrac{3}{t} = \dfrac{1}{3}$

Write in lowest terms.

25. $\dfrac{5}{25}$ **26.** $\dfrac{7}{14}$ **27.** $\dfrac{6}{9}$ **28.** $\dfrac{11}{22}$ **29.** $\dfrac{25}{75}$

30. $\dfrac{3a}{6a}$ **31.** $\dfrac{4bc}{12b}$ **32.** $\dfrac{xy}{3y}$ **33.** $\dfrac{5t}{10t^2}$ **34.** $\dfrac{abc}{5abc}$

35. Use the numbers 3, 5, 6, and 10 to write three pairs of equivalent fractions.

Use prime factors to write each fraction in lowest terms.

36. $\dfrac{15}{25}$ **37.** $\dfrac{12}{16}$ **38.** $\dfrac{6}{15}$ **39.** $\dfrac{3a^2b}{5b}$ **40.** $\dfrac{6mn}{9m}$ **41.** $\dfrac{8p^3q}{12p^2}$

CALCULATOR Use cross products. Compare using = or ≠.

42. $\dfrac{18}{30} \;\blacksquare\; \dfrac{15}{25}$ **43.** $\dfrac{16}{21} \;\blacksquare\; \dfrac{12}{15}$ **44.** $\dfrac{13}{24} \;\blacksquare\; \dfrac{11}{18}$ **45.** $\dfrac{18}{32} \;\blacksquare\; \dfrac{27}{48}$

Solve.

46. The world production of gold in 1988 was about 58 million troy ounces. The United States produced about 6 million troy ounces. What fraction of the world's production came from the United States? Write your answer in lowest terms.

47. For a money-raising project, the senior class baked a huge pizza. The class divided the pizza into 60 pieces. The swim team bought 24 pieces. What fraction of the pizza did the swim team buy? Write your answer in lowest terms.

48. A survey of students revealed that the favorite music of half the group was rock. One-third preferred jazz and the rest liked country music. Draw a diagram to represent this data.

49. _PROJECT_ Take a survey of the students in one of your classes. Determine the number of left-handed people. Compare this with the total number of students in the class. Write this information as a fraction.

MIXED REVIEW

Find the factors.

1. 32   **2.** 27

Find the prime factors. Then write using exponents.

3. 36   **4.** 54

Estimate.

5. $21.5 \cdot 12.8$

6. $42.8 + 13.6 + 18.23$

7. What are the GCF and the LCM of 18 and 12?

8. The lowest recorded temperature for Hawaii is 12°F. The lowest recorded temperature for Wisconsin is 66° lower. What is the record for Wisconsin?

OBJECTIVE:
To write mixed
numbers, improper
fractions, and
decimals using
models and
computation.

5-2 *Fractions and Decimals*

▼ If you work more than 40 h/week, your rate of pay may be $1\frac{1}{2}$ times your regular rate. The number $1\frac{1}{2}$ is a *mixed number*.

▼ You can use models to write mixed numbers as *improper fractions*.

Example 1 **Write $3\frac{1}{4}$ as an improper fraction using a model.**

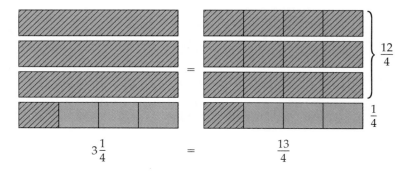

$$3\frac{1}{4} \qquad = \qquad \frac{13}{4}$$

▼ You can also write mixed numbers as improper fractions using equivalent fractions.

Example 2 **Write $3\frac{1}{4}$ as an improper fraction.**

Solution $3\frac{1}{4} = \frac{3}{1} + \frac{1}{4}$

$= \frac{12}{4} + \frac{1}{4}$ $\quad \frac{12}{4}$ and $\frac{3}{1}$ are equivalent fractions:

$= \frac{13}{4}$ $\qquad \frac{3}{1} = \frac{3 \cdot 4}{1 \cdot 4} = \frac{12}{4}$

▼ You can divide to write improper fractions as mixed numbers or decimals.

Example 3 **Write $\frac{7}{2}$ as a mixed number and as a decimal.**

Solution $\frac{7}{2} = 7 \div 2 = 3\frac{1}{2} = 3.5$

▼ You can write decimals as fractions in lowest terms.

Example 4 **Write each decimal as a fraction or mixed number in lowest terms.**

      a. 0.12   **b.** 1.625

Solution   **a.** $0.12 = \frac{12}{100}$ **b.** $1.625 = 1 + \frac{625}{1,000}$

$\qquad\qquad\qquad = \frac{12 \div 4}{100 \div 4}$ $\qquad\qquad\qquad\qquad = 1 + \frac{625 \div 125}{1,000 \div 125}$

$\qquad\qquad\qquad = \frac{3}{25}$ $\qquad\qquad\qquad\qquad\qquad = 1\frac{5}{8}$

THINK How do you decide which models you will use to replace the whole models?

THINK Why is 3 the same as $\frac{3}{1}$?

▼ Sometimes it's necessary to write fractions as decimals before you solve word problems.

THINK What is the decimal equivalent for $5\frac{3}{4}$? for $12\frac{3}{4}$?

Example 5   You are at a delicatessen and ask for $\frac{3}{4}$ lb of potato salad. The scale reads 0.75. Are you getting the amount you requested?

Solution $\frac{3}{4} = 3 \div 4 = 0.75$ Use a calculator. Divide the numerator by the denominator.

Since $\frac{3}{4}$ equals 0.75, you received the right amount.

▼ Some fractions result in decimal patterns that repeat. Three dots at the right of a decimal indicate that digits repeat. You can also write a bar over the digits that repeat.

Example 6   Use a calculator to write each fraction as a decimal.

   a. $\frac{2}{3}$ **b.** $\frac{15}{11}$

Solution   **a.** $\frac{2}{3} = 2 \div 3 = 0.6666\ldots$

   $\frac{2}{3} = 0.\overline{6}$ Write a bar over the 6.

   b. $\frac{15}{11} = 15 \div 11 = 1.3636\ldots$

   $\frac{15}{11} = 1.\overline{36}$ Write a bar over the repeating digits 3 and 6.

CLASS EXERCISES

Use a model to write as an improper fraction or mixed number.

1. $2\frac{3}{5}$ **2.** $1\frac{5}{8}$ **3.** $\frac{21}{4}$ **4.** $\frac{17}{6}$

Write as an improper fraction or mixed number.

5. $7\frac{1}{2}$ **6.** $\frac{11}{4}$ **7.** $\frac{19}{8}$ **8.** $\frac{21}{5}$

Write each decimal as a fraction in lowest terms.

9. 0.10   **10.** 0.5   **11.** 2.75   **12.** 3.25

CALCULATOR   **Write each fraction or mixed number as a decimal.**

13. $\frac{7}{16}$ **14.** $4\frac{7}{16}$ **15.** $\frac{5}{12}$ **16.** $8\frac{5}{12}$

THINK AND DISCUSS

1. Where would you place the bar in the repeating decimal 12.032032 . . . ?

2. Use models to show the relationship between an improper fraction and a mixed number.

WRITTEN EXERCISES

Use each model to answer the questions.

1.

a. Let each piece represent $\frac{1}{4}$. What improper fraction is shown?

b. What mixed number is shown?

2.

a. Let each piece represent $\frac{1}{3}$. What improper fraction is shown?

b. What mixed number is shown?

MIXED REVIEW

Compare. Use <, >, or =.

1. $|5 - (-8)|$ ▇ 2^3

2. $6 - 15$ ▇ $\frac{27}{3}$

Write in lowest terms.

3. $\frac{16}{24}$ **4.** $\frac{3a}{a^2}$

Write as a decimal.

5. $\frac{3}{5}$ **6.** $1\frac{1}{2}$

7. The Lake Meade Reservoir has a capacity of 34,850,000,000 m³. Write this number in scientific notation.

3. Draw a model to show that $\frac{14}{5} = 2\frac{4}{5}$.

4. Write the length of the segment as an improper fraction and as a mixed number.

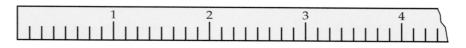

Write each mixed number as an improper fraction.

5. $1\frac{5}{8}$ **6.** $4\frac{3}{5}$ **7.** $5\frac{7}{8}$ **8.** $2\frac{9}{16}$

9. $6\frac{2}{3}$ **10.** $3\frac{7}{12}$ **11.** $2\frac{9}{11}$ **12.** $6\frac{1}{4}$

Write each improper fraction as a mixed number.

13. $\frac{17}{3}$ **14.** $\frac{16}{7}$ **15.** $\frac{23}{5}$ **16.** $\frac{31}{8}$

17. $\frac{19}{11}$ **18.** $\frac{37}{12}$ **19.** $\frac{10}{3}$ **20.** $\frac{53}{25}$

Write each decimal as a fraction or mixed number in lowest terms.

21. 0.8   **22.** 0.17   **23.** 5.15   **24.** 10.01

25. 2.5   **26.** 0.002   **27.** 6.05   **28.** 25.025

CALCULATOR Write as a decimal.

29. $\frac{7}{25}$ **30.** $\frac{3}{5}$ **31.** $\frac{5}{8}$ **32.** $\frac{9}{20}$

33. $\frac{5}{9}$ **34.** $\frac{7}{11}$ **35.** $5\frac{3}{8}$ **36.** $24\frac{7}{15}$

37. Copy and complete the chart. The first row is done for you.

Decimal	Read As	Fraction
0.23	twenty-three hundredths	$\frac{23}{100}$
▨	eighteen hundredths	▨
▨	▨	$5\frac{73}{100}$
▨	nine tenths	▨

38. Write an improper fraction with the greatest possible value using the digits 3, 5, and 6. Write this as a mixed number and as a decimal.

39. *DATA FILE 5 (pp. 180–181)* Write fractions to represent the number of instruments of each type in a typical symphony orchestra.

   a. woodwinds   **b.** brasses   **c.** percussion   **d.** bowed strings

40. *WRITE* Describe three situations when you would use fractions. Describe three situations when you would use decimals.

DATA **Use the circle graph at the right.**

41. Did about half the people respond that they see a movie less than once per month?

42. Did at least $\frac{1}{4}$ of the people asked say they see a movie two to three times a week?

43. Do one out of ten people see a movie once a week?

44. *CALCULATOR*

   a. Write each fraction as a decimal.

   b. Do at least 0.5 of the respondents see a movie more than once a week?

45. *PROJECT* Choose five movies or sports teams or a topic of your own. Collect data about the favorites in your class. Write fractions and decimals to describe the choices.

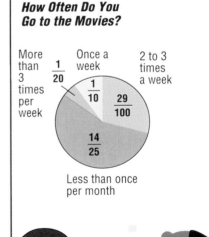

How Often Do You Go to the Movies?

More than 3 times per week $\frac{1}{20}$ · Once a week $\frac{1}{10}$ · 2 to 3 times a week $\frac{29}{100}$ · $\frac{14}{25}$ · Less than once per month

Rational Numbers

OBJECTIVE:
To study the meaning
of rational numbers.

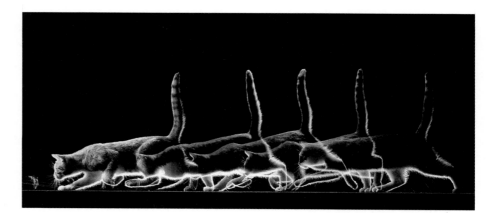

▼ The photograph above was taken with a strobe light that flashed at $\frac{1}{1,000}$ of a second intervals. We call the fraction $\frac{1}{1,000}$ a *rational number*.

THINK In $\frac{a}{b}$, why can't b equal zero?

Rational Number	A rational number is a number you write in the form $\frac{a}{b}$, where a is any integer, and b is a nonzero integer.

▼ Fractions are rational numbers. Other numbers are rational if you can express them as fractions.

Proper fractions	$\frac{2}{3}, -\frac{1}{2}$
Improper fractions	$\frac{4}{3}, \frac{10}{8}$
Mixed numbers	$1\frac{5}{6}, 2\frac{3}{11}$
Integers	$-6 = -\frac{6}{1}, 0 = \frac{0}{1}$
Variables	$\frac{a}{4}, \frac{3a}{4}, \frac{5a}{b}, \frac{2a}{3b}$
Some decimals	$0.5 = \frac{1}{2}, -9.8 = -\frac{98}{10}, 0.\overline{8} = \frac{8}{9}$

THINK What are some equivalent fractions for $\frac{a}{b}$?

▼ You can express a rational number as a set of equivalent fractions.

Example 1 $\frac{1}{2} = \frac{2}{4} = \frac{3}{6} = \cdots$ Both numerator and denominator are positive.

$\frac{1}{2} = \frac{-1}{-2} = \frac{-2}{-4} = \frac{-3}{-6} = \cdots$ Both numerator and denominator are negative.

▼ You can write negative rational numbers in three ways.

Example 2 $-\frac{7}{9} = \frac{-7}{9} = \frac{7}{-9}$

▼ You can show rational numbers on a number line.

Example 3 Graph each point on a number line.

     a. 0.5 **b.** $-1\frac{1}{2}$ **c.** $\frac{3}{4}$

Solution

▼ You can find the absolute value of a rational number.

Example 4 The absolute value of $-\frac{5}{6}$ is $\frac{5}{6}$.

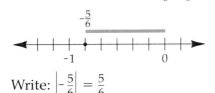

The distance from $-\frac{5}{6}$ to 0 is $\frac{5}{6}$.

Write: $\left|-\frac{5}{6}\right| = \frac{5}{6}$

THINK What is the opposite of $-\frac{a}{b}$?

▼ The fraction bar is a grouping symbol similar to parentheses.

Example 5 Evaluate the expression $\frac{x+5}{y}$ for $x = 7$ and $y = -8$.

Solution

$\dfrac{x+5}{y} = \dfrac{7+5}{-8}$ Substitute values.

$= \dfrac{12}{-8}$ Compute following order of operations.

$= -1\frac{1}{2}$ Write as a mixed number.

CLASS EXERCISES

Give a rational number to represent each situation.

  1. a loss of one-and-one-half pounds

  2. moving the time ahead a quarter of an hour on a clock

Write a rational number for each point on the number line.

  3. A **4.** B **5.** C **6.** D

Give the opposite and the absolute value.

  7. $1\frac{1}{3}$ **8.** $-\frac{3}{5}$ **9.** $\frac{5}{-9}$ **10.** $-2\frac{2}{3}$

 11. $\frac{1}{4}$ **12.** $\frac{4}{-5}$ **13.** $\frac{5}{8}$ **14.** $1\frac{1}{2}$

THINK AND DISCUSS

1. Is zero a rational number? Why or why not?

2. Is a set of equivalent fractions equal to the same decimal?

3. How many rational numbers are there between 1 and 2?

Evaluate for $a = 6$, and $b = -5$. Write in lowest terms.

15. $\dfrac{a+b}{3}$ **16.** $\dfrac{a-b}{4}$ **17.** $\dfrac{a+9}{b}$

WRITTEN EXERCISES

Write a rational number to represent each situation.

1. the number of dollars in nine quarters.

2. a loss of two dollars and seventy-five cents

Write a rational number for each point on the number line.

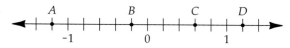

3. A **4.** B **5.** C **6.** D

Graph each point on a number line.

7. $1\frac{1}{2}$ **8.** -0.5 **9.** -3.5 **10.** $\frac{3}{4}$

Write the opposite and the absolute value.

11. $\frac{-4}{9}$ **12.** -1.73 **13.** $1\frac{2}{3}$ **14.** $-2\frac{1}{5}$

15. Which rational numbers are equal to $-\frac{4}{5}$?

   a. $\frac{4}{-5}$ **b.** 0.8 **c.** $-\frac{16}{20}$ **d.** $\frac{-4}{-5}$

16. Which rational numbers are equal to $\frac{9}{5}$?

   a. $\frac{-9}{-5}$ **b.** $-9 \cdot \frac{1}{-5}$ **c.** -1.8 **d.** $\frac{18}{10}$

Evaluate. Write in lowest terms.

17. $\frac{a}{b}$ for $a = 20$, $b = 25$ **18.** $\frac{a^2}{b^2}$ for $a = 4$, $b = -5$

19. $\frac{a+3}{b}$ for $a = 5$, $b = -2$ **20.** $\frac{(a+3)(a-3)}{a^2-9}$ for $a = 5$

Write each rational number in lowest terms.

21. $\frac{4a}{8b}$ **22.** $\frac{2 \cdot 5 \cdot a}{4 \cdot 25 \cdot b}$ **23.** $\frac{4 \cdot a^2}{16 \cdot a \cdot b}$ **24.** $\frac{5 \cdot a^2 \cdot b}{25 \cdot a \cdot b^2}$

Write *sometimes*, *always*, or *never* to tell when each is true.

25. $\frac{3a}{3b} = \frac{a}{b}$ **26.** $\frac{a^2}{b} > \frac{a}{b}$ **27.** $\frac{a}{b} = \left|\frac{a}{b}\right|$ **28.** $\frac{a}{b}(-1) > 0$

Complete.

29. All ▩ rational numbers are less than zero.

30. The set of rational numbers is made up of the positive rational numbers, the negative rational numbers, and ▩.

31. The opposite of a ▩ rational number is positive.

32. The absolute value of a negative rational number is ▩.

33. A number is less than zero. Its opposite is a mixed number greater than zero. Is the number a rational number?

34. *DATA FILE 5 (pp. 180–181)* Write fractions that represent these musical notes: whole note, half note, quarter note, eighth note, and sixteenth note.

35. Copy and complete the chart. Write *yes* or *no*.

Number	Rational Number	Integer	Whole Number	Natural Number
2	▩	▩	▩	▩
$-\frac{1}{2}$	▩	▩	▩	▩
0.5	▩	▩	▩	▩
$\frac{-12}{-3}$	▩	▩	▩	▩
$0 \cdot \frac{a}{b}$	▩	▩	▩	▩

36. *WRITE* a sentence about rational numbers. How are rational numbers different from integers? How are they similar?

TEST YOURSELF

Write in lowest terms.

1. $\frac{12}{15}$ **2.** $\frac{18}{24}$ **3.** $\frac{6}{20}$ **4.** $\frac{5a^3b^2}{15ab^2}$ **5.** $\frac{35mn^3}{4m}$

Write three fractions equivalent to the given fraction.

6. $\frac{5}{8}$ **7.** $-1\frac{2}{5}$ **8.** $\frac{9}{12}$ **9.** $\frac{2b}{3c}$ **10.** $\frac{16r}{20s}$

Write the opposite and the absolute value.

11. $\frac{2}{3}$ **12.** $-2\frac{5}{6}$ **13.** $1\frac{7}{16}$ **14.** $-2\frac{3}{4}$

OBJECTIVE:
To compare and
order fractions and
decimals.

5-4 Comparing and Ordering Rational Numbers

▼ The Houston Rockets won 10 out of 12 home games. The Denver Stars won 8 out of 10 games. Which team won a greater fraction of games?

$$\text{Houston's games} \rightarrow \frac{10}{12}$$

$$\text{Denver's games} \rightarrow \frac{8}{10}$$

Compare $\frac{10}{12}$ and $\frac{8}{10}$ using fraction strips.

$$\frac{10}{12} > \frac{8}{10}$$

▼ You can also compare fractions by finding their *least common denominator (LCD)*.

Least Common Denominator	The least common denominator of two or more fractions is the LCM of the denominators.

Example 1 Compare $\frac{5}{12}$ and $\frac{4}{9}$.

Solution
1. Find the LCD. The LCD of $\frac{5}{12}$ and $\frac{4}{9}$ is 36.

2. Find equivalent fractions.
$$\frac{5}{12} = \frac{15}{36}$$
$$\frac{4}{9} = \frac{16}{36}$$

3. Compare. $\frac{16}{36} > \frac{15}{36}$, so $\frac{4}{9} > \frac{5}{12}$.

▼ To compare fractions and decimals, you can first write each in the same form.

Example 2 Compare 0.8 and $\frac{3}{5}$.

Solution
1. Use a calculator to write $\frac{3}{5}$ as a decimal.
$$3 \div 5 = 0.6$$

2. Compare.
Since $0.8 > 0.6$, $0.8 > \frac{3}{5}$.

▼ Writing fractions as decimals often makes it easier to order the fractions from least to greatest.

Example 3 Order $\frac{13}{40}$, $\frac{9}{32}$, $\frac{5}{16}$, $\frac{8}{25}$ from least to greatest.

Solution Use a calculator to write each fraction as a decimal.

$\frac{13}{40} = 0.325 \quad \frac{9}{32} = 0.28125 \quad \frac{5}{16} = 0.3125 \quad \frac{8}{25} = 0.32$

$0.28125 < 0.3125 < 0.32 < 0.325$ **Order the decimals.**

$\frac{9}{32} \quad < \quad \frac{5}{16} \quad < \quad \frac{8}{25} \quad < \quad \frac{13}{40}$ **Order the fractions.**

▼ You can also order fractions on a number line.

Example 4 Order $\frac{1}{4}$, -0.2, 1.1, and $-\frac{3}{5}$ from least to greatest.

Solution Use a calculator to write fractions as decimals.

$\frac{1}{4} = 0.25, -\frac{3}{5} = -0.6$

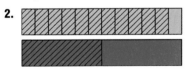

THINK How does writing fractions as decimals help when ordering on the number line?

CLASS EXERCISES

Write the two fractions modeled and compare them.

1.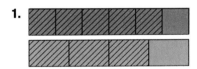

2.

Compare. Use >, <, or =.

3. $\frac{5}{8}$ ▨ $\frac{3}{4}$ **4.** $\frac{7}{15}$ ▨ $\frac{2}{3}$ **5.** $\frac{5}{18}$ ▨ $\frac{1}{3}$

6. $\frac{33}{40}$ ▨ $\frac{5}{8}$ **7.** 0.3 ▨ $\frac{-1}{-3}$ **8.** 0.22 ▨ $\frac{2}{9}$

9. 0.63 ▨ $\frac{7}{-11}$ **10.** $3\frac{1}{4}$ ▨ 3.2 **11.** 4.985 ▨ $4\frac{985}{1,000}$

Order from least to greatest.

12. $\frac{2}{5}$, $\frac{7}{20}$, $\frac{3}{10}$ **13.** $\frac{11}{16}$, $\frac{5}{8}$, $-\frac{13}{24}$ **14.** $\frac{3}{4}$, $\frac{7}{10}$, $\frac{-29}{40}$

15. $\frac{6}{11}$, $\frac{11}{20}$, $\frac{5}{9}$, $\frac{14}{-25}$ **16.** $\frac{7}{33}$, $\frac{-2}{-9}$, $\frac{11}{50}$, $\frac{4}{17}$ **17.** $\frac{20}{37}$, $\frac{6}{11}$, $\frac{27}{50}$, $-\frac{51}{90}$

THINK AND DISCUSS

1. Suppose you are comparing a fraction and a decimal. Why is it easier to write the fraction as a decimal than to write the decimal as a fraction?

2. Some fractions result in decimals with several places. When comparing, are all of the digits important? Consider $\frac{1}{7}$ ▨ 0.142.

Solve.

1. $0.3x = 2.1$

2. $18.08 = a + 7.5$

Find each answer.

3. the opposite of $-7\frac{1}{3}$

4. $-1\frac{2}{5} + \blacksquare = 0$

5. $\left|-2\frac{7}{9}\right|$

6. $-4\frac{2}{3} = \frac{\blacksquare}{3}$

7. Write $-2\frac{3}{8}$ as a decimal.

8. How many miles will you travel in 3.5 h at a speed of 55 mi/h?

WRITTEN EXERCISES

Use a model to compare.

1. $\frac{3}{5} \blacksquare \frac{5}{8}$ **2.** $\frac{5}{6} \blacksquare \frac{7}{10}$

Compare. Use >, <, or =.

3. $\frac{13}{18} \blacksquare \frac{7}{9}$ **4.** $\frac{11}{12} \blacksquare \frac{5}{6}$ **5.** $-\frac{7}{9} \blacksquare -\frac{2}{3}$ **6.** $-\frac{5}{6} \blacksquare -\frac{19}{24}$

7. $\frac{3}{8} \blacksquare \frac{5}{12}$ **8.** $\frac{3}{4} \blacksquare \frac{5}{6}$ **9.** $-\frac{5}{12} \blacksquare \frac{7}{9}$ **10.** $\frac{3}{4} \blacksquare \frac{7}{10}$

MENTAL MATH Compare. Use >, <, or =.

11. $-\frac{3}{19} \blacksquare \frac{1}{200}$ **12.** $\frac{-4}{-17} \blacksquare -\frac{5}{2}$ **13.** $\frac{(-1) \cdot (-1)}{3} \blacksquare \frac{1}{3}$

CALCULATOR Compare. Use >, <, or =.

14. $\frac{17}{24} \blacksquare \frac{24}{35}$ **15.** $-\frac{11}{16} \blacksquare -\frac{19}{28}$ **16.** $\frac{15}{22} \blacksquare \frac{23}{34}$ **17.** $\frac{11}{25} \blacksquare \frac{17}{30}$

18. $\frac{3}{8} \blacksquare 0.39$ **19.** $\frac{3}{4} \blacksquare 0.752$ **20.** $-\frac{5}{12} \blacksquare -0.34$ **21.** $2\frac{3}{14} \blacksquare 2.22$

CALCULATOR Order from least to greatest.

22. $\frac{5}{6}, \frac{7}{8}, \frac{19}{24}$ **23.** $-\frac{5}{12}, -\frac{3}{8}, -\frac{1}{4}$ **24.** $-\frac{5}{11}, \frac{6}{13}, -\frac{8}{17}$

25. $-\frac{7}{10}, -\frac{11}{15}, -\frac{7}{12}, -\frac{13}{20}$ **26.** $\frac{17}{20}, \frac{23}{30}, \frac{23}{40}, \frac{13}{24}$ **27.** $2\frac{3}{50}, -2\frac{7}{8}, -2\frac{9}{16}, 2\frac{19}{25}$

Find a rational number between the given rational numbers.

28. $\frac{1}{2}$ and 1 **29.** -1 and -2 **30.** $2\frac{5}{12}$ and $2\frac{3}{4}$ **31.** $-1\frac{3}{4}$ and -2

Compare the rational numbers $\frac{5}{8}$ and $\frac{x}{4}$. Find the values of x that make each statement true.

32. $\frac{5}{8} = \frac{x}{4}$ **33.** $\frac{5}{8} > \frac{x}{4}$ **34.** $\frac{5}{8} < \frac{x}{4}$

35. **DATA FILE 5 (pp. 180–181)** Write as a fraction in lowest terms the number of tapes sold in 1976 compared with the number of tapes sold in 1986.

36. In the high school band there are 15 clarinets. The band has 80 members. Compare the number of clarinets to the number of band members. Write the number as a fraction in lowest terms and as a decimal.

OBJECTIVE:
To add and subtract
fractions and mixed
numbers.

5-5 Adding and Subtracting Rational Numbers

▼ Two thirds of the earth's surface is covered by oceans. Another tenth of the earth's surface is covered by glaciers. What fraction of the earth is covered by oceans and glaciers?

The total amount is the sum of the two fractions.

$\frac{2}{3} + \frac{1}{10} = \frac{20}{30} + \frac{3}{30}$ **Find a common denominator.**

$= \frac{23}{30}$

▼ You can add rational numbers using a model.

Example 1 $\frac{1}{4} + \frac{1}{6} = \blacksquare$

THINK Why must the last fraction bar have 12 sections?

Solution

Find the fraction bar that aligns with the sum.

So, $\frac{1}{4} + \frac{1}{6} = \frac{5}{12}$.

▼ You can also subtract rational numbers expressed as fractions.

Example 2 $\frac{1}{12} - \frac{1}{3} = \blacksquare$

THINK Why do you subtract only the numerators?

Solution $\frac{1}{12} - \frac{1 \cdot 4}{3 \cdot 4} = \frac{1}{12} - \frac{4}{12}$ Write equivalent fractions and subtract numerators.

$= -\frac{3}{12}$ Write in lowest terms.

$= -\frac{1}{4}$

▼ You can add fractions that contain variables.

Example 3 $\frac{x}{5} + \frac{3}{4} = \blacksquare$

Solution $\frac{x \cdot 4}{5 \cdot 4} + \frac{3 \cdot 5}{4 \cdot 5} = \blacksquare$ Write equivalent fractions.

$\frac{4x}{20} + \frac{15}{20} = \frac{4x + 15}{20}$ Add numerators.

▼ To add mixed numbers, combine the integers and fractions separately.

Example 4 $2\frac{3}{4} + 4\frac{5}{12} = \blacksquare$

Solution

$$2\frac{3}{4} = \quad 2\frac{9}{12}$$ Write equivalent fractions.

$$+4\frac{5}{12} = +4\frac{5}{12}$$

$$\overline{\qquad\qquad 6\frac{14}{12}}$$ Add integers and fractions separately.

$$6 + 1\frac{2}{12}$$ Write improper fractions as mixed numbers and add whole numbers.

So, $2\frac{3}{4} + 4\frac{5}{12} = 7\frac{1}{6}$ Write the fraction in lowest terms.

▼ With subtraction, you may need to rename before subtracting.

Example 5 $5\frac{1}{6} - 2\frac{2}{3} = \blacksquare$

Solution

$$5\frac{1}{6} = \quad 5\frac{1}{6} = \quad 4\frac{7}{6}$$ Write equivalent fractions.

$$-2\frac{2}{3} = -2\frac{4}{6} = -2\frac{4}{6}$$

$$\overline{\qquad\qquad\qquad\qquad = \quad 2\frac{3}{6}}$$

So, $5\frac{1}{6} - 2\frac{2}{3} = \quad 2\frac{1}{2}$ Write the fraction in lowest terms.

THINK AND DISCUSS

1. Is the sum or difference of two rational numbers also a rational number?

2. Do the commutative and associative properties also apply to rational numbers? Use examples to support your answer.

CLASS EXERCISES

Use a model to find the sum or difference.

1. $\frac{1}{3} + \frac{1}{6}$ **2.** $\frac{2}{3} - \frac{1}{6}$ **3.** $\frac{11}{12} + \frac{5}{6}$ **4.** $1\frac{3}{8} - \frac{7}{8}$

Find the sum or difference.

5. $\frac{1}{3} + \frac{3}{4}$ **6.** $\frac{4}{5} + 3\frac{7}{10}$ **7.** $\frac{3}{4} - \frac{2}{5}$ **8.** $5\frac{1}{3} - 2\frac{3}{4}$

9. $\frac{x}{3} + \frac{5}{6}$ **10.** $\frac{3}{4}x + \frac{2}{3} + \frac{1}{2}x$ **11.** $11\frac{3}{4} - \left(-19\frac{5}{8}\right)$ **12.** $5 - 3\frac{3}{4}$

Estimate the sum or difference.

13. $5\frac{5}{9} + 8\frac{2}{31}$ **14.** $21.76 - 15\frac{3}{41}$ **15.** $-\frac{11}{3} + (-3.25)$ **16.** $15\frac{3}{4} - 38\frac{1}{2}$

17. $2\frac{1}{3} + 7\frac{1}{8}$ **18.** $-\frac{7}{8} - \left(-\frac{1}{4}\right)$ **19.** $14.7 + 3\frac{1}{5}$ **20.** $8\frac{11}{12} + 4\frac{1}{12}$

WRITTEN EXERCISES

Use a model to find the sum or difference.

1. $\frac{3}{8} + \left(-\frac{1}{2}\right)$ **2.** $-\left(\frac{2}{3}\right) - \frac{1}{6}$ **3.** $\frac{3}{4} + \frac{1}{2}$ **4.** $1\frac{1}{2} - \frac{3}{4}$

Write a number sentence for each model shown.

5.    **6.**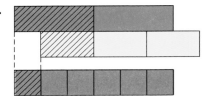

Find each sum or difference.

7. $\frac{7}{8} + \frac{5}{12}$ **8.** $\frac{5}{6} + \frac{-1}{8}$ **9.** $\frac{2}{3} - 1\frac{1}{9}$ **10.** $4\frac{3}{5} - 2\frac{7}{10}$

11. $\frac{2}{3} + 1\frac{5}{6}$ **12.** $\frac{x}{4} + \frac{x}{6}$ **13.** $14\frac{5}{9} - 5\frac{1}{3}$ **14.** $\frac{4x}{5} + \left(-\frac{6x}{10}\right)$

15. $\frac{5}{9}y - \frac{1}{6}y$ **16.** $2\frac{3}{5} + 4\frac{7}{15}$ **17.** $2\frac{1}{8} - 6\frac{3}{4}$ **18.** $\frac{3b}{4} - \frac{5b}{6}$

Estimate each sum or difference.

▼▼   *SAMPLE* $12\frac{3}{4} - 5\frac{3}{8} \approx 13 - 5 = 8$

19. $28\frac{5}{18} - 12\frac{7}{17}$ **20.** $-145.76 + \left(-76\frac{8}{19}\right)$ **21.** $52.097 - \left(-98\frac{5}{23}\right)$

22. $35.1 - 12\frac{8}{11}$ **23.** $52\frac{25}{48} + 22\frac{7}{16}$ **24.** $42\frac{3}{11} + 57\frac{9}{16}$

MENTAL MATH Find each sum or difference.

25. $5\frac{1}{4} + 19\frac{2}{3} + 4\frac{3}{4}$ **26.** $7\frac{2}{8} + 4\frac{5}{8} + \left(-6\frac{7}{8}\right)$

CALCULATOR Check whether the following are correct.

27. $25\frac{7}{12} - \left(-18\frac{13}{18}\right) = 44\frac{11}{36}$ **28.** $17\frac{11}{24} + \left(-11\frac{17}{30}\right) = 5\frac{107}{120}$

29. $23\frac{5}{8} - 12\frac{3}{5} = 11\frac{1}{3}$ **30.** $16\frac{7}{12} - \left(-14\frac{3}{8}\right) = 30\frac{23}{24}$

31. Which of the following are equal to $1\frac{1}{2}$?

  a. $4\frac{3}{8} - 3\frac{1}{4}$ **b.** $\frac{-3}{-2} - \frac{1}{2}$ **c.** $2\frac{1}{x} - \frac{3}{x}, x = 4$ **d.** $\frac{x - 1.5}{3.5 - x}, x = \frac{1}{2}$

32. Classify each statement as *sometimes*, *always*, or *never* true.

  a. $\left|\frac{4}{5}x\right| \geq \frac{4}{5}x$ **b.** $\frac{2x}{3} < x$ **c.** $\frac{1}{x} < x, x \neq 0$ **d.** $\frac{2}{x} < \frac{3}{x}, x > 0$

MIXED REVIEW
Calculate each answer.
1. Write the opposite and the absolute value of $3\frac{1}{5}$.
2. $5\frac{8}{11} + \blacksquare = 0$
3. Write the rational number $\frac{-7}{10}$ in two other ways.
4. $-6\frac{2}{3} = \frac{\blacksquare}{3}$
5. Compare $-\frac{13}{9}$ and $-\frac{30}{21}$.
6. When is $\frac{y}{8} > \frac{1}{2}$?
7. What is the LCM of 15 and 20?
8. Sara earns \$4.95 an hour and works for 29 hours. Estimate her pay.

PROBLEM SOLVING HINT
Try guess and test.

Compare. Use >, <, or =.

33. $\frac{3^2}{5}$ ◼ $\frac{17}{20}$

34. $-\frac{5}{14}$ ◼ $-\frac{7}{15}$

35. $\frac{3}{8} + \frac{2}{3}$ ◼ $\frac{4}{5}$

36. $\frac{a}{3}$ ◼ $\frac{a}{4}$, $a > 0$

37. $\frac{a}{5}$ ◼ $\frac{a^2}{5}$, $a < 0$

38. $\left|\frac{a}{b}\right|$ ◼ $\frac{|a|}{|b|}$, $b \neq 0$

39. Lynn wishes to wallpaper her room. Estimate the perimeter of Lynn's room. The length is $9\frac{3}{8}$ ft and the width is $11\frac{7}{12}$ ft.

40. **MENTAL MATH** Make a chart. List the following fractions in three categories: close to 0, close to $\frac{1}{2}$, close to 1.

$$\frac{3}{5}, \frac{17}{21}, \frac{5}{14}, \frac{27}{53}, \frac{17}{15}, \frac{28}{59}, \frac{8}{55}$$

41. What fraction of an hour is fifteen minutes? What fraction is seventy-five minutes?

42. In the lower bass section of the band, 15 students play trombone and 4 play tuba. Two students play both instruments. What fraction of the group play tuba?

43. What numbers must be in the blanks to form a magic square?

PROBLEM SOLVING HINT
Use a Venn diagram.

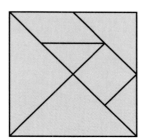

$\frac{1}{2}$	◼	$\frac{2}{3}$
◼	$\frac{5}{12}$	◼
$\frac{1}{6}$	◼	$\frac{1}{3}$

Critical Thinking

EXPLORING VISUALIZATION

An ancient geometric puzzle known as the tangram divides a large square into seven pieces. You can use the pieces to create a variety of geometrical designs. The large triangles are $\frac{1}{4}$ of the tangram. Two of the large triangles equal half of the large square. Written in fractions this would be $\frac{1}{4} + \frac{1}{4} = \frac{1}{2}$.

1. Copy the tangram on graph paper. What fraction of the tangram does each piece represent?

Draw or model the tangram pieces that show each equation.

2. $\frac{1}{4} = \frac{1}{8} + \frac{1}{16} + \frac{1}{16}$

3. $\frac{1}{4} + \frac{1}{4} = \frac{1}{8} + \frac{1}{8} + \frac{1}{8} + \frac{1}{16} + \frac{1}{16}$

Create a figure to show each expression.

4. $\frac{1}{8} + \frac{1}{16}$

5. $\frac{1}{8} + \frac{1}{16} + \frac{1}{16}$

6. $\frac{1}{4} + \frac{1}{8} + \frac{1}{8}$

7. Compare your figures with those of other students in the class.

OBJECTIVE:
To solve problems by
working backwards.

5-6 *Working Backwards*

■ With some problems, you have to work backwards
from the given information to get an answer.

PROBLEM

The Tanaka family is planning a trip to the Grand Canyon. It will
take 5 h of driving. In addition, they plan to make three half-hour
rest stops. They plan on arriving at 3:30 P.M. What time should they
plan to leave?

SOLUTION

READg ▶ Answer these questions to understand the given information:

What do you want to find?	The departure time for the trip.
What is the arrival time?	3:30 P.M.
How much time will be spent driving?	5 h
How much time will be spent resting?	$1\frac{1}{2}$ h

PLAN ▶ Add up the time needed for the trip.
Work back from the arrival time to find the departure time.

SOLVE ▶ Total time: $5 + 1\frac{1}{2} = 6\frac{1}{2}$
Work backwards from the arrival time:

9:00 A.M.   3:30 P.M.

9:30 10:30 11:30 12:30 1:30 2:30

LOOK BACK ▶ Did you solve the problem? Count forward from 9:00 A.M. The
elapsed time between 9:00 A.M. and 3:30 P.M. is $6\frac{1}{2}$ hours. ✓

CLASS EXERCISES

1. What other strategy could you use to solve this problem?

2. How could you use estimation to find the approximate departure
   time?

3. Suppose it will take $6\frac{1}{2}$ h of driving. At what time should the
   Tanakas leave?

4. The Tanakas will need $2\frac{1}{2}$ hours to get dressed and have
   breakfast. They will also need another $1\frac{1}{4}$ h to pack the
   car. At what time should the Tanakas get up in order to leave at
   9:00 A.M.?

Solve each problem by working backwards.

1. Solve this riddle: "I think of a number, add 5, multiply by 3, divide by 4, and subtract 1. The answer is 8." What is the original number?

2. Carla spent $\frac{1}{3}$ of her money at the amusement park. Afterward, she had $15 left. How much money did she have originally?

3. A ball is bouncing on the floor. After each bounce, the ball is $\frac{2}{3}$ as high as the previous bounce. On the fifth bounce, the ball is 2 ft off the floor. How high was the ball before the first bounce?

Solve each problem. Use an appropriate strategy.

4. Use the map at the left. It took the Tanakas 7 h to reach the Grand Canyon. If their average speed was 55 mi/h, could Seattle be their home town?

5. Joan is twice as old as her brother Harry. When Joan is twice as old as she is now, she will be six years older than Harry. How old is Joan now?

6. Look at the following list of numbers: {1, 1, 1, 2, 3, 5, 6}. How many combinations of numbers will make the following equation true?

You cannot use a number on the list more than once for each equation.

7. **CALCULATOR** Find the first three quotients. Predict the quotients for the remaining equations.

   a. $1 \div 9 = $ ▦   **b.** $2 \div 9 = $ ▦   **c.** $3 \div 9 = $ ▦

   d. $4 \div 9 = $ ▦   **e.** $5 \div 9 = $ ▦   **f.** $6 \div 9 = $ ▦

8. You have two nickels, three dimes, and a quarter. Using at least one of each coin, how many different amounts of money can you make?

9. Look for the number pattern and find the next three numbers.

   $\frac{2}{3}, 1\frac{5}{12}, 2\frac{1}{6}, 2\frac{11}{12}$

10. Alex, Bart, Clarence, and Dan enter a classroom. All four choose one of the four desks at the back. Each day they sit in a different order. How many days can they do this before they must repeat a previous pattern?

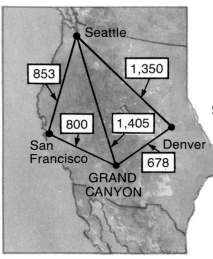

Seattle

853

1,350

800

1,405

San
Francisco

Denver

678

GRAND
CANYON

Driving distance in miles

Practice

Write in lowest terms.

1. $\dfrac{3}{15}$ 2. $\dfrac{4}{18}$ 3. $\dfrac{8}{12}$ 4. $\dfrac{20}{45}$

5. $\dfrac{9}{15}$ 6. $\dfrac{24}{42}$ 7. $\dfrac{15y^2}{35y}$ 8. $\dfrac{5m}{5m}$

9. $\dfrac{3a}{9a}$ 10. $\dfrac{6xy}{20x}$ 11. $\dfrac{12m}{18m^2}$ 12. $\dfrac{cd}{3c^2d}$

Write each mixed number as an improper fraction.

13. $2\dfrac{3}{5}$ 14. $1\dfrac{7}{8}$ 15. $4\dfrac{2}{3}$ 16. $5\dfrac{7}{9}$

17. $8\dfrac{1}{4}$ 18. $12\dfrac{5}{8}$ 19. $20\dfrac{7}{12}$ 20. $15\dfrac{3}{4}$

Write each improper fraction as a mixed number.

21. $\dfrac{12}{5}$ 22. $\dfrac{19}{2}$ 23. $\dfrac{25}{4}$ 24. $\dfrac{41}{12}$

25. $\dfrac{53}{8}$ 26. $\dfrac{35}{6}$ 27. $\dfrac{57}{7}$ 28. $\dfrac{28}{9}$

Write the opposite and absolute value of each number.

29. $2\dfrac{3}{8}$ 30. $-5\dfrac{4}{5}$ 31. $-18\dfrac{2}{3}$ 32. $24\dfrac{7}{15}$

33. $-13\dfrac{5}{9}$ 34. $22\dfrac{1}{6}$ 35. $-\dfrac{11}{15}$ 36. $31\dfrac{8}{9}$

Compare. Use >, <, or =.

37. $\dfrac{2}{3} \blacksquare \dfrac{3}{4}$ 38. $-\dfrac{7}{15} \blacksquare -\dfrac{3}{5}$ 39. $\dfrac{7}{8} \blacksquare \dfrac{13}{16}$

40. $-\dfrac{5}{6} \blacksquare -\dfrac{7}{8}$ 41. $\dfrac{11}{15} \blacksquare \dfrac{7}{10}$ 42. $-\dfrac{5}{9} \blacksquare \dfrac{7}{12}$

Find the sum or difference.

43. $\dfrac{5}{12} + \dfrac{7}{12}$ 44. $\dfrac{3}{8} - \dfrac{5}{8}$ 45. $\dfrac{8}{9} + \dfrac{2}{9}$

46. $\dfrac{3}{5} - \left(-\dfrac{7}{10}\right)$ 47. $-\dfrac{5}{8} + \dfrac{1}{4}$ 48. $\dfrac{7}{15} - \dfrac{2}{5}$

49. $-2\dfrac{1}{2} - 3\dfrac{3}{4}$ 50. $7\dfrac{5}{8} - 2\dfrac{1}{4}$ 51. $3\dfrac{5}{6} - 2\dfrac{3}{8}$

52. $3\dfrac{3}{8} - 2\dfrac{7}{12}$ 53. $4\dfrac{7}{15} + 2\dfrac{3}{10}$ 54. $-4\dfrac{2}{3} + 6\dfrac{5}{8}$

55. $10 - 3\dfrac{4}{7}$ 56. $4\dfrac{3}{8} - 5$ 57. $-5\dfrac{1}{2} - 5\dfrac{1}{2}$

58. $-14\dfrac{5}{8} + 2\dfrac{3}{5}$ 59. $18\dfrac{9}{16} + 11\dfrac{3}{4}$ 60. $15\dfrac{3}{8} - 8\dfrac{3}{4}$

OBJECTIVE:
To multiply and
divide fractions and
mixed numbers.

5-7 *Multiplying and Dividing Rational Numbers*

▼ About $\frac{3}{4}$ of the world's fresh water is found in glaciers. Antarctica has $\frac{9}{10}$ of the world's glaciers. What fraction of the world's fresh water is in Antarctica? To find the solution, multiply $\frac{3}{4}$ by $\frac{9}{10}$.

$$\frac{3}{4} \cdot \frac{9}{10} = \frac{3 \cdot 9}{4 \cdot 10}$$
$$= \frac{27}{40}$$

Antarctica has more than half of the world's fresh water.

▼ You can also use a model to multiply rational numbers.

Example 1 $\quad \frac{4}{5} \cdot \frac{2}{3} = \blacksquare$

Solution

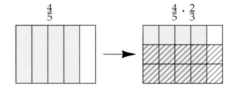

Count the number of rectangles that include both patterns.

So, $\frac{4}{5} \cdot \frac{2}{3} = \frac{8}{15}$.

▼ You can multiply fractions that have variables.

Example 2 $\quad -\frac{2}{3} \cdot \frac{x}{7} = \blacksquare$

Solution $\quad -\frac{2}{3} \cdot \frac{x}{7} = -\frac{2 \cdot x}{3 \cdot 7}$ Multiply the numerator and denominator.

$$= -\frac{2x}{21}$$

Product of Two Rational Numbers	For any two rational numbers $\frac{a}{b}$ and $\frac{c}{d}$, $\quad \frac{a}{b} \cdot \frac{c}{d} = \frac{a \cdot c}{b \cdot d} \qquad b \neq 0,\ d \neq 0$

▼ You can multiply mixed numbers.

Example 3 $\quad 2\frac{1}{4} \cdot \left(-2\frac{2}{3}\right) = \blacksquare$

Solution $\quad 2\frac{1}{4} \cdot \left(-2\frac{2}{3}\right) = \frac{9}{4} \cdot \left(-\frac{8}{3}\right)$ Write mixed numbers as improper fractions.

$$= -\frac{72}{12}$$
$$= -6$$

FLASHBACK

$(+) \cdot (+) = +$
$(+) \cdot (-) = -$
$(-) \cdot (+) = -$
$(-) \cdot (-) = +$

▼ **THINK** Why must you multiply both numerators and denominators?

▼ You can sometimes simplify fractions before multiplying.

Example 4 $\frac{3}{14} \cdot \frac{2}{3} \cdot \left(-\frac{1}{2}\right) = $ ▨

Solution $\dfrac{\overset{1}{\cancel{3}} \cdot \overset{1}{\cancel{2}} \cdot 1}{14 \cdot \underset{1}{\cancel{3}} \cdot (-\cancel{2})} = -\dfrac{1}{14}$ Divide common factors from the numerator and denominator.

▼ You can divide two rational numbers.

Example 5   Use pattern blocks to model $\frac{4}{6} \div \frac{1}{3}$.

Solution   Two $\frac{1}{3}$ pieces fit in $\frac{4}{6}$.

$\frac{4}{6} \div \frac{1}{3} = 2$

▼ You can divide two fractions by multiplying by the *reciprocal* of the second factor.

Example 6 $\frac{2}{5} \div \frac{3}{7} = $ ▨

Solution   The reciprocal of $\frac{3}{7}$ is $\frac{7}{3}$.

$\frac{2}{5} \cdot \frac{7}{3} = \frac{14}{15}$ Multiply by the reciprocal.

Dividing Two Rational Numbers	For any two rational numbers $\frac{a}{b}$ and $\frac{c}{d}$, $\frac{a}{b} \div \frac{c}{d} = \frac{a}{b} \cdot \frac{d}{c}$ $b \neq 0, c \neq 0, d \neq 0$

THINK What is the reciprocal of a whole number?

CLASS EXERCISES

Use a model to find the product or quotient.

1. $\frac{2}{3} \cdot \frac{3}{4}$ **2.** $\frac{1}{2} \cdot \frac{3}{8}$ **3.** $\frac{1}{2} \div \frac{1}{3}$ **4.** $2\frac{1}{2} \cdot \frac{1}{6}$

Find the product or quotient.

5. $\frac{1}{3} \cdot \frac{1}{2}$ **6.** $\frac{5a}{7} \cdot -\frac{3a}{5}$ **7.** $\frac{5a}{9} \div \frac{4a}{5}$ **8.** $1\frac{1}{2} \div \frac{3}{8}$

9. $-\frac{5}{8} \div \frac{3}{4}$ **10.** $1\frac{1}{5} \cdot \frac{3}{8}$ **11.** $-4\frac{1}{6} \cdot 1\frac{4}{5}$ **12.** $-3\frac{2}{3} \div \left(-2\frac{4}{9}\right)$

THINK AND DISCUSS

1. Is the product of two rational numbers a rational number? Is the quotient?

2. If two proper fractions are less than 1, is their product less than 1?

Solve.

1. $x - 7.2 = -5.8$

2. $y + (-6.2) = 3.7$

3. $3\frac{1}{3} + \left(-2\frac{5}{6}\right)$

4. $\frac{17}{24} \overset{?}{=} \frac{13}{18}$

5. Convert $\frac{13}{40}$ to a decimal.

6. What is the GCF of 30 and 24?

7. $\left|-2\frac{1}{2}\right| + \left|2\frac{1}{2}\right|$

8. Paul's height is $5\frac{11}{12}$ ft, Jim's height is $5\frac{13}{16}$ ft, and Sam's height is $5\frac{7}{8}$ ft. Who is the tallest?

FLASHBACK

Order of operations:

1. grouping symbols

2. exponents

3. multiplication and division

4. addition and subtraction

WRITTEN EXERCISES

Use a model to find the product or quotient.

1. $\frac{1}{2} \cdot \frac{2}{3}$

2. $\frac{5}{6} \cdot \frac{1}{6}$

3. $4 \div \frac{1}{2}$

4. $2\frac{1}{2} \div \frac{1}{2}$

Find the answer.

5. $\frac{1}{3} \cdot \frac{6}{11}$

6. $\frac{8}{15} \div \frac{2}{3}$

7. $\frac{3}{8} + \frac{9}{16}$

8. $\frac{-9}{10} \div \frac{5}{12} \div \frac{1}{2}$

9. $\frac{3a}{5} - \frac{7a}{10}$

10. $\frac{5q}{8} \div \frac{3}{5}$

11. $3\frac{1}{3} + 2\frac{1}{2}$

12. $1\frac{3}{8} \div 2\frac{1}{16}$

13. $\frac{2}{5} \cdot 2\frac{1}{2}$

14. $2\frac{1}{3} \cdot \frac{3}{7}$

15. $\frac{-4}{9}\left(-2\frac{1}{4}\right) - \frac{1}{4}$

16. $-1\frac{3}{5} \cdot \left(\frac{-5}{8}\right) + \frac{4}{5}$

Estimate the answer by rounding to the nearest integer.

17. $-12\frac{3}{4} \cdot \left(-3\frac{1}{3}\right)$

18. $25\frac{1}{10} \div \left(-5\frac{2}{5}\right)$

19. $-11\frac{7}{18} + 2\frac{7}{10}$

20. $45\frac{3}{8} \cdot \left(-2\frac{6}{7}\right)$

21. $-75\frac{1}{12} - \left(-15\frac{1}{10}\right)$

22. $-33\frac{1}{16} \cdot \left(-12\frac{5}{7}\right)$

23. $18\frac{2}{5} \div 11\frac{1}{2}$

24. $-42\frac{2}{3} + 65\frac{3}{8}$

25. $25\frac{3}{8} \cdot 4\frac{5}{7} + 5\frac{1}{3}$

Compare. Use >, <, or =.

26. $\frac{3}{4} \cdot \frac{4}{5} \ \blacksquare \ \frac{3}{4} \div \frac{4}{5}$

27. $\frac{9}{7} \cdot \left(-\frac{56}{3}\right) \ \blacksquare \ -30 + 2\frac{1}{2}$

28. $\frac{1}{2} \cdot \frac{1}{2} \cdot \frac{1}{2} \ \blacksquare \ \frac{1}{2^3}$

29. $\frac{x}{4} \div 2\frac{1}{2} \ \blacksquare \ \frac{2}{3}x, \ x > 0$

30. $-\frac{2a}{3} \cdot 1\frac{1}{8} \ \blacksquare \ \frac{1a}{4} \cdot \left(-1\frac{3}{7}\right), \ a > 0$

31. $3\frac{3}{10} \cdot \left(-3\frac{2}{11}\right) \ \blacksquare \ -4\frac{2}{3} \cdot 2\frac{1}{4}$

Solve. Write each answer in simplest form.

32. $\frac{1}{2} \cdot \frac{1}{4} \cdot \left[\frac{1}{3} + \left(-\frac{1}{6}\right)\right]$

33. $\frac{4}{5} \div \left(\frac{-4}{9}\right) + \frac{4}{9} \cdot \frac{3}{5}$

34. $\frac{3}{10} - \frac{4}{5} \cdot \frac{8}{5} \div 2\frac{1}{2}$

35. $\frac{3}{5} + \frac{1}{4} \cdot \left(-\frac{4}{5}\right) \div \frac{2}{15}$

36. Classify the following as *sometimes*, *always*, or *never* true, assuming $a \neq 0$ and $b \neq 0$.

   a. $\frac{5a}{b} \cdot \frac{4}{25} = \frac{20a}{b}$

   b. $\frac{5a}{3b} \div \frac{15a}{9b} = 1$

   c. $\frac{a}{b} \cdot \frac{a}{b} = \left|\frac{a}{b}\right| \cdot \left|\frac{a}{b}\right|$

37. **MENTAL MATH** Solve each problem.

   a. How many quarters are there in $50?

   b. How many nickels are there in $25?

   c. How many $.75 drinks will $9 buy?

Exploring Infinity

■ Using a computer or a graphing calculator, you can create a bar graph of the *unit fractions*, or fractions with a numerator of 1. The first six unit fractions are shown below.

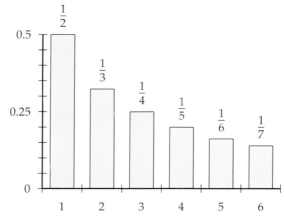

1. Continue the bar graph for the first 10 unit fractions.

2. What happens to the size of the bar for each new fraction?

3. What will the graph look like for 20 unit fractions?

4. Will this trend continue for 100 unit fractions? for 1,000?

5. Can a bar have a height of zero?

6. **Write** a description of the graph of the unit fractions for an increasing denominator.

■ The graphs of the unit fractions are equivalent to these equations:

$$\text{height of bar } 1 = 1 \cdot \frac{1}{2}$$

$$\text{height of bar } 2 = 1 \cdot \frac{1}{3}$$

$$\text{height of bar } 3 = 1 \cdot \frac{1}{4}$$

$$\text{height of bar } 4 = 1 \cdot \frac{1}{5}$$

$$\text{height of bar } 5 = 1 \cdot \frac{1}{6}$$

$$\text{height of bar } 6 = 1 \cdot \frac{1}{7}$$

7. Why does the height of the bars decrease as the denominator of the unit fraction increases?

8. Write an equation that shows the height for *any* bar.

■ You can also create a bar graph made up of the product of two unit fractions. For example, look at the spreadsheet shown below.

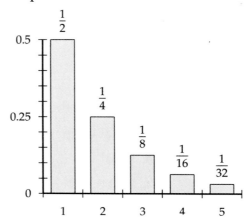

	A
1	= 1/2
2	= A1*A1
3	= A1*A1*A1
4	= A1*A1*A1*A1
5	= A1*A1*A1*A1*A1
6	

A bar graph of the spreadsheet data looks like this.

9. How would you continue the spreadsheet data for five more bars?

10. What happens to the bars in the graph? **Compare** this to the change in the graph for the unit fractions.

11. Write each of the five fractions on the bar graph using exponents. Then write an equation to show the height of any bar on the graph.

■ For each graph, the height of the bars approaches zero as the denominators become larger, or approach *infinity*. A number is said to approach infinity if the number increases without limit. The symbol for infinity is ∞.

12. Why does the value of a unit fraction approach zero as the denominator approaches infinity?

13. Decide which of the following expressions will approach zero as x approaches infinity. (Use a computer to create a bar graph for $x = 1$ to 5, if necessary.)

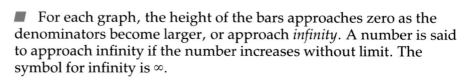

a. $\frac{1}{3}x$ **b.** $\frac{1}{3x}$ **c.** $\frac{x^2}{2x}$ **d.** $\frac{1}{3^x}$ **e.** $\frac{3}{x}$

OBJECTIVE:
To simplify expressions with negative exponents.

5-8 *Rational Numbers with Exponents*

▼ The mass in grams of a proton is 1.67×10^{-24}. To understand numbers like this, you must learn about rational numbers with exponents.

▼ You can divide rational numbers with exponents.

Example 1   Simplify $7^8 \div 7^3$.

Solution
$$\frac{7^8}{7^3} = \frac{\overset{1}{\cancel{7}} \cdot \overset{1}{\cancel{7}} \cdot \overset{1}{\cancel{7}} \cdot 7 \cdot 7 \cdot 7 \cdot 7 \cdot 7}{\underset{1}{\cancel{7}} \cdot \underset{1}{\cancel{7}} \cdot \underset{1}{\cancel{7}}}$$ Divide common factors.

$$= \frac{7 \cdot 7 \cdot 7 \cdot 7 \cdot 7}{1} = \frac{7^5}{1}$$

$$= 7^5$$

Notice that $\frac{7^8}{7^3} = 7^{8-3}$, or 7^5. This suggests the following rule.

Rule of Exponents for Division	To divide numbers or variables with the *same* base, subtract exponents.
	Arithmetic　　　　　**Algebra**
	$\frac{4^5}{4^2} = 4^{5-2} = 4^3$ 　　 $\frac{a^m}{a^n} = a^{m-n}$ 　 $a \neq 0$

Example 2   Simplify.

    a. $\dfrac{x^6}{x^3}$ **b.** $\dfrac{a^4 b^2}{a^2 b}$

Solution　**a.** $x^{6-3} = x^3$ **b.** $\dfrac{a^4}{a^2} \cdot \dfrac{b^2}{b} = (a^{4-2})(b^{2-1}) = a^2 b$

▼ Sometimes the exponents in the numerator and denominator are equal.

Example 3   Simplify $\frac{3^4}{3^4}$.

FLASHBACK

Any nonzero number divided by itself is equal to one.

Solution　**1.** $3^{4-4} = 3^0$ 　　Use the rules of exponents for division.

         2. $\dfrac{3^4}{3^4} = 1$ 　　Divide common factors.

Since $\frac{3^4}{3^4} = 3^0$ and $\frac{3^4}{3^4} = 1$, you know that $3^0 = 1$. This suggests the following definition of zero as an exponent.

Zero as an Exponent	Any nonzero number with zero as an exponent equals 1.
	$a^0 = 1$ for all $a \neq 0$.

▼ Sometimes the exponent in the denominator is greater than the exponent in the numerator.

Example 4 Simplify $\frac{2^2}{2^3}$.

Solution **a.** Use the rule.

$$\frac{2^2}{2^3} = 2^{2-3}$$

$$= 2^{-1}$$

b. Use the meaning of exponents.

$$\frac{2^2}{2^3} = \frac{\overset{1}{\cancel{2}} \cdot \overset{1}{\cancel{2}}}{\underset{1}{\cancel{2}} \cdot \underset{1}{\cancel{2}} \cdot 2}$$

$$= \frac{1}{2}$$

Since $\frac{2^2}{2^3} = 2^{-1}$ and $\frac{2^2}{2^3} = \frac{1}{2}$ you know that $2^{-1} = \frac{1}{2}$. This suggests the following about negative exponents.

▼
THINK Why must 0^0 be undefined?

Negative Exponents	For any nonzero integers a and n: $a^{-n} = \frac{1}{a^n}$

Example 5 Simplify. Write with positive exponents.

a. $\frac{m^2}{m^5}$

b. $4x^{-3}$

Solution a. $\frac{m^2}{m^5} = m^{2-5}$

$$= m^{-3}$$

$$= \frac{1}{m^3}$$

b. $4x^{-3} = 4 \cdot \frac{1}{x^3}$

$$= \frac{4}{x^3}$$

▼

THINK AND DISCUSS

1. Can you simplify $\frac{x^3}{y^4}$?

2. How many ways can you write $^-8x^{-3}$?

3. Explain why 3^{-2} is not a negative number.

CLASS EXERCISES

Evaluate.

1. 2^{-3} **2.** 5^{-2} **3.** 7^0 **4.** -3^0

5. $\frac{2^5}{2^2}$ **6.** $\frac{5^{-3}}{5^{-2}}$ **7.** $8^4 \div 8^2$ **8.** 0^0

Write with positive or negative exponents. Leave no exponents in the denominator.

9. $\frac{a^3}{a^7}$ **10.** $\frac{m^5}{m^2}$ **11.** $\frac{b^5}{c^2}$ **12.** $\frac{a^5b^7}{a^6b^{-3}}$

Write with positive exponents.

13. a^{-3} **14.** $5b^{-7}$ **15.** $\frac{6x^2}{x^4}$ **16.** $\frac{2y^5}{8y^3}$

17. $x^{-3}y^2$ **18.** 5^{-2} **19.** $4a^{-3}$ **20.** $15x^2y^{-4}$

WRITTEN EXERCISES

Evaluate.

1. 6^{-2}

2. 3^{-1}

3. $(-2)^0$

4. $\dfrac{4^3}{4^5}$

5. $2^{-3} \cdot 3$

6. -7^0

7. $(-5)^{-2}$

8. $3^0 \cdot 5^2 \cdot 2^{-4}$

Write with positive or negative exponents. Leave no exponents in the denominator.

9. $\dfrac{1}{a^3}$

10. $\dfrac{b^5}{b^7}$

11. $\dfrac{5x^2}{10x^{-5}}$

12. $\dfrac{3y^4z}{y^6z^2}$

13. $\dfrac{x^5y^{-2}}{x^3y^8}$

14. $\dfrac{y^{-2}z^{-4}}{y^3z^{-2}}$

15. $\dfrac{15b^6c}{3b^2c^{-4}}$

16. $\dfrac{4xy^{-5}}{20x^7y^{-2}}$

Write with positive exponents.

17. $\dfrac{20m^5}{4m^3}$

18. $\dfrac{3b^2}{4b^7}$

19. $\dfrac{3x^2y^3}{x^5y}$

20. $\dfrac{b^{-3}c^7}{b^5c^{-2}}$

21. Write each of these numbers without an exponent.

    a. -5^2 **b.** $(-5)^2$ **c.** 5^{-2} **d.** $(-5)^{-2}$

Simplify.

22. $(3a)^2$

23. $(5a)^{-2}$

24. $-(2y^4)^0$

25. $(a^2b^{-3})^5$

26. $x^2 \cdot x^{-3}$

27. $\left(\dfrac{3a}{b}\right)^2 \cdot \left(\dfrac{a^2}{b^{-3}}\right)$

28. $(2x^2y^{-3}) \cdot (x^3y^4)$

29. Study the table at the right.

    a. Describe the pattern in the first column of the table.

    b. Describe the pattern in the second column. If this pattern continues, what will be the next three entries?

    c. How are these values related to 3?

    d. Create a similar table for values of n and 2^n. How are the values in the table related to 2?

4	81
3	27
2	9
1	3
0	
-1	
-2	

True or *false*? Explain your answer.

30. $\dfrac{a^3 \cdot a^4}{a^2} = \dfrac{a^3 + a^4}{a^2}$

31. $x^8 \cdot x^2 = x^5 \cdot x^5$

32. $1^0 = 1^{-1}$

33. $x^5 \cdot x^3 = x^{15}$

34. $x^3 \cdot y^4 = (xy)^7$

35. $5^0 = 7^0$

36. $(-r^3)^2 > 0$

37. $-(r^2)^3 < 0$

38. $1^8 = 1^{23}$

Write in standard notation.

39. The weight of all the ocean water on Earth is 1.58×10^{18} t.

40. The radius of Earth's orbit is 1.5×10^{11} m.

Use the article below to answer each question.

Future Glows for Natural Gas

As oil prices continue to rise, American investors look again at an abundant resource, natural gas. In the United States, natural gas now accounts for $\frac{1}{4}$ of daily energy use. Petroleum products account for about $\frac{2}{5}$.

Not only can gas replace oil for home heating, it can also fuel cars and power electric generating plants. Natural Gas burns more cleanly than oil, emitting less carbon dioxide.

When gas replaces coal in electric generating plants, sulphur emissions are immediately cut.

41. How much of the energy of the United States do natural gas and petroleum products provide?

42. *PROJECT* Research natural gas. Find out how it can be used to fuel automobiles. What are the costs of converting from gasoline to natural gas?

Critical Thinking
EXPLORING PATTERNS IN SCIENTIFIC NOTATION

1. Continue the pattern and describe what happens when the exponents are negative.

$$
\begin{aligned}
1.2 \times 10^3 &= 1{,}200 \\
1.2 \times 10^2 &= 120 \\
1.2 \times 10^1 &= 12 \\
1.2 \times 10^0 &= \blacksquare \\
1.2 \times 10^{-1} &= \blacksquare \\
1.2 \times 10^{-2} &= \blacksquare
\end{aligned}
$$

2. $1.2 \times 10^{-3} = 0.0012$. Extend the pattern above to see if it agrees.

3. Write 3.7×10^{-4} in standard notation.

4. 1.67×10^{-24} g is the mass of a proton. How many zeros would follow the decimal point and come before the 1 if this were written in standard notation?

5. The mass of the sun is 1.00×10^{30} kg and the mass of an electron is 9.11×10^{-28} g. Why do scientists prefer scientific notation to standard notation for very large and very small numbers?

OBJECTIVE:
To solve equations
involving addition
and subtraction of
rational numbers.

5-9 *Addition and Subtraction Equations*

▼   In four months Jules grew $\frac{2}{3}$ in. How could you represent his new height?

Let x = Jules' height four months ago. You can represent Jules' new height by the following variable expression.

$$x + \frac{2}{3}$$

▼   You can write an equation using a variable expression.

Example 1   **Write an equation to represent the situation.**

At high tide the water level rose $3\frac{1}{2}$ ft to a height of 25 ft.

Solution   Let x = the previous height.
Then $x + 3\frac{1}{2} = 25$ is an equation to represent the water level at high tide.

▼   You can solve rational number equations by using or drawing a model.

Example 2   **Solve the equation using a model.**

$$x + \frac{1}{2} = \frac{11}{12}$$

Solution

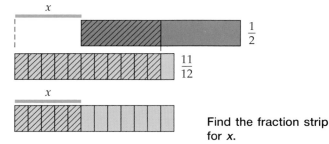

Find the fraction strip for x.

So, $x = \frac{5}{12}$.

▼   You know how to solve integer equations by isolating the variable. You can use the same procedure for solving equations with rational numbers.

Example 3   Solve $x + \frac{4}{15} = \frac{7}{10}$.

Solution $x + \dfrac{4}{15} - \dfrac{4}{15} = \dfrac{7}{10} - \dfrac{4}{15}$ Subtract $\frac{4}{15}$ from each side to isolate x.

$$x = \frac{7}{10} - \frac{4}{15}$$

$$= \frac{21}{30} - \frac{8}{30}$$ Find a common denominator.

$$= \frac{13}{30}$$

▼ You can also solve equations involving subtraction of rational numbers.

Example 4 Solve $z - \left(-3\frac{7}{10}\right) = -2\frac{1}{5}$.

Solution $z - \left(-3\frac{7}{10}\right) + \left(-3\frac{7}{10}\right) = -2\frac{1}{5} + \left(-3\frac{7}{10}\right)$ Add $-3\frac{7}{10}$ to each side.

$$z = -2\frac{1}{5} + \left(-3\frac{7}{10}\right)$$

$$= -2\frac{2}{10} + \left(-3\frac{7}{10}\right)$$ Find a common denominator.

$$= -5\frac{9}{10}$$

THINK AND DISCUSS

1. How is a rational number equation similar to an equation with integers?

2. How could you write the equation $x + \frac{1}{2} = 1\frac{5}{8}$ as an equation with decimals?

3. How could you write the equation $x + \frac{1}{2} = 10$ as an integer equation?

CLASS EXERCISES

Use a model to solve each equation.

1. $x + \frac{1}{4} = \frac{2}{3}$ **2.** $y + \frac{1}{3} = \frac{3}{4}$ **3.** $z + \left(-\frac{1}{3}\right) = 8$

Solve each equation.

4. $a + \frac{1}{8} = \frac{5}{6}$ **5.** $b + \left(-\frac{4}{5}\right) = 6$ **6.** $c - \frac{9}{10} = \frac{4}{3}$

7. $x + \left(-1\frac{1}{2}\right) = \frac{1}{4}$ **8.** $y - 4\frac{7}{8} = -2$ **9.** $z + \left(-7\frac{5}{9}\right) = -7\frac{5}{9}$

10. $g - \left(9\frac{2}{3}\right) = -10\frac{4}{5}$ **11.** $h + \left(-12\frac{1}{10}\right) = -12\frac{3}{10}$

WRITTEN EXERCISES

Write and solve an equation for each model.

1. 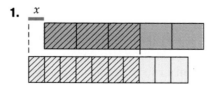   **2.**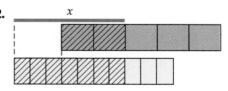

Solve each equation.

3. $m + \frac{3}{4} = \frac{1}{4}$ **4.** $p - \frac{2}{3} = 1\frac{1}{3}$ **5.** $n + \frac{5}{8} = 6$

6. $a + \frac{5}{8} = \frac{7}{12}$ **7.** $b + \left(-\frac{1}{6}\right) = \frac{3}{8}$ **8.** $c - \frac{3}{16} = -5$

9. $d - \left(\frac{-3}{10}\right) = \frac{-7}{8}$ **10.** $e - 6\frac{1}{4} = 3$ **11.** $f - \left(-4\frac{5}{12}\right) = 5\frac{3}{8}$

12. $g + 8\frac{1}{6} = 3\frac{4}{9}$ **13.** $h + \left|-2\frac{3}{4}\right| = 5\frac{7}{10}$ **14.** $k + 4.5 = 3.3$

15. $m + (-0.7) = \left|-5.4\right|$ **16.** $n - 7.23 = 10.88$

17. $p - 16.5 = -11\frac{1}{2}$ **18.** $z - 12.3 = 13\frac{1}{5}$ **19.** $q + 6.4 = 12\frac{2}{5}$

MENTAL MATH Solve each equation.

20. $a + \frac{3}{5} = \frac{4}{5}$ **21.** $b - \frac{9}{10} = -\frac{7}{10}$ **22.** $c + 2\frac{11}{12} = 3\frac{5}{12}$

23. $d + 5\frac{7}{16} = -2\frac{11}{16}$ **24.** $e - \frac{5}{8} = \frac{3}{4}$ **25.** $f + \frac{5}{6} = -\frac{7}{12}$

26. For which equations does $x = 3\frac{1}{2}$?

    a. $x + 3\frac{1}{2} = 0$ **b.** $x + \left(-\frac{7}{2}\right) = 0$ **c.** $x + \left(-\frac{4}{5}\right) = 3\frac{1}{2}$

27. WRITE Suppose you are solving the equation $x + \frac{1}{2} = \left(-3\frac{4}{5}\right)$. Without solving the equation, how can you tell that x is less than zero?

MENTAL MATH Which equations have a solution greater than 0?

28. $x + 4\frac{1}{5} = 5\frac{1}{2}$ **29.** $x - 5\frac{7}{9} = 6\frac{1}{4}$ **30.** $x + \left(-5\frac{3}{4}\right) = -5\frac{3}{4}$

Write an equation and solve.

31. Billie's tote bag weighed $3\frac{3}{16}$ lb when she left for school. When she returned home it weighed $5\frac{11}{16}$ lb. How much did she add to the weight of her tote bag? Let b represent the number of pounds she added to the weight in her tote bag.

32. On January 2, 0.26 in. of rain fell. The total rainfall for the year was 3.5 in. How much rain fell on January 1?

33. In June Jonathan's height was $68\frac{1}{2}$ in. During the school year he had grown $1\frac{5}{8}$ in. What was Jonathan's height the previous September?

Solve.

34. Some freshmen were trying out for the school track team.

After Round 1, $\frac{1}{2}$ were eliminated.

After Round 2, $\frac{1}{3}$ of those remaining were eliminated.

After Round 3, $\frac{1}{4}$ of those remaining were eliminated.

After Round 4, $\frac{1}{5}$ of those remaining were eliminated.

After Round 5, $\frac{1}{6}$ of those remaining were eliminated.

The 10 who remained became the track team. How many freshmen originally tried out?

MIXED REVIEW
Find each answer.
1. *True* or *false*?
$\left|-5\frac{3}{5}\right| = \left|5\frac{3}{5}\right|$
2. What is the opposite of $-3\frac{8}{13}$?
3. Compare $\frac{13}{36}$ and $\frac{37}{56}$.
4. Compare $\frac{7}{20}$ and $-\frac{5}{12}$.
5. $\frac{23}{30} + \left(-\frac{14}{25}\right)$
Simplify.
6. $\frac{a^3}{a^7}$ **7.** $\frac{x^3 y^7}{x^5 y^2}$
8. On Monday it rains $1\frac{1}{2}$ in. and on Tuesday it rains $1\frac{5}{8}$ in. What is the total rainfall for the two days?

PROBLEM SOLVING HINT
Try working backwards.

5-10 *Multiplication Equations*

▼ An 18-karat gold bracelet is three-fourths pure gold. Suppose a bracelet has $3\frac{1}{2}$ oz of gold. How could you represent the total weight of the bracelet with an equation?

Let x = the weight of the bracelet. Then, $\frac{3}{4} \cdot x = 3\frac{1}{2}$ is an equation that represents the situation.

▼ You can solve multiplication equations by isolating the variable and using the multiplication property of equality.

Example 1 Solve $\frac{7}{8}x = -\frac{4}{5}$.

Solution

$$\frac{8}{7} \cdot \frac{7}{8}x = \frac{8}{7} \cdot \left(-\frac{4}{5}\right)$$ Multiply both sides by the reciprocal of $\frac{7}{8}$.

$$\frac{\overset{1}{\cancel{8}} \cdot \overset{1}{\cancel{7}}}{\underset{1}{\cancel{7}} \cdot \underset{1}{\cancel{8}}}x = \frac{8 \cdot (-4)}{7 \cdot 5}$$

$$x = -\frac{32}{35}$$

▼ When equations involve mixed numbers, rewrite them as improper fractions. Then solve the equation.

Example 2 Solve $-\frac{5x}{9} = 3\frac{1}{2}$.

FLASHBACK

$-\frac{5x}{9} = -\frac{5}{9}x$

Solution

$$-\frac{5x}{9} = 3\frac{1}{2}$$

$$-\frac{5x}{9} = \frac{7}{2}$$ Write $3\frac{1}{2}$ as an improper fraction.

$$\left(-\frac{9}{5}\right) \cdot \left(-\frac{5}{9}\right)x = -\frac{9}{5} \cdot \frac{7}{2}$$ Multiply by the reciprocal.

$$x = -\frac{63}{10}$$

$$= -6\frac{3}{10}$$

▼ Some equations are false and do not have a solution.

Example 3 Solve $\frac{1}{2}|x| = -\frac{2}{9}$.

Solution

$$\frac{1}{2}|x| = -\frac{2}{9}$$

$$\frac{2}{1} \cdot \frac{1}{2}|x| = \frac{2}{1} \cdot \left(-\frac{2}{9}\right)$$ Multiply by the reciprocal.

$$|x| = -\frac{4}{9}$$

Since the absolute value of a number is never negative, $|x| \neq -\frac{4}{9}$. This is a false equation. It has no solution.

CLASS EXERCISES

Solve each equation.

1. $\frac{1}{5}x = \frac{2}{3}$

2. $-\frac{2}{7}x = \frac{3}{8}$

3. $\frac{7}{8}z = 2\frac{3}{4}$

4. $-1\frac{6}{7} \cdot x = \frac{9}{10}$

5. $4\frac{5}{8} \cdot z = 6\frac{2}{5}$

6. $\frac{2}{3}x = 2$

7. $\frac{2}{3} \cdot |x| = \frac{7}{12}$

8. $\frac{5}{9} \cdot |y| = -1\frac{1}{2}$

9. $1\frac{1}{3} \cdot |m| = 2\frac{2}{3}$

THINK AND DISCUSS

1. How would you solve the equation $\frac{3}{5} = \frac{x}{2}$?

2. How would you solve the equation $\frac{2}{3}x = 3x$? What is the value of x?

3. What is the reciprocal of x? of $\frac{1}{x}$?

WRITTEN EXERCISES

Solve each equation.

1. $\frac{2}{7}b = \frac{3}{8}$

2. $-\frac{5}{7}x = \frac{9}{10}$

3. $\frac{2}{9}z = 1\frac{4}{5}$

4. $6\frac{3}{5} \cdot x = \frac{1}{2}$

5. $\frac{2}{3}x = -8$

6. $1\frac{1}{2} \cdot m = \frac{3}{4}$

7. $\frac{3x}{4} = \frac{3}{8}$

8. $-\frac{7x}{8} = 1$

9. $\frac{1}{6}x = \frac{2}{3}$

10. $\frac{3}{4}x = -2\frac{1}{3}$

11. $\frac{1}{2}x = -0.4$

12. $\frac{-2}{3}x = 7$

Without solving, how do you know that $x < 0$?

13. $-\frac{3}{4}x = 6$

14. $\frac{-5}{-7}x = -\frac{3}{5}$

15. $\frac{5}{8}x = -1\frac{1}{2}$

For what values of x is each equation true?

16. $\frac{|x|}{5} = \frac{2}{3}$

17. $-\frac{3}{5}|x| = -1\frac{2}{3}$

18. $\frac{5}{8}|x| = -\frac{4}{5}$

19. $-2\frac{3}{4} \cdot |x| = 3\frac{1}{7}$

20. $-1\frac{2}{3} \cdot |x| = \frac{-25}{27}$

21. $4\frac{2}{5} \cdot |x| = -2\frac{1}{5}$

MIXED REVIEW

Calculate each answer.

1. $7\frac{1}{3} \cdot \left(-1\frac{3}{11}\right)$ **2.** $\frac{-5}{6} \cdot \left(-1\frac{7}{20}\right)$

3. $4\frac{1}{6} \div \frac{3}{8}$ **4.** $2.4 + 3.7$

5. $x + \left(\frac{-5}{12}\right) = \frac{7}{18}$

6. $y - (-1.6) = 3.8$

7. Compare $\frac{-7}{16}$ and $\frac{-5}{12}$.

8. Three-fifths of the freshman class intend to help with a fund raising project. There are 210 students in the class. How many will help?

Write an equation and solve each problem.

22. A sheet of plywood is $\frac{3}{4}$-in. thick. How many sheets would make a stack 9 in. high? Let s represent the number of sheets of plywood.

23. A fast-growing ivy plant grew $\frac{5}{8}$ in. each day. How many days did it take the plant to grow 12 in? Let d represent the number of days.

24. How many dimes are in $12.50? Let d represent the number of dimes.

Solve each equation. Is a >, <, or = to b?

25. $\frac{2}{3}a = \frac{5}{9}$, $\frac{3}{5}b = \frac{8}{10}$

26. $1\frac{1}{2}a = ^-6\frac{2}{3}$, $\frac{^-3}{8}b = 1\frac{2}{3}$

Solve.

27. One-fifth of the students at Lincoln High are graduating. This represents 70 students. How many students attend Lincoln High?

28. In a tree replanting project, $\frac{2}{3}$ of the trees planted survived the winter. There are 150 trees still living. Find the original number of trees planted.

29. Sara has a handful of coins. Three-fifths of the coins are dimes, one-third are nickels, and the rest are pennies. What fraction of the coins are pennies?

30. Two-thirds of the science club's members are older than fifteen. One-fifth of the members are younger than 15. Six members are exactly 15 years old. Find the number of students in the science club.

31. **_PROJECT_** While watching your favorite half-hour TV program, compute the number of minutes spent on commercials. Then count the number of different products advertised in each set of commercials.

   a. What fraction of the 30 min is program time?

   b. What fraction of the 30 min is spent on commercials?

   c. How many products are advertised?

   d. Write the number of products advertised compared to the minutes of commercial time as a fraction.

   e. Compare your results with others in the class.

Complete each analogy.

32. one-fifth : terminating decimal : : two-thirds : ▨

33. numerator : denominator : : part : ▨

34. multiplication : division : : addition : ▨

35. sum : product : : addition : ▨

36. $\frac{1}{10} : 0.10 : : \frac{1}{4} :$ ▨

37. $0.75 : \frac{3}{4} : : 0.875 :$ ▨

38. $11 : \text{prime} : : 20 :$ ▨

39. $3^4 : 81 : : 4^3 :$ ▨

40. $\frac{2}{4} : \frac{1}{2} : : \frac{3}{6} :$ ▨

41. $\frac{15}{8} : \frac{19}{7} : : 1\frac{7}{8} :$ ▨

42. $\frac{1}{3} : 0.\overline{3} : : \frac{2}{3} :$ ▨

43. $0.\overline{45} : \frac{5}{11} : : 0.\overline{63} :$ ▨

Use the article below and the data at the right to answer each question.

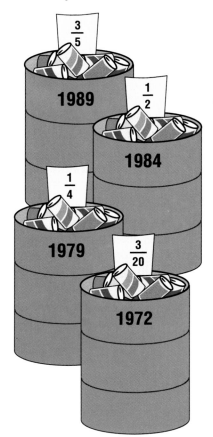

Aluminum Recycling on Rise

In 1989, Americans recycled about three-fifths of the aluminum cans produced. They returned 49 billion cans and earned $900 million. The trend toward recycling has steadily increased since 1972 when the number of recycled cans was only $\frac{3}{20}$ of the number produced. Recycling saves money and saves our environment.

44. Write each fraction as a decimal.

45. How much greater is the fraction recycled in 1989 than 1979?

46. One year $\frac{2}{5}$ of the cans produced were recycled. Would you predict the year was between 1979 and 1984 or between 1984 and 1989?

47. Would the data suggest that recycling doubled from 1979 to 1984? Why or why not?

48. *ESTIMATION* About how much is each recycled can worth?

49. The fraction of recycled cans in 1995 is predicted to be $1\frac{1}{2}$ times the number for 1989. What fraction of the cans produced would you expect to be recycled in 1995?

TEST YOURSELF

Solve each equation.

1. $\frac{2}{3} + x = 1\frac{5}{8}$

2. $a - 3\frac{1}{2} = 6\frac{3}{4}$

3. $m - (-2.5) = 1\frac{5}{8}$

4. $\frac{2}{3}x = 1\frac{5}{8}$

5. $-\frac{3}{8}y = \frac{7}{12}$

6. $2\frac{2}{3} \cdot p = -2\frac{1}{4}$

7. $\frac{x}{5} = 3\frac{3}{8}$

8. $\frac{9}{14} \cdot |x| = -4\frac{1}{2}$

9. $-\frac{2}{5} \cdot |x| = 3\frac{1}{5}$

Evaluate.

10. 3^{-2}

11. $(-1)^0$

12. $\frac{3^4}{3}$

13. $3^0 \cdot 5^{-1} \cdot 2^3$

Write with positive exponents.

14. $\frac{5n^3}{n^2}$

15. $\frac{9a^2}{3a^5}$

16. $\frac{8x^3y^2}{xy^5}$

17. $\frac{a^{-3}b^2}{a^2b^{-4}}$

OBJECTIVE:
To apply operations with rational numbers to stock market problems.

5-11 *The Stock Market*

■ Companies sell shares of stock to raise money. Stock prices appear as mixed numbers such as $3\frac{1}{8}$ for $3.125. When people buy stock, they usually use a broker who charges a commission for buying or selling stock.

KEY

- **Stock** name of company
- **Div** payment made to investors for each share held
- **High** highest price per share for the day
- **Low** lowest price per share for the day
- **Close** price of a share at the close of the day
- **Chg.** the amount of change from the previous day's closing price

Stock	Div	High	Low	Close	Chg.
DQ	1.02	$5\frac{5}{8}$	$5\frac{1}{2}$	$5\frac{1}{2}$	$-\frac{1}{8}$
MCJ	1.26	10	$9\frac{3}{4}$	$9\frac{7}{8}$	$-\frac{1}{8}$
EDL	.90	$11\frac{7}{8}$	$11\frac{5}{8}$	$11\frac{3}{4}$	$+\frac{1}{4}$
JMB	.68	$46\frac{7}{8}$	$45\frac{1}{4}$	$46\frac{5}{8}$	$+1\frac{3}{8}$
BBH	2.76	$53\frac{1}{4}$	$52\frac{3}{4}$	53	$+\frac{1}{4}$

Newspapers publish the results of stock trading daily in lists like the one at the left.

Example 1 Mr. Jitters bought 100 shares of MCJ for $9\frac{3}{4}$ per share plus a broker's fee of $19.50. He later sold the stock for $11\frac{1}{2}$ per share minus a $23 broker's fee. Did Mr. Jitters gain or lose money? How much?

Solution

$$100\left(9\frac{3}{4}\right) + 19.50 = 100(9.75) + 19.50 \quad \text{buying price}$$
$$= 994.50$$

$$100\left(11\frac{1}{2}\right) - 23 = 100(11.50) - 23 \quad \text{selling price}$$
$$= 1{,}127$$

$$1{,}127 - 994.50 = 132.50 \quad \text{difference}$$

Mr. Jitters gains $132.50.

■■■■■■ Decision Making ■ **DECISION MAKING** ■ Decision Making ■ Decision Making ■ Decision Making ■

THE STOCK MARKET

■ **COLLECT DATA**

1. Assume you have $10,000 to invest. You must choose at least four stocks and buy at least 100 shares of each stock. Find out what a PE ratio is and how you might use it to choose a stock. Also consider whether or not the stock pays a dividend. Balance your portfolio by choosing stocks in different industries.

2. Use the financial pages of the newspaper to choose your stocks. Assume a broker's fee of 0.02. Determine the cost of your investment including the broker's fee. Make a table and keep track of your portfolio for three months.

CLASS EXERCISES

Write each share price as a decimal.

1. $9\frac{7}{8}$ **2.** $4\frac{1}{2}$ **3.** $27\frac{3}{8}$ **4.** $198\frac{1}{8}$ **5.** $76\frac{3}{4}$

Find each difference. Write the gain or loss in dollars and cents.

6. $22\frac{7}{8}$ to $29\frac{1}{2}$ **7.** $115\frac{1}{4}$ to $98\frac{3}{4}$ **8.** $33\frac{1}{8}$ to $29\frac{7}{8}$

9. $37\frac{5}{8}$ to $32\frac{1}{2}$ **10.** $49\frac{3}{4}$ to $52\frac{1}{8}$ **11.** $65\frac{1}{2}$ to $67\frac{3}{8}$

Solve.

12. An investor bought 2,500 shares of XYZ Company on Monday. She kept track of the daily changes and on Friday decided to sell. Use the table at the right to answer each question. Each change number is the change from the day before.

XYZ Stock		
Day	Opening Price	Change
Mon	$29\frac{1}{2}$	
Tues		$-\frac{1}{4}$
Wed		$+4\frac{1}{8}$
Thurs		$+2\frac{1}{2}$
Fri		$-\frac{3}{4}$

   a. What was the price at the end of the week for a share of XYZ stock?

   b. How much money did the investor pay for the 2,500 shares on Monday?

   c. How much will the 2,500 shares of stock sell for on Friday?

   d. What else do you need to know to find out whether the investor made or lost money on the stock?

13. A share of stock in the ABC Company has an average weekly change of $-\frac{5}{8}$ over 14 weeks. How much less is 100 shares worth at the end of the 14-week period than at the beginning?

■ *Decision Making* ■ *Decision Making* ■ *Decision Making* ■ *Decision Making* ■ *Decision Making* ■ *Decision Making* ■

■ ANALYZE DATA

3. Which of your stocks increased in value? Which decreased?

4. How would factors such as an oil spill or news of a company's new product affect stock prices? What factors influenced the way your stocks changed?

■ MAKE DECISIONS

5. Stocks are risky investments because their value can increase or decrease. Suppose you invested $5,000 in stocks and $5,000 in a savings account. How might your financial position differ at the end of the three months? Do you think it's a good idea to invest all of your money in one stock? Why or why not?

WRITTEN EXERCISES

Write each share price as a decimal.

1. $62\frac{5}{8}$ **2.** $104\frac{3}{8}$ **3.** $77\frac{1}{8}$ **4.** $15\frac{3}{4}$ **5.** $88\frac{7}{8}$

Find each difference. Write the gain or loss in dollars and cents.

6. $17\frac{7}{8}$ to $12\frac{1}{2}$ **7.** $57\frac{3}{4}$ to $61\frac{3}{8}$ **8.** $96\frac{1}{2}$ to $95\frac{7}{8}$

9. Use the stock table on page 222.

    a. Determine the cost of buying 500 shares of each stock at the closing price. Assume a broker's commission of 0.02.

    b. Determine the dividend earned on 500 shares of each stock.

10. Use the **DATA** below to solve.

Stock	Price	Changes			
	Mon	**Tues**	**Wed**	**Thurs**	**Fri**
VEX	$9\frac{3}{8}$	$+\frac{1}{2}$	$-\frac{1}{8}$	$+2$	$+1\frac{7}{8}$
VYE	$36\frac{1}{2}$	$-1\frac{3}{8}$	$+\frac{3}{4}$	$+\frac{1}{2}$	$-\frac{1}{8}$
WITT	$111\frac{1}{4}$	$+\frac{5}{8}$	$+1\frac{1}{8}$	$+\frac{3}{4}$	$-\frac{1}{4}$
WKM	67	$-1\frac{1}{2}$	$-\frac{1}{8}$	$+\frac{1}{4}$	$-1\frac{7}{8}$
X-L	$101\frac{7}{8}$	$-3\frac{1}{4}$	$-1\frac{1}{2}$	$+3\frac{1}{8}$	$+\frac{3}{4}$

    a. What was the net change for each stock for the week?

    b. What was the closing price for each stock on Friday?

    c. Which stock showed the greatest change by Friday?

    d. Which stock had the greatest gain during the week? Explain.

    e. Which stock had the greatest loss during the week? Explain.

11. Why is the amount of a broker's commission different on the sale of stock than on the purchase when the rate is the same?

12. **WRITE** A stockholder in the ABC Company decides to sell all stock in the company based on the steady drop in market price. Is it certain that the investor is making the right move? Describe what things you think might influence the investor's decision.

13. **DATA FILE 3 (pp. 96–97)** Look at the value of the proof sets in 1965, 1968, and 1990. Which proof set seems to be the best investment? Why do you think the value of some sets increased while others decreased?

Problem Solving Practice

Solve. The list at the left shows some possible strategies you can use.

**PROBLEM SOLVING
STRATEGIES**

Look for a Pattern
Guess and Test
Simplify the Problem
Account for All Possibilities
Make an Organized List
Work Backwards
Make a Table
Write an Equation
Solve by Graphing
Draw a Diagram
Make a Model
Simulate the Problem

1. In science class there is a jar of bacteria that doubles each day. If the jar is full on the 28th day, on what day is it half full?

2. Phillip has 4 pairs of pants, 5 shirts, and 2 sweaters. How many different three-piece outfits can he make?

3. What is a four-digit number in which the first digit is half the second, the third digit is the product of the first two, and the last is the sum of the first two?

4. You check your coin collection. The total is $16. Surprisingly, you have an equal number of nickels, quarters, and half-dollars. How many coins do you have?

5. In a race Marie was faster than Sophie. Clara beat Lena but lost to Sophie. Who came in last?

6. RPM means the number of revolutions a record makes in one minute. How many more revolutions does a 45-rpm record make in 6 min than a $33\frac{1}{3}$-rpm record?

7. Clara had $30. She bought 3 packets of Morning Glory seeds at $1.98 each, 4 packets of Marigold seeds at $2.49 each, tomato plants for $5.95, and fertilizer for $2.89. How much change did she receive?

8. John found the following prices on a list of sports equipment: $3, $2, $6, $4, $9, $8. Although the list seemed a bit odd, John was sure there was a pattern. What are the next three numbers?

9. The magic square shown below has the sum of 15. An anti-magic square uses the numbers from 1–9, but the totals in any direction, including the diagonals, are different. Make an anti-magic square.

Magic Square		
4	3	8
9	5	1
2	7	6

Anti-Magic Square

10. **DATA FILE 9 (pp. 360–361)** Create a data base of the different types of golf clubs. Include these field names: club, loft, and distance. Arrange the data by distance from least to greatest.

11. Ralph bought $3\frac{1}{2}$ lb of cheese. He used $2\frac{3}{4}$ lb for cheese spread. He used the rest for sandwiches. How much did he use for sandwiches?

Chapter 5 Review

Complete each statement. Use the vocabulary words given.

1. You can form ■ by multiplying or dividing the numerator and denominator by the same nonzero factor.

2. When a fraction is in ■, the only common factor of the numerator and denominator is 1.

3. A ■ is a number you write in the form $\frac{a}{b}$ where a is an integer and b is a nonzero integer.

4. The ■ of two or more fractions is the LCM of the denominators.

5. To divide numbers or variables with the same base, subtract ■.

VOCABULARY

rational number
exponents
equivalent fractions
lowest terms
least common
  denominator

Equivalent Fractions   5-1

To form equivalent fractions, multiply or divide the numerator and denominator by the same nonzero factor.

Rename the variable to form equivalent fractions.

6. $\frac{3}{4} = \frac{a}{8}$

7. $\frac{2}{3} = \frac{4}{b}$

8. $\frac{3}{x} = \frac{12}{32}$

9. $\frac{y}{5} = \frac{16}{20}$

10. $\frac{5}{6} = \frac{c}{30}$

Fractions and Decimals   5-2

To write an improper fraction as a mixed number or as a decimal, divide the numerator by the denominator. To write a decimal as a fraction, write the decimal as a fraction with a denominator as a power of ten. Write the fraction in lowest terms.

Write each improper fraction as a mixed number and as a decimal.

11. $\frac{15}{4}$

12. $\frac{3}{2}$

13. $\frac{12}{5}$

14. $\frac{17}{6}$

15. $\frac{21}{8}$

Write each decimal as a fraction or a mixed number.

16. 0.6

17. 2.375

18. 5.25

19. 0.7

20. 0.35

Rational Numbers   5-3, 5-4

To compare rational numbers, write as fractions with a common denominator and compare the numerators, or write the fractions as decimals and compare.

Compare. Use >, <, or =.

21. $\frac{2}{3}$ ■ $\frac{3}{4}$

22. 0.9 ■ $\frac{8}{9}$

23. $-\frac{4}{5}$ ■ -0.8

24. $\left|\frac{5}{9}\right|$ ■ $\left|\frac{5}{11}\right|$

Adding and Subtracting Rational Numbers 5-5

To add or subtract rational numbers, write equivalent fractions with the same denominator, and add or subtract the numerators.

Write each sum or difference.

25. $2\frac{1}{3} + \frac{3}{4}$
26. $16\frac{4}{5} - 9\frac{2}{3}$
27. $8\frac{1}{6} + 7\frac{3}{12}$
28. $11\frac{5}{6} - 5\frac{3}{8}$

Problem Solving 5-6, 5-11

To solve some problems, you have to work backwards.

To determine the price of 100 shares, multiply the number of shares by the quoted price.

Solve.

29. It will take the Smiths 9 h to drive to Washington. They plan to make five $\frac{1}{2}$-h stops. They plan to arrive at 5:30 P.M. At what time should they plan to leave?

30. Ms. Nelson bought 500 shares of Plato Publishing at $39\frac{7}{8}$ per share. Find the cost of the 500 shares.

Multiplying and Dividing Rational Numbers 5-7

For any two rational numbers $\frac{a}{b}$ and $\frac{c}{d}$, $\frac{a}{b} \cdot \frac{c}{d} = \frac{a \cdot c}{b \cdot d}$ and $\frac{a}{b} \div \frac{c}{d} = \frac{a}{b} \cdot \frac{d}{c}$.

Find each product or quotient.

31. $\frac{3}{5} \cdot 1\frac{1}{2}$
32. $2\frac{2}{3} \cdot 3\frac{3}{8}$
33. $5\frac{1}{4} \div \frac{7}{8}$
34. $\frac{4}{5} \div 1\frac{3}{5}$

Simplifying Expressions with Exponents 5-8

To divide numbers or variables with the *same* base, subtract exponents. For any nonzero integers a and n: $a^{-n} = \frac{1}{a^n}$.

Write with positive exponents.

35. x^{-5}
36. $6a^{-1}$
37. $\frac{4m^6}{2m^2}$
38. $\frac{10b^2}{5b^3}$
39. $\frac{12x^2y^5}{4x^4y^2}$

Solving Equations 5-9, 5-10

To solve equations, use the properties of equality.

Solve each equation.

40. $x - \frac{4}{5} = \frac{1}{3}$
41. $\frac{3}{4}x = 2\frac{1}{2}$
42. $\frac{2}{5}x = -1\frac{1}{4}$
43. $x + 4\frac{2}{3} = 6$

Write a rational number for each point on the number line.

1. A **2.** B **3.** C **4.** D **5.** E **6.** F

ESTIMATION Tell whether each fraction is close to 0, $\frac{1}{2}$, or 1.

7. $\frac{7}{8}$ **8.** $\frac{7}{12}$ **9.** $\frac{21}{25}$ **10.** $\frac{2}{15}$ **11.** $\frac{16}{31}$ **12.** $\frac{5}{9}$

Write each fraction as a decimal. Write each decimal as a fraction.

13. $\frac{2}{5}$ **14.** $\frac{3}{4}$ **15.** $\frac{7}{8}$ **16.** 0.9 **17.** -0.4 **18.** 0.75

Compare. Use >, <, or =.

19. $\frac{4}{5} \blacksquare \frac{2}{3}$ **20.** $0.66 \blacksquare \frac{2}{3}$ **21.** $-\frac{7}{10} \blacksquare -0.07$ **22.** $0.875 \blacksquare \frac{7}{8}$

Find each answer.

23. $\frac{3}{8} + \frac{5}{6}$ **24.** $\frac{3}{4} \cdot 2\frac{5}{8}$ **25.** $3\frac{4}{5} - 2\frac{1}{2}$ **26.** $4\frac{2}{3} \div 1\frac{5}{6}$

27. $3 - \frac{5}{9}$ **28.** $-1\frac{1}{3} \div \left(-\frac{5}{9}\right)$ **29.** $-\frac{3}{5} - \left(-1\frac{1}{3}\right)$ **30.** $3\frac{3}{4} \cdot 2\frac{4}{5}$

31. $4\frac{3}{8} \cdot 2\frac{4}{5}$ **32.** $4\frac{3}{7} + 5\frac{4}{7}$ **33.** $-1\frac{5}{9} \cdot 2\frac{5}{8}$ **34.** $-1\frac{7}{8} + \left(-3\frac{5}{6}\right)$

Solve each equation.

35. $-\frac{7}{6} + x = \frac{5}{6}$ **36.** $\frac{3}{5}a = 9$ **37.** $n + \left(-\frac{7}{8}\right) = \frac{5}{6}$ **38.** $\frac{2}{3}k = -6$

39. $m - \left(-\frac{3}{4}\right) = 1\frac{1}{2}$ **40.** $\frac{3}{8}y = -15$ **41.** $-5b = -3\frac{1}{3}$ **42.** $r - 6.5 = -9.3$

Solve.

43. Suppose you take a number, subtract 8, multiply by 7, add 10, divide by 5, and the answer is 9. What is the original number?

44. Josie spent $\frac{3}{4}$ of her money on clothes. She had $21 left. How much money did she originally have?

45. Write a word problem for the equation $x - 1.70 = 3.50$.

46. Find the price of 1,000 shares of Universal Tractor stock at $21\frac{5}{8}$ per share.

Chapters 1–5   Cumulative Review

Choose the correct answer. Write A, B, C, or D.

1. Evaluate $(-1)^{27}$.

  A. 1   **B.** 1×10^{27}

  C. -1 **D.** not given

2. Write $\frac{3x^2y}{12xy^2}$ in lowest terms.

  A. $\frac{1}{4}$ **B.** $\frac{2y}{4xy}$

  C. $\frac{x}{4y}$ **D.** not given

3. Which number is written in scientific notation?

  A. 0.5×10^6 **B.** 1.5×10^6

  C. 1.5×6^6 **D.** not given

4. Solve $\frac{2}{3}x = 2\frac{2}{9}$.

  A. $\frac{3}{10}$ **B.** $3\frac{1}{3}$

  C. $2\frac{8}{9}$ **D.** not given

5. Write $\frac{28}{3}$ as a mixed number.

  A. $3\frac{1}{3}$ **B.** $4\frac{1}{3}$

  C. $7\frac{2}{3}$ **D.** not given

6. $(0.0056)(-3.5)$

  A. -0.196 **B.** -0.00196

  C. -0.0196 **D.** not given

7. Identify the property used.
$$(x^2y^3)x^0 = x^2y^3$$

  A. associative   **B.** identity

  C. commutative   **D.** not given

8. The GCF of 25 and 50 is ▨.

  A. 10   **B.** 5

  C. 2   **D.** not given

9. Which number is divisible by 3 and 9?

  A. 663   **B.** 879

  C. 864   **D.** not given

10. Without computing, state the sign of $2(-4)(-9) + 100$.

  A. positive   **B.** negative

  C. zero   **D.** not given

11. Linda is 12 years older than Jill. The sum of their ages is 38. Find their ages.

  A. 12 and 26   **B.** 12 and 38

  C. 5 and 17   **D.** not given

12. Simplify $\frac{5a^3b^{-2}}{15a^2b^3}$.

  A. $\frac{a}{3b^5}$ **B.** $3ab^{-1}$

  C. $\frac{ab}{3}$ **D.** not given

13. Compare $\left|2\frac{1}{4}\right|$ ▨ $\left|-\frac{9}{4}\right|$.

  A. $>$ **B.** $<$

  C. $=$ **D.** not given

14. Find the number of times at bat in the formula $a = \frac{h}{n}$ for $a = 0.25$ and $h = 25$.

  A. 625   **B.** 50

  C. 100   **D.** not given

15. Find the LCD of $\frac{7}{12}$ and $\frac{5}{18}$.

  A. 35   **B.** 6

  C. 72   **D.** not given

16. $3\frac{1}{2} - 5\frac{3}{8} = $ ▨.

  A. $-2\frac{1}{8}$ **B.** $-1\frac{7}{8}$

  C. $-2\frac{7}{8}$ **D.** not given

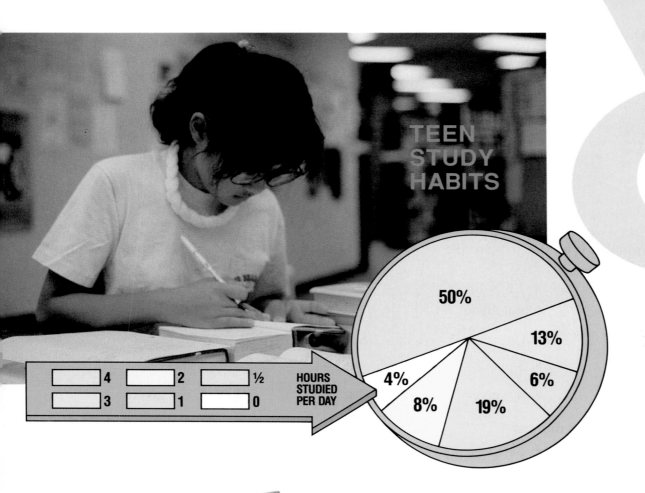

TEEN
STUDY
HABITS

| | 4 | | 2 | | ½ |
| | 3 | | 1 | | 0 |

HOURS
STUDIED
PER DAY

50%

13%

6%

19%

4%

8%

WHO'S GOING TO THE STORE?

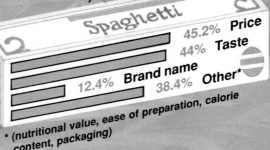

FORECAST MAGAZINE polled
1,000 high school students
about their grocery
shopping.
Here are some of the results.

Do you ever shop for food
for your family?

FEMALES

Yes 94%

No 6%

MALES

Yes 90%

No 10%

What is the most important factor in
selecting a food item? (Many teens chose
more than one.)

45.2% Price

44% Taste

12.4% Brand name   Other*

38.4% Other*

* (nutritional value, ease of preparation, calorie
content, packaging)

CHAPTER 6

Ratios, Proportions, and Percent

▶ **TEENAGE RESEARCH UNLIMITED (TRU)** of Northbrook, IL, developed the Teenage Buying Control Index (TBC). TRU asked teens whether they or their parents make the buying decision for a list of products. An index number of 100 means the teen makes the decision. An index number of 0 means the parent makes the decision.

TEENAGE BUYING CONTROL INDEX (TBC)		
ITEM	**MALES**	**FEMALES**
Book	63	63
Poster	78	78
Camera Film	54	53
Health and Beauty Aids	31	42
Food	39	39
Clothing	38	39
Audio/Video	55	48
School Supplies	46	52

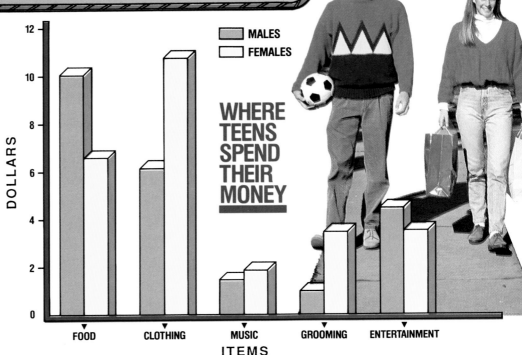

WHERE TEENS SPEND THEIR MONEY

Think about it...

Look at the data from TRU. Why are some items on the TBC rated higher than others? How do you think advertisers might use the index?

OBJECTIVE:
Use activities to explore ratios.

Exploring Ratios

▼ What do batting averages, pass completions, first down statistics, and free-throw averages have in common? They are all *ratios*. Each statistic compares two numbers by division.

MATERIALS

- Waste basket
- Wadded up sheet of paper
- Math journal to record work

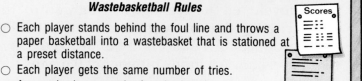

Wastebasketball Rules

○ Each player stands behind the foul line and throws a paper basketball into a wastebasket that is stationed at a preset distance.
○ Each player gets the same number of tries.
○ A recorder keeps track of each player's attempts and successes.
○ Each player computes the ratio $\frac{\text{baskets}}{\text{attempts}}$.

Play a game of wastebasketball and compute your own ratios.

Player	Attempts	Baskets	Free-throw Average (Ratio)

1. **Compare** with another group. Are the averages close?

2. Change the conditions. Then play more games.

   a. Change the distance to the basket.

   b. Change the number of attempts.

3. Compute new statistics. Which variable has the greatest impact? Is it different for different people?

4. Compute team statistics. **Compare** with other groups. Are the averages close?

5. **Discuss** what you can conclude from the statistics. If you make 2 baskets out of 2 tries, is your ratio better than someone who gets 7 out of 10? 15 out of 20?

6. **Write** Would it be fair to judge a player's ability on one game's free-throw average? Why or why not?

7. **PROJECT** How does the ratio relate to the number of tries? Look up lifetime free-throw averages for five basketball players. Compare to averages for players in one game and over a season. What impact does the number of attempts have on the average?

6-1 Ratios, Proportions, and Rates

▼ Statistics show that 10 out of 25 people in the United States have brown eyes. The numbers 10 and 25 form a *ratio*. You can write a ratio in three different ways:

$$10 \text{ to } 25; \quad 10:25; \quad \frac{10}{25}$$

You can express a ratio as a fraction in lowest terms.

$$\frac{10}{25} = \frac{2}{5}$$

READ 10 is to 25 as 2 is to 5. You can say that two out of five people have brown eyes.

Ratio	A ratio is a comparison of two quantities by division.
	Arithmetic **Algebra**
	1 to 2; 1 : 2; $\frac{1}{2}$ a to b; $a:b$; $\frac{a}{b}$ $b \neq 0$

▼ You can write ratios that compare $\frac{part}{part}$, $\frac{part}{whole}$, and $\frac{whole}{part}$.

Example 1   In a survey of 100 students, 60 reported having after school jobs. Write three ratios for the data.

Solution

$$\frac{60 \text{ students with jobs}}{40 \text{ students without jobs}} \qquad \frac{\text{part}}{\text{part}}$$

$$\frac{60 \text{ students with jobs}}{100 \text{ all students surveyed}} \qquad \frac{\text{part}}{\text{whole}}$$

$$\frac{100 \text{ all students surveyed}}{60 \text{ students with jobs}} \qquad \frac{\text{whole}}{\text{part}}$$

▼ When two ratios are equal they form a *proportion*.

Proportion	A proportion is a statement that two ratios are equal. If two ratios are equal, their cross products are equal.
	Arithmetic **Algebra**
	6 is to 9 as 8 is to 12 a is to b as c is to d
	6 : 9 : : 8 : 12 $a : b : : c : d$
	$\frac{6}{9} = \frac{8}{12}$ $\frac{a}{b} = \frac{c}{d}$ $b \neq 0, d \neq 0$

Example 2   The directions for making orange juice from concentrate call for 4 cans of water to 1 can of concentrate. So, for 2 cans of concentrate you would need 8 cans of water. The following proportion describes the situation.

$$\frac{1}{4} = \frac{2}{8}$$

▼ You can write *rates* and *unit rates* to describe many situations.

▼

THINK What rate describes money earned? mileage?

▼

THINK What proportion would you write to describe the number of minutes it takes to blink once?

Rate	A rate is a ratio that compares quantities in different units. A unit rate compares a quantity to one.

Example 3 On average, a person blinks 100 times in 4 min. How many times does a person blink in one minute?

Solution $\dfrac{100}{4} = \dfrac{t}{1} = \dfrac{\text{number of blinks}}{\text{number of minutes}}$ Write a ratio to describe the the situation.

$4t = 100$ Write cross products.

$\dfrac{4t}{4} = \dfrac{100}{4}$ Divide both sides by 4.

$t = 25$

On average, a person blinks 25 times per minute.

Example 4 A car travels 264 mi on 12 gal of gas. Find the unit rate in miles per gallon.

Solution $\dfrac{264}{12} = \dfrac{x}{1}$

$264 \boxed{\div} 12 \boxed{=} 22$

$x = 22$ mi/gal

▼

THINK AND DISCUSS

1. You know that 2 in 5 people have brown eyes. How many people do *not* have brown eyes? Explain.

2. The ratios $\frac{a}{b}$ and $\frac{c}{d}$ form a proportion. How can you use cross products to express the relationship between *a*, *b*, *c*, and *d* as an equation without using fractions?

3. A student claims that a ratio would remain unchanged if 1 is added to both the numerator and the denominator of the fraction as in $\frac{a}{b} = \frac{a+1}{b+1}$. Is the student correct? Explain your decision.

CLASS EXERCISES

Write each ratio as a fraction in lowest terms.

1. 9 : 27   **2.** 10 out of 16   **3.** 12 is to 8

4. 6 people in 50 are over 65 years of age.

5. 1 person in 18 plays the piano.

Write three ratios to describe each figure.

6. 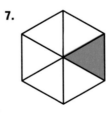   **7.** 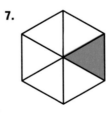   **8.**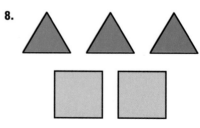

Write each ratio as a unit rate.

9. A bathtub contains 20 gal of water. The tub empties in 4 min. What is the rate of flow per minute?

10. A sprinter completes 200 m in 22 s.

11. A keyboarder types 1,575 words in 25 min.

WRITTEN EXERCISES

Write each ratio as a fraction in lowest terms.

1. 3 : 8   **2.** 7 is to 9   **3.** 8 out of 11   **4.** 14 out of 18

5. 15 : 25   **6.** 36 is to 48   **7.** 60 is to 24   **8.** 16 : 12

9. 25 homes out of 125 have a personal computer.

10. 3 out of 12 people live in a rural area.

11. 4 people out of 24 attend school.

12. 20 homes in 25 have a TV.

13. 6 of 24 people live in a household composed of three people.

14. 7 of 35 people live in a household composed of four people.

15. 6 of 42 people live in a household composed of five or more people.

Write three ratios to describe each figure.

16.    **17.**    **18.**

Use graph paper to draw a model of each ratio.

19. $\frac{3}{6}$ **20.** 12 : 36   **21.** 5 out of 8   **22.** 9 : 10

23. PROJECT Survey at least ten people. Find the number of people living in each household. Use your data to write ratios showing the number of people who live in a household composed of three or fewer people, of four people, and of more than four people. Compare your ratios with the statistics in Exercises 13–15.

Compare. Write = or ≠. Then tell which pairs of ratios form a proportion.

24. $\frac{4}{7}$ ▧ $\frac{20}{35}$ **25.** $\frac{3}{2}$ ▧ $\frac{16}{10}$ **26.** $\frac{3}{4}$ ▧ $\frac{12}{15}$ **27.** $\frac{8}{3}$ ▧ $\frac{56}{21}$

28. $\frac{9}{24}$ ▧ $\frac{15}{40}$ **29.** $\frac{32}{20}$ ▧ $\frac{20}{12}$ **30.** $\frac{40}{24}$ ▧ $\frac{75}{45}$ **31.** $\frac{7}{8}$ ▧ $\frac{8}{9}$

CALCULATOR Write = or ≠. Then tell which pairs of ratios form a proportion.

32. $\frac{75}{90}$ ▧ $\frac{90}{108}$ **33.** $\frac{120}{144}$ ▧ $\frac{145}{75}$ **34.** $\frac{215}{155}$ ▧ $\frac{270}{165}$ **35.** $\frac{192}{144}$ ▧ $\frac{256}{192}$

Express each as a unit rate.

36. 20 mi in 5 h

37. 42 gal in 7 min

38. a fall of 144 ft in 3 s

39. 12 hits in 66 times at bat

40. 68 baskets in 119 throws

41. 245 mi in 56 h

42. 676 mi in 13 h

43. 78 hits in 260 times at bat

Write three ratios to describe each situation.

44. For every five victories, the baseball team lost one game.

45. For every fifty radios sold, two were returned for a refund.

46. A bookstore sells paperbacks, hardbacks, and magazines. For every three paperbacks sold, five hardbacks are also sold. For every ten hardbacks sold, twenty magazines are sold.

Write a ratio to describe each situation. Decide if the rates form a proportion. Solve each problem.

47. In one classroom, 4 of the 24 students are boys. In another classroom, 6 of the 30 students are boys. Is the ratio of boys to total number of students the same in both classes?

48. A subcompact car travels 196 mi on 7 gal of gas. A compact travels 336 mi on 12 gal of gas. Is the fuel economy of both cars the same?

49. Two cans of beans cost $1.69. Five cans cost $3.98. Is the ratio of cans to cost the same? If not, which is the better buy? Explain.

50. *DATA FILE 3 (pp. 96–97)* Suppose you turn in $\frac{1}{2}$ of a 20-dollar bill. How much will you get?

51. Use the article below to answer each question.

   a. Write the ratio of sap to syrup in three different ways.

   b. Write the cost of syrup per pint as a ratio.

   c. Write the cost of syrup per gallon as a ratio.

A Sappy Story

Vermont is renowned as a major producer of maple syrup. It is a little known fact, however, that more than 100 farms in Connecticut also produce maple syrup. Sugarers collect sap daily and boil it down to make syrup. In a good year, one small sugarer in Connecticut collects 300 gal of sap from 200 trees. The sap boils down to just 7 gal of syrup. The syrup is sold for $4.50 per half pint or $44 per gallon.

OBJECTIVE:
To use proportions to solve problems.

6-2 *Solving Proportions*

▼ An average adult's heart beats 8 times every 6 s. At this rate, how many times does it beat in 120 s? You can write a proportion to describe the situation. Let x = the number of heartbeats in 120 s.

$$\frac{8}{6} = \frac{x}{120} \qquad \leftarrow \text{number of heartbeats}$$
$$\qquad\qquad \leftarrow \text{ number of seconds}$$
$$6x = 8 \cdot 120 \qquad \text{Write the cross products.}$$
$$6x = 960 \qquad \text{Divide both sides by 6.}$$
$$x = 160$$

The average person's heart beats 160 times in 120 s.

▼ You can use cross products to solve a proportion.

Example 1 A canary's heart beats 130 times in 12 s. At this rate, how many times does it beat in 30 s?

Solution
$$\frac{130}{12} = \frac{x}{30} \qquad\qquad\qquad \text{Write a proportion.}$$
$$130 \cdot 30 = 12x \qquad\qquad \text{Write the cross products.}$$
$$3{,}900 \div 12 = 12x \div 12 \qquad \text{Divide both sides by 12.}$$
$$325 = x$$

A canary's heart beats 325 times in 30 s.

▼ You can use a calculator to help you solve a proportion.

Example 2 Solve $\frac{x}{3.5} = \frac{35}{8.75}$ for x.

Solution
$$\frac{x}{3.5} = \frac{35}{8.75}$$
$$8.75x = 3.5 \cdot 35 \qquad\qquad\qquad \text{Write the cross products.}$$
$$3.5 \,\boxed{\times}\, 35 \,\boxed{\div}\, 8.75 \,\boxed{=}\, 14 \qquad \text{Use a calculator to solve.}$$
$$x = 14$$

THINK How is writing cross products an application of the multiplication property of equality?

Solving Proportions	To solve a proportion:
	1. Write the cross products.
	2. Solve the equation.

▼ Express quantities in the same units before solving proportions.

Example 3 Ribbon costs $3 for 15 in. Find the cost of 3 ft of ribbon.

Solution
$$\frac{15 \text{ in.}}{\$3} = \frac{3 \text{ ft}}{d} \qquad\qquad \text{Write a proportion.}$$
$$\frac{15}{3} = \frac{36}{d} \qquad\qquad\qquad \text{Write 3 ft as 36 in.}$$
$$15d = 108 \qquad\qquad\qquad \text{Solve the proportion for } d.$$
$$d = 7.20$$

It costs $7.20 for 3 ft of ribbon.

CLASS EXERCISES

Solve.

1. $\frac{4}{11} = \frac{x}{16.5}$ **2.** $\frac{7}{12} = \frac{17.5}{y}$ **3.** $\frac{z}{5.4} = \frac{13}{18}$ **4.** $\frac{2}{v} = \frac{1}{8}$

Write a proportion to describe each situation. Then solve.

5. 3 oz of nuts cost $1.70; 5 oz cost x dollars.

6. A student runs 24 yd in $2\frac{1}{2}$ s; 100 yd in x seconds.

7. 50 calories in 4 oz of orange juice; x calories in 14 oz.

8. A lion's heart beats 12 times in 16 s; x times in 60 s.

Each pair of figures is in proportion. Find the missing length.

9.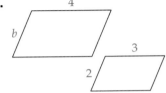

10.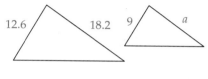

WRITTEN EXERCISES

Solve.

1. $\frac{4}{15} = \frac{a}{75}$ **2.** $\frac{4}{3} = \frac{b}{21}$ **3.** $\frac{13}{c} = \frac{39}{60}$ **4.** $\frac{3}{6} = \frac{7}{d}$

5. $\frac{6}{25} = \frac{e}{80}$ **6.** $\frac{4}{9} = \frac{f}{15}$ **7.** $\frac{3}{8} = \frac{50}{g}$ **8.** $\frac{24}{17} = \frac{108}{h}$

9. $\frac{7}{9} = \frac{j}{22.5}$ **10.** $\frac{11}{18} = \frac{k}{49.5}$ **11.** $\frac{6}{13} = \frac{7.8}{m}$ **12.** $\frac{20}{27} = \frac{1.1}{n}$

Each pair of figures is in proportion. Find the missing length.

13. $x \,\boxed{}$ $\underset{12}{\boxed{}}\,3$
  4

14.

Write a proportion to describe each situation. Then solve.

15. 4 oz of cheese costs $1.85; $1\frac{1}{2}$ lb costs t dollars.

16. A baseball player gets 54 hits in 225 times at bat; x hits in 500 times at bat.

17. A student runs 5 km in 18 min 36 s; 8 km in v min.

18. 20 lb of dog food costs $27.50; 12 lb costs x dollars.

19. 96 oz costs $2.25; y pounds costs $10.

20. A rectangle measuring 20 cm by 28 cm is reduced to one measuring 9 cm by z cm.

21. Three tea bags are used to make a gallon of iced tea. How many tea bags are needed to make four gallons?

22. At the Copy Shoppe, 18 copies cost $1.08. At the same rate, how much will 40 copies cost?

23. The cost of 3 posters is $9.60. Find the cost of 15 posters.

24. *DATA FILE 10 (pp. 404–405)* What would be the home range, in acres, for a pack of 30 gray wolves?

25. A microchip inspector found three defects in a batch containing 750 chips. How many defects should the inspector find in a batch of 10,000 chips?

26. A truck driver estimated that it would take him 12 h to drive 1,160 km. After 5 h, he had driven 480 km. Is he on target? Explain.

27. *PROJECT* How would you describe your class? Use the list of questions at the right or questions of your own. Interview your classmates and tally all the responses. Write ratios to describe the results.

Use the relationship $x \blacktriangleright y = \frac{x + y}{x}$ for exercises 28–35. Evaluate each expression.

▼▼ *SAMPLE* $3 \blacktriangleright 5 = \frac{3 + 5}{3} = \frac{8}{3}$

28. $2 \blacktriangleright 3$ **29.** $3 \blacktriangleright 4$ **30.** $5 \blacktriangleright -4$ **31.** $-7 \blacktriangleright 9$

Write *yes* or *no* to tell if each is proportional to $\frac{1}{3}$.

32. $-1 \blacktriangleright -3$ **33.** $2 \blacktriangleright 6$ **34.** $-15 \blacktriangleright 10$ **35.** $5 \blacktriangleright -3$

Solve.

36. If $\frac{y}{25} = \frac{6}{30}$, find the ratio of y to 6.

37. If $\frac{10}{100} = \frac{r}{30}$, find the ratio of r to 10.

38. If $\frac{15}{75} = \frac{30}{f}$, find the ratio of f to 75.

39. If $\frac{12}{p} = \frac{1}{3}$, find the ratio of p to 3.

40. An artist mixes red and blue paint to make purple paint in the ratio of 2 : 3. This tells you that for every 2 parts of red there are 3 parts of blue. What does each ratio tell you about the mixture of red and blue paint?

    a. $6 : 9$ **b.** $1 : 1.5$ **c.** $10 : 15$ **d.** $20 : 30$

Complete.

41. $3:15 = 1:5$ because $15 = 3 \cdot 5$ and $\blacksquare = \blacksquare \cdot 15$

42. $15:6 = 5:2$ because $\blacksquare = 15 \cdot 2$ and $\blacksquare = 6 \cdot \blacksquare$

43. $8:2 = 16:4$ because $\blacksquare = \blacksquare \cdot 4$ and $\blacksquare = \blacksquare \cdot 2$

44. $6.5:2.5 = 19.5:7.5$ because $\blacksquare = 6.5 \cdot \blacksquare$ and $2.5 \cdot \blacksquare$

Human Heartbeats

Age (years)	Heartbeat
Newborn	140/min
1 y	120/min
6 y	100/min
10 y	90/min
12 y	85/min
Adult	80/min

Use the *DATA* at the left to solve each problem.

45. In how many seconds will a newborn's heart beat 35 times?

46. In how many seconds will a 12-year-old's heart beat 25 times?

47. How many times does an adult's heart beat in 270 s?

48. How many more times does a newborn's heart beat in 45 s than a 6-year-old child's heart?

49. About how many times will an adult's heart beat in one year?

50. *PROJECT* Find examples of heartbeat rates during different activities, such as sleeping, running, reading, and so on. Then take your pulse to determine your own heartbeat rate. Compare to see how close your rate is to the average heartbeat rates.

Critical Thinking

EXPLORING VENN DIAGRAMS

Study the numbers in each circle. How are they alike? How are they different?

Write a sentence to describe each.

1. the numbers in Circle A

2. the numbers in Circle B

3. the numbers in Circle C

4. Describe the numbers that fit in the intersection of A and B.

5. What numbers fit in the intersection of B and C?

6. Would 11 fit in B? in the intersection of B and C?

7. Are there other numbers that fit in the intersection of A and B? Why or why not?

8. Draw your own Venn diagram to classify sets of numbers. Trade with a classmate and describe each other's diagrams.

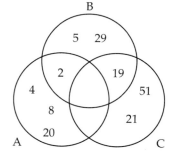

6-3 Scale Drawing

■ Maps and floor plans are examples of *scale drawings*. Sizes in scale drawings are usually smaller than the actual sizes. However, if you sketch something you're observing through a microscope, your measurements will be greater than the actual measurements.

Example 1   On the map below, 1 cm represents about 84 km. What is the air distance between Lubbock and Abilene?

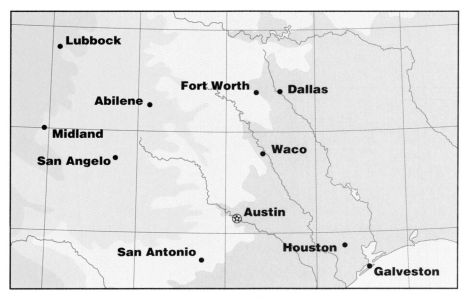

SCALE: 1 cm: 84 km

Solution   Measure the distance on the map with a centimeter ruler. The map distance is about 2.9 cm. Write and solve a proportion.

$$\frac{1}{84} = \frac{2.9}{d} \qquad \text{Let } d = \text{actual distance.}$$

$$1 \cdot d = 84 \cdot 2.9 \qquad \text{Use cross products.}$$

$$d = 243.6$$

The air distance is about 244 km.

CLASS EXERCISES

Use the map above. Round to the nearest 5 km.

1. What is the air distance from Midland to Dallas?

2. Which city on the map is about 285 km from Ft. Worth?

3. A plane flies from San Angelo to Houston and then on to Galveston. About how far does it travel in all?

BEDROOM AND BATH AREA

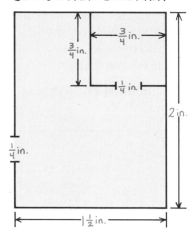

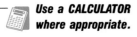

WRITTEN EXERCISES

The length of the bedroom and bath area in the diagram at the left is 2 in. The actual length is 20 ft. Use the diagram to solve.

1. What is the scale for the diagram?

2. How many feet wide are the doors leading into the bedroom and into the bath?

3. How wide is the widest part of the bedroom?

4. Could a bed 6 ft long and 3 ft wide fit into the narrow section of the bedroom? Does it matter along which wall the bed is placed? Explain.

5. Suppose you want to make a scale drawing of a rectangular dance floor that is 90 ft long and 75 ft wide. Can you fit the drawing on a piece of paper that measures $8\frac{1}{2}$ in. by 11 in. if your scale is 1 in. : 9 ft? Explain.

6. In a scale drawing, Marco plans to use $\frac{1}{2}$ in. to represent 1 ft. The room he wants to show in the drawing is 16 ft 3 in. long. To the nearest half-inch, what will be the length in the scale drawing?

▪▪▪▪▪▪ Decision Making ▪ *DECISION MAKING* ▪ Decision Making ▪ Decision Making ▪ Decision Making ▪

SCALE DRAWING

▪ COLLECT DATA

1. Choose a furnished room in your home. Measure its length and width to the nearest inch. Measure the width of each door and window. Then measure the distance that each door, window, and unmovable piece of furniture is from the nearest corner.

2. Measure the movable furniture so that you can tell how much floor space it occupies.

▪ ANALYZE DATA

3. Make a scale drawing of the room, showing windows, doors, and any unmovable furniture. Then make and cut out a scale model for each piece of movable furniture. Position the cutouts on the scale drawing to show the location of each piece of furniture.

Each piece of a model railroad built on the HO scale is $\frac{1}{87}$ the size of an actual railroad part. The N scale, where models are $\frac{1}{160}$ the size of the real thing, is another popular scale.

7. Which models are smaller, HO or N scale models?

8. Each car on a full-size passenger train is 80 ft long.

   a. What is the length, in inches, of a model passenger car, using the HO scale? using the N scale?

   b. What is the length of a model train with eight cars, using the HO scale? using the N scale?

9. A diesel electric locomotive is 60 ft long. How long is the model locomotive using the N scale?

10. A boxcar on a freight train is 40 ft long. A model boxcar is $\frac{1}{4}$ ft long. In what scale was the model built, HO or N?

11. You are building a table for your HO-scale model train set. Your railroad includes a passenger train 12 cars long. Each car is 1.2 ft long. How long must your table be for the cars to fit end-to-end?

12. Toy trains are larger than most model trains. Using the O scale, a toy train is $\frac{1}{48}$ the size of an actual train. A toy locomotive is 1.04 ft long. How long is the real locomotive?

■ **Decision Making** ■ **Decision Making** ■ **Decision Making** ■ **Decision Making** ■ **Decision Making** ■ **Decision Making** ■

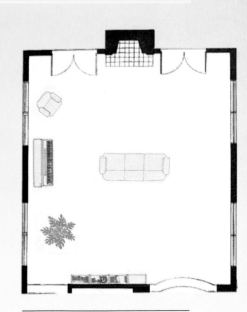

4. Look at the furniture in the room. Analyze the placement of each piece to make the most efficient use of light, traffic patterns, and so on.

5. Move your cutouts to try different furniture arrangements. What floor plan do you like the best? Why?

■ **MAKE DECISIONS**

6. Decide on two pieces of furniture that might be good additions to the room. Find out their dimensions as accurately as you can.

7. Make flat, to-scale cutouts for the new furniture. Work with the cutouts to decide on one or two good ways to arrange all the items in the room. You may remove two other pieces of furniture from the room if necessary. State some of the points you considered in making your decision.

OBJECTIVE:
Use models to explore percents.

___

MATERIALS

- Graph paper

- Math journal to record work

___

Exploring Percents

▼   A *percent* is a ratio that compares a number to 100. You can use a decimal model to show percents.

1. Each grid has 100 squares. Write a ratio and a percent to describe the shaded part.

   a.   **b.**   **c.**

2. Use graph paper to model each percent.

   a. 20%   **b.** 60%   **c.** 73%   **d.** 5%

3. Compare with others in your group. Do all your models look the same? Do they all show the same percents?

4. Write a ratio and a percent to describe the shaded part of each figure.

   a.   **b.**   **c.**   **d.**

   e. *Discuss* how ratios and percents are like fractions.

▼   You can model percents greater than 100 and less than 1.

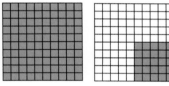

   100%   +   25%   = 125% $\frac{1}{2}$ of 1% = 0.5%

5. Use graph paper to model each percent.

   a. 150%   **b.** 170%   **c.** 0.25%   **d.** 0.75%

▼   You can use number sense to estimate percents. You know that $\frac{1}{100}$ is 1% so $\frac{1}{200}$ is less than 1%.

6. Which fractions are less than 1%? *Write* a rule to tell when a fraction equals a percent less than 1%.

   a. $\frac{2}{400}$ **b.** $\frac{300}{500}$ **c.** $\frac{1}{1,000}$ **d.** $\frac{500}{1,000}$

OBJECTIVE:
To express ratios and
rates as percents.

6-4 Percent

▼ In a recent survey, 25 people out of 100 said they buy a newspaper every day. When you compare a number to 100, you are finding a *percent*.

Percent (%) means *per hundred*. You can express 25 out of 100 as 25% (25 percent). You can say that 25% of the people buy a daily newspaper.

Percent	A percent is a ratio that compares a number to 100.

▼ You can express a ratio as a percent.

Example 1   **Express each ratio as a percent.**

    a. 5 out of 100   **b.** 4 out of 5

Solution   **a.** $\dfrac{5}{100} = 5\%$ **b.** $\dfrac{4}{5} = \dfrac{x}{100}$ Write and solve a proportion.

$$= \dfrac{80}{100}$$

$$= 80\%$$

▼ You can write proportions to solve percent problems.

Example 2   In a survey, 57 out of 90 ninth graders said they received an allowance. What percent is this?

Solution $\dfrac{57}{90} = \dfrac{n}{100}$ Write a proportion.

$90n = 5{,}700$ Write cross products.

$\dfrac{90n}{90} = \dfrac{5{,}700}{90}$ Divide both sides by 90.

$n = 63.\overline{3}$

$\approx 63\%$ Write a percent.

▼ You can write a decimal as a fraction with a denominator of 100 before writing as a percent.

Example 3   **Write each decimal as a percent.**

    a. 0.62   **b.** 0.03   **c.** 0.005   **d.** 1.25

Solution   **a.** $0.62 = \dfrac{62}{100}$ **b.** $0.03 = \dfrac{3}{100}$

$$= 62\% \qquad\qquad\qquad\qquad = 3\%$$

     c. $0.005 = \dfrac{0.5}{100}$ **d.** $1.25 = \dfrac{125}{100}$

$$= 0.5\% \qquad\qquad\qquad\qquad = 125\%$$

During the time of Columbus, the words *per cento,* derived from the Latin form *per centum,* were used to indicate *per hundred.* Later, the words were abbreviated and the term slowly changed its form to the symbol we use today.

Columbus's era

Today

THINK AND DISCUSS

1. Why is it possible to write a decimal as a percent by moving the decimal two places to the right? Justify your answer and give examples.

2. Which do you think is easiest to compare: ratios, decimals, or percents? Explain.

▼ You can use the following rule to write decimals as percents.

Decimals to Percents	To write decimals as percents, move the decimal point two places to the right and write the percent sign.

▼ You can use a calculator to write fractions as decimals before writing as percents.

Example 4 **Write as a percent.**

    a. $\dfrac{3}{8}$ **b.** $\dfrac{5}{400}$ **c.** $1\dfrac{2}{3}$ **d.** $2\dfrac{1}{4}$

Solution   **a.** $3 \div 8 = 0.375$
              $= 37.5\%$

        b. $5 \div 400 = 0.0125$
                       $= 1.25\%$

    c. $5 \div 3 = 1.6\ldots$
              $\approx 167\%$

        d. $9 \div 4 = 2.25$
                   $= 225\%$

CLASS EXERCISES

Write each fraction as a percent. Round to the nearest tenth.

1. $\dfrac{23}{100}$ **2.** $\dfrac{1}{4}$ **3.** $\dfrac{11}{20}$ **4.** $\dfrac{1}{6}$

Write each ratio as a percent. Round to the nearest tenth.

5. $28 : 40$ **6.** $60 : 150$ **7.** $75 : 39$ **8.** $20 : 36$

Write each decimal as a percent.

9. 1.68 **10.** 0.36 **11.** 0.70 **12.** 0.002

13. Write a percent to describe each situation.

    a. 4 out of 16 people live in a rural area.

    b. What percent do *not* live in a rural area?

WRITTEN EXERCISES

Write each ratio as a percent. Round to the nearest tenth.

1. $15 : 20$ **2.** $6 : 30$ **3.** $30 : 48$ **4.** $22 : 80$

5. $28 : 48$ **6.** $32 : 56$ **7.** $84 : 60$ **8.** $72 : 54$

Write each decimal as a percent. Round to the nearest tenth.

9. 0.33 **10.** 0.35 **11.** 0.06 **12.** 0.0075

13. 0.045   **14.** 0.375   **15.** 1.88   **16.** 2.59

Write each fraction as a percent. Round to the nearest tenth.

17. $\frac{79}{100}$ **18.** $\frac{29}{50}$ **19.** $\frac{3}{10}$ **20.** $\frac{7}{20}$

21. $\frac{17}{25}$ **22.** $\frac{3}{50}$ **23.** $\frac{111}{100}$ **24.** $\frac{27}{80}$

CALCULATOR Write each fraction as a percent. Round to the nearest
tenth.

25. $\frac{2}{9}$ **26.** $\frac{5}{6}$ **27.** $\frac{7}{16}$ **28.** $\frac{18}{11}$

ESTIMATION About what percent of each flag is red?

29.   **30.**   **31.**

   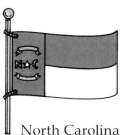   

Tennessee   North Carolina   Arizona

Copy and complete the table.

	Fraction	Decimal	Percent
32.	$\frac{4}{5}$		
33.		0.10	
34.		0.5	
35.	$\frac{3}{4}$		
36.			67
37.			25

Solve. Round to the nearest tenth.

38. Jamie scored 31 correct on a 45-item test. The passing grade is
70%. Did Jamie pass?

39. A scale drawing needs to be enlarged by a factor of 1.12. Express
this as a percent.

40. A map was drawn to a scale of 0.725% of the original. Express this
as a decimal.

41. A student committee has 15 members. Nine voted in favor of a
smoking ban. What percent is this?

42. In a ball-throwing contest, Player A scores 30 hits out of 35 shots. Player B scores 0.85 of her throws and Player C's rate is 85.5%. Which player has the best record?

43. At a local high school, 560 out of 1,060 students voted to support a community fund drive. What percent of the students did not support the fund drive?

44. A crowd filled the 8,000 seats at a football stadium. There were 1,500 children and 5,600 men present. Write a ratio and a percent that describes how many seats were filled by:

   a. men   **b.** children   **c.** women

45. A student is a member of a 4-person relay team. What percent of the distance will she run in a race?

Compare. Use >, <, or =.

46. $\frac{7}{12}$ ■ 60%   **47.** 0.0325 ■ 32.5%   **48.** $\frac{5}{8}$ ■ 0.625

49. 0.05% ■ 50%   **50.** $\frac{7}{8}$ ■ 68%   **51.** 15 : 30 ■ 85%

52. $\frac{3}{2}$ ■ 1.5   **53.** 140 : 130 ■ 104%   **54.** 0.1756 ■ 176%

WRITE Does each sentence makes sense? Explain why or why not.

55. A student ran 150% farther today than yesterday.

56. Since 15% of the students play tennis, 85% of the students do not play tennis.

57. A student got 200% of the items correct on a test.

58. A student missed 12 items on a test and got an A.

Complete each analogy.

59. dime : dollar : : 10 : ■   **60.** foot : yard : : ■ : 3

61. 50 : 20 : : 25 : ■   **62.** 10 : decade : : 100 : ■

63. 1 : 7 : : day : ■   **64.** 1 : 365 : : ■ : year

Use the DATA at the left. Write a ratio of pure gold to total karat weight for jewelry that has each marking.

65. 10 K   **66.** 14 K   **67.** 18 K   **68.** 24 K

69. WRITE a sentence that tells what percent of gold each of the markings indicate.

70. a. Which label indicates that less than 50% of the item consists of gold?

   b. Which label indicates that an item is 100% gold?

NOTES & QUOTES

The proportion of gold to other metals is marked in karats. Pure gold is marked 24 K. This is read as 24 karats. Gold is often mixed with other metals to make it more durable.

Karats	Gold	Other	Total
24 K	24	0	24
18 K	18	6	24
14 K	14	10	24
10 K	10	14	24

Practice

Write as a fraction in lowest terms.

1. 18 is to 45   **2.** 17 : 24   **3.** 24 out of 60

4. 92 : 38   **5.** 21 out of 49   **6.** 14 is to 52

Compare. Use = or ≠. Then tell if the pair of ratios form a proportion.

7. $\frac{11}{9}$ ▮ $\frac{55}{54}$ **8.** $\frac{5}{15}$ ▮ $\frac{3}{9}$ **9.** $\frac{6}{9}$ ▮ $\frac{24}{36}$ **10.** $\frac{52}{4}$ ▮ $\frac{26}{2}$

11. $\frac{4}{5}$ ▮ $\frac{20}{25}$ **12.** $\frac{12}{4}$ ▮ $\frac{9}{3}$ **13.** $\frac{7}{28}$ ▮ $\frac{4}{16}$ **14.** $\frac{16}{26}$ ▮ $\frac{8}{12}$

Solve.

15. $\frac{a}{7} = \frac{1}{3.5}$ **16.** $\frac{6}{7.2} = \frac{5}{b}$ **17.** $\frac{3}{c} = \frac{2}{8}$ **18.** $\frac{7}{5} = \frac{d}{45}$

19. $\frac{22}{18} = \frac{2.75}{e}$ **20.** $\frac{3a}{39} = \frac{3}{6}$ **21.** $\frac{8}{5g} = \frac{16}{20}$ **22.** $\frac{2.4}{3} = \frac{12}{h}$

Write as a percent. Round to the nearest tenth.

23. $\frac{9}{5}$ **24.** $\frac{1}{3}$ **25.** $\frac{3}{8}$ **26.** $\frac{125}{100}$

27. $\frac{46}{60}$ **28.** $\frac{7.5}{10}$ **29.** $\frac{11}{20}$ **30.** $\frac{5}{6}$

Write as a percent. Round to the nearest tenth.

31. 2 : 30   **32.** 15 : 5   **33.** 34 : 40   **34.** 2 : 3

35. 5 : 8   **36.** 1 : 25   **37.** 4 : 32   **38.** 7 : 35

Write as a decimal.

39. $22\frac{1}{2}\%$ **40.** 165%   **41.** 73.6%   **42.** 9%

Express as a fraction in lowest terms, as a decimal, and as a percent. Round to the nearest tenth of a percent.

43. 15 : 45   **44.** 6 : 10   **45.** 3 : 9   **46.** 13 : 10

47. 48 : 72   **48.** 19 : 95   **49.** 32 : 54   **50.** 16 : 28

Compare the following. Use >, <, or =.

51. $\frac{24}{36}$ ▮ 65%   **52.** $\frac{11}{12}$ ▮ 90%   **53.** $0.45\frac{1}{3}$ ▮ $45\frac{1}{3}\%$

54. 0.52 ▮ $\frac{13}{25}$ **55.** 19.6% ▮ 0.195   **56.** 5 : 18 ▮ 28%

57. 0.75 ▮ $\frac{3}{4}$ **58.** 0.25 ▮ $\frac{1}{5}$ **59.** 38% ▮ 0.038

OBJECTIVE:
To explore number relationships.

Exploring Number Relationships

■ At a homecoming dance, two-thirds of the ninth-grade boys have dates with a ninth-grade girl. Half of the ninth-grade girls have dates with a ninth-grade boy. What part of the entire ninth-grade class are boys who do *not* have dates with ninth-grade girls?

You can organize and analyze the data to make it easier to decide on a strategy to solve the problem.

1. **Analyze** the data and answer these questions.

   a. Do you know the number of ninth-grade students that are in the school?

   b. Do you know whether there are more boys or girls in the ninth grade at the school? **Explain** how you know and use a model to justify your answer.

2. List some strategies you think might help you solve the problem.

■ Sometimes substituting a number in a problem can help you understand the relationships in a problem.

3. Is this technique like any of the strategies you listed? If so, describe the ones that are similar.

4. a. Choose a possible number of ninth-grade boys and substitute this number into the problem. **Compare** with another group.

   b. Could there be a total of exactly ten boys in the ninth grade? exactly twelve boys? **Explain.**

5. **Analyze** the data after you substitute a number into the problem.

   a. How many ninth-grade boys have dates with ninth-grade girls?

   b. How many ninth-grade girls have dates with ninth-grade boys? **Explain** how you found the number of girls when you know the number of boys. Use a model if necessary.

   c. What is the total number of ninth-grade girls at the school?

   d. What is the total number of ninth-grade students?

   e. How many ninth-grade boys do *not* have a date with a ninth-grade girl? **Describe** how you found this answer. **Compare** with another group.

   f. What fractional part of the entire ninth grade is boys who do not have a date with a ninth-grade girl?

   g. **Write** a ratio in three different forms to describe your answer.

6. Choose a *different* possible number of ninth-grade boys and try substituting this number into the problem.

   a. Complete each step in Exercise 5 using your new chosen number.

   b. *Compare* the results you get from Exercises 5 and 6. What do you notice about the ratios?

7. Refer to the problem. ***Write*** a ratio that describes each of the following.

   a. the part of the entire ninth-grade class that are girls who do *not* have a date with a ninth-grade boy

   b. the part of the entire ninth-grade class that are boys who do have dates with a ninth-grade girl

   c. the part of the entire class that are girls who do have a date with a ninth-grade boy

   d. a ratio of boys to girls

■ You can often use more than one strategy to solve a problem.

8. Try using some of the other strategies you listed to solve the same problem.

9. *Describe* how you might use a diagram or draw a picture to help you solve the problem.

   a. What kind of picture would be appropriate?

   b. How can your picture display the ratio of boys to girls?

10. *Summarize* your findings.

   a. *Explain* how substituting numbers can sometimes help to clarify the relationships within the problem.

   b. List the strategies that were effective in solving the problem. ***Discuss*** which ones were helpful and which ones were not. ***Explain.***

   c. *Write* a similar problem. Trade with a partner and solve each other's problem.

6-5 Using Proportions to Find Percent

▼ In a recent year, there were 8,763 commercial radio stations in the United States. Of these, 295 stations had a rock format. To find the percent of stations with a rock format, you can find the ratio of some number to 100.

You can write a proportion to solve the problem.

$$\frac{295}{8,763} = \frac{n}{100}$$ Write a proportion.

$$8,763n = 29,500$$ Write cross products.

$$\frac{8,763n}{8,763} = \frac{29,500}{8,763}$$ Divide both sides by 8,763.

$$n = 3.366$$ Solve for n.

$$= 3\%$$ Round to the nearest whole number. Write as a percent.

Proportions and Percents	To find the ratio of a number to 100, use the formula. $$\frac{\text{part}}{\text{whole}} = \frac{n}{100}$$

▼ You can use proportions to solve other percent problems.

Example 1   About 5% of the 8,763 radio stations had a golden oldie format. How many stations played golden oldies?

Solution

$$\frac{p}{8,763} = \frac{5}{100}$$ Write a proportion.

$$8,763\left(\frac{p}{8,763}\right) = 8,763\left(\frac{5}{100}\right)$$ Multiply both sides by 8,763.

$$p = \frac{43,815}{100}$$

$$= 438.15 \approx 438$$

About 438 radio stations played golden oldies.

Example 2   Memphis, TN, had 12 AM radio stations in one year. These stations accounted for 60% of the AM and FM stations in Memphis. How many AM and FM stations did Memphis have at this time?

Solution

$$\frac{12}{b} = \frac{60}{100}$$ Write a proportion.

$$60b = 1,200$$ Write the cross products.

$$\frac{60b}{60} = \frac{1,200}{60}$$ Divide both sides by 60.

$$b = 20$$ Solve for b.

Memphis had 20 AM and FM radio stations.

▼ To compare ratios and percents, write both in the same form.

Example 3 At Pineapples, all books and posters are marked down 30%. At Avocados, the same items are marked $\frac{1}{3}$ off. Which store offers the greater markdown?

Solution To compare the sale prices, write $\frac{1}{3}$ as a percent.

$$\frac{1}{3} = \frac{x}{100}$$

$$x = 100\left(\frac{1}{3}\right)$$

$$x = 33\frac{1}{3}\%$$

Since $33\frac{1}{3}\% > 30\%$, Avocados offers the greater markdown.

CLASS EXERCISES

Write and solve a proportion. Round to the nearest tenth.

1. What percent of 40 is 30?
2. What percent of 20 is 40?
3. Find 80% of 20.
4. Find 300% of 50.
5. What is $33\frac{1}{3}\%$ of 75?
6. What is 40% of 60?
7. 25% of f is 8. What is f?
8. 250% of t is 50. What is t?

Solve.

9. A bank account balance of $400 earns $24 interest in one year. What is the rate of interest?

10. A bicycle cost $200 last year. The same bike costs $250 this year. What percent of last year's cost is this year's cost?

11. A student pole vaulted 5 ft yesterday. Today she vaulted 20% higher. How high was her vault today?

THINK AND DISCUSS

1. Is $a\%$ of b the same as $b\%$ of a? Explain.

2. When might it be easier to solve a percent problem by writing it as a fraction with a denominator other than 100?

WRITTEN EXERCISES

Write a proportion to solve. Round to the nearest tenth.

1. What percent of 25 is 13?
2. Find 18% of 150.
3. 116% of a is 125. What is a?
4. Find 116% of 75.
5. What percent is 40 of 120?
6. 49% of b is 31.85. What is b?
7. Find 60% of 15.
8. $12\frac{1}{2}\%$ of n is 6. What is n?

9. Find $58\frac{1}{3}\%$ of 54.   10. What percent of 250 is 75?

11. What percent of 20 is 7?   12. What percent of 80 is 130?

13. Find 125% of 16.   14. Find 92% of 625.

15. What percent of 40 is 70?   16. 35% of x is 52.5. What is x?

Compare. Use >, <, or =.

17. $\frac{14}{25}$ ▨ 56%   18. 0.3125 ▨ 32.5%   19. $\frac{1}{9}$ ▨ 0.111

20. 0.4205 ▨ 42.5%   21. 30 : 36 ▨ 85%   22. $\frac{8}{7}$ ▨ 114%

23. $\frac{13}{8}$ ▨ 1.625   24. 125 : 120 ▨ 104%   25. $\frac{7}{8}$ ▨ 75%

26. **WRITE** a paragraph explaining why a proportion is frequently set up with at least one ratio having a denominator of 100.

MENTAL MATH Solve.

27. What percent of 50 is 10?   28. What percent of 10 is 15?

29. What percent is 6 of 24?   30. What percent is 18 of 9?

31. Find 120% of 20.   32. Find 9% of 300.

33. 200% of p is 24. What is p?   34. $\frac{1}{4}\%$ of n is 3.75. What is n?

CALCULATOR Write a proportion and solve. Round to the nearest tenth.

35. What percent of 92 is 17?   36. What percent of 68 is 89?

37. Find 93% of 47.89.   38. Find 53% of 76,550.

39. Find 138% of 61.   40. Find 189% of 82.

41. Find 80 increased by 65%.   42. Find 36 reduced by $16\frac{2}{3}\%$.

43. 43% of q is 18.06. What is q?   44. 2.5% of z is 912.5. What is z?

Solve.

45. The interest on an account of $1,500 is $120 for one year. What is the rate of interest?

46. The population of a city was 28,000 in 1950 and 70,000 in 1990. What percent is the 1990 population of the 1950 population?

47. A salesperson gets an 8% commission on sales after the first $5,000 per month. What commission would the salesperson receive on sales of $20,000?

48. **DATA FILE 4 (pp. 138–139)** About what percent of the world's population speaks Chinese? what percent speaks English?

MIXED REVIEW

Find each answer.

1. $x^2 + 3$ for $x = 7$

2. $a + b^2$ for $a = 3$ and $b = 6$

Write each as a percent.

3. $2\frac{7}{12}$ 4. 4.523

5. 0.08   6. 45.6

7. The ski club has 50 members. There are 19 students going on a ski trip. What percent of the club members are going on the trip?

WRITE a sentence telling whether or not the statement makes sense.

49. Sam got a 25% markdown on the price of a new car. Pat got $2,500 off. Pat got a better deal.

50. On a recent math test, 15 students passed in one class and 22 passed in another. The second class did better on the test.

51. The human body is about 60% water by weight. That means that a person who weighs 100 lb is about 60 lb water.

To Insure Proper Service

Some say TIPS means *To Insure Proper Service*. No matter what your translation, you need to know the rules. On a long awaited cruise vacation, you just want to have fun. You think you've accounted for everything. Everything, that is, except for the small print that reads GRATUITIES NOT INCLUDED. Don't despair. Follow these simple guidelines for tipping and you'll be in for a smooth sailing vacation!

Resort Tipping Guidelines

Restaurants	15%-20% of the check before taxes
Caddies	$4-$5 per bag or 15% of the greens fees
Hairdresser	15%
Laundry	15%-20%
Taxis	15% of the fare ($.25 minimum)
Bellhops and porters	$.50-$1 per bag

Use the chart at the right to solve.

52. What would be the tip for a $25 haircut?

53. You tipped your server $4.50. About what was the cost of your meal?

TEST YOURSELF

Write each ratio as a fraction in lowest terms.

1. 7 out of 21 students have a TV in their bedroom.

2. 5 out of 100 students plan to be doctors.

Write a proportion to describe each situation. Then solve.

3. One pint of paint costs $2.89. Find the cost of a quart of paint.

4. Three light bulbs cost $5.25. Find the cost of one light bulb.

Write each as a percent.

5. $\frac{3}{4}$ **6.** 0.89   **7.** $\frac{7}{8}$ **8.** 0.03   **9.** 0.007

Write and solve a proportion.

10. Find 18% of 30.   **11.** 25% of *n* is 25. Find *n*.

OBJECTIVE:
To evaluate percents
using models and
equations.

6-6 *Percents and Equations*

▼ You can use a triangle diagram to relate the parts of a percent problem.

You know that 12 is 50% of 24. You can read this from the diagram as $\frac{12}{50\%} = 24$. You can also see the following relationships from the diagram.

50% of 24 is 12 → 50% · 24 = 12

50% equals 12 divided by 24 → 50% $= \frac{12}{24}$

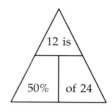

▼ You can draw a diagram to model the parts of any percent problem. The diagram always has the same form. To use the diagram, decide which part of the problem fits in each section. Then write and solve the appropriate equation.

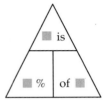

Example 1 In a recent survey, about 28% of the households surveyed were watching the top-rated TV program. Researchers used the information to estimate that about 25,312,000 households were watching the program. This assumes how many households in the total viewing population?

Solution Let x = the number of households

Draw a diagram and use it to write an equation.

$\frac{25,312,000}{28\%} = x$

25,312,000 ÷ 0.28 = 90,400,000

There are about 90,400,000 households in the viewing population.

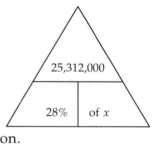

Example 2 About 18% of the 90,400,000 households in the viewing population watched the thirteenth-place program. About how many households watched this program?

Solution Let x = the number of households. that watched the program.

Draw a diagram and use it to write an equation.

18% of 90,400,000 = x
0.18 × 90,400,000 ÷ 16,272,000

About 16,272,000 households watched the thirteenth-place program.

Example 3   About 21,114,600 households in the viewing population watched the eighth-place program. What percent of the 90,400,000 households watched this program?

Solution   Let x = the percent viewing the program. Draw a diagram and use it to write an equation.

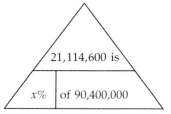

$$x = \frac{21,114,600}{90,400,000}$$
$$\approx 0.234$$

About 23.4% of the households saw the program.

CLASS EXERCISES

Write and solve an equation for each triangle diagram.

1.
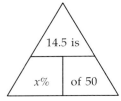

2.
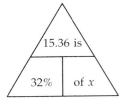

> **THINK AND DISCUSS**
> **1.** When might it be easier to use the proportion method than the equation method to solve a percent problem?
> **2.** Describe a shortcut for finding the sale price of an item marked 20% off.

Draw a triangle diagram and use it to solve.

3. What percent of 25 is 40?

4. Find 30% of 30.

5. What is $66\frac{2}{3}\%$ of 63?

6. Find 150% of 90.

7. Sneakers are on sale for 60% of their regular price. They are selling for $36. What is their regular price?

8. A banker loaned $650 last year. The balance is $400 this year. What percent of the original loan is still outstanding?

9. **WRITE** In your own words, describe how to use a triangle diagram to solve percent problems.

WRITTEN EXERCISES

Write and solve an equation for each triangle diagram.

1.
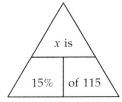

2.
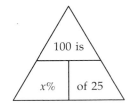

Draw a triangle diagram and use it to solve.

3. What percent of 20 is 11?

4. Find 56% of 75.

5. 135% of t is 63. What is t?

6. What percent of 25 is 17?

7. Find 500% of 12.

8. 85% of z is 106,250. What is z?

Solve. Round to the nearest tenth.

9. What percent of 4 is 9?

10. $33\frac{1}{3}$% of s is $7\frac{1}{2}$. What is s?

11. Find $26\frac{2}{3}$% of 81.

12. $12\frac{1}{4}$% of b is 9.1875. What is b?

13. Find 5.5% of 44.

14. $16\frac{2}{3}$% of m is 6. What is m?

15. What percent of 150 is 96?

16. What percent of 45 is 24?

17. Find 15% of 150.

18. What percent of 8 is 20?

19. Find 225% of 36.

20. 35% of d is 105,000. What is d?

MIXED REVIEW
Simplify.

1. $|43| + |a|$ for $a = -9$

2. $p^2 + p^3$ for $p = 5$

Use proportions to find each percent.

3. What percent of 360 is 45?

4. Find 35% of 60.

Subtract.

5. $0.85 - 0.23$

6. $1.25 - 0.351$

7. A book was marked at 85% of list price. It sold for $12.75. What was the list price?

MENTAL MATH Solve.

21. What percent of 60 is 30?

22. Find 20% of 20.

23. 100% of t is 100. What is t?

24. What percent of 3 is 30?

25. Find $33\frac{1}{3}$% of 66.

26. 200% of g is 24. What is g?

27. What percent of 55 is 11?

28. Find 5% of 10.

29. 18% of n is 18. What is n?

30. What percent of 100 is 35?

31. Find 10% of 125.

32. 25% of z is 200. What is z?

33. What percent of 9 is 3?

34. Find 20% of 80.

CALCULATOR Solve. Round to the nearest tenth.

35. What percent of 117 is 54?

36. 18% of a is 15. What is a?

37. Find 16% of 83.

38. What percent of 59 is 176?

39. 23% of a is 23. What is a?

40. Find 86% of 29.

Solve.

41. The rate of interest on a savings account is $5\frac{1}{4}$%. What is the simple interest for a year on $750?

42. An item on sale for $7.50 is 70% of the original price. What was the original price?

43. **DATA FILE 6 (pp. 230–231)** Is it accurate to say that females spend about 50% more per week on clothes than males do?

44. Identical sweaters are on sale in two different stores. In the first store, the sweater is on sale at 70% of the list price of $25. In the second store, the sweater is on sale at 60% of the list price of $30. Which sweater is the better buy?

45. A tie and a wallet were originally the same price. The tie is now 75% of its original price; the wallet is now 70% of its original price. The wallet has a sale price $17.50. What was the original price of each item? What is the sale price of the tie?

DATA **Use the table at the right.**

46. True or false? Write *T* or *F*.

   a. The number of households with VCRs increased more than 100% from 1978 to 1980.

   b. The number of households with VCRs in 1978 is less than 1% of the number of households with VCRs in 1986.

47. ESTIMATION Suppose the average cost of a VCR was $1,200 in 1978. Estimate the value of the sales of VCRs in 1978.

48. Use the data to make a bar graph.

49. The number of households with VCRs in 1981 was about 57% of the households with VCRs in 1982. How many households had VCRs in 1981?

50. Which of the following could you *not* conclude from the data?

   a. VCRs are very popular in the United States.

   b. More VCRs are produced in the United States than in any other country.

   c. The number of movies available on videotape probably increased from 1978 to 1986.

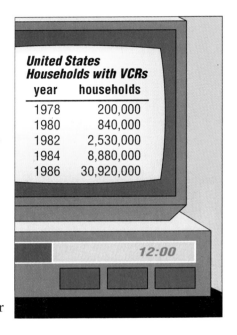

United States Households with VCRs

year	households
1978	200,000
1980	840,000
1982	2,530,000
1984	8,880,000
1986	30,920,000

Critical Thinking

EXPLORING VISUAL PERCEPTION

1. Study the unfolded pattern. Then decide which, if any, of the three-dimensional figures would result if you fold the pattern.

a.   **b.**   **c.**

2. Use graph paper to make a pattern for a visual perception problem like the one above. Trade with a classmate and try to solve the problem.

OBJECTIVE:
To find percent of
increase or decrease.

6-7 Percent of Change

▼ Over a ten-year period, the average tuition at a private four-year college increased from $2,476 to $7,693. You can write and solve an equation to find the *percent of change*.

1. Subtract to find the amount of change. $7,693 - 2,476 = 5,217$

2. Write an equation.

   percent of change $= \dfrac{\text{amount of change}}{\text{original amount}}$ $n = \dfrac{5,217}{2,476}$

3. Solve the equation. Round to the nearest hundredth. $5,217 \div 2,476 = 2.107\ldots$ $n \approx 2.11$

4. Write as a percent.   211%

Tuition rose by about 211% over the ten-year period.

Percent of Change	Use the following equation to find percent of change. percent of change $= \dfrac{\text{amount of change}}{\text{original amount}}$

▼ You can use the same approach to find the percent of decrease.

Example 1 High school enrollment fell from 13.3 million students to 11.4 million in 20 y. Find the percent of change.

Solution $13.3 - 11.4 = 1.9$ Find the amount of change.

$$d = \frac{1.9}{13.3}$$ Write an equation.

$1.9 \div 13.3 = 0.1428\ldots$ Solve the equation.
$d \approx 0.14$ Round to the nearest hundredth.

14%   Write as a percent.

High school enrollment fell about 14%.

▼ Always use the same units when working with measures.

Example 2 An animal weighed 5 lb at birth. A week later it weighed 5 lb 6 oz. What was the percent of change?

Solution $86 - 80 = 6$ Write measures in the same units. Find the amount of change.

$$c = \frac{6}{80}$$ Write an equation.

$6 \div 80 = 0.075$ Solve the equation.
$c = 0.075$

7.5%   Write as a percent.

The animal had a 7.5% gain in weight.

▼ The percent of change may be part of a multi-step problem.

Example 3 An investment grew from $100 to $110 in the past year because of interest earned. The investment will earn interest at the same rate for the next year. What will be the value of the investment at the end of next year?

Solution
1. Find the percent of increase: $\frac{10}{100} = 10\%$.
2. Find the interest for the next year: 10% of $110 = $11.
3. Find the value of the investment: $110 + $11 = $121.

At the end of next year, the investment will be worth $121.

THINK Why is the denominator always the original amount in percent of change problems?

CLASS EXERCISES

Find the percent of increase.

1. 30 is increased to 39.

2. 45 is increased to 144.

Find each percent of decrease.

3. 60 is decreased to 48.

4. 96 is decreased to 78.

Find each percent of change.

5. 72 to 99   **6.** 64 to 40   **7.** 144 to 300   **8.** 400 to 120

Find the percent of change for the first set of numbers. Use the same percent of change to complete the second set of numbers.

9. 50 to 60 : : 60 to ▨ .

10. 250 to 200 : : 200 to ▨ .

THINK AND DISCUSS

1. 100 is increased by 10%. Then the result is decreased by 10%. Is the final result 100? Explain.

2. 100 is decreased by 10%. Then the result is increased by 10%. Is the final result 100? Explain.

3. Are the values of the answers to Questions 1 and 2 the same? Explain.

WRITTEN EXERCISES

Find each percent of increase. Round to the nearest tenth.

1. 50 is increased to 66.

2. 80 is increased to 95.

3. 32 is increased to 76.

4. 45 is increased to 105.

Find each percent of decrease. Round to the nearest tenth.

5. 90 is decreased to 75.

6. 64 is decreased to 24.

7. 120 is decreased to 95.

8. 280 is decreased to 126.

Find each percent of change. Round to the nearest tenth.

9. 38 to 95   **10.** 111 to 74   **11.** 27 to 72   **12.** 180 to 54

13. 25 to 30   **14.** 40 to 45   **15.** 50 to 45   **16.** 40 to 30

Find the percent of change from the first number to the second. Use the same rate of change to find the next number in the pattern. Round each answer to the same number of decimal places.

17. 38, 57, ▦   **18.** 70.6, 105.9, ▦   **19.** 103.6, 77.7, ▦

Item	Price ($)	
	1980	**1990**
calculator	13	4
110 camera	40	28
radio with headphones	100	35
video game system	29	99
sneakers	29	52
candy bar	0.25	0.50
movie ticket	2	4.50
cassette tape	8.98	9.99
basic watch	16	20
ballpoint pen	0.29	0.39

DATA Use the table at the left.

20. a. Find the percent of change for each item. Round each answer to the nearest hundredth. Label your answer as increase or decrease.

     b. **WRITE** Which items increased in price? Which items decreased in price? Why do you think some items increased in price and some decreased?

CALCULATOR Find each percent of change. Label your answer as increase or decrease. Round to the nearest tenth.

21. 87 to 108   **22.** 59 to 127   **23.** 77 to 13

24. 132.8 to 93.3   **25.** 131.75 to 40.45   **26.** 18 to 47.69

Solve. Round each answer to the nearest tenth.

27. A stock increased in value from $130 to $166. What was the percent of change?

28. The value of artwork appreciated from $295 to $495. What was the percent of change?

29. Investments decreased in value from $1,750 to $1,232. What was the percent of change?

30. A stock traded at the following prices each day for a week: Monday, $846; Tuesday, $819; Wednesday, $838; Thursday, $864; Friday, $850.

     a. Find the percent of change for each day.

     b. On which day was the percent of change the greatest?

     c. On which day was the percent of change the least?

     d. What was the percent of change from the value on Monday to the value on Friday?

31. A worker received a raise from $22,000 to $25,000. What is the percent of change?

32. A family bought a house for $78,000 in 1985. In 1991, the family sold the house for $88,900. Find the percent of change.

MIXED REVIEW

Evaluate.

1. $|-3| + |x|$ for $x = -5$

2. $[(3 + 12)(8 \div 2)]^2$

Compare. Use >, <, or =.

3. $42 : 54$ ▦ $56 : 64$.

4. $\frac{3}{11}$ ▦ $27\frac{1}{4}\%$

5. Find 45% of 45.

6. There are about 20,000 human-made objects in orbit around Earth. All but 300 are junk. What percent are junk?

33. A gallon of gas cost $.32 in 1972. In 1991, a gallon of gas cost $1.58. What is the percent of change?

34. The population of Growtown increased from 10,000 to 13,000 in one year, while the population of Slowtown decreased from 30,000 to 24,000 in one year.

    a. Find the respective rates of increase or decrease.

    b. If both towns maintain the same rate of change, when will the population of Growtown exceed that of Slowtown?

35. *DATA FILE 3 (pp. 96–97)* Find the percent of change for the value of each proof set from 1965 to 1968.

36. *DATA* Use the table on page 259. Find the percent of change for each time period.

    a. from 1978 to 1980   **b.** from 1980 to 1982

    c. from 1982 to 1984   **d.** from 1984 to 1986

37. *DATA* Use the table at the right to solve.

    a. Find the percent of change for each occupation from 1986 to 2000. Round to the nearest whole percent.

    b. Is the percent of change the only factor that you would consider when making a career decision?

    c. *WRITE* What impact might these projections have on a person's career planning?

38. *PROJECT* Research the expected employment demands in the profession of your choice. Find out what training and education is necessary to qualify for this position.

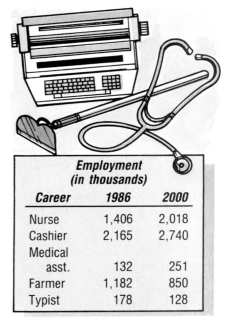

Employment (in thousands)		
Career	**1986**	**2000**
Nurse	1,406	2,018
Cashier	2,165	2,740
Medical asst.	132	251
Farmer	1,182	850
Typist	178	128

TEST YOURSELF

Write and solve an equation.

1. Find 33% of 120.

2. Find 125% of 42.

3. What percent of 50 is 10?

4. 15% of q is 9.75. What is q?

5. What percent of 12 is 8?

6. 80% of w is 120. What is w?

Solve. Round to the nearest tenth of a percent.

7. A pair of sneakers was reduced from $125 to $85. What was the percent of change?

8. Tickets to regular season games are $36. Tickets to playoff games are $50. What is the percent of change?

OBJECTIVE:
To solve problems by drawing a diagram.

6-8 Draw a Diagram

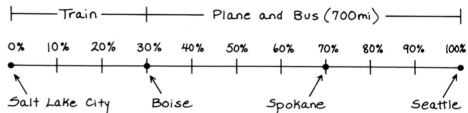

■ You can solve many types of problems using diagrams.

PROBLEM

A sales representative travels by train from Salt Lake City, Utah, to Boise, Idaho. This distance is about 30% of her entire trip. She then flies 400 mi to Spokane, Washington. She completes the remaining 300 mi of her trip to Seattle, Washington, by bus. What percent of her trip did she cover by bus?

SOLUTION

Answer these questions to understand the given information.

READ ▶ What facts do you have?

Salt Lake City to Boise → 30% by train

Boise to Spokane → 400 mi by air

Spokane to Seattle → 300 mi by bus

What do you want to find? What percent of the trip (the part covered by bus) does 300 mi represent?

PLAN ▶ Make a diagram to organize the information.

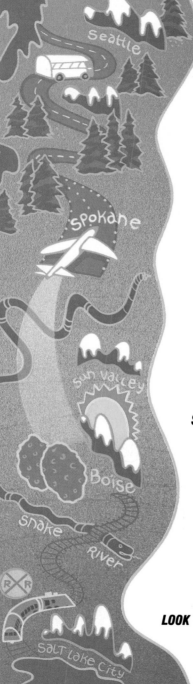

├────── Train ──────┼────── Plane and Bus (700mi) ──────┤

0% 10% 20% 30% 40% 50% 60% 70% 80% 90% 100%

↑ Salt Lake City   ↑ Boise   ↑ Spokane   ↑ Seattle

SOLVE ▶ How far did she travel by air and by bus?   700 mi

What percent represents the total she traveled by air and bus?   70%

The distance between two marks on your diagram represents what percent of the total distance?   10%

How many miles does the distance between two marks represent?   100 mi (700 ÷ 7)

How many miles did she travel in all?   1,000 mi (100 · 10)

What percent of the trip did she cover by bus? $\frac{300}{1,000} = 30\%$

LOOK BACK ▶ Does your answer make sense? Look at the problem another way to check.

Think of a proportion.

70% : 700 as 30% : 300. So, 300 mi by bus is 30%.

CLASS EXERCISES

1. Refer to the problem in the example on page 264.
   a. What percent of the trip was covered by plane?
   b. How many miles were covered by train?

2. A student has 80 miles to walk. She walks 50% of the distance the first day and 25% of the remaining distance the second day. How far does she have to walk to finish her trip?

3. A student put points P and Q on a line to the right of point X. Three times the distance from point X to point P is four times the distance from point X to point Q. What is the ratio of $PQ : XQ$?

4. There are 25 students in an algebra class. Ten students are members of the math club. Twelve students are members of the chess club. Five students are members of both clubs. How many of the students in the algebra class are members of neither club?

WRITTEN EXERCISES

Use a CALCULATOR where appropriate.

Solve using a diagram.

1. Container A has twice the capacity of container B. Container A is full of sand and container B is empty. Suppose $\frac{1}{8}$ of the sand in container A is poured into container B. What fractional part of container B will contain sand?

2. Six students are in the finals of the chess tournament. Each student plays one game against every other student. How many games will be played?

3. Points P, Q, R, and S appear in that order on a line. The ratio of $PQ : QR$ is $3 : 4$, and the ratio of $QR : RS$ is $2 : 5$. The length of $PQ = 6$ in. Find the length of PS.

4. A wooden cube that measures 5 cm along each edge is painted blue. The painted cube is then cut into centimeter cubes. How many of the small cubes are painted on three faces?

5. A homeowner is building a fence around a rectangular lot that measures 48 ft by 60 ft. He digs a post hole at each corner and one every 4 ft in between corners. How many post holes must he dig?

Solve. Use any strategy you wish.

6. After George poured 48 gal of water into an empty tank, the tank was 75% full. How many gallons does the tank hold?

7. Maureen cut a 20-cm wire into exactly three pieces. The first piece is 3 cm shorter than the second piece. The third piece is 4 cm shorter than the second piece. Find the length of the shortest piece.

8. At a local high school, 60% of the students are girls. Of these girls, 75% own a cassette player. What percent of all the students are girls who do *not* own cassette players?

9. Twelve of Ms. Brown's students tried out for both the gymnastics and the baseball teams. Half of the students made the baseball team. One-third made the gymnastics team. One-fourth made neither team. How many students made both teams?

10. Belinda takes the bus $\frac{2}{5}$ of the distance from home to school. She then walks 2 blocks to her friend's house and rides with her friend the remaining 7 blocks to school. What fractional part of the trip did Belinda ride with her friend?

11. A student has 5 mi to walk. The student walks half the distance the first hour and a fourth of the remaining distance the next hour. How far does the student have to walk to finish the trip?

12. On Saturday, a student pays off a loan of $12.50. He then earns $20 mowing a lawn. At the mall, he buys two pairs of socks for $3.98 each and a pair of shoes for $45.79. He has $24.32 left. How much money did he have to start with?

13. A student was standing in the middle of a line. Twenty-three students were ahead of him. How many students were in the line?

14. A board is cut in half. Then each piece is cut in half again. Then each of these pieces is cut in half.

    a. How many cuts are made?

    b. How many pieces are there?

15. A chain fence encloses a square pen. The 8 posts on each side of the pen are spaced 6 ft apart and are 6 in. in diameter. There is a post at each corner of the pen.

    a. How many posts are there?

    b. What are the dimensions of the pen?

16. *DATA FILE 9 (pp. 360–361)* Suppose you are teeing off on the 8th hole at St. Andrew's golf club. Would you be more likely to use a 1 wood or a 3 wood?

Problem Solving Practice

PROBLEM SOLVING STRATEGIES

Look for a Pattern
Guess and Test
Simplify the Problem
Account for All Possibilities
Make an Organized List
Work Backwards
Make a Table
Write an Equation
Solve by Graphing
Draw a Diagram
Make a Model
Simulate the Problem

Solve. The list at the left shows some strategies you may use.

1. What is the maximum possible number of digits in the product of two positive integers each having two digits?

2. To make an orange dye, 3 parts of red dye are mixed with 2 parts of yellow dye. To make a purple dye, 2 parts of blue dye are mixed with 1 part of red dye. Suppose equal amounts of orange and purple are mixed. What fractional part of the mixture is red dye?

3. When n is divided by 7, the remainder is 4. What is the remainder when $2n$ is divided by 7?

4. The ratio of Clark's weight to Kim's weight is 3 : 2. The ratio of Kim's weight to Janine's weight is 1 : 2. Compare Clark's weight with Janine's weight.

5. Working together, two painters earned $1,000 for painting a new house. The first painter worked for seven days. The second painter worked for three days. What is the first painter's fair share of the $1,000?

6. Refer to the two circle graphs at the left.

   a. What percent of Earth's water supply is fresh water?

   b. What percent of Earth's fresh water is found in rivers, lakes, and streams?

   c. What percent of Earth's total water supply is found in rivers, lakes, and streams? How did you find the answer?

   d. What is the ratio of salt water to fresh water? the ratio of salt water to the water from icecaps and glaciers?

7. **DATA FILE 4 (pp. 138–139)**

   a. In 1989, the world population was about 5 billion. Approximately what percent of the population spoke Japanese?

   b. Is this more than the percent of the population that spoke both English and Spanish?

8. **DATA FILE 10 (pp. 404–405)**

   a. What is the total area (in mi^2) of the earth covered by oceans? Of the total area, approximately what percent is the Pacific Ocean? the Atlantic Ocean?

   b. The total surface area of Earth is 1.96951×10^8 mi^2. Approximately what percent of Earth's surface area do the oceans cover?

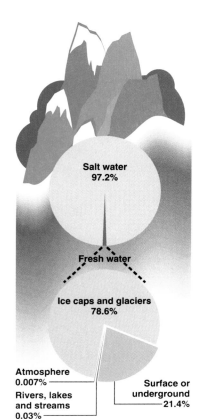

Salt water
97.2%

Fresh water

Ice caps and glaciers
78.6%

Atmosphere
0.007%

Rivers, lakes
and streams
0.03%

Surface or
underground
21.4%

Chapter 6 Review

Write true or false. If false, change the underlined word to make the statement true.

1. A <u>proportion</u> is a comparison of two quantities by division.

2. If two ratios are equal, their <u>cross products</u> are equal.

3. $\frac{miles}{hour}$ is an example of a <u>ratio</u>.

4. A <u>rate</u> is a ratio that compares a number to 100.

5. The percent of change is the amount of change divided by the <u>original amount</u>.

Ratios, Proportions, and Rates   6-1

To compare two quantities, write a ratio. To determine if two ratios form a proportion, multiply the cross products. If the cross products are equal, the ratios form a proportion.

To compare quantities measured in different units, use a rate.

Compare. Write = or ≠. Then tell whether or not the ratios form a proportion.

6. $\frac{3}{8} \blacksquare \frac{9}{24}$

7. $\frac{5}{7} \blacksquare \frac{20}{35}$

8. $\frac{3}{4} \blacksquare \frac{15}{20}$

9. $\frac{2}{3} \blacksquare \frac{18}{17}$

10. $\frac{5}{6} \blacksquare \frac{100}{130}$

Write each ratio as a unit rate.

11. 150 mi in 3 h

12. 115 mi on 5 gal

13. 270 words in 3 min

14. $9.45 for 5 lb

Solving Proportions   6-2

To solve a proportion, write the cross products, then solve.

Solve.

15. $\frac{5}{6} = \frac{n}{42}$

16. $\frac{3}{2} = \frac{18}{x}$

17. $\frac{15}{a} = \frac{30}{98}$

18. $\frac{y}{9} = \frac{30}{90}$

19. $\frac{21}{25} = \frac{m}{150}$

Scale Drawing   6-3

To use a scale drawing, measure the distance on the drawing. Then use the scale given to write and solve a proportion.

Use the scale 1 cm : 75 km.

20. The distance on the map from Centerville to Toptown is 2.5 cm. What is the actual distance?

21. The actual distance from Summit to Crown Heights is 37.5 km. What is the map distance?

Writing Percents

To write decimals as percents, move the decimal point two places to the right and write a percent sign. To write a fraction as a percent, first write the fraction as a decimal. Then write the decimal as a percent.

Write each decimal as a percent.

Write each fraction as a percent.

22. 0.05   **23.** 0.98   **24.** 1.45   **25.** $\frac{3}{4}$ **26.** $\frac{5}{8}$ **27.** $\frac{3}{25}$

Using Proportions to Find Percent

To find the ratio of a number to 100, use the following formula.

$$\frac{\text{part}}{\text{whole}} = \frac{n}{100}$$

Write and solve a proportion.

28. Find $12\frac{1}{2}\%$ of 48.   **29.** 20% of x is 30. What is x?   **30.** What percent is 90 of 270?

Using Equations to Find Percent

Use a triangle diagram to relate the parts of a percent problem.

Write and solve an equation. Round to the nearest tenth.

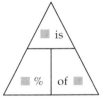

31. 35% of a is 70. What is a?   **32.** Find 68% of 300.

33. What percent is 9 of 180?   **34.** What percent of 55 is 10?

35. Find 3% of 89.   **36.** 125% of y is 100. What is y?

Finding Percent of Change

$$\text{percent of change} = \frac{\text{amount of change}}{\text{original amount}}$$

Find the percent of change.

37. 18 to 24   **38.** 120 to 90   **39.** 148 to 37   **40.** 285 to 342   **41.** 1,000 to 250

Problem Solving

To solve a problem, draw a diagram to represent the information.

Solve.

42. Alicia rides 25% of a 100-mi trip the first day. She rides $33\frac{1}{3}\%$ of the remaining distance the second day. What percent of the original distance does she have to ride to finish her trip?

43. *DATA* Refer to the circle graphs on page 267. What percent of Earth's fresh water supply is on the surface or underground?

Chapter 6   Test

Write each ratio as a unit rate.

1. A car travels 84 mi on 3 gal of gas.

2. A car travels 220 mi in 4 h.

Compare. Write = or ≠.

3. $\frac{7}{8}$ ■ $\frac{42}{40}$

4. $\frac{3}{5}$ ■ $\frac{45}{75}$

5. $\frac{12}{18}$ ■ $\frac{18}{12}$

6. $\frac{5}{9}$ ■ $\frac{25}{81}$

Write a proportion to describe each situation. Then solve.

7. Three cans of dog food sell for 99¢. Find the cost of 15 cans.

8. A photo that measures 5 in. by 7 in. is enlarged to 7.5 in. by b.

9. A student reads 45 pages in 2 h; x pages in 3 h.

The length of the kitchen in the diagram at the right is $1\frac{1}{4}$ in. The actual length is 20 ft. Use the diagram to solve.

10. What is the scale of the diagram?

11. What is the actual size of the dining area?

12. How wide is the kitchen at its narrowest part?

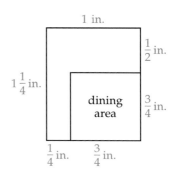

Write each decimal as a percent.

13. 0.37   **14.** 0.005   **15.** 1.02

Write each fraction as a percent.

16. $\frac{5}{8}$ **17.** $\frac{2}{3}$ **18.** $\frac{7}{9}$

19. WRITE a paragraph describing how to use a triangle diagram to solve a percent problem.

Solve.

20. What percent of 400 is 20?

21. Find $33\frac{1}{3}\%$ of 12.

22. 20% of c is 24. What is c?

23. What percent of 3 is 15?

24. Find 125% of 50.

25. 60% of y is 75. What is y?

Find each percent of change. Round to the nearest tenth.

26. 60 to 36   **27.** 18 to 24   **28.** 15 to 25   **29.** 85 to 50   **30.** 88 to 300

Solve.

31. Suppose you have posts of length 6 in., 9 in., and 11 in. How can you use the posts to measure a 4-in. length?

32. Two oranges weigh the same as an apple and a grape. An apple weighs the same as 11 grapes. How many grapes equal the weight of an orange?

Chapters 1–6 Cumulative Review

Choose the correct answer. Write A, B, C, or D.

1. Which number is divisible by 3 and 5?

   A. 725   **B.** 726

   C. 720   **D.** not given

2. Write $\frac{7}{8}$ as a percent.

   A. $87\frac{1}{2}\%$ **B.** 70%

   C. 78%   **D.** not given

3. Which is *not* a ratio that describes

             □□□□ △△△?

   A. 4:3   **B.** 4:7

   C. 4 + 3   **D.** not given

4. Simplify $\frac{5a^3b^4}{10a^2b^3}$.

   A. $\frac{a}{2b^{-1}}$ **B.** $\frac{1}{2}ab$

   C. $\frac{1}{2}a^{5b-1}$ **D.** not given

5. Evaluate $\frac{2x^3 - 0.01}{x^2}$ for $x = -0.2$.

   A. 0.65   **B.** -0.41

   C. 0.065   **D.** not given

6. The figures are in proportion. Find the missing length.

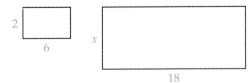

   A. 6   **B.** 10

   C. 12   **D.** not given

7. Solve $1.5 = 0.2x - 0.5$.

   A. 1   **B.** 5

   C. -10   **D.** not given

8. Compare $\frac{\sqrt{25}}{2^3}$ ▧ $\frac{\sqrt{9}}{2^2}$.

   A. >   **B.** <

   C. =   **D.** not given

9. Find the LCM of $6x^3y^2$ and $8x^2y^5$.

   A. $2x^2y^2$ **B.** $24x^3y^5$

   C. $48x^5y^7$ **D.** not given

10. Evaluate $3 + 4 \cdot 5 - 5 + 6 \div 3$.

   A. 20   **B.** 12

   C. 8   **D.** not given

11. The sum of two numbers is 9. The product is 20. What are the numbers?

   A. 3 and 6   **B.** 2 and 10

   C. 4 and 5   **D.** not given

12. Identify the model.

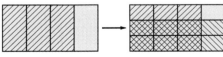

   A. $\frac{3}{4} + \frac{2}{3}$ **B.** $\frac{3}{4} - \frac{6}{12}$

   C. $\frac{3}{4} \cdot \frac{2}{3}$ **D.** not given

WHEN STANDARD TIME was first established in 1884, there were 24 time zones—one for every 15° of longitude. The prime meridian at 0° longitude is used to determine noon. Time for other zones depends on the number of zones east or west of the prime meridian.

The line opposite 0° at 180° (called the international date line) is used to determine midnight. To make standard time practical for daily use, many nations, states, and cities changed the time zones to include local boundaries.

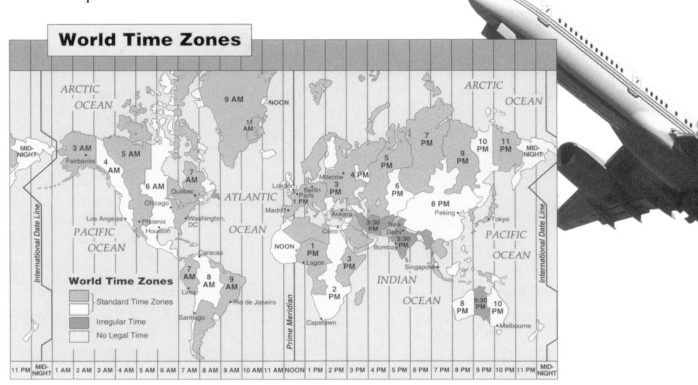

World Time Zones

Legend:
- Standard Time Zones
- Irregular Time
- No Legal Time

Federal regulations ban smoking on all domestic flights.

Passengers 11 years of age, or younger, and 62 years of age, or older, are eligible for discounts on most major airlines. Children under two fly for free.

Air Travel Information

Equations and Inequalities

UNITED STATES BUSIEST AIRPORTS	PASSENGER BOARDINGS (Millions of Passengers)		RANK	
AIRPORT	1987	2000	1987	2000
Chicago O'Hare	27.5	43.6	1	1
Atlanta	23.9	34.6	2	3
Los Angeles	21.2	27.1	3	4
Dallas/Ft. Worth	20.8	23.6	4	5
Denver	16.1	35.7	5	2
New York/Kennedy	14.4	17.6	6	12
San Francisco	14.0	20.3	7	7
Newark	12.2	23.4	8	6
New York/La Guardia	11.6	16.0	9	15
Miami	11.6	18.9	10	9

OBJECTIVE:
Use models to explore and solve two-step equations.

MATERIALS

- Algebra tiles
- Math journal to record work

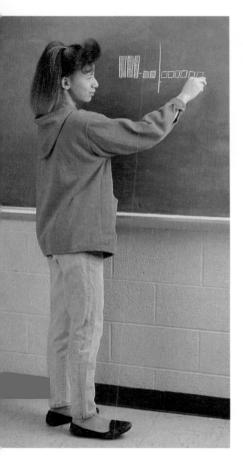

Exploring Two-step Equations

▼ You can use algebra tiles to model a two-step equation.

a. $2x + 3 = 5$

b. $2x - 4 = 6$

1. **Describe** what each tile represents in each equation. **Analyze** how these equations and models are different from the ones you have seen before.

2. **Model** each equation. **Compare** your models with those of another group.

   a. $3n + 4 = 7$ **b.** $4x - 2 = 6$ **c.** $5r - 2 = 8$

▼ You can also use algebra tile models to help you solve a two-step equation.

3. **Analyze** the model for $2x + 3 = 5$. To solve the equation, you must isolate the variable.

   a. **Discuss** what isolating a variable means.

   b. **Describe** the first step you would take in isolating the variable expression $2x$. What operation did you perform?

   c. **Discuss** what you need to do to solve the resulting equation for x. What is the value of x?

4. **Analyze** the model for $2x - 4 = 6$.

   a. **Discuss** why it is helpful to think of this equation as $2x + (-4) = 6$.

   b. **Describe** the two steps needed to solve the equation.

   c. What is the solution of $2x - 4 = 6$?

5. Use models to solve each equation.

   a. $3r + 4 = 10$ **b.** $2b - 7 = 3$ **c.** $4n - 6 = -2$

6. **Analyze** your solutions for Exercise 5.

   a. What was the first thing you did to solve each equation?

   b. **Summarize** Write a rule describing the steps you used to solve a two-step equation.

7-1 Two-step Equations

▼ A student pays $.86 for three school stickers and a school emblem. An emblem costs $.29. What is the price for each sticker? If we represent the price of one sticker with variable p, we can write the following equation.

$$3p + 29 = 86$$

You can solve this equation by using the subtraction and division properties of equality.

$$3p + 29 = 86$$
$$3p + 29 - 29 = 86 - 29 \qquad \text{Subtract 29 from both sides.}$$
$$3p = 57$$
$$\frac{3p}{3} = \frac{57}{3} \qquad \text{Divide both sides by 3.}$$
$$p = 19$$

Check $3p + 29 = 86$

$3 \, \boxed{\times} \, 19 \, \boxed{+} \, 29 \, \boxed{=} \, 86 \, \checkmark \qquad$ Replace p with 19.

Each sticker costs $.19.

Julia B. Robinson (1920–1985), a mathematics researcher at the University of California, Berkeley, showed that there was no automatic method of determining whether or not an equation had a whole number solution.

▼ You can also solve two-step equations using the addition and multiplication properties of equality.

Example 1 **Write an equation to describe the situation. Solve.**

Suppose you divide a number by 4 and then subtract 5 to get 8. What is the original number?

Solution Let $n =$ the original number.
Then the equation $\frac{n}{4} - 5 = 8$ describes the situation.

$$\frac{n}{4} - 5 = 8$$
$$\frac{n}{4} - 5 + 5 = 8 + 5 \qquad \text{Add 5 to both sides.}$$
$$\frac{n}{4} = 13$$
$$4\left(\frac{n}{4}\right) = 13(4) \qquad \text{Multiply both sides by 4.}$$
$$n = 52$$

Check $\frac{n}{4} - 5 = 8$

$52 \, \boxed{\div} \, 4 \, \boxed{-} \, 5 \, \boxed{=} \, 8 \, \checkmark \qquad$ Replace n with 52.

Solving a Simple Two-step Equation	To solve a simple two-step equation: **1.** Undo addition or subtraction. **2.** Undo multiplication or division.

Example 2 **Choose the correct equation. Solve.**

Three friends rent a canoe. Each person also rents a paddle for $4. Each person pays a total of $20. What is the cost of renting the canoe without the paddles?

a. $3n - 4 = 20$ **b.** $3n + 12 = 20$

c. $\frac{n}{3} + 4 = 20$ **d.** $\frac{n}{3} - 4 = 20$

Solution Let $n =$ the total cost of the canoe rental.
Then the correct equation is c.

$$\frac{n}{3} + 4 = 20$$

$$\frac{n}{3} + 4 - 4 = 20 - 4 \qquad \text{Subtract 4 from each side.}$$

$$\frac{n}{3} = 16$$

$$3\left(\frac{n}{3}\right) = 16(3) \qquad \text{Multiply both sides by 3.}$$

$$n = 48 \qquad \text{The check is left for you.}$$

The cost of renting a canoe without the paddles is $48.

CLASS EXERCISES

State the first step in solving each equation.

1. $\frac{a}{6} + 9 = 13$ **2.** $4b - 6 = 2$

3. $2c + 1 = 5$ **4.** $\frac{d}{3} - 10 = 5$

Choose the correct equation. Solve.

a. $3x + 1 = 14$ **b.** $x - 1 = 14$

c. $\frac{x}{3} + 1 = 14$ **d.** $\frac{x}{3} - 1 = 14$

5. Sarita, Clara, and Joe baked muffins, which they shared equally. Clara ate one on the way home. She had 14 muffins left. How many muffins did Sarita, Clara, and Joe bake?

6. Kyle sent away for three tapes. The cost of the order, with $1 for shipping, was $14. What was the price of each tape?

Solve each equation.

7. $9x - 15 = 39$ **8.** $\frac{y}{7} - 6 = 8$ **9.** $\frac{2}{3}n + \frac{3}{8} = \frac{15}{16}$

10. $4 - \frac{z}{3} = 13$ **11.** $-35 = 4x + 1$ **12.** $2.4r - 5.6 = 11.2$

THINK AND DISCUSS

1. What is the first step in solving the equation $ax - b = c$ for x?

2. How can you solve the equation $5x + 2 = -28$ using addition and multiplication?

3. Is the solution of the equation $18n - 1 = 402$ a negative number? Explain.

13. $6n - 5 = 55$ **14.** $\frac{x}{3} + 2 = 14$ **15.** $16d - 28 = 174$

WRITTEN EXERCISES

Solve each equation.

1. $3n + 5 = 23$

2. $18 = 4t + 2$

3. $-86 + 4k = 102$

4. $30 = 18 + 2b$

5. $5 + \frac{k}{9} = -31$

6. $2 + \frac{m}{3} = 0$

7. $12d - 6 = 138$

8. $4x - 2 = 28.4$

9. $15 = 6 + \frac{m}{6}$

10. $-19 = 4 + 3x$

11. $4 - \frac{k}{5} = 18$

12. $15 = -11c + 4$

13. $12 - 11s = 45$

14. $10 = 3 + \frac{d}{2}$

15. $\frac{-3}{4}n + \frac{1}{4} = 1\frac{3}{4}$

16. $\frac{x}{-6} + 7 = 0$

17. $0 = 91 + 13t$

18. $5p - 0.48 = 0.12$

19. $\frac{2n}{5} - 23 = 11$

20. $2.1 + 3b = 1.8$

21. $\frac{t}{8} - \frac{3}{4} = \frac{1}{2}$

MENTAL MATH Solve each equation.

22. $2n + 3 = 15$

23. $\frac{y}{5} - 2 = 10$

24. $4x - 1 = 27$

25. $\frac{m}{10} + 3 = 6$

26. $2x - 7 = 11$

27. $3a - 2 = 13$

CALCULATOR Solve each equation.

28. $31.5 - 4.2x = -65.1$

29. $238.7 + 1.8k = 3.02 \cdot 10^5$

30. $0 = -5.67x + 0.25$

31. $47.2 = \frac{4r}{5} + 81.9$

Write a situation for each equation.

32. $3g + 4 = 16$

33. $\frac{r}{4} + 0.35 = 5.15$

Choose the correct equation. Solve.

34. A student bought some pencils for $.39 each and a pad of drawing paper for $1.19. The total cost for the supplies was $3.92. How many pencils did the student buy?

  a. $39x + 1.19 = 3.92$ **b.** $1.19x + 39y = 3.92$

  c. $0.39x + 1.19 = 3.92$ **d.** $0.039x + 1.19 = 3.92$

35. A student is saving $15 each week from earnings and already has $150. In how many weeks will the balance be $210?

  a. $150 + 210 = 15n$ **b.** $150 - 15n = 210$

  c. $150 + 15n = 210$ **d.** $15n - 150 = 210$

MIXED REVIEW

Solve each equation.

1. $12n + 60 = 300$

2. $25n - 30 = 70$

Find each answer.

3. Solve $\frac{12}{x} = \frac{18}{27}$.

4. What is 15% of $42?

5. 24 is 25% of what number?

Simplify each expression.

6. $4m + 5 - m$

7. $13 - 5x + 2$

8. How much warmer is it when the temperature is 90° than when the temperature is -6°?

Write a two-step equation with each number as its solution.

36. -2   **37.** 7   **38.** 0.3

Write an equation to describe the situation. Do not solve.

39. Seven less than three times a number equals 19. Find the number.

40. Linda had $235 in her savings account. She withdrew the same amount each week for 15 weeks. Her balance was then $55. How much money did Linda withdraw each week?

Write an equation to describe the situation. Solve.

41. Two is twelve times a number less four. Find the number.

42. Phillip wants to buy a bicycle for $189. He has $24 and plans to save $15 each week. In how many weeks will he be able to buy the bicycle?

43. Phyllis wants to buy a camera for $78. She has already saved $36. She plans to save $8 each week. In how many weeks will she be able to buy the camera?

44. A taxi ride costs $.40 for each quarter-mile and $.85 for each additional passenger. Yolanda and Cara paid $5.25 altogether. How far did they travel?

45. Thirty is three times a number less nine. Find the number.

46. Greg bought four greeting cards, all at the same price, and a package of wrapping paper for $1.79. He spent a total of $5.19. How much was each greeting card?

Solve each equation for x.

47. $ax + b = c$ **48.** $\frac{x}{a} - b = c$, $a \neq 0$

49. *DATA FILE 3 (pp. 96–97)* Nicholas turned in five halves of one-dollar bills that had accidentally been torn, along with $6 worth of pennies. How much money will he receive?

7-2 Simplifying and Solving Equations

OBJECTIVE:
To solve two-step equations by combining like terms and using the distributive property on one side.

▼ A bowler scores 20 points more in her second game than in her first game. Her total for both games is 310. What is her score in the first game? Let *s* represent the score in the first game and $s + 20$ represent the score in the second game. Then the following equation describes the situation.

$$s + s + 20 = 310$$

You can solve this equation by combining like terms.

$$
\begin{aligned}
s + s + 20 &= 310 \\
2s + 20 &= 310 && \text{Combine like terms.} \\
2s + 20 - 20 &= 310 - 20 && \text{Subtract 20 from both sides.} \\
2s &= 290 \\
\frac{2s}{2} &= \frac{290}{2} && \text{Divide both sides by 2.} \\
s &= 145
\end{aligned}
$$

THINK What if we let *s* represent the score in the second game. How would the score of the first game be expressed? What would be the new equation?

Check $s + s + 20 = 310$

$145 \boxed{+} 145 \boxed{+} 20 \boxed{=} 310 \checkmark$ Replace *s* with 145.

▼ Sometimes you need to use the distributive property before combining like terms.

Example 1 $2(x + 7) - 4x = 8$

Solution

$$
\begin{aligned}
2x + 14 - 4x &= 8 && \text{Distributive property} \\
-2x + 14 &= 8 && \text{Combine like terms.} \\
-2x + 14 - 14 &= 8 - 14 && \text{Subtract 14 from each side.} \\
-2x &= -6 \\
\frac{-2x}{-2} &= \frac{-6}{-2} && \text{Divide both sides by -2.} \\
x &= 3
\end{aligned}
$$

Check $2(x + 7) - 4x = 8$ Replace *x* with 3.

$$
\begin{aligned}
2(3 + 7) - 4(3) &= 8 \\
2(10) - 12 &= 8 \\
20 - 12 &= 8 \\
8 &= 8 \checkmark
\end{aligned}
$$

Solving a Multi-step Equation	To solve a multi-step equation:
	1. Remove parentheses using the distributive property.
	2. Combine like terms.
	3. Undo addition or subtraction.
	4. Undo multiplication or division.

▼ You can use an equation to solve word problems.

Example 2 The sale price of a sweater is $48. The price is 20% less than the original price. What was the original price?

Solution Let p = the original price.
Then $p - 0.2p = 48$ describes the situation.

$$p - 0.2p = 48$$
$$0.8p = 48 \qquad \text{Combine like terms.}$$
$$\frac{0.8p}{0.8} = \frac{48}{0.8} \qquad \text{Divide both sides by 0.8.}$$
$$p = 60$$

Check $p - 0.2p = 48$
$60 \ominus 0.2 \otimes 60 \boxminus 48 \checkmark$ Replace p with 60.

▼
THINK How would you write the equation in Example 2 using a fraction instead of a decimal for 20%?

▼

THINK AND DISCUSS

1. How can you solve the equation $25x + 2 = -73$ using addition and multiplication?

2. Is the solution of the equation $14(2x - 1) = 56$ a negative number? Explain.

CLASS EXERCISES

Simplify the left side of each equation. Do not solve.

1. $4x + 5x = 45$

2. $-2(x - 7) = 8$

3. $5 + x - 2x = 8$

4. $\frac{x}{3} - \frac{x}{6} = -7$

Solve and check each equation.

5. $9x - 2x = -42$

6. $4x + 1 - x = 19$

7. $15 = x - 7x$

8. $3(n - 2) = 36$

9. $1.2x + 2.6x = 4.56$

10. $\frac{x}{2} - \frac{x}{4} = -\frac{1}{8}$

Choose the equation that describes the situation. Solve.

11. This year's soybean crop of 224,000 t represents an increase of 40% over last year's crop. How many tons of soybeans were produced last year?

    a. $n = 224,000 - 0.4n$ **b.** $n = 224,000 + 0.4n$

    c. $n + 0.4n = 224,000$ **d.** $n - 0.4n = 224,000$

12. Sally paid $22.40 for a sweatshirt. It had been discounted by 30%. What was the original price of the sweatshirt?

    a. $x + 0.30x = 22.40$ **b.** $x + 30x = 22.40$

    c. $x - 0.30x = 22.40$ **d.** $x = 22.40(0.30x)$

13. Joe bought 2 cartons of milk on Monday and 3 cartons on Tuesday. He spent $1.75. How much was each carton of milk?

    a. $2c + 2c = 1.75$ **b.** $2c + 3c = 0.175$

    c. $5c = 17.5$ **d.** $1.75 = 2c + 3c$

WRITTEN EXERCISES

Solve and check each equation.

1. $5x - x = 11$
2. $-4(y - 1) = 28$
3. $7 = 2(y + 6)$
4. $4(y + 2) = 2$
5. $9 = \frac{1}{3}(h - 4)$
6. $0.9t + 2.3t = -6.4$
7. $16 = 2(y - 1) - 6$
8. $6 = a + a + 4$
9. $n + 2 - 3n = -8$
10. $9 - b + 8b = 23$
11. $9(2m + 5) = -14$
12. $2x + 4 + 3x = -26$
13. $36 = y - 5y - 12$
14. $\frac{1}{5}(x + 2) = 2$
15. $8 - 3(x - 4) = 6$
16. $21 = 9 - 2(4a + 2)$
17. $7(2k - 1) + 4 = 7$
18. $15 = -8(c - 1) + 9$
19. $-0.5x + 4 + 2x = 9$
20. $\frac{2}{3}n + \frac{3}{8}n = \frac{15}{16}$

MENTAL MATH Find each value.

21. If $\frac{1}{6}(4x + 5) = 0.5$, find the value of $4x + 5$.
22. If $3(x + 5) = 18$, find the value of $3x$.
23. If $21 = 2(4 + x) + 7$, find the value of $2x$.

CALCULATOR Solve each equation.

24. $25.8x + 17.3 - 4.2x = -65.1$
25. $238.7 + 1.8(k - 0.2) = 371.9$
26. $0 = 2.4x + 9.8x - 0.25$
27. $-13.5 = 0.8x + 6.7 - 1.3x$
28. $12.3 + 18.6x - 3.5(2.8x + 8.5) = 7(2.55 + 2.5)$
29. $2.34(2.2x - 4.66) + 2.352x + 2.4044 = 0.25 + 1.25$

Write a situation for each equation.

30. $x + 2x + 3x = 18$
31. $5(x - 1) = 10$

Choose the equation which describes the situation. Solve.

32. Julio bought some pencils for $.39 each and the same number of erasers for $.19 each. The total for his supplies was $4.06. How many pencils did Julio buy?

   a. $39x + 19 = 4.06$
   b. $0.39x + 0.19x = 4.06$
   c. $0.39 + 0.19x = 4.06$
   d. $0.39x + (0.39)(0.19) = 4.06$

33. Use the table at the right. What was the original price of a pair of running shoes?

   a. $0.3p = 21$
   b. $30p = 21$
   c. $\frac{p}{30} = 21$
   d. $\frac{p}{0.3} = 21$

NOTES & QUOTES

The procedure for solving an equation is known as an *algorithm*. The term is based on the name of a Persian mathematician, al-Khowârizmî (c. 780–850).

SALE
ATHLETIC SHOES
30% OFF

Shoe Type	Savings
Basketball	$15
Track	$ 9
Running	$21

42. DATA FILE 3 (pp. 96–97)

MIXED REVIEW

Find the LCM of each set of numbers.

1. 6, 8

2. 2, 5, 6

Solve and check.

3. $3n + 8 = -44$

4. $16 = \frac{n}{4}$

Write an algebraic expression.

5. Ten less than one-fourth of a number

6. 12 times a number decreased by 5 times the same number

7. A student pays $3.75 for lunch and $6.92 for a snack after school. He has $16.48 left. How much money did he start with?

Write an equation to describe the situation. Solve.

34. I'm thinking of a number. If I subtract 7 and multiply the result by 3, I get 18. What is the number?

35. Team A defeated Team B by 13 points. The total number of points scored by both teams was 171. How many points were scored by Team B?

36. Find two consecutive integers whose sum is -39.

37. Bill paid $53 for a sweater. It was 20% off the original price. What was the original price of the sweater?

38. Jo Ann paid $16.25 for an alarm clock. The original price was $25. What was the percent discount?

39. I'm thinking of a number. If the number is decreased by 8 and the result is tripled, I get 36. What is the number?

Each of these solutions contains a common error. Find each error. State the correct solution.

40. $7x - 1 = 15$
$7x = 14$
$x = 2$

41. $3(x - 1) - 5 = 14$
$3x - 1 - 5 = 14$
$3x - 6 = 14$
$3x = 20$
$x = \frac{20}{3}$

42. DATA FILE 3 (pp. 96–97) An employee at the United States Mint worked 3.2 h on Monday, 6.8 h on Tuesday, and 6 h on Wednesday. How many sheets of one-dollar bills were produced in this time? How many one-dollar bills were produced?

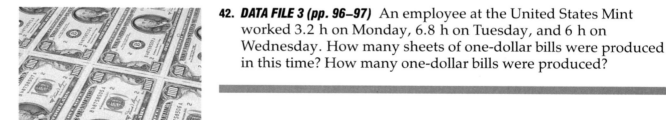

TEST YOURSELF

Solve each equation.

1. $4a - 7 = -15$

2. $52 = \frac{b}{3} - 2$

3. $8.35 + 0.12s = 9.07$

4. $3x + 3x + 9 = -9$

5. $-8 = -2(y + 5)$

Write an equation to describe the situation. Solve.

6. Carmen had $185 in her account. She withdrew the same amount each week for 11 weeks. She then deposited $40. At that time, her balance was $93. How much money did Carmen withdraw each week?

Problem Solving Practice

READ PLAN LOOK BACK SOLVE

PROBLEM SOLVING STRATEGIES

Look for a Pattern
Guess and Test
Simplify the Problem
Make an Organized List
Work Backwards
Account for All Possibilities
Make a Table
Write an Equation
Solve by Graphing
Draw a Diagram
Make a Model
Solve Another Way
Simulate the Problem

Solve. Use an appropriate strategy or a combination of strategies.

1. A student is building a square pen 21 ft long on each side. He puts one post at each corner and one post every 3 ft in between. How many posts will he use?

2. Find two whole numbers whose sum is 125 and whose difference is 23.

3. There are six basketball teams in a tournament. Each team will compete twice against each of the other teams. What is the total number of games to be played?

4. A student counts 18 legs on the chairs and three-legged stools at the Science Fair exhibit booth. How many chairs are there? how many stools?

5. The perimeter of a rectangle is 340 cm. The length is 20 more than twice the width of the rectangle. Find the length.

6. A supermarket clerk stacks cans of beans for a display. The clerk puts 10 cans on the bottom row, 9 cans on top of them, and so on. How many cans does the clerk use if the top layer has one can?

7. A student bought some cassette tapes for $7.95 each and a cassette player for $45.98. The total is $77.78. How many cassette tapes did the student buy?

8. A ninth-grade student rides her bike every other day for exercise. Her friend rides his bike every third day. They both rode their bikes on January 2. How many other days in January will they both ride their bikes on the same day?

9. In a competition, one runner runs 280 m farther than another. Together they run 2,870 m. How many meters did each run?

10. A student bought a skirt for $21.49 and two blouses for $18.98 each. She then had $23.15. How much money did she have before she made the purchases?

11. The sum of the numbers on two facing pages is 149. Their product is 5,550. What are the page numbers?

12. There are 156 students at band practice. There are twice as many females as males at the practice session. How many males are there?

13. A painter can paint a square wall that measures 100 ft on a side in 1 h. How long will it take to paint a square wall that measures 50 ft on a side?

7-3 Writing Equations

■ You can solve many types of problems using equations.

PROBLEM

The Standard Oil Building has eight times as many stories as the first skyscraper. The Sears Tower has 110 stories, which is 20 more than the total number of stories of the other two skyscrapers. How many stories does the first skyscraper have?

SOLUTION

READ ▶ Answer these questions to understand the given information:

What do you want to find?	how many stories are in the first skyscraper
How many stories are in the Standard Oil Building?	eight times as many as are in the first skyscraper
How many are in the Sears Tower?	110 stories
How many more stories are in the Sears Tower than in the other two skyscrapers?	20 more stories

PLAN ▶ Write an equation.

Let n = the number of stories in the first skyscraper.
Then $8n$ = the number of stories in the Standard Oil Building.
The equation $n + 8n + 20 = 110$ describes the situation.

SOLVE ▶ Solve the equation.

$$n + 8n + 20 = 110$$
$$9n + 20 = 110 \quad \text{Combine like terms.}$$
$$9n + 20 - 20 = 110 - 20 \quad \text{Subtract 20 from each side.}$$
$$9n = 90$$
$$\frac{9n}{9} = \frac{90}{9} \quad \text{Divide both sides by 9.}$$
$$n = 10$$

The first skyscraper has 10 stories.

LOOK BACK ▶ How many stories are in the Standard Oil Building? 80 stories

---

CLASS EXERCISES

Write an equation for each sentence. Do not solve.

1. Two-thirds of a number is decreased by 7 to obtain 13.
2. 45 less twice a number is equal to 15.

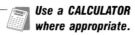
WRITTEN EXERCISES

Write an equation. Do not solve.

1. The difference between 8 times a number and $\frac{1}{2}$ of the number is 16. Find the number.

2. When half of n is added to three times n, the sum is thirty-five. Find n.

Write an equation. Solve.

3. A pair of boots cost $5 more than a pair of shoes. The total cost for both is $114.90. Find the price of the boots.

4. A coin bank contains $2.80 in dimes and quarters. The bank contains the same number of each coin. How many of each coin does the bank contain? *Hint:* Let n = the number of dimes. Since each dime has a value of $.10, the value of n dimes is $.10n$. Since the number of quarters is also n, the value of n quarters is $.25n$.

5. A pencil and an eraser together cost $.95. The pencil costs $.45 more than the eraser. Find the cost of the eraser.

6. A piggy bank contains the same number of pennies, dimes, and quarters for a total of $13.32. How many of each kind of coin is in the bank?

7. A cheese pizza costs $8.75. Each additional topping costs $1.25. If a pizza costs $12.50, how many toppings are on the pizza?

8. A wire of uniform thickness and composition weighs 48 lb. The wire is cut into two pieces. The piece that is 120 yd long weighs 32 lb. Find the original length of the wire.

9. The booster club sold 75% of the tickets printed for the raffle. They did not sell 175 tickets. How many tickets did they have printed?

10. A car rental agency charges $27.95 a day plus $.14/mi. Pat's bill for 3 days was $154.83. How many miles did she drive?

11. Jan has $240 in the bank to pay for her tuba lessons. A lesson costs $15. How many lessons can she afford with her savings?

12. The perimeter of a rectangle is 64 cm. The length is 4 cm less than twice the width. Find the length and width.

13. A number s is multiplied by $\frac{2}{3}$. Then $\frac{2}{5}$ is subtracted from the product. The result is $\frac{11}{45}$. What number is s?

14. Water flows over the Niagara Falls at a rate of 1.5 million gal/s. How many gallons flow over the falls in 1 h 15 s?

Solve.

15. Miss Zawtocki teaches a total of 40 students. The ratio of female students to male students is 1 to 4. How many female students does she teach?

16. The weight of an object on the moon is about $\frac{1}{6}$ of its weight on Earth. If an astronaut weighs 134 lb on Earth, how much would she weigh on the moon to the nearest tenth of a pound?

17. *DATA FILE 1 (pp. 2–3)* What is the danger of frostbite if the air temperature is 10°F and the wind speed is 25 mi/h?

18. Approximately 27 million acres of rain forest are cut and burned each year. If this rate continues, how many acres will be destroyed in the next decade?

19. Mr. Macintosh has 42 rows of apple trees in his orchard. Each row contains 24 trees. Mr. Macintosh is expecting to harvest 18,144 bu of apples this year. On the average, how many bushels of apples does each tree produce?

Critical Thinking

EXPLORING CLOCK ARITHMETIC

Visualize a 12-hour clock face. Start at 10:00. Count forward 16 h. What time will it be?

To find the time using clock arithmetic, follow these steps.

1. To find the *clock time,* add the starting time to the number. $10 + 16 = 26$

2. Use the following formula to determine what the time will be.

clock time − (hours on clock face)(groups of 12 in clock time)
$26 - (12)(2) = 2$, so the time will be 2 o'clock.

Solve.

1. It is 3:00. What time will it be in 7 h?

2. It is 6:00. What time will it be in 17 h?

3. It is 4:00. How many hours ago was it 9 o'clock?

4. a. Suppose a clock shows five hours on its face. How could you adapt the formula so that you could use clock arithmetic? Write the formula.

   b. It is 4 o'clock. What time will it be in 17 h?

   c. It is 1 o'clock. What time was it 29 hours ago?

OBJECTIVE:
To solve equations
with an unknown on
both sides.

7-4 Equations with Variables on Both Sides

▼ The Ricardos have three children whose ages are consecutive even integers. The sum of the children's ages is equal to four times the youngest child's age. What are the ages of the Ricardos' children?

Let a = the youngest child's age.
Then $a + 2$ = the middle child's age.
Then $a + 4$ = the oldest child's age.

We can write the following equation to describe this situation.

$$a + a + 2 + a + 4 = 4a$$

You can solve this equation by using a model.

Model the equation.

Combine like terms.

Subtract 3a from each side of the equation.

The value of a is 6. So the ages of the Ricardo children are 6, 8, and 10.

▼ You can also solve equations with variables on both sides by using algebraic properties.

Example 1 **Solve $3x + 7 = 5x - 1$.**

Solution

$$3x + 7 = 5x - 1$$
$$3x + 7 - 3x = 5x - 1 - 3x \qquad \text{Subtract } 3x \text{ from each side.}$$
$$7 = 2x - 1$$
$$7 + 1 = 2x - 1 + 1 \qquad \text{Add 1 to each side.}$$
$$8 = 2x$$
$$\frac{8}{2} = \frac{2x}{2} \qquad \text{Divide each side by 2.}$$
$$4 = x$$

Check $3x + 7 = 5x - 1$
$$3(4) + 7 = 5(4) - 1 \qquad \text{Replace } x \text{ with 4.}$$
$$12 + 7 = 20 - 1$$
$$19 = 19\checkmark$$

▼ When more than one term on a side of an equation contains a variable, you need to combine like terms before you add or subtract.

Example 2 Solve $5x - 2 - 3x = 2x + 7 - x$.

Solution

$$5x - 2 - 3x = 2x + 7 - x$$
$$2x - 2 = x + 7 \qquad \text{Combine like terms.}$$
$$2x - 2 - x = x + 7 - x \qquad \text{Subtract } x \text{ from each side.}$$
$$x - 2 = 7$$
$$x - 2 + 2 = 7 + 2 \qquad \text{Add 2 to each side.}$$
$$x = 9$$

Check $5x - 2 - 3x = 2x + 7 - x$
$$5(9) - 2 - 3(9) = 2(9) + 7 - 9 \qquad \text{Replace } x \text{ with 9.}$$
$$45 - 2 - 27 = 18 + 7 - 9$$
$$16 = 16 \checkmark$$

▼ You may need to use the distributive property to remove parentheses before combining like terms.

Example 3 Solve $n + 2(n + 2) = n + 16$.

Solution

$$n + 2(n + 2) = n + 16$$
$$n + 2n + 4 = n + 16 \qquad \text{distributive property}$$
$$3n + 4 = n + 16 \qquad \text{Combine like terms.}$$
$$3n + 4 - n = n + 16 - n \qquad \text{Subtract } n \text{ from each side.}$$
$$2n + 4 = 16$$
$$2n + 4 - 4 = 16 - 4 \qquad \text{Subtract 4 from each side.}$$
$$2n = 12$$
$$\frac{2n}{2} = \frac{12}{2} \qquad \text{Divide both sides by 2.}$$
$$n = 6 \qquad \text{The check is left for you.}$$

THINK How is adding and subtracting variables similar to adding and subtracting numbers from both sides of an equation?

Solving Equations with Variables on Both Sides	To solve equations with variables on both sides:
	1. Use the distributive property to remove parentheses.
	2. Combine like terms.
	3. Use the addition and/or subtraction properties so that variables are on one side and constants on the other.
	4. Use the multiplication or division property.

THINK AND DISCUSS

1. To solve the equation $6x = x - 10$, what should you do first?

2. How are the steps for solving equations related to the strategy, *Simplify the Problem*?

CLASS EXERCISES

State the first step in solving each equation.

1. $4x = 9x + 50$

2. $2x - 9 = 27$

3. $4 - x + 6x = 10 + x - 1$

4. $3(2x - 0.3) = 15 - (x + 2)$

Write an equation for each diagram. Solve.

5.

6.

Solve and check each equation.

7. $n + 12 = 5n$

8. $-2r + 7 = r - 8$

9. $9 - (x - 4) = 3(x - 1)$

10. $\frac{1}{4}(d + 2) = \frac{3}{4}d - 6$

WRITTEN EXERCISES

Write an equation for each diagram. Solve.

1.

2.

MENTAL MATH Solve.

3. $x + x + x = x + 6$

4. $3x + 20 = 8x$

5. $x + 7 = 2x + 6$

6. $2(x + 4) = 3x$

Solve each equation.

7. $5x + 8 = 7x$

8. $3a = a + 22$

9. $8.6 + 2.1x = -0.05x$

10. $m + m + 18 = 4m$

11. $4w + 8 = 6w - 4$

12. $7r = 2(r - 10)$

13. $6(h + 3) = -2(h + 31)$

14. $-2(y + 6) = y + 3 + 2y$

15. $9 - (2y - 3) = y$

16. $4 - 7t = 2(t - 7)$

17. $2g + 6 = -g - 8$

18. $5(n - 3) = 2n - 6$

19. $7b = b + 16 + 2b$

20. $0.3k + 1.4 = 4.2 - 0.1k$

21. $4(8 - k) = 2k + 16$

22. $m - 16 = 3m + 18 + 2m$

23. $\frac{1}{5}(x + 8) = \frac{4}{5}x - \frac{1}{5}$

24. $\frac{1}{2}(2h + 4) = \frac{1}{3}(h - 4)$

Is the given number a solution of the equation?

25. $b + 6 = 3(b - 4), b = 9$

26. $10 - 6m = 2(m - 3), m = -3$

27. $-f + 3f = f + 27, f = 27$

28. $a - 8 - 2 = \frac{1}{2}(a - 2), a = 18$

CALCULATOR Solve.

29. $3.6a - 6.2 - 0.1a = 1.5 + 0.2(a + 6)$

30. $4 - 0.6a = 3(1.5a + 0.9) + 7.93$

MIXED REVIEW

Write an algebraic expression.

1. twice the result of increasing a number by 4

2. $14 more than the cost of a cassette

Write an equation. Solve.

3. Six less than three times a number is twelve.

4. Fifty-six is eight more than six times a number.

Replace each ▓ with <, >, or =.

5. $\frac{12}{-4}$ ▓ $-2 - 1$

6. 3 ▓ $\sqrt{9}$

7. A student pays $168 for a coat and jacket. The jacket costs $18 less than the coat. What is the price of the coat?

Write an equation to describe the situation. Solve.

31. Find three consecutive integers whose sum is 165.

32. Find three consecutive odd integers whose sum is 87.

33. One more than one-half of a number is one less than two-thirds of the number. What is the number?

34. If a number is subtracted from 18, the result is four less than the number. What is the number?

35. Twice a number less eight is 16 less than three times the number. What is the number?

36. Find four consecutive integers whose sum is negative two.

37. ***DATA FILE 9 (pp. 360–361)*** Twice the measure of the loft of a 6 iron minus *x* is equal to the measure of the loft of a 9 iron.

Use the article below.

38. a. Use Diophantine symbols. Write the numerals 56, 129, and 683.

   b. ***WRITE*** Will a letter in any number written in Diophantine symbolism ever come before a letter of later rank in the alphabet? Explain.

   c. Determine how many years Diophantus lived. *Hint:* Let his age *a* equal the expression in the article below. Simplify the expression and solve for *a*.

Diophantine Symbolism Using Roman Signs

1	2	3	4	...	9
a	b	c	d	...	i

10	20	30	...	90
j	k	l	...	r

100	200	300	...
s	t	u	...

The Father of Algebra

Diophantus was a Greek mathematician who lived in the third century. He is called the father of algebra because he was the first mathematician to use symbols. For example, Diophantus expressed numerals as shown in the table at the left. The number 234 would have been written as *tld*.

We know how long Diophantus lived from a description of his life in terms of an algebraic riddle. The riddle states, "Diophantus' youth lasted one sixth of his life. He grew a beard after one twelfth more. After one seventh more of his life he married. Five years later he had a son. The son lived exactly one-half as long as his father and Diophantus died four years after his son. All of this adds up to the years Diophantus lived."

Adding the parts of Diophantus' life results in the following expression:

$$\frac{1}{6}a + \frac{1}{12}a + \frac{1}{7}a + 5 + \frac{1}{2}a + 4$$

MATERIALS

- Paper
- Ruler
- Math journal to record
  work

Exploring Inequalities

▼ Study the number line models to see what happens to each inequality sign for $-2 < 4$ when you multiply each side of the inequality by a positive or negative number.

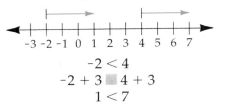

a. Add 3, a positive number.

$$-2 < 4$$
$$-2 + 3 \; \blacksquare \; 4 + 3$$
$$1 < 7$$

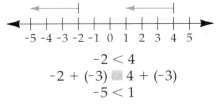

b. Add -3, a negative number.

$$-2 < 4$$
$$-2 + (-3) \; \blacksquare \; 4 + (-3)$$
$$-5 < 1$$

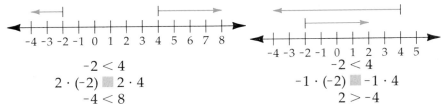

c. Multiply each side by 2, a positive number.

$$-2 < 4$$
$$2 \cdot (-2) \; \blacksquare \; 2 \cdot 4$$
$$-4 < 8$$

d. Multiply each side by -1, a negative number.

$$-2 < 4$$
$$-1 \cdot (-2) \; \blacksquare \; -1 \cdot 4$$
$$2 > -4$$

1. **Describe** what you notice about the direction of the arrows in the inequalities modeled above.

2. Try adding other positive and negative numbers to the inequality $-2 < 4$. **Model** on the number line. **Explain** what happens to the inequality sign.

3. **Explore** what happens to the inequality sign if you subtract the same number from each side of an inequality.

4. Try multiplying each side of $-2 < 4$ by other positive and negative numbers and model on the number line. **Explain** what happens to the inequality sign.

5. **Explore** what happens if you divide each side of the inequality $-2 > 4$ by 2 and by -2.

6. **Summarize** Write a rule that tells what happens to an inequality sign if you perform the following operations on each side of the inequality.

   a. Add or subtract either a positive number or a negative number.

   b. Multiply or divide by a positive number.

   c. Multiply or divide by a negative number.

7. How are the rules for inequalities similar to the rules for equations? How are they different?

OBJECTIVE:
To write and graph simple inequalities with one variable.

7-5 *Inequalities and Their Graphs*

▼ No one under 17 is admitted to theaters showing R-rated films unless they are accompanied by an adult. If you let *a* represent age, you can write the *inequalities* $a < 17$ and $a > 0$ to describe this situation.

Inequality	An inequality is a statement that two expressions are not equal.

▼ You can graph an inequality on a number line.

Example 1 **Graph each inequality.**

    a. $y < 3$ **b.** $x > -1$

Solution **a.**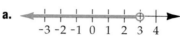

The value for *y* is any real number less than 3. We place an open dot above 3 to show that 3 is not a solution.

    b.

The value for *x* is any real number greater than -1. We place an open dot above -1 to show that -1 is not a solution.

THINK Why is graphing an inequality an easier way to show the solutions than listing them?

▼ You can also graph inequalities that include an equal sign.

Example 2 **Graph each inequality.**

    a. $a \leq -2$ **b.** $g \geq -6$

Solution **a.**

The value for *a* is -2 or any real number less than -2. We place a solid dot above -2 since -2 is a solution.

    b.

The value for *g* is -6 or any real number greater than -6. We place a solid dot above -6 since -6 is a solution.

FLASHBACK

$\leq$ *is less than or equal to*

$\geq$ *is greater than or equal to*

Example 3 **State whether the endpoint of the graph of each inequality would be a solid dot or an open dot.**

    a. $y + 3 > 12$ **b.** $3a \geq -21$ **c.** $6x \leq 18$

Solution   **a.** open   **b.** solid   **c.** solid

▼ You can write an inequality for a graph.

Example 4 Write an inequality for each graph.

a.   b.

Solution a. $x > 0$ b. $x \leq -1$

▼ You can write an inequality for a sentence or a sentence for an inequality.

Example 5 a. Write an inequality for p is greater than -2.
b. Write a sentence for the inequality $b \leq 8$.

Solution a. $p > -2$ b. b is less than or equal to 8.

▼ You can write an inequality to describe a situation.

Example 6 Write an inequality to describe the situation.

There are more than 15 girls in the class.
Let g = the number of girls in the class.

Solution $g > 15$

CLASS EXERCISES

Read each inequality aloud.

1. $t > -16$ **2.** $57 \leq n$ **3.** $y < 28$

Tell whether each inequality is true or false.

4. $-2 + 7 > 6$ **5.** $0.03 > 0.1$ **6.** $-2^4 < (-2)^4$

Match each inequality with the appropriate graph.

7. $x \geq -4$ a.

8. $x \leq -4$ b.

9. $x > 0.4$ c.

10. $t \geq -0.4$ d.

THINK AND DISCUSS
1. Is the inequality $a > b$ equivalent to $b < a$?
2. How is an inequality with one variable different from an equation?

Write an inequality for each word phrase.

11. x is less than 5.   **12.** y is more than -3.

WRITTEN EXERCISES

Tell whether each inequality is true or false.

1. $-5 + 2 < -2$ **2.** $|-8 \times 2| \geq 10$ **3.** $\sqrt{16} \leq 4$

4. $3(-5) + 1 > -2(-6) - 18$ **5.** $(0.5)(2 + 8) < -2^2 + 2$

CALCULATOR True or false.

6. $-8.46 - 4.51 < 5(1.13) - 1.76$ **7.** $3(-0.04 + 7.12) > -2.87(-2.35)$

8. $-0.8(8.3 + 6.8) \geq 4.3(-3)$ **9.** $|-14.3 + 4.9| < 4.47(2.1)$

Write each inequality as a word sentence.

10. $2.5 > m$ **11.** $6.2 \leq j$ **12.** $5 \leq k$

13. $|x| \geq 2$ **14.** $8r < 29$ **15.** $72 \geq g$

State an inequality for each graph.

16.
```
  <-+-Ø-+-+-+-+-+-+-+->
   -5 -4 -3 -2 -1 0 1 2 3
```

17.
```
  <-+-+-+-+-+-+-+-●-+->
   -5 -4 -3 -2 -1 0 1 2 3
```

18.
```
  <-+-+-+-+-●-+-+-+-+->
   -5 -4 -3 -2 -1 0 1 2 3
```

Graph each inequality on a number line.

19. $x < 7$ **20.** $y > 2$ **21.** $a \geq -2$

22. $j \leq 0$ **23.** $x > -1$ **24.** $a < 2$

25. $m > -5$ **26.** $b \geq 6$ **27.** $p \leq 4$

28. $x > 1$ **29.** $j \geq -1$ **30.** $c < 1$

Write an inequality for each sentence.

31. Three is less than ten.

32. The total t is greater than seven.

33. A number p is positive.

34. A number c is at least a dozen.

35. The price p is not more than $30.

36. The number of seats s in the auditorium is no more than 3,500.

37. *DATA FILE 4 (pp. 138–139)* Three times x is less than the population of Monaco per square kilometer.

State two inequalities for each graph.

38.
```
  <-+-+-+-●-Ø-+-+->
   -3 -2 -1 0 1 2 3
```

39.
```
  <-+-+-Ø-●-+-+-+-+->
   -15 -10 -5 0 5 10 15
```

MIXED REVIEW

Solve.

1. $2x - 5 = 29$

2. $x - 3(5 - x) = 2 + 7x$

Write as an expression.

3. 4 less than twice a number

4. 14 less a number

Simplify.

5. $\sqrt{16} - |-4|$

6. $n + (n + 2) + (n + 4)$

Solve.

7. A recipe calls for $\frac{2}{3}$ c of milk. Jane needs to triple the recipe. How much milk will she need?

Replace  with <, >, or = to make the statement
$3 + x$ ■ $7 + x$ true.

40. if $x = 4$ **41.** if $x = 0$ **42.** if $x = -5$ **43.** if $x < 0$

Replace ■ with <, >, or = to make the statement $3x$ ■ $7x$ true.

44. if $x = 7$ **45.** if $x = 0$ **46.** if $x = -2$ **47.** if $x < -1$

Replace ■ with < or > to make each statement true.

48. If $a < b$, then b ■ a. **49.** If $x > y$, and $y > z$, then x ■ z.

Write an inequality to describe each situation.

50. Fewer than 45 people attended the show. Let n equal the number of people who attended the show.

51. A student has $5 but does not have enough money to purchase three pairs of socks. Let m equal the cost of three pairs of socks.

52. At least 127 students attended the rock concert. Let s equal the number of students.

53. A student picked at least 15 bushels of apples. Let b equal the number of bushels picked.

54. A student pays for three movie tickets with a twenty-dollar bill. The change is less than $1. Let t equal the cost of a movie ticket.

55. No more than 50 students walked in the walkathon. Let s equal the number of students.

56. *DATA FILE 7 (pp. 272–273)* Let h equal the flight time in hours.
  a. On flights of how many hours is smoking not permitted?
  b. On flights of how many hours is smoking permitted?

COMPUTER You can use a computer to compare data. The table at the right shows yearly salaries for six people. Each person's tax is based on salary. Let s equal salary.

57. a. Run the following BASIC program. Use the data in the table for S.

```
10 PRINT "SALARY";
20 INPUT S
30 IF S < 20000 THEN PRINT "TAX = ";S*.15
40 IF S > 20000 THEN PRINT "TAX = ";S*.2
```

  b. *CALCULATOR* Did the program calculate the correct tax for each employee?

  c. The IF command allows the program to decide which tax rate to use. What role do the inequalities play in the program?

Name	Salary
Smith, J.	$25,700
Chien, H.	32,500
Garcia, R.	22,000
O'Malley, M.	19,500
Jones, K.	38,500
Strauss, J.	17,000

Tax Rates

If $s < 20{,}000$, 15%	
If $s > 20{,}000$, 20%	

Solving One-step Inequalities

NOTES & QUOTES

Dimitri Ivanovich Mendeleev (1834–1907) was a Russian chemist. He classified the elements by their similarities. Mendeleev left gaps in his periodic table for elements that would be discovered in later years.

▼ In 1869, Dimitri Mendeleev arranged the 63 known elements into the first *periodic table*. By 1984, advances in science had gradually increased the size of the table to 109 elements. How many elements could have been added to Mendeleev's table by 1982?

We can let n equal the number of elements added to the periodic table. Then the following inequality represents the number of elements that could have been added to the table by 1982.

$$63 + n < 109$$
$$-63 + 63 + n < 109 - 63$$
$$n < 46$$

Fewer than 46 elements could have been added to the table by 1982.

▼ You can solve inequalities by using the *addition properties for inequalities.*

Example 1 Solve the inequality $n - 15 < 73$.

Solution

$$n - 15 < 73$$
$$n - 15 + 15 < 73 + 15 \qquad \text{Add 15 to each side.}$$
$$n < 88$$

Addition Properties for Inequalities	Arithmetic
	1. $7 > 3$, so $7 + 4 > 3 + 4$.
	2. $2 < 5$, so $2 + 6 < 5 + 6$.
	Algebra
	1. If $a > b$, then $a + c > b + c$.
	2. If $a < b$, then $a + c < b + c$.

▼ You can solve inequalities by using the *subtraction properties for inequalities.*

Example 2 Solve the inequality $-26 > y + 15$.

Solution

$$-26 > y + 15$$
$$-26 - 15 > y + 15 - 15 \qquad \text{Subtract 15 from each side.}$$
$$-41 > y$$

Subtraction Properties for Inequalities	Arithmetic
	1. $12 > 4$, so $12 - 3 > 4 - 3$.
	2. $8 < 9$, so $8 - 2 < 9 - 2$.
	Algebra
	1. If $a > b$, then $a - c > b - c$.
	2. If $a < b$, then $a - c < b - c$.

▼ You can solve inequalities which involve multiplication using the *multiplication properties for inequalities*.

Multiplication Properties for Inequalities	**Arithmetic**
	1. $3 < 4$, so $3(5) < 4(5)$.
	2. $7 > 2$, so $7(4) > 2(4)$.
	3. $6 < 7$, so $6(-2) > 7(-2)$.
	4. $7 > 5$, so $7(-3) < 5(-3)$.
	Algebra
	1. If c is positive and $a < b$, then $ac < bc$.
	2. If c is positive and $a > b$, then $ac > bc$.
	3. If c is negative and $a < b$, then $ac > bc$.
	4. If c is negative and $a > b$, then $ac < bc$.

Example 3   Solve the inequality $\frac{x}{6} > -4$.

Solution $\frac{x}{6} > -4$

$6\left(\frac{x}{6}\right) > -4(6)$ Multiply each side by 6.

$x > -24$

THINK How are the rules for solving inequalities similar to those for solving equations? How are they different?

▼ You can solve inequalities which involve division using the *division properties for inequalities*.

Division Properties for Inequalities	**Arithmetic**
	1. $3 < 6$, so $3 \div 3 < 6 \div 3$.
	2. $6 > 2$, so $6 \div 2 > 2 \div 2$.
	3. $6 < 12$, so $6 \div (-3) > 12 \div (-3)$.
	4. $16 > 8$, so $16 \div (-4) < 8 \div (-4)$.
	Algebra
	1. If c is positive and $a < b$, then $\frac{a}{c} < \frac{b}{c}$.
	2. If c is positive and $a > b$, then $\frac{a}{c} > \frac{b}{c}$.
	3. If c is negative and $a < b$, then $\frac{a}{c} > \frac{b}{c}$.
	4. If c is negative and $a > b$, then $\frac{a}{c} < \frac{b}{c}$.

Example 4   Solve the inequality $-5x < 20$.

Solution $-5x < 20$

$\frac{-5x}{-5} > \frac{20}{-5}$ Divide each side by -5. Change the direction of the inequality symbol.

$x > -4$

You need to change the direction of the inequality sign only when multiplying or dividing by a negative number.

CLASS EXERCISES

State whether the inequality symbol remains the same or is reversed when you do the following to each side of an inequality.

1. add -5 **2.** multiply by -7 **3.** divide by 3

4. subtract 12   **5.** divide by -1 **6.** add 8

What was done to both sides of the first inequality to obtain the second?

7. $x - 5 \geq 6; x \geq 11$ **8.** $8 > -4x; -2 < x$

Tell whether each number is a solution of $3 - x > 1$.

9. 3   **10.** 2   **11.** 0   **12.** -4

Solve each inequality.

13. $\dfrac{x}{-6} > 3$ **14.** $-3.2x < 14.4$ **15.** $x - 8.4 > -2.7$

THINK AND DISCUSS

1. The rules for multiplying and dividing both sides of an inequality do not mention zero. Discuss these cases.

2. Is -6 a solution of the inequality $x \div 3 > 2$? Explain.

WRITTEN EXERCISES

State whether the inequality symbol remains the same or is reversed when you do the following to each side of an inequality.

1. A negative number is subtracted from both sides.

2. Both sides are multiplied by a positive number.

3. Both sides are divided by a negative number.

What was done to both sides of the first inequality to obtain the second?

4. $x + 8 \leq 11; x \leq 3$ **5.** $9 > -3x; -3 < x$

6. $4x \geq 48; x \geq 12$ **7.** $\frac{1}{3}x \leq 18; x \leq 54$

Tell whether each number is a solution of $5 - 2x \leq 1$.

8. 3   **9.** 2.5   **10.** 0   **11.** -4

Solve each inequality.

12. $x + 6 \geq 7$ **13.** $3 \leq x - 5$ **14.** $\dfrac{x}{3} \geq -5$

15. $-3x < 0$ **16.** $-4x \leq -16$ **17.** $x - 9 > -5$

18. $\frac{1}{2}x \geq -3$ **19.** $x - 7 < -15$ **20.** $9x \leq 27$

21. $5 + x > -7$ **22.** $\dfrac{b}{3} \leq -31$ **23.** $-3 \geq \dfrac{g}{-7}$

MIXED REVIEW

Find the GCF of each set of numbers.

1. 10, 35

2. 4, 7, 8

Graph each inequality.

3. $x < 2$

4. $x \geq -5$

Solve each equation.

5. $3x - 5 = 4 - 2x$

6. $3(1 - x) = 6x + 11$

7. Find two whole numbers whose sum is 164 and whose difference is 12.

24. DATA FILE 7 (pp. 272–273) Write each as an inequality.

a. Use two inequalities to describe the passengers eligible for discounted airline fares. Let p = the age of passengers eligible for discounted fares.

b. Two times the number of passengers boarding in Miami in 1987 is less than the number boarding in Chicago/O'Hare in 1987.

DATA The circle graph at the right shows the source of energy for every 100 kilowatts (kw) of energy produced in the United States.

25. Let x and y be two sources of energy from the graph. Determine the source related to x and y based on the inequalities: $x < y$; $x + y > 10$; $xy > 200$; $y - x \geq 35$.

26. What percent of the energy is obtained from oil and natural gas?

27. COMPUTER How many more kilowatts of nuclear energy would be required to increase nuclear energy's share to at least 25%? Assume that the other sources of energy have the same number of kilowatts shown on the circle graph. *Hint:* use a spreadsheet and a graphics program.

28. PROJECT What sources of energy are not included in the graph?

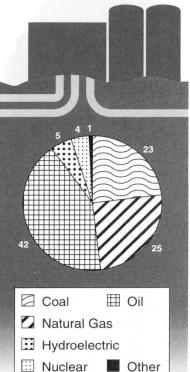

Sources of Energy in the United States for Every 100 kw

Coal ⊞ Oil
Natural Gas
Hydroelectric
Nuclear ■ Other

TEST YOURSELF

Solve each equation.

1. $12w = 7w + 25$

2. $8 - 3t = t - 2t - 6$

3. $(y + 6)3 + 2y = 2y + 6$

4. $12 - 2x = -(x - 4)$

Solve each inequality.

5. $y - 3 > -7$

6. $y + 4 < 8$

7. $\frac{s}{-6} > -7$

8. $7h > \frac{1}{3}$

9. $64 \leq -8k$

10. $y - (-5) > -7$

Write an inequality to describe the situation. Solve.

11. Seven less than a number is greater than negative two. Find the number.

12. When this number is divided by negative four, the result is at least 30. Find the number.

13. Negative eight is greater than or equal to a number divided by negative three. Find the number.

7-7 *Solving Two-step Inequalities*

▼ A research company budgeted $1,000 for an on-line computer information service. The service charges a $250 monthly service fee plus $75 for each hour of use. How many hours can the research company use the service and stay within budget?

Let h = the number of hours.
Then $250 + 75h \le 1,000$ describes the situation.

The steps for solving a two-step inequality are similar to the steps for solving a two-step equation.

$$250 + 75h \le 1,000$$
$$250 + 75h - 250 \le 1,000 - 250 \qquad \text{Subtract 250 from each side.}$$
$$75h \le 750$$
$$\frac{75h}{75} \le \frac{750}{75} \qquad \text{Divide each side by 75.}$$
$$h \le 10$$

The company can use the computer service for, at most, 10 h.

Example 1 **Solve each inequality.**

    a. $6 - x > 3$ **b.** $\frac{1}{2}y - 3 \le -5$

Solution   **a.** $6 - x - 6 > 3 - 6$ **b.** $\frac{1}{2}y - 3 + 3 \le -5 + 3$
$$-x > -3$$
$$(-1)(-x) < (-1)(-3) \qquad\qquad \frac{1}{2}y \le -2$$
$$x < 3 \qquad\qquad\qquad (2)\left(\frac{1}{2}y\right) \le (2)(-2)$$
$$y \le -4$$

▼ You can use inequalities to describe situations.

Example 2   Divide a number by -5. Then add 4 to the quotient. The result is no more than 7. Find the number.

Solution   Let n = the original number.
Then $\frac{n}{-5} + 4 \le 7$ describes the situation.

$$\frac{n}{-5} + 4 \le 7$$

$$\frac{n}{-5} + 4 - 4 \le 7 - 4 \qquad \text{Subtract 4 from each side.}$$

$$\frac{n}{-5} \le 3$$

$$-5 \cdot \frac{n}{-5} \ge -5 \cdot 3 \qquad \text{Multiply each side by -5.}$$

$$n \ge -15$$

The number is greater than or equal to -15.

▼ Sometimes you will use an inequality to solve a problem with only one correct answer.

Example 3 Find the two smallest consecutive integers whose sum is greater than 55.

Solution Let i = the lesser of the two integers.
Then $i + 1$ = the next consecutive integer.
The inequality $i + i + 1 > 55$ describes the situation.

$$i + i + 1 > 55$$
$$2i + 1 > 55 \qquad \text{Combine like terms.}$$
$$2i + 1 - 1 > 55 - 1 \qquad \text{Subtract 1 from each side.}$$
$$2i > 54$$
$$\frac{2i}{2} > \frac{54}{2} \qquad \text{Divide each side by 2.}$$
$$i > 27$$

The two consecutive integers are 28 and 29.

CLASS EXERCISES

What was done to each side of the first inequality to obtain the second?

1. $2 + x \le 9;\ x \le 7$

2. $16 + x > -5;\ x > -21$

3. $-3x > 24;\ x < -8$

4. $8x - 3 \le 19;\ 8x \le 22$

Solve each inequality for x.

5. $\frac{2x}{3} + 1 > 3$

6. $4x - 1 \le 3$

7. $6x + 2 \ge 0$

8. $\frac{1}{2}x - 3 < 1$

9. $20 - 3x > 2$

10. $3x - 1 < 11$

11. $5 - (x - 1) \ge 9$

12. $-4(2x + 7) < -12$

13. $3 + x > -6$

Write an inequality to describe the situation. Solve.

14. Find the two greatest consecutive odd integers whose sum is less than -11.

THINK AND DISCUSS

1. Why is addition or subtraction usually performed before multiplication or division when solving an inequality?

2. Are there any situations where it might be easier to multiply or divide before adding and subtracting? Explain.

3. Find two positive and two negative solutions of the inequality $|x + 3| < 5$.

WRITTEN EXERCISES

What was done to each side of the first inequality to obtain the second?

1. $8 - x \le 11;\ -x \le 3$

2. $6 + 3x > 5;\ 3x > -1$

3. $4x + 7 > 0;\ 4x > -7$

4. $\frac{2x}{5} < 2;\ x < 5$

Solve each inequality for variable x.

5. $\frac{x}{3} + 2 > 3$

6. $9x + 3 \geq 21$

7. $\frac{1}{2}x - 4 \geq -1$

8. $\frac{1}{2}x - \frac{1}{4} < -\frac{3}{4}$

9. $-3x + 15 < 0$

10. $2x - 9 > -7$

11. $5x \leq 15 - 8$

12. $11 - 3x > 5$

13. $6x - 10 - x > 14$

14. $8 + 2x \leq 10$

15. $-5x + 3 \geq 28$

16. $2x + x + 5 > 18$

17. $1 + 8x > 25$

18. $4 + 7x \geq 32$

19. $\frac{1}{9}x + 13 \geq 5$

20. $2x + \frac{1}{2} > \frac{3}{2}$

21. $-21 - 3x < 0$

22. $10x - 8 - x < 19$

23. $19 - 8x > -5$

24. $7 + 2x - x \geq 9$

25. $18x - 5x - 4 > 22$

26. $6 - 4x > 14$

27. $\frac{1}{3}x + 11 < 31$

28. $\frac{1}{6}x - 2 < 4$

29. $2x + 2x + 2 < 18$

30. $11x + 13 > -86$

Choose the inequality which describes the situation. Solve.

31. You divide a number by -3. Then you subtract 1 from the quotient. The result is at most 5. Find the number.
(Let x = the number.)

   a. $\frac{-3}{x} - 1 < 5$

   b. $\frac{x}{-3} - 1 \leq 5$

   c. $\frac{x}{3} - 1 \leq -5$

   d. $\frac{x}{-3} - 1 > 5$

32. Laura has $16 in her savings account. She earns $4.50 per hour babysitting. Laura wants to purchase a sweater for $55. What is the least number of hours Laura must babysit in order to buy the sweater? Let x = the number of hours Laura must babysit.

   a. $16x + 4.50 \geq 55$

   b. $4.50x \geq 55 + 16$

   c. $4.50x + 16 \geq 55$

   d. $55 \geq 16 + 4.50x$

Write an inequality to describe the situation. Solve.

33. Five less than twice a number is at least 13. Find the number.

34. An artist withdrew $14 from a bank in each of the last three weeks and still has more than $65. How much did he start with?

35. Students in a math class need an average test score of at least 90 points to earn an A. A student's test scores are 88, 91, and 85. What could the student score on the next test to have an A average?

36. A salesperson earns a salary of $600 per month, plus a commission of 2% of sales. How much must the salesperson sell to have a monthly income of at least $1,700?

37. Find the least whole number solution of $6x - 19 > \text{-}7$.

38. Find the greatest integer solution of $\text{-}5x + 7 > 22$.

Write a problem that could be solved using the inequality.

39. $n + n + 2 < 15$ **40.** $50h + 40h > 360$

41. DATA FILE 10 (pp. 404–405)

    a. What is the least number of acres of rain forests cut down in an eight-hour working day?

    b. How many eight-hour days would it take to destroy an area of rain forest equivalent to the home range of a grizzly bear?

Critical Thinking

EXPLORING QUANTITATIVE COMPARISONS

▼ A *quantitative comparison* is a type of question that appears on some standardized tests. This type of question requires that you evaluate two quantities, compare them, and choose the correct lettered response. Common answer choices are listed below.

(A) The number in Column A is greater.

(B) The number in Column B is greater.

(C) The two numbers are equal.

(D) The relationship cannot be determined based on the available information.

Compare each pair of expressions. The first one is done for you.

	Column A	Column B	Response Choice
1.	$x + 2$	$x + 5$	B, no matter what replacement you choose for x, $x + 5 > x + 2$.
2.	$2x$	$5x$	
3.	$|\text{-}5 - 2|$	$|5| - |2|$	
4.	$3x$	$\frac{x}{3}$	
5.	$5(x - 3)$	$5x - 15$	
6.	$\frac{x-2}{2-x}; x \neq 2$	$4 - \sqrt{16}$	

Practice

Solve and check each two-step equation.

1. $6x + 4 = 40$ **2.** $7x - 10 = 25$ **3.** $57 - 11x = 13$

4. $6 + 5x = 66$ **5.** $\frac{2}{9}x - 9 = 45$ **6.** $7 - \frac{3}{5}x = 13$

7. $19 + 2x = 57$ **8.** $7x - 17 = -3$ **9.** $-21 = -6t - 3$

Solve and check each multi-step equation.

10. $8x - 20 + 2x = 60$ **11.** $42 = -6(5 - x)$

12. $\frac{2}{7}(x + 5) = 8$ **13.** $\frac{2}{3}x - \frac{1}{12}x = 4$

14. $5x - 2x + 11 = 59$ **15.** $19 = x + x - 7$

16. $3(3x - 8) = 21$ **17.** $1.5x - 0.7x = 8$

18. $18 - 3x = 4(x + 8)$ **19.** $6.5 - (0.1x + 2) = -1.6x$

20. $2(6 + x) = 17 - 3x$ **21.** $x + 9 = 2x - 43 + x$

22. $\frac{3}{4}(x - 4) = \frac{1}{4}x + 23$ **23.** $\frac{1}{2}(6x - 6) = \frac{1}{4}(x + 54)$

24. $8x - 7 = 2x - 1$ **25.** $7x + 5 = 8x - 3$

Graph each inequality.

26. $x \le -3$ **27.** $x < 6$ **28.** $x > 0$

29. $x \ge 5$ **30.** $x > -4$ **31.** $x \le 10$

Solve each inequality for x.

32. $x + 6 > 2$ **33.** $-2x < 8$ **34.** $x - 7 \le 6$

35. $\frac{1}{3}x > -6$ **36.** $x - \frac{1}{5} < \frac{4}{5}$ **37.** $6x \le 18$

38. $10 > 5x$ **39.** $8x \ge 32$ **40.** $x - 2 > 5$

41. $6 + 3x > 12$ **42.** $18 - 5x < -2$ **43.** $x + x - 7 \le 21$

44. $\frac{1}{2}x - 9 < 27$ **45.** $\frac{4}{5}x + 4 \ge 16$ **46.** $8x + 54 < 53$

Write an equation to describe the situation. Solve.

47. Martha is saving $22 each week from her paycheck. She already has $47 in her account. In how many weeks will her balance be $201?

48. Fifty-three is four times a number minus nineteen. Find the number.

49. Find four consecutive integers whose sum is -490.

50. Four times the sum of a number and five is equal to 100. Find the number.

OBJECTIVE:
To apply
mathematical skills
when purchasing a
car.

7-8 *Buying a Car*

Option	Price
Air Conditioning	$744
AM/FM Radio-cassette	$155
Automatic Transmission	$732
Metallic Color	$91
Sunroof	$549

THINK What must a
dealership do to a car to
prepare it for sale?

■ Buying a car is one of the first major purchases an individual makes. There are several things to consider when making such an expensive purchase.

A car dealership will give you a *base price* on a car. This is the price of the car without any additional features. Additional features, or *options*, have an additional charge. The table at the left lists the cost of several options that dealers frequently offer.

Example 1 Mr. Perry wants to buy a car with automatic transmission, an AM/FM radio-cassette, and a sunroof. What is the total cost of these options?

Solution $732 + 155 + 549 = 1,436$ Add the cost of the options.

The total cost of these options is $1,436.

■ You will automatically pay a *destination* and *delivery charge* on a new car. This charge pays for the cost of shipping the car from the manufacturer and for preparing the automobile for sale. Most states require you to pay a *sales tax* on a new car.

Example 2 James is purchasing a car for $8,667. The sales tax is 6%. How much sales tax will James pay?

Solution $6\% = 0.06$ Write 6% as a decimal.
$8,667(0.06) = 520.02$ Multiply the cost of the car by 0.06.

James will pay $520.02 in sales tax.

■ Many people take out a loan to help pay for a car. They then make monthly payments. To determine the monthly payment, multiply the number of thousands of dollars being borrowed by a factor which can be found in an *amortization table* like the one shown below.

Amortization Table (per $1,000)

number of months	interest rate		
	10%	11%	12%
12	87.92	88.39	88.85
24	46.15	46.61	47.08
36	32.27	32.74	33.22
48	25.37	25.85	26.34

Example 3 What is the factor for a 10% loan over 36 mo?

Solution Find the number of months. Read across to the 10% column. The factor is 32.27.

Example 4 Lynn wants to borrow $12,000 from her bank. The bank is offering an 11% interest rate. Lynn plans to take out a 36-mo loan. What will be her monthly payment?

Solution

1. Determine the number of thousands of dollars that are being borrowed on $12,000.

   12,000 is the same as 12 thousands.

2. Find the factor on an 11% interest rate over 36 mo using the amortization table.

   32.74

3. Multiply the number of thousands of dollars being borrowed by the factor.

   $12 \cdot 32.74 = 392.88$

Lynn's monthly payment will be $392.88.

CLASS EXERCISES

Refer to the options list on page 305.

1. What would a sunroof and an AM/FM radio-cassette cost?

2. How much sales tax must you pay on a $10,000 car at 6%?

3. How many thousands are in $14,500?

4. What is the factor on a loan at 12% interest over 48 mo?

■ ■ ■ ■ ■ ■ Decision Making ■ **DECISION MAKING** ■ Decision Making ■ Decision Making ■ Decision Making ■

BUYING A CAR

■ **COLLECT DATA**

1. Choose a car you would like to own. Interview salespeople at three dealerships. Organize your data in a chart.

Dealership	base price	options	price of options	dest/del charge

2. Find out the sales tax in your state.

3. Contact three banks in your area and find out what interest rates they offer on new car loans.

■ **ANALYZE DATA**

The base price of a car includes the dealership's profit.

4. Did the base prices on the car you chose vary?

WRITTEN EXERCISES

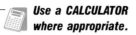

Use a **CALCULATOR**
where appropriate.

Determine the sales tax on each amount at a rate of 6%.

1. $8,675   **2.** $7,988   **3.** $16,654   **4.** $12,560

Determine how many thousands each amount represents.

5. $9,000   **6.** $8,500   **7.** $11,750   **8.** $14,250

Determine each factor using the amortization table on page 305.

9. a loan at 12% over 24 mo   **10.** a loan at 11% over 48 mo

11. Gerald wants to buy a car with a base price of $9,518. The car is metallic black. Gerald is having a sunroof installed. The destination and delivery charge is $342.

   a. Gerald has enough money saved to pay for the sales tax. How much sales tax will Gerald pay at a rate of 6%?

   b. Gerald took out a loan at 10% over 48 mo for the remaining cost of the car. What will he pay per month?

12. Alicia bought a car with a base price of $14,670. She had an AM/FM radio-cassette installed. The destination and delivery charge was $397. Alicia paid 5% sales tax. She withdrew $4,483.10 from her savings and took out a 12% loan over 36 mo for the rest. What does Alicia pay per month?

■ *Decision Making* ■ *Decision Making* ■ *Decision Making* ■ *Decision Making* ■ *Decision Making* ■ *Decision Making* ■

5. Why might one dealership offer a lower base price than another?

6. Did the prices on the options you chose vary from place to place?

7. Is there a relationship between the base price that a dealership offered and the price that they charged for the options?

8. Why might loan rates differ at different banks?

■ **MAKE DECISIONS**

Suppose you are buying the car of your choice. You may add any options. You have enough money saved for sales tax.

9. What is the price of the car, including the options you chose, the destination and delivery charge, and sales tax?

10. Determine what your monthly payment would be if you took out a loan for the full amount needed at 11.5% over 48 mo.

11. How much did you pay the bank for their loan service?

7-8 Buying a Car

Chapter 7 Review

Complete each statement. Use the vocabulary words given.

1. A two-step equation involves two .

2. To solve $3(x + 2) - 2x$, first remove the parentheses using the  property.

3. To solve $2x - 3 + 4x = x + 2 - 3x$, first ▧ like terms.

4. An inequality is a statement that two expressions are ▧.

5. If c is ▧ and $a > b$, then $ac < bc$.

6. The steps for solving a two-step inequality are similar to the steps for solving a two-step ▧.

VOCABULARY

negative
combine
operations
distributive
equation
not equal

Two-step Equations 7-1

To solve a two-step equation,
1. undo addition and subtraction;
2. undo multiplication and division.

Solve each equation.

7.

8.

9. $5a + 3 = 28$

10. $\frac{x}{4} - 9 = -6$

11. $7n - 2 = 19$

12. $\frac{5b}{6} + 7 = 22$

Simplifying and Solving Equations 7-2

To solve a multi-step equation,
1. remove parentheses using the distributive property;
2. combine like terms;
3. undo addition and subtraction;
4. undo multiplication and division.

Solve each equation.

13. $3(x - 5) + 2x = 20$

14. $2x - 8 - 3x = 2$

15. $(2x - 1)2 + 5x = 1$

16. $9 - 5x + 1 = 15$

17. $5(x + 2) - 3x = 38$

18. $8x + 5 - 5x = 3$

Problem Solving Strategy: Writing Equations 7-3

To write an equation for a word problem, you need to recognize words that imply the variable(s), the operation(s), and the equality.

Solve.

19. The difference between 3 times n and 2 times the quantity $n + 5$ is 3. Find n.

20. A sweater cost $12 more than a shirt. The total cost of two sweaters and three shirts is $144. Find the cost of the shirt.

Equations with Variables on Both Sides **7-4**

To solve equations with variables on each side,

1. use the distributive property to remove parentheses;
2. combine like terms;
3. use the addition and subtraction property so that all variables are on one side and constants on the other;
4. use the multiplication and division property.

Solve each equation.

21.

22. $3x + 5 = 7x - 11$

23. $n + 3(n - 2) = 5n + 4$

Inequalities and Their Graphs **7-5**

To graph an inequality, use an open dot for $>$ and $<$, use a closed dot for $\geq$ and $\leq$. If the symbol is $>$ or $\geq$, graph all points to the right of the boundary. If the symbol is $<$ or $\leq$, graph all points to the left of the boundary.

Match each inequality with the appropriate graph.

24. $x \geq 1$ **25.** $x < -3$ **26.** $x > -3$ **27.** $x \leq -1$

Solving One-step Inequalities **7-6**

To solve an addition or subtraction inequality, add or subtract the same value from both sides of the inequality.

To solve a multiplication or division inequality, multiply or divide both sides of the inequality by the same nonzero value. If the value is positive, keep the inequality symbol. If the value is negative, reverse the inequality symbol.

Solve each inequality.

28. $x - 3 < -8$ **29.** $x + 2 \geq -1$ **30.** $-3x > 12$ **31.** $\frac{x}{4} \leq -2$

Solving Two-step Inequalities **7-7**

To solve a simple two-step inequality,   1. undo addition and subtraction;
                                               2. undo multiplication and division.

Solve each inequality.

32. $5x - 7 \leq 18$ **33.** $2y + 4 > 12$ **34.** $\frac{b}{-3} + 5 > 8$ **35.** $\frac{2a}{3} - 1 < 7$

Solve each equation.

1.

2.

3.

4. $5x + 9 = -6$

5. $0.5 + 2n = 3$

6. $\frac{3}{4}y - 5 = 7$

7. $7p - 3 = 18$

8. $-3(b - 6) = 27$

9. $1.5(c + 2) = 6$

10. $7z + 8 - 2z = 23$

11. $5x - 9 = 3x$

12. $2(6 - 2x) = 5x - 6$

Write an equation to describe each situation. Solve.

13. Kendra bought a scarf for \$35.75. The original price was \$55. What was the percent discount?

14. The perimeter of a rectangle is 132 cm. The length is 3 cm more than twice the width. Find the length and width.

Match each inequality with the appropriate graph.

15. $x \geq 2$

    a.
![number line -3 to 3, closed circle at 2, arrow left]

16. $x > -2$

    b.
![number line -3 to 3, open circle at -2, arrow right]

17. $x > 2$

    c.
![number line -3 to 3, closed circle at 2, arrow right]

18. $x \leq -2$

    d.
![number line -3 to 3, open circle at 2, arrow right]

Solve each inequality.

19. $5 \leq x + 1$

20. $3a > 4$

21. $y - 6 < 9$

22. $-2n \leq 10$

23. $\frac{b}{3} \geq \frac{1}{3}$

24. $\frac{p}{-2} < -5$

25. $-2x + 14 < 6$

26. $9y - 8 > -17$

27. $\frac{1}{5}c - 1 \geq 2$

28. $-9 + 6r \leq -33$

29. $-7m + 6 < 48$

30. $9k + 5 > -67$

Write an inequality for each sentence. Graph each inequality.

31. The total, t, is greater than 5.

32. The perimeter, p, is less than 64.

33. The number of passengers, p, on the bus is less than or equal to 45.

34. The number of students, s, that ran in the road race was not less than 55.

35. The number of questions, q, answered correctly is less than or equal to 35.

Chapters 1–7   *Cumulative Review*

Choose the correct answer. Write A, B, C, or D.

1. Write an equation for the model.

  A. $2x + 3 = 4$ **B.** $2x - 3 = 4$

  C. $2x = 3 - 4$ **D.** not given

2. What is the prime factorization of 108?

  A. $2 \cdot 3$ **B.** $2^3 \cdot 3^2$

  C. $2^2 \cdot 3^3$ **D.** not given

3. Solve $\frac{10}{15} = \frac{x}{3}$.

  A. 2 **B.** $\frac{1}{2}$

  C. 5 **D.** not given

4. Write $\frac{3a^3b}{12ac^2}$ in lowest terms.

  A. $\frac{3ab}{4ac}$ **B.** $\frac{ab}{4c}$

  C. $\frac{a^2b}{4c^2}$ **D.** not given

5. Solve $3x - 1 + 2x = x + 11$.

  A. 3 **B.** 2

  C. 0 **D.** not given

6. Write 0.0050 as a percent.

  A. 50% **B.** 5%

  C. 0.5% **D.** not given

7. Find the next number.
0.5, 1.2, 2, 2.9, 3.9, . . .

  A. 4.9 **B.** 4

  C. 5 **D.** not given

8. Count the number of squares.

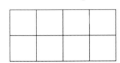

  A. 8 **B.** 11

  C. 10 **D.** not given

9. Simplify $x^2(x - 24)$.

  A. $x^3 - x^2y$ **B.** $x^3 - 2x^2y$

  C. $x^3 - 2y^2$ **D.** not given

10. Find a number between $-1\frac{1}{2}$ and -2.

  A. $-\frac{3}{4}$ **B.** $-1\frac{1}{4}$

  C. $-1\frac{3}{4}$ **D.** not given

11. What percent is 35 of 105?

  A. 3% **B.** 33%

  C. $33\frac{1}{3}\%$ **D.** not given

12. If c is negative and $a < b$, then

  A. $ac > bc$ **B.** $ac < bc$

  C. $ac \le bc$ **D.** not given .

13. Simplify $(a^2b^3)^2(ab^2)$.

  A. a^5b^7 **B.** a^5b^8

  C. a^3b^5 **D.** not given

14. There are 12 students that belong to the Math Club and 18 that belong to the Science Club. There are 5 students that belong to both clubs. How many notices need to be printed for a joint meeting?

  A. 30 **B.** 13

  C. 7 **D.** not given

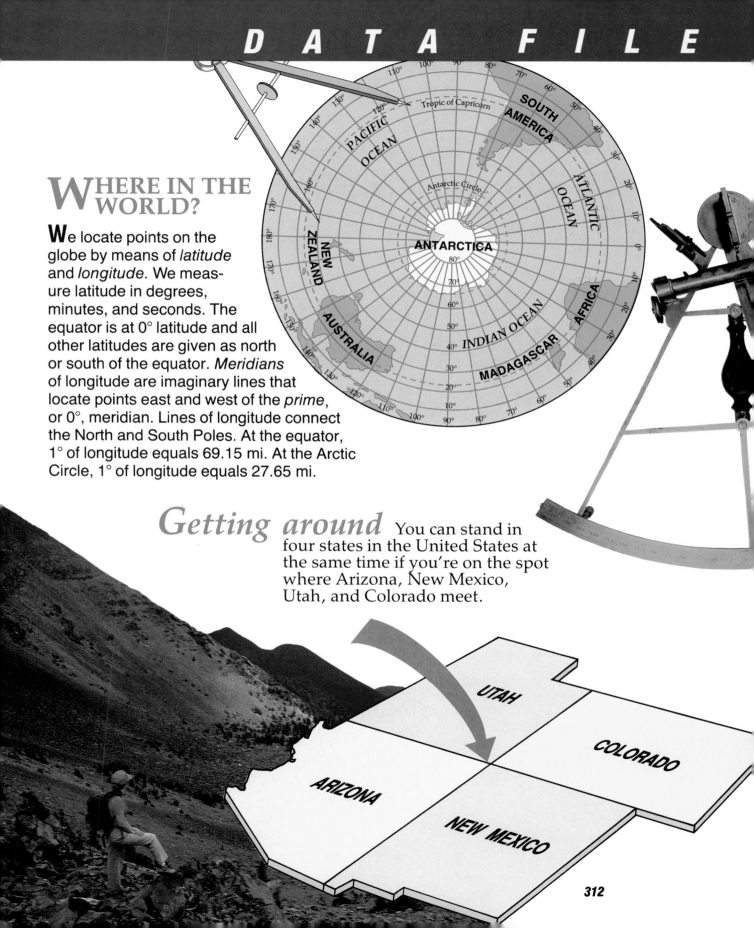

WHERE IN THE WORLD?

We locate points on the globe by means of *latitude* and *longitude*. We measure latitude in degrees, minutes, and seconds. The equator is at 0° latitude and all other latitudes are given as north or south of the equator. *Meridians* of longitude are imaginary lines that locate points east and west of the *prime*, or 0°, meridian. Lines of longitude connect the North and South Poles. At the equator, 1° of longitude equals 69.15 mi. At the Arctic Circle, 1° of longitude equals 27.65 mi.

Getting around

You can stand in four states in the United States at the same time if you're on the spot where Arizona, New Mexico, Utah, and Colorado meet.

312

Graphing in the Coordinate Plane

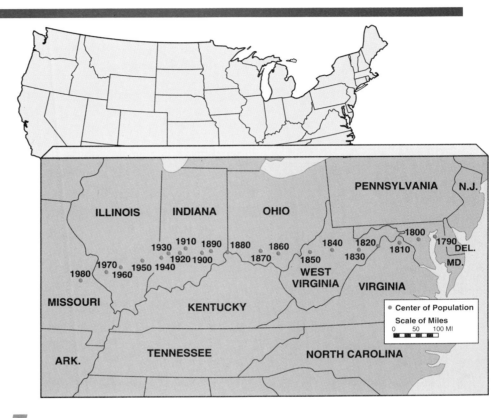

UNITED STATES CENSUS DATA	
YEAR	**POPULATION**
1790	3,929,214
1800	5,308,483
1810	7,239,881
1820	9,638,453
1830	12,866,020
1840	17,069,453
1850	23,191,876
1860	31,443,321
1870	39,818,449
1880	50,155,783
1890	62,947,714
1900	75,994,575
1910	91,972,266
1920	105,710,620
1930	122,775,046
1940	131,669,275
1950	150,697,361
1960	179,323,175
1970	203,302,031
1980	226,545,805
1990	249,632,692

THE CENTER OF POPULATION is the point in the United States at which the population is evenly balanced. This means that if the country were flat, and everyone had the same weight, the country would exactly balance at the center of population.

Think about it...

Look at the Center of Population map. Why do you think the center of population moves? Do you think the center of population will ever stop moving west?

OBJECTIVE:
To explore communication problems.

MATERIALS

- Geoboard
- Math journal to record work

Exploring Verbal Communication

▼ Oral communication is an important tool. It involves an accurate portrayal of a situation by the speaker and careful analysis by the listener.

▼ You can improve your communication skills by choosing a partner and playing this game on a geoboard.

What's My Shape?

Number of Players:	2
Objective:	Each player will end up with the same shape in the same location on their geoboard.
Rules:	**1.** Players sit back-to-back so that neither player can see the other's geoboard.
	2. Player 1 creates a shape on the geoboard using a rubber band. The rubber band may not intersect itself and it may not double back. Examples are shown below.

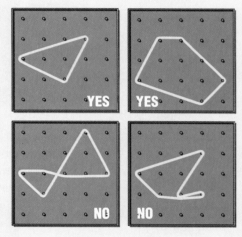

3. Player 1 describes the shape to player 2.

4. Player 2 listens carefully to the description and tries to duplicate the shape in the correct location on his or her geoboard.

5. Player 2 may ask player 1 to repeat the instructions, but may not ask any other questions.

6. After player 2 has completed the shape, both players turn around and compare the shapes on their geoboards.

1. **Write** a description of the method player 1 used to communicate the location of the points on the geoboard. Include answers to the following questions in your description.

   a. Did player 1 give instructions to move right or left?

   b. Did player 1 give instructions to move up or down?

   c. Did player 1 refer to columns and rows?

2. **a.** **Describe** some of the problems player 1 had in describing the shape and location.

   b. **Explain** how player 1 could improve his or her oral communication skills.

3. **Describe** some of the problems player 2 had in interpreting player 1's instructions.

4. Together, write a set of clear instructions so that the shape and location can be duplicated without any problem.

5. Reverse roles and repeat the activity. Answer Questions 1–4.

▼ Good communication skills are necessary when you are giving directions to someone.

6. **a.** **Explain** how playing this game is similar to giving directions to get from your school to your home.

   b. **Explain** how it is different.

   c. **Write** a clear set of instructions telling someone how to get from your school to your home.

   d. **DATA FILE 1 (pp. 2–3) Write** a clear set of instructions telling someone how to use the wind chill chart to determine the degree of danger of frostbite if the air temperature is -15°F and the wind speed is 25 mi/h.

▼ You can try other games to improve listening skills.

7. One student reads a short news article to the listener. The listener writes a short paragraph describing what he or she heard.

   a. **Compare** what is written with the original article.

   b. **Explain** how the listener can improve his or her listening skills.

8. Form a group of ten students. One student whispers the contents of a short newspaper story to another. That student whispers to another what he or she heard. Repeat the process until the last student has heard the story. That student then relates the story he or she heard to the group.

   a. **Compare** the accuracy of the last story with the original.

   b. **Describe** how the group can improve its communication skills.

OBJECTIVE:
To locate and graph a point given the coordinates and to identify the coordinates of a given point.

Benjamin Banneker (1731–1806) was a famous mathematician, astronomer, and surveyor. In 1791 he was asked by President George Washington to help plan the streets and buildings of the nation's new capital, Washington, D.C.

8-1 The Coordinate Plane

▼ Mapmakers use letters and numbers to designate regions on maps. According to the index, Southeastern Avenue in Indianapolis, Indiana, is in Region B2.

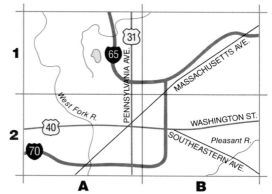

▼ Mathematicians represent a region using a *coordinate plane*.

Coordinate Plane	A coordinate plane is the plane which results when two perpendicular number lines intersect at their zero points. The number lines form a grid on the plane.

▼ We call the horizontal number line the *x-axis*, with the positive direction to the right. We call the vertical number line the *y-axis*, with the positive direction upward. The x- and y-axes intersect at the *origin*. The x- and y-axes divide the coordinate plane into four *quadrants*.

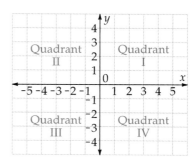

▼ We use *ordered pairs* to locate points in the coordinate plane.

Ordered Pair	An ordered pair is a pair of numbers (x,y) assigned to a point on a coordinate plane.

In the ordered pair (x,y), the value that corresponds with x is called the x-coordinate. The value that corresponds with y is called the y-coordinate. You can locate a point on the coordinate plane when given an ordered pair.

FLASHBACK

The absolute value of a number is its distance from zero on a number line.

Locating a Point on the Coordinate Plane	To locate $P(x,y)$ on the coordinate plane: 1. Begin at origin. 2. Locate x on the x-axis. 3. Move up or down the absolute value of y units.

▼ Use the coordinate plane below for the examples.

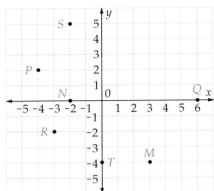

Example 1 **Locate each point on the coordinate plane. State the letter of the point.**

    a. $(-2,5)$ **b.** $(0,-4)$ **c.** $(-3,-2)$ **d.** $(6,0)$

Solution   **a.** Start at the origin. Move 2 units left and up 5. S

      b. Start at the origin. Move zero units left or right and 4 units down. T

      c. Start at the origin. Move 3 units left and 2 units down. R

      d. Start at the origin. Move 6 units right and zero units up or down. Q

▼ Identifying the quadrant in which a point falls is similar to identifying a region on a map.

Example 2   In which quadrant or on which axis does each point fall?

    a. $(2,6)$ **b.** $(-4,0)$ **c.** $(0,0)$

    d. $(3,-1)$ **e.** $(-5,-2)$ **f.** $(0,5)$

Solution   **a.** quadrant I   **b.** x-axis   **c.** both axes

      d. quadrant IV   **e.** quadrant III   **f.** y-axis

▼ You can use an ordered pair to locate a point on the coordinate plane.

Example 3 **Name the coordinates of each point.**

    a. point M **b.** point P **c.** point N

Solution   **a.** Point M is 3 units to the right (positive) of the origin and 4 down (negative). The ordered pair is $(3,-4)$.

      b. Point P is 4 units to the left (negative) of the origin and 2 units up (positive). The ordered pair is $(-4,2)$.

      c. Point N is 2 units to the left (negative) of the origin and zero units up or down. The ordered pair is $(-2, 0)$.

CLASS EXERCISES

State the letter of the point named by each ordered pair.

1. (-1,-4)   **2.** (3,0)

3. (-1,4)   **4.** (-4,-1)

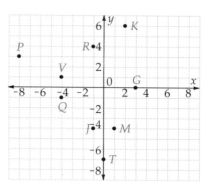

State the coordinates of each point.

5. T   **6.** V

7. M   **8.** K

MENTAL MATH State the coordinates of each point described.

9. the point which is 5 units to the left of the y-axis and down 2 units from the x-axis

10. the point on the y-axis that is 4 units below the x-axis

In which quadrant or on which axis does each point fall?

11. (-2.6,3.4)   **12.** $\left(5\frac{1}{4}, 2\frac{1}{2}\right)$ **13.** $\left(0, -4\frac{2}{3}\right)$ **14.** (1.36,19.41)

15. P(-1,3), Q(4,3), and R(4,-2) are three vertices of a square. Find the coordinates of the fourth vertex.

WRITTEN EXERCISES

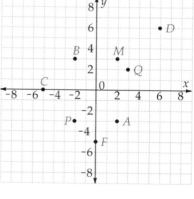

State the letter of the point named by each ordered pair.

1. (3,2)   **2.** (0,-5)

3. (2,3)   **4.** (-2,-3)

State the coordinates of each point.

5. A   **6.** B

7. C   **8.** D

Draw a coordinate plane. Graph each point.

9. F(-3,2)   **10.** G(-1.5,0)   **11.** H(1,7)   **12.** J(-3.5,-4)

13. K(5,-6)   **14.** L(0,0)   **15.** $M\left(\frac{1}{2},3\right)$ **16.** N(7,0)

17. State the coordinates of four points in the coordinate plane that are 3 units from the origin.

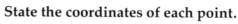

MENTAL MATH State in which quadrant or on which axis $P(x,y)$ lies if the following conditions are true.

18. x is negative and y is zero.

19. x is positive and y is negative.

20. x is positive and y is positive.

21. x is negative and y is positive.

22. x is negative and y is negative.

In which quadrant or on which axis does each point fall?

23. $(13,25)$

24. $(-17.654,-0.02)$

25. $(0,|-2|)$

26. (x,y) if $x > 0$, $y < 0$

27. (x,y) if $x < 0$, $y < 0$

28. (x,y) if $x = 0$, $y > 0$

Graph and connect each point in the order given. Connect the last point to the first. Name the figure.

29. $(-1,2)$, $(1,5)$, $(7,5)$, $(5,2)$

30. $(2,2)$, $(2,-1)$, $(-5,-1)$, $(-5,2)$

31. $(-4,1)$, $(1,1)$, $(-3,-1)$

32. $(2,-4)$, $(7,-1)$, $(4,4)$, $(-1,1)$

33. $P(0,5)$, $Q(5,0)$, and $R(-5,0)$ are three vertices of a square. Find the coordinates of the fourth vertex.

34. **PROJECT** Draw a dot-to-dot picture on a coordinate grid. Write the coordinates of each point in order. Exchange with a classmate and draw each other's picture.

MIXED REVIEW

Solve for **y**.

1. $4.5 + 7y = 18.5$

2. $5a - 10 = 30$

Solve for **x**.

3. $-3x + 8 > 29$

4. $\frac{2}{3}x - 19 \le -13$

Solve for **y** if **x = 3**.

5. $7x + y = 24$

6. $21x + 2y = -7$

Solve.

7. The perimeter of a rectangle is 62 in. Its length is twice its width, less 5 in. Find the actual length and width.

Critical Thinking

EXPLORING GRAPHING

1. **Describe** what you think will happen to a figure if you perform an operation on one or both coordinates of each point.

2. Graph the points $(-2,1)$, $(-2,3)$, $(1,3)$, $(1,1)$. Connect them in the order given. Connect the last point to the first.

3. Find the new coordinates and graph.

   a. Multiply each x-coordinate by -1.

   b. Multiply each y-coordinate by -1.

   c. Multiply each coordinate by -1.

   d. Multiply each coordinate by 2.

4. **Compare** the figures in Exercise 3. **Write** a short paragraph describing your results.

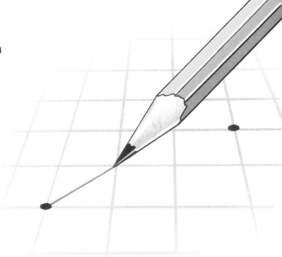

OBJECTIVE:
To solve linear
equations in two
variables.

8-2 Solving Equations

▼ The normal low temperature at the base of Mt. Rushmore in July is 21°C. The temperature drops an average of 1°C for every 100 m of vertical ascent. You can write an equation using two variables to describe this situation. Let y = temperature and let x = meters above the foot of the mountain.

$$y = 21 - 0.01x$$

▼ An ordered pair that makes an equation in two variables a true statement is a *solution* of the equation.

Example 1 **Tell whether each ordered pair is a solution for the equation $y = 21 - 0.01x$.**

a. (300,18)   **b.** (500,15)

Solution Substitute the first number of each ordered pair for x and the second number for y.

a. $y = 21 - 0.01x$
        $18 = 21 - 0.01(300)$
        $18 = 21 - 3$
        $18 = 18$ ✓

b. $y = 21 - 0.01x$
        $15 = 21 - 0.01(500)$
        $15 = 21 - 5$
        $15 = 16$ ✗

True, so the ordered pair (300,18) is a solution.

False, so the ordered pair (500,15) is not a solution.

What is the average temperature 300 m above the base of Mt. Rushmore in July?

▼ You can find solutions for an equation with two variables by using a table to organize your data.

THINK Why is it sometimes helpful to choose 0 as a value for x?

Example 2 **Find three solutions to the equation $y = 3x + 6$.**

Solution 1. Choose three values for x. Try -3, 0, and 4.

2. Use a table to organize your data.

3. Substitute x values into the equation to find y values.

x	y	(x,y)
-3	■	(■,■)
0	■	(■,■)
4	■	(■,■)

$y = 3x + 6$
$y = 3(-3) + 6$
$y = -9 + 6$
$y = -3$

$y = 3x + 6$
$y = 3(0) + 6$
$y = 0 + 6$
$y = 6$

$y = 3x + 6$
$y = 3(4) + 6$
$y = 12 + 6$
$y = 18$

The ordered pairs (-3,-3), (0,6), and (4,18) are solutions.

▼ You may need to solve an equation for *y* in order to find solutions of the equation.

Example 3 **Solve the equation $3x + 5y = 30$ for *y* in terms of *x*.**

Solution

$$3x + 5y = 30$$
$$3x + 5y - 3x = 30 - 3x \qquad \text{Subtract 3x from each side.}$$
$$5y = 30 - 3x$$
$$\frac{5y}{5} = \frac{30 - 3x}{5} \qquad \text{Divide each side by 5.}$$
$$y = \frac{30}{5} - \frac{3x}{5}$$
$$y = 6 - \frac{3}{5}x$$
$$y = -\frac{3}{5}x + 6$$

> **FLASHBACK**
>
> Solving an equation for a specific variable means to isolate that variable on one side of the equation.

Example 4 **Find three solutions of the equation $4x - \frac{2}{3}y = 6$.**

Solution

1. Solve for *y* in terms of *x*.

$$4x - \frac{2}{3}y = 6$$
$$3\left(4x - \frac{2}{3}y\right) = 6(3) \qquad \text{Multiply each side by 3.}$$
$$12x - 2y = 18$$
$$12x - 2y - 12x = 18 - 12x \qquad \text{Subtract 12x from each side.}$$
$$-2y = 18 - 12x$$
$$\frac{-2y}{-2} = \frac{18 - 12x}{-2} \qquad \text{Divide each side by -2.}$$
$$y = \frac{18}{-2} + \frac{-12x}{-2}$$
$$= -9 + 6x$$
$$= 6x - 9$$

2. Find three solutions of the equation $y = 6x - 9$.

   a. Choose three values for *x*. Try -3, 0, and 2.

   b. Use a table to organize your data.

x	y	(x,y)
-3	▨	(▨,▨)
0	▨	(▨,▨)
2	▨	(▨,▨)

   c. Substitute *x* values into the equation to find *y* values.

$y = 6x - 9$	$y = 6x - 9$	$y = 6x - 9$
$y = 6(-3) - 9$	$y = 6(0) - 9$	$y = 6(2) - 9$
$y = -18 - 9$	$y = 0 - 9$	$y = 12 - 9$
$y = -27$	$y = -9$	$y = 3$

   The ordered pairs (-3,-27), (0,-9), and (2,3) are solutions of the equation $y = 6x - 9$.

THINK AND DISCUSS

1. How is a table helpful in determining ordered pair solutions?

2. How can you clear the decimals in $0.25x + 0.75y = 6.75$?

3. Find the value of k that makes the given point a solution of the equation:

a. $x + ky = 6$; $(-3,3)$

b. $x - ky = 12$; $(4,2)$

MIXED REVIEW

Solve.

1. $5x + 9 = 6x + 25$

2. $12 - \frac{3}{4}y = 34 + 2y$

3. Graph $(-1,3)$, $(2,0)$, and $(1,1)$ in the coordinate plane.

4. In the third quadrant, the x-coordinate is always ▦ and the y-coordinate is always ▦.

5. Write three ordered pairs whose y-coordinate is twice the x-coordinate.

6. Name the coordinates of the point on the y-axis 8 units above the x-axis.

7. A student gets out of bed and spends 48 min getting ready for school, 25 min walking to school, and 55 min in her first class. The class ends at 9:25 A.M. At what time did the student get up?

CLASS EXERCISES

Tell whether each ordered pair is a solution of $4x - 3y = 6$.

1. $(5,7)$ **2.** $(3,2)$ **3.** $(0.5,-1.3)$

Find the value of y that corresponds to each value of x for the equation $6x + 2y = 12$.

4. $x = -3$ **5.** $x = 2.5$ **6.** $x = 0$

Solve for y in terms of x.

7. $-5x + \frac{y}{3} = 9$ **8.** $-4x - 0.5y = -2$ **9.** $\frac{1}{4}x + \frac{1}{4}y = \frac{1}{2}y$

Find four solutions for each equation.

10. $x - y = 9$ **11.** $3x + y = 12$ **12.** $3x + y = 24$

WRITTEN EXERCISES

MENTAL MATH Is each ordered pair a solution of $x + 2y = 57$?

1. $(5,0)$ **2.** $(-1,28)$ **3.** $(57,0)$

MENTAL MATH Is each ordered pair a solution of $x + 2y = 5$?

4. $(-1,2)$ **5.** $(-3,4)$ **6.** $(2,-3)$

CALCULATOR Is each ordered pair a solution of $x + 2y = 5$?

7. $(1.2,1.9)$ **8.** $(-4.5,4.5)$ **9.** $(13.2,4.1)$

Find the value of y that corresponds to each value of x.

10. $3x - 4y = 24$ if $x = -2$ **11.** $5 - y = \frac{1}{2}x$ if $x = 12$

12. $2x + y = 5$ if $x = 2$ **13.** $x + 8y + 6 = 0$ if $x = -22$

14. $2.9x + 2y = 5$ if $x = 0$ **15.** $0.25x + 0.5y = 6.75$ if $x = 4$

Solve for y in terms of x.

16. $x = 11 - 3y$ **17.** $x + y - 5 = 4x$

18. $5x + 3y = 2x - 10$ **19.** $2(x - y) = -x + 10$

20. $x - y - 8 = 6(2x + 4)$ **21.** $7y - x - 1 = y - (2x + 1)$

Solve for y in terms of x. Find four solutions of each equation.

22. $4x + \frac{1}{2}y = 3$ **23.** $x + 2y = -5$ **24.** $3x - y = -1$

25. $2x - 3y = 12$ **26.** $x + y = 32$ **27.** $x + 4y = 16$

28. PROJECT Many situations rely on coordinate systems. As you press B5 in a vending machine, the letter refers to a row of items and the number to a position in the row. Find other examples in which a coordinate system is used to locate positions. Write the results in your math journal.

Use the article below to answer each question.

Mountains Under the Sea

A mountain range exists in the Pacific Ocean, far, far beneath the surface of the water. In 1960, Jacque Piccard and Donald Walsh made a record dive in these mountains at the site of the Marianas Trench. Piccard and Walsh descended to 10,916 m. The depth of the dive is remarkable because of the tremendous amount of pressure that exists at these depths. The pressure of the air at sea level is 1 kg/cm², but it increases 0.1 kg/cm² for every meter an object descends in salt water.

29. The equation $P = 1 + 0.1x$ gives the pressure in kg/cm² at x m below sea level.

a. Find four possible solutions for this equation.

b. Find the pressure at the record-breaking depth achieved by Piccard and Walsh.

c. *DATA FILE 10 (pp. 404–405)* Find the pressure at the greatest known depth of the Atlantic Ocean.

TEST YOURSELF

State the letter of the point named by each ordered pair.

1. $(-3,3)$ **2.** $(0,-2)$

3. $(-2,1)$ **4.** $(-3,0)$

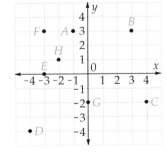

State the coordinates of each point.

5. A **6.** B

7. C **8.** D

Solve for y in terms of x. Find three solutions of each equation.

9. $3x + 2y = 4$ **10.** $\frac{1}{2}x + y = -3$ **11.** $x + 3y = 7$

OBJECTIVE:
To graph a linear
equation and find x
and y-intercepts.

8-3 Graphing Linear Equations

▼ You can graph an equation to show the solutions.

Example 1 Graph the equation $2x + y = 3$.

Solution
1. Solve for y in terms of x.

$$2x + y = 3$$
$$2x + y - 2x = 3 - 2x$$
$$y = 3 - 2x$$
$$y = -2x + 3$$

2. Find three solutions to the equation.

   a. Choose three values. Try -1, 0, and 2.

   b. Use a table to organize your data.

x	y	(x,y)
-1	▨	(▨,▨)
0	▨	(▨,▨)
2	▨	(▨,▨)

THINK How many points must you have to draw a line?

   c. Substitute each x value into the equation to find y.

$$y = -2x + 3 \qquad y = -2x + 3 \qquad y = -2x + 3$$
$$y = -2(-1) + 3 \qquad y = -2(0) + 3 \qquad y = -2(2) + 3$$
$$y = 2 + 3 \qquad y = 0 + 3 \qquad y = -4 + 3$$
$$y = 5 \qquad y = 3 \qquad y = -1$$

Three solutions are (-1,5), (0,3), and (2,-1).

3. Graph the points. Draw a line connecting them.

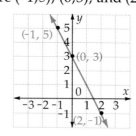

Each ordered pair on the graph is a solution of the linear equation $2x + y = 3$.

▼ We call the equations you have been solving *linear equations*.

Linear Equation	A linear equation is an equation for which the graph is a line. The standard form of a linear equation is $Ax + By = C$, where A, B, and C are real numbers and A and B are not both equal to zero.

Example 2 Write each linear equation in standard form.

   a. $x = 12 - 2y$

   b. $x + y - 2 = 0$

Solution
   a.
$$x = 12 - 2y$$
$$x + 2y = 12 - 2y + 2y$$
$$x + 2y = 12$$

   b.
$$x + y - 2 = 0$$
$$x + y - 2 + 2 = 0 + 2$$
$$x + y = 2$$

Example 3   Is the point $(6,1)$ on the graph of $x - 2y = 4$?

Solution $x - 2y = 4$ Substitute 6 for *x* and 1 for *y*.
  $6 - 2(1) = 4$
  $6 - 2 = 4$
  $4 = 4\checkmark$

True, so $(6,1)$ is on the graph of $x - 2y = 4$.

▼ You can use the *x*- and *y*-intercepts when graphing an equation.

x-intercept	The *x*-intercept is the *x*-coordinate of a point where a graph crosses the *x*-axis.

y-intercept	The *y*-intercept is the *y*-coordinate of a point where a graph crosses the *y*-axis.

Example 4   **Find the *x*-intercept and the *y*-intercept for the equation $2x - 3y = 12$. Use the intercepts to sketch the graph.**

Solution   To find the *x*-intercept, substitute 0 for *y*.

$2x - 3y = 12$
$2x - 3(0) = 12$
$2x - 0 = 12$
$2x = 12$
$\dfrac{2x}{2} = \dfrac{12}{2}$
$x = 6$

The *x*-intercept is 6.

To find the *y*-intercept, substitute 0 for *x*.

$2x - 3y = 12$
$2(0) - 3y = 12$
$0 - 3y = 12$
$-3y = 12$
$\dfrac{-3y}{-3} = \dfrac{12}{-3}$
$y = -4$

The *y*-intercept is -4.

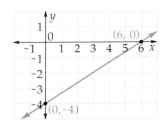

▼ You can graph an equation which contains only one variable.

Example 5   **Graph each equation on the same coordinate plane.**

a. $4x = 12$ **b.** $3y = -6$

Solution   **a.** When you solve this equation for *x*, you get $x = 3$. Any ordered pair having an *x*-coordinate equal to 3 will be a solution.

b. When you solve this equation for *y*, you get $y = -2$. Any ordered pair having a *y*-coordinate equal to -2 will be a solution.

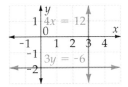

▼ **THINK** What are two solutions of the equation $4x = 12$? of the equation $3y = -6$?

CLASS EXERCISES

THINK AND DISCUSS

1. Describe and give an example of an equation of a line with

a. no *y*-intercept.

b. no *x*-intercept.

2. Is the graph of $y = x^2 - 4$ a line? Use intercepts to help you decide. Explain.

3. Is the graph of the equation $xy = 12$ a line? Use guess and test to find four ordered pairs that are solutions. Graph the points.

4. Explain how the *x*- and *y*-intercepts can be helpful when graphing.

The figure at the right shows the graph of the equation $y = 3x - 2$.

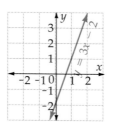

1. Write the equation in standard form.

2. Tell whether each point is on the graph.

  a. $(0,-2)$ **b.** $(1,0)$

  c. $\left(\frac{4}{3},2\right)$ **d.** $(-0.5,-3.5)$

3. What are the *x*-intercept and the *y*-intercept?

Find the *x*-intercept and *y*-intercept for each equation.

4. $4x - 3y = 12$ **5.** $2x + \frac{1}{2}y = -3$

6. $\frac{1}{3}x = 2$ **7.** $1.5y + 6 = 0$

Solve for *y* in terms of *x*. Graph each equation.

8. $8x + 4y = 16$ **9.** $9.3x + 3.1y = 15.5$

10. $\frac{1}{4}x - 3y = 6$ **11.** $6x + \frac{2}{3}y = 8$

WRITTEN EXERCISES

The figure at the right shows the graph of the equation $3 + y = -\frac{1}{2}x$.

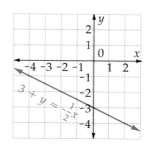

1. Write the equation in standard form.

2. Tell whether each point is on the graph.

  a. $(1,2.5)$ **b.** $(-2,2)$

  c. $(-4,-1)$ **d.** $(-2,-2)$

3. What are the *x*-intercept and the *y*-intercept?

Find the *x*-intercept and *y*-intercept for each equation.

4. $3x + 5y = 15$ **5.** $0.75x - 0.25y + 1 = 0$

6. $6x + 8 = 0$ **7.** $y = \frac{2}{3}x$

Solve for y in terms of x. Graph each equation.

8. $2x - \frac{1}{3}y = 1$

9. $10 - 2(x + 2y) = -3y - (x - 8)$

10. $y : x = 3 : 2$

11. $y - 3(0.25x + 1) = -8 - \frac{3}{4}x$

Graph each equation on a separate set of coordinate axes.

12. $3x - 5y = 15$

13. $3x + \frac{1}{2}y = -3$

14. $\frac{1}{3}x + 1 = -2$

15. $y = 0$

16. $|x| = 2$

17. $|y| = 3$

18. $|x| + |y| = 3$

19. $|x + y| = 3$

MENTAL MATH Write an equation for each line described.

20. the line parallel to the y-axis and 2 units to the left of the y-axis

21. the line 2 units to the right of the line $x = -3$

22. the line 7 units below the line $y = 2$

23. the line parallel to the x-axis and 6 units below the x-axis

24. the line perpendicular to the x-axis and passing through the point $(-3,0)$

Write an equation using two variables for each situation. Graph the equation on a coordinate plane. Use the graph to find one solution of the word problem.

25. Find two numbers whose difference is 3.

26. Find two numbers such that one is three times the other.

27. Louis buys six pieces of fruit. Some are apples and some are oranges. Let x equal the number of oranges and y equal the number of apples.

28. A collection of nickels and dimes is valued at $1. Let x equal the number of nickels and y equal the number of dimes.

29. Ben cut a ribbon so that one piece was twice as long as the other. Let x equal the shorter piece and y equal the longer piece.

30. Gina's sister earned $6 at her lemonade stand. She sold small cups of lemonade for $.25 and large cups for $.40. Let x equal the number of small cups sold and y equal the number of large cups sold.

31. A 12-m fence encloses a rectangular garden. Let x equal the width of the garden and y equal the length of the garden.

32. **DATA FILE 3 (pp. 96–97)** A collection of 1936 and 1961 proof sets was valued at $20,264 in 1990. Let x equal the number of 1936 proof sets and y equal the number of 1961 proof sets.

THINK In Exercise 27, can the values of x and y be negative numbers? fractions? Why or why not?

FLASHBACK

perimeter of a rectangle = $2l + 2w$

OBJECTIVE:
To use coordinate graphs to explore linear equations, intercepts, and slope.

MATERIALS

- Graph paper

- Math journal to record work

Standard form	Solved for *y*	*y*-intercept	Ratio

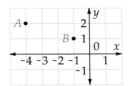

Exploring Slope

▼ The graph below shows the linear equation $-2x + y = 4$.

Copy and complete a table like the one at the left.

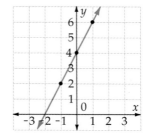

1. **a.** In what form is the equation written? Write the equation in the table.

   b. Solve the equation for y in terms of x. Write the equation in the table.

2. **a.** *Describe* what a y-intercept is.

   b. Determine from the graph what the y-intercept of the equation $y = 2x + 4$ is. Write the y-intercept in the table.

3. **a.** *Write* the coordinates of three points found on the line.

   b. *Explain* how to get from the first point to the second. Use only two sentences. Give vertical directions first using the words *up* and *down*. Then give horizontal directions, using *left* and *right*. What is the ratio in fraction form of the vertical change to the horizontal change?

Example   To get from *B* to *A*:   To get from *A* to *B*:

1. Go up 1. (+1)   1. Go down 1. (-1)

2. Go left 3. (-3)   2. Go right 3. (+3)

3. The ratio is $\frac{1}{-3}$ or $-\frac{1}{3}$.   3. The ratio is $\frac{-1}{3}$ or $-\frac{1}{3}$.

   c. *Explain* how to get from the second point to the third. What is the ratio of the vertical change to the horizontal change?

   d. *Explain* how to get from the third point to the first. What is the ratio of the vertical change to the horizontal change?

   e. *Discuss* how the ratios in (b), (c), and (d) are alike. How are they different?

   f. *Write* the ratio of the vertical change to the horizontal change in simplest form. Write the result in your table.

4. Repeat Steps 1–3 for each equation shown.

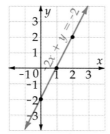 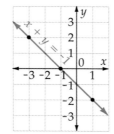 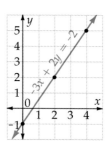

▼   We call the ratio of the vertical change to the horizontal change the *slope* of the line.

5. **a. *Analyze*** the table and discuss the relationship between each equation when it is solved for y in terms of x and its y-intercept.

   b. *Analyze* the table and discuss the relationship between each equation when it is solved for y in terms of x and its slope.

   c. Is the y-intercept the same for the equation $y = 3x - 4$ and $y = 3x + (-4)$?

6. Name the y-intercept and slope of each linear equation.

   a. $y = 12x - 4$ **b.** $y = 2x + 14$

▼   Knowing the y-intercept and the slope are useful when sketching the graph of a line.

7. **a. *Discuss*** why solving an equation for y is helpful when graphing the equation.

8. Sketch each equation by using the y-intercept and slope.

   a. $-4x + y = 10$ **b.** $-5x + y = -10$

▼   You can write the equation of a line by studying its graph.

9. **a.** What is the y-intercept?

   b. What is the slope?

   c. *Write* an equation for the line graphed at the right.

   d. *Discuss* how you could check that the equation is correct.

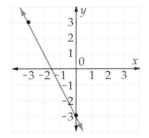

▼   You can write the equation of a line when you know the y-intercept and the slope.

10. ***Write*** the equation of each line described.

    a. The y-intercept is 7 and the slope is 8.

    b. The y-intercept is -1 and the slope is 6.

OBJECTIVE:
Find the slope and
y-intercept for the
graph of a linear
equation.

8-4 Slope and y-intercept

▼ The ski hill pictured at the left has a vertical rise of 4 m for every 20 m of horizontal run. You can find the steepness or *slope* of the ski hill by using the ratio of the vertical change to the horizontal change. The ratio for the ski hill is $\frac{4}{20}$ or $\frac{1}{5}$.

Slope	The slope of a line is the ratio of the vertical change in *y* to the corresponding horizontal change in *x*.

▼ You can also find the slope of a straight line in the coordinate plane by counting the units of vertical change and the units of horizontal change from one point to another.

Example 1 Find the slope of the line shown on each graph.

a.   b.

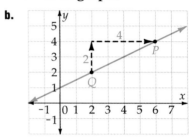

Solution a. Choose any two points on the line. Try $P(3,-5)$ and $Q(1,-2)$. If you begin at P, and move three units up and two units to the left, you reach Q.

$$\text{slope} = \frac{\text{vertical change}}{\text{horizontal change}} = \frac{3}{-2} \text{ or } -\frac{3}{2}$$

b. Choose any two points on the line. Try $P(6,4)$ and $Q(2,2)$. If you begin at Q, and move 2 units up and 4 units to the right, you reach P.

$$\text{slope} = \frac{\text{vertical change}}{\text{horizontal change}} = \frac{2}{4} \text{ or } \frac{1}{2}$$

▼ You can use a formula to find the slope if you know the coordinates of any two points on the line.

Slope Formula	Use the following formula to calculate slope.
	$\text{slope} = \frac{\text{difference in } y\text{-coordinates}}{\text{difference in } x\text{-coordinates}}$

Example 2 Find the slope of a line that contains the points $R(-2,1)$ and $S(4,3)$.

Solution $\text{slope} = \frac{\text{difference in } y\text{-coordinates}}{\text{difference in } x\text{-coordinates}} = \frac{3-1}{4-(-2)} = \frac{2}{6} \text{ or } \frac{1}{3}$

Example 3 Determine the slope of the line containing the given points. Graph the line on a coordinate plane.

    a. (2,4) and (-3,4)   **b.** (3,2) and (3,-1)

Solution   **a.** slope $= \dfrac{4-4}{-3-2} = \dfrac{0}{-5} = 0$

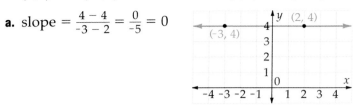

The slope of a horizontal line is zero.

    b. slope $= \dfrac{-1-2}{3-3} = \dfrac{-3}{0}$

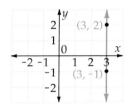

Because division by zero is undefined, a vertical line has no slope.

▼ You can draw the graph of a line if you know the slope of the line and a point on the line.

Example 4 **Graph the line with slope $\frac{3}{4}$ and y-intercept -4.**

Solution Locate the point (0,-4) and label it P. Move 3 units up and 4 units to the right. You are now at (4,-1), or Q. Draw the line containing P and Q.

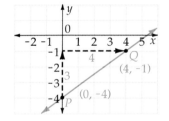

FLASHBACK

The y-intercept is the y-coordinate of a point where a graph crosses the y-axis.

▼ When you solve an equation for y it is in *slope-intercept* form.

Slope-intercept Form	A linear equation in the form $y = mx + b$ is in slope-intercept form. The slope is m and the y-intercept is b.

Example 5 **Sketch the graph of the equation $y = 3x + 1$.**

Solution The slope is 3 or $\frac{3}{1}$. The y-intercept is 1. Locate the point (0,1) and label it P. Move 3 units up and 1 unit to the right. You are now at (1,4), or Q. Draw the line containing P and Q.

THINK AND DISCUSS

True or false?

1. The greater the absolute value of *m*, the greater the steepness of the line.

2. A line with a positive slope runs downward from left to right.

3. If a line has a *y*-intercept of zero, it does not cross the *x*-axis.

4. Given $y = mx + b$, the slope of the line is *m* and the *y*-intercept is *b*.

CLASS EXERCISES

Find the steepness and *y*-intercept of each line.

1. 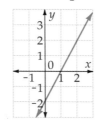   **2.** 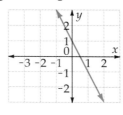   **3.**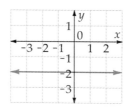

Find the slope of the line containing the given points.

4. (4,5) (6,13)   **5.** (-3,5) (-4,-1)   **6.** (-10,-6) (-13,-10)

Write each linear equation in slope-intercept form. Name the slope and *y*-intercept.

7. $3x + y = 3$ **8.** $2y + 4x = 12$ **9.** $-10 + y = -2x$

10. Graph the line with slope -2 and containing the point (1,-3).

WRITTEN EXERCISES

MIXED REVIEW

Find the LCM.

1. 4, 10, 16

2. 7, 12, 18

Tell whether or not each equation is linear. Explain how you know.

3. $Ax + By + C = 0$

4. $y = -2$

5. $xy = -12$

6. $x + y = -6$

7. $3(x - 2y) + y = 7 - x$

8. $x = y^2$

Solve.

9. The price of gold per oz increases from \$350 to \$420. Find the percent of increase.

MENTAL MATH Find the steepness and *y*-intercept of each line.

1. 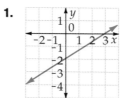   **2.** 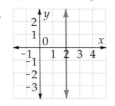   **3.**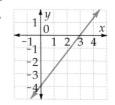

Plot each pair of points. Draw the line containing them. Then find its slope and *y*-intercept.

4. (-1,3), (1,-1)   **5.** (-6,2), (0,4)   **6.** (0,3), (5,0)

Find the slope of the line containing the given points.

7. (2,1) (3,1)   **8.** (-2,5) (-2,-1)   **9.** (3,5) (6,15)

10. (-5,-2) (1,4)   **11.** (1,-2) (2,-4)   **12.** (-1,15) (3,5)

Graph each line described.

13. the line having slope -3 and containing the point (-6,5)

14. the line having slope 5 and containing the point (-4,-5)

15. the line having slope $\frac{2}{3}$ and containing the point (0,-4)

Graph each line described.

16. the line having slope 0 and containing the point (5,3)

17. the line having no slope and containing the point (4,-2)

18. the line having slope -3 and containing the origin

Write each linear equation in slope-intercept form. Name the slope and y-intercept.

19. $-2x + y = 1$

20. $6x + y = \frac{1}{6}$

21. $3 + y = -2x$

22. $-2x + 3y = 18$

23. $-3x + 4y - 1 = 0$

24. $4y = 2x$

Sketch the graph of each equation.

25. $y = 2x + 4$

26. $y = \frac{1}{2}x$

27. $y = -5x - 3$

28. $y = -x + 1$

29. $y = -\frac{2}{5}x - 2$

30. $y = x - \frac{3}{4}$

31. a. Graph each pair of lines on one coordinate grid.

  Pair 1   Pair 2

  $y = 2x - 5$ $y = -3x + 1$

  $y = 2x + 3$ $y = -3x - 2$

  b. Describe the lines.

  c. Compare the slopes of each pair of equations.

  d. Draw a conclusion.

Write an equation in standard form for each line described. *Hint:* **First write the equation in slope-intercept form.**

32. having slope 3 and y-intercept -4

33. having slope 0 and y-intercept 6

34. having slope -2 and y-intercept -1.

35. having no slope and containing the point (-3,0).

36. having slope -8 and y-intercept $\frac{1}{2}$

37. PROJECT Call a local taxi company to find out the rates for trips of distances up to 1.5 mi. Make a table and draw the graph. Find the slope and the y-intercept. Compare with other members of your group.

38. The table at the right shows a student's savings between the sixth and tenth weeks. The student saved at the same rate during this time.

  a. Find the rate of savings per week.

  b. Find the slope of the line passing through points (6,5) and (10,11). How does the slope compare with the savings?

Student's Savings

Weeks (x)	Savings (y)
6	$5
10	$11

8-5 Solve by Graphing

OBJECTIVE:
To solve problems using a graph.

■ You can solve many types of problems using graphs.

PROBLEM

Two years ago the value of a new car was $12,000. Its current value is $9,000. Predict the value of the car three years from now if it continues to depreciate at the same rate.

SOLUTION

READimage What do you want to find? | the value of the car in three years

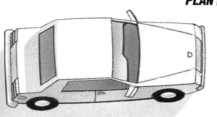

PLANimage Decide on a strategy. | Make a graph. Let x = the age of the car and y = the dollar value.

What was the value of x when the car was new? the value of y? | $x = 0$ $y = 12,000$

What is the current value of x when y is 9,000? | $x = 2$

SOLVEimage What will be the value of x in three years? | $x = 2 + 3 = 5$

Use the information to write two ordered pairs. | $(0, 12,000)$ and $(2, 9,000)$

Plot the points. Connect them. Extend the line so that you can find other values.

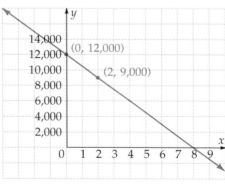

Find the value of y when $x = 5$ | $y = 4,500$

The value of the car in three years will be $4,500.

LOOK BACKimage Check your answer by solving another way. | In two years the car depreciates $3,000, or $1,500 per year. If it drops at the same rate for three more years, it would be worth $9,000 - 3(1,500)$ or $4,500.

CLASS EXERCISES

Refer to the problem on page 334.

1. What will the car be worth five years from now?

2. When the car is worth $6,000, how old will the car be?

3. How old must the car be before its value has depreciated to $0? Explain why this is probably not an accurate prediction.

WRITTEN EXERCISES

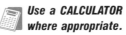
Use a CALCULATOR where appropriate.

Solve by using the strategy of graphing.

1. The relationship between the Fahrenheit and Celsius temperature scales is linear. The freezing point of water is 32°F or 0°C. The boiling point of water is 212°F or 100°C.

   a. Make a graph showing this information.

   b. What is the approximate Fahrenheit temperature that is equivalent to 10°C?

   c. What is the approximate Celsius temperature that is equivalent to 70°F?

2. The Jackson family bought a house in 1968 for $32,000. In 1988 they sold it for $192,000. Assume that the increase in value was constant over the 20-year period.

   a. Make a graph showing this information.

   b. What was the value of the house in 1980?

   c. Assume the value of the house continues to increase at the same rate. Predict the value of the house in the year 2000.

   d. Is it reasonable to assume that the increase in value over time is constant? Explain.

Solve using any strategy.

3. The temperature at 6:00 A.M. was 48°F. At 9:00 A.M. it was 60°F. The temperature climbed at a constant rate from 6:00 A.M. to 11:00 A.M. What was the temperature at 10:00 A.M.?

4. An airplane flying at an altitude of 30,000 ft begins its descent at the rate of 1,500 ft/min. Assume the plane continues to descend at the same rate. In how many minutes will the plane be on the ground?

5. If 4 is subtracted from three times a number, the result is two more than the number. Find the number.

6. A supermarket charges $1.19 for a 12-oz jar of salsa and $1.89 for a 20-oz jar. The manufacturer has just come out with a 16-oz size. What would you suggest the supermarket should charge for the new size? Justify your answer.

7. The sales tax on an item costing $17.50 is $1.23. Find the sales tax on an item that costs $30. Round your answer to the nearest cent.

8. A shoe store employs high-school students as part-time salespeople. The starting pay is $3.85/h. Every six months a worker is eligible for a raise of $.35 an hour, if the work has been satisfactory. What can a good salesperson expect to be earning per hour two years after starting at the store?

9. A slope of $\frac{1}{10}$ is suitable for a ramp to allow wheelchair access to a building. How far from a doorway will a ramp extend if the doorway is $3\frac{1}{2}$ ft above the ground?

10. A delivery van travels 240.8 mi using 10.6 gal of gas. The tank holds 13.6 gal. How many miles can the van expect to travel on a full tank of gas? Round your answer to the nearest mile.

11. A store is holding its annual 30% off sale.

a. What will you save on an item if the regular price is $89.95? Round your answer to the nearest dollar.

b. A student saved $50 on a dress she bought at the sale. Estimate its original price.

12. The high school hired a rock band for a concert. The school guaranteed the band a fee of $1,500, plus $4.50 for each ticket sold. There are 1,132 seats in the auditorium. What is the greatest possible amount of money the band can earn for its single concert performance? the least amount?

13. A student has $5.90 in dimes and quarters. There are 32 coins altogether. How many of each coin does the student have?

14. *PROJECT* Look up record times for the 100-m dash in the Olympics for the years 1980 and 1984.

a. Assume that the record time continues to decrease at the same rate. Graph the data from the first two years. Use the horizontal axis to represent the year. Use the vertical axis to represent the time.

b. Extend the graph to predict the record time for the 1988 Olympic games. Compare your result with the actual Olympic record in 1988.

c. *WRITE* a paragraph about your findings in your journal.

15. *DATA FILE 9 (pp. 360–361)* Ron played eighteen holes of golf at St. Andrew's golf club for five consecutive days. About how many miles did Ron walk on the golf course?

Problem Solving Practice

READ
PLAN
SOLVE
LOOK BACK

PROBLEM SOLVING STRATEGIES

Look for a Pattern
Guess and Test
Simplify the Problem
Make an Organized List
Work Backwards
Account for All Possibilities
Make a Table
Write an Equation
Solve by Graphing
Draw a Diagram
Make a Model
Solve Another Way
Simulate the Problem

Solve. Use an appropriate strategy or a combination of strategies.

1. In a collection of dimes and quarters, there are seven more quarters than there are dimes. How many dimes and quarters are there if the collection is worth $3.50?

2. Anna has $75 in the bank. She saves $5 the first week, $10 the second week, and $15 the third week. At this rate, how much money will she have in the bank at the end of 12 weeks?

3. A landscaper wants to plant a bush every 1.5 ft around the edge of a circular garden. It is 72 ft around the edge of the garden. How many plants should the landscaper purchase?

4. A student withdraws $15 from his bank account. He then buys lunch for $4.75, a ticket to the movies for $7.50, and a snack after the movie for $3.45. He has $14.23 left. How much money did he have before he withdrew the $15?

5. The sum of three consecutive integers is 111. What are the integers?

6. A plumber charges $35 for a service call, plus $60 per hour for her time.
   a. Find the cost of a two-hour service call.
   b. How much time was spent on a call if the bill was $125?

7. The height of a toddler is 36 in. The mother's height is double the toddler's height, less 7 in. How tall is the mother?

8. You can buy 12 pencils for $.80. How much will you pay for 27 pencils?

9. One square has sides four times as long as the sides of a second square. The combined area of the squares is 272 ft^2. Find their dimensions.

10. The sum of the squares of two consecutive integers is 145. Find the integers.

11. Mr. Harrow earns $22,500 a year. He gets paid weekly. He pays 6.3% of his salary to social security. How much money is taken out of each pay check for social security?

12. There are four candidates running for president of the student council. Three candidates are running for vice-president. How many different ways can the two offices be filled?

13. A grocery store sells apples at $1.92 a dozen. Oranges are $2.16 a dozen. What is the cost of 4 apples and 3 oranges?

OBJECTIVE:
To study computer-simulated motion.

Exploring Simulations

■ Scientists and engineers use computers to *simulate*, or re-create the motion of an object such as rolling a ball off a table.

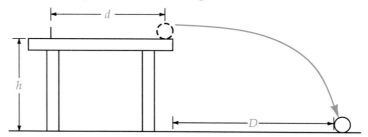

MATERIALS

- Computer and graphing software or a graphing calculator
- Measuring tape or ruler
- Rubber ball or tennis ball
- Stopwatch
- Math journal to record work

DATAPOINT

Keep track of your data in a table.

d	D	h	t
⋮	⋮	⋮	⋮

Sonya Kovalevsky (1850–1891) was a mathematical genius. In 1888 she wrote the brilliant essay "On the Problem of the Rotation of a Solid Body about a Fixed Point," which won the highest award of the French Academy of Sciences.

1. **Model** the situation shown above. Measure the distances *d* and *h*. Roll a ball off a table along distance *d*. Use a stopwatch to measure *t*, the time it takes the ball to hit the ground after it rolls off the table. Measure *D*, the distance from the table to where the ball hits the ground.

   a. Continue the experiment, but each time increase the speed of the ball. What happens to the time it takes the ball to hit the ground? What happens to *D*?

   b. When does $D = 0$? Is there a limit to the value of *D*?

2. Increase the value of *h* by using a higher table. Repeat the experiment.

   a. How does increasing *h* affect *t*? How does increasing *h* affect *D*?

   b. How does increasing the speed of the ball affect *D*?

■ You can use a computer or graphing calculator to graph the *trajectory*, or path, of the ball. The equation for this trajectory is $y = -16x^2 + 10$. The figure below shows the part of the graph that simulates the ball's trajectory.

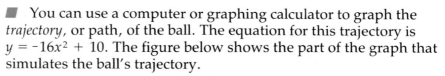

3. In the equation $y = -16x^2 + 10$, the value 10 indicates the height of the table. Write equations for table heights of 15 ft, 20 ft, and 35 ft.

4. Graph the equations from Exercise 3. What do you notice about the trajectory as *h* increases?

■ The equation $y = -16x^2 + 10$ assumes a speed of 1 ft/s. The equation for *any* speed is $y = -\frac{16}{v^2}x^2 + h$, where h is the height of the table and v is the speed of the ball.

5. a. *Write* equations for each speed and height.

Speed (ft/s)	1	2	3	4	4	4	6	7	8
Height (ft)	10	10	10	10	15	20	20	20	20

b. Graph each equation.

c. *Analyze* what happens to D as the speed of the ball increases but the height remains the same. Is this what you would expect to happen?

d. What happens to D as the height of the table increases but the speed of the ball remains the same? Is this what you would expect to happen?

e. What happens to D as both the table height and the speed of the ball increase? Is this what you would expect to happen?

6. *Explore* What happens to D for very large values of v? What happens to the ball's trajectory for large values of v?

■ A computer or graphing calculator simulation can help you predict the outcome of an experiment. The three trajectories below are for a ball moving with speeds 1 ft/s, 2 ft/s, and 3 ft/s off a 4-ft high table.

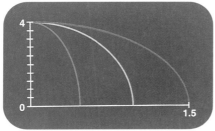

7. a. *Estimation* What are the values for D in each case?

b. *Model* each situation in the graph. To get the right speed, measure d and use a stopwatch. Time the motion of the ball to 1 s, 2 s, or 3 s, depending on the speed.

c. How do your results compare to those of the computer simulation? How do they differ?

d. *Discuss* the advantages to using a computer to simulate an experiment.

DATAPOINT

You can use a spreadsheet and graphics package to graph equations. Use the spreadsheet format below to create a line graph for as many points as you want.

	A	B
1	0	= −16*A1^2 +10
2	0.01	= −16*A2^2 +10
3	0.02	= −16*A3^2 +10
4	0.03	= −16*A4^2 +10
5	0.04	= −16*A5^2 +10
6	0.05	= −16*A6^2 +10
7	0.06	= −16*A7^2 +10
8	0.07	= −16*A8^2 +10
9	0.08	= −16*A9^2 +10
10	0.09	= −16*A10^2 +10
11	0.1	= −16*A11^2 +10
12		

DATAPOINT

A satellite in orbit around Earth is actually falling. It never hits the ground because it is moving forward fast enough to keep it from dropping.

OBJECTIVE:
To solve two
equations in two
variables by
graphing.

8-6 Solving Systems of Linear Equations

▼ Two linear equations using the same variables form a *system of linear equations*.

System of Linear Equations	A system of linear equations is two or more linear equations using the same variables.

Example 1 State whether each pair of linear equations is a system of linear equations.

a. $2x + y = 8$
$x - 3y = -9$

b. $x + 8y = 12$
$6a + b = -3$

Solution **a.** Yes, this is a system of linear equations. Both equations contain variables x and y.

b. No, this is not a system of linear equations. The equations do not contain the same variables.

▼ A *solution* of a system of linear equations makes all of the equations in the system true.

Solution	A solution of a system of linear equations is any ordered pair of numbers that satisfies all equations in the system.

Example 2 Tell whether the ordered pair (2,5) is a solution for the system of linear equations $2x + y = 9$ and $4x - y = 3$.

Solution Substitute the ordered pair into each equation.

$$2x + y = 9 \qquad 4x - y = 3$$
$$2(2) + 5 = 9 \qquad 4(2) - 5 = 3$$
$$4 + 5 = 9 \qquad 8 - 5 = 3$$
$$9 = 9 ✓ \qquad 3 = 3 ✓$$

Since (2,5) makes both equations true, it is a solution of the system of linear equations.

FLASHBACK

Every point on the graph of an equation represents an ordered pair of numbers that is a solution of the equation.

▼ You can solve a system of linear equations by graphing.

Example 3 Solve the system $2x + 3y = 6$ and $3x - y = -2$ by graphing.

Solution Graph each equation on the same set of axes. The lines intersect at (0,2). The point (0,2) is the only solution of the system.

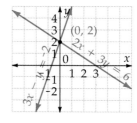

▼ Some systems of linear equations have no solution.

Example 4 Solve the system of linear equations $x + y = 1$ and $x + y = 4$ by graphing.

Solution Graph each equation on the same set of axes. The lines are parallel and do not intersect. There is no solution to this system.

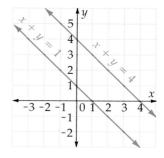

▼ Some systems of equations have infinitely many solutions.

Example 5 Solve the system of linear equations $x - 2y = 4$ and $2x - 4y = 8$ by graphing.

Solution Graph each equation on the same set of axes. The graph of each equation is the same line. Therefore, every point on the line satisfies both equations. There are infinitely many solutions to this system.

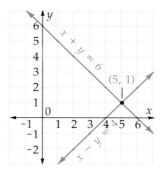

▼ Systems of equations can help you solve word problems.

Example 6 Find two numbers whose sum is 6 and difference is 4.

Solution Let x represent the first number and y represent the second number. Write a system of linear equations.

$$x + y = 6 \leftarrow \textbf{Sum}$$
$$x - y = 4 \leftarrow \textbf{Difference}$$

Graph each equation on the same set of axes. The lines intersect at $(5,1)$. The numbers are 5 and 1.

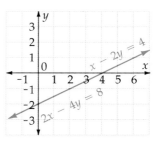

Check $x + y = 6$	$x - y = 4$
$5 + 1 = 6$	$5 - 1 = 4$
$6 = 6$✓	$4 = 4$✓

CLASS EXERCISES

Find the solution for each system.

1. $y = x + 1$ and $y = 3x - 7$

2. $x + y = -3$ and $y = 3x - 7$

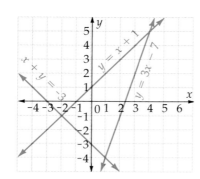

Write the coordinates of each point.

3. a point that satisfies $y = x + 1$ but not $y = 3x - 7$

4. a point that satisfies $y = 3x - 7$ but not $x + y = -3$

THINK AND DISCUSS

1. All the examples had integer solutions. When do you think graphing might not be useful for solving a system of equations?

2. A system of two linear equations in two variables has no solution. Describe the graphs of the equations.

3. Two distinct ordered pairs are solutions of a system of two linear equations. Describe the graphs of the equations.

Tell whether the ordered pair is a solution of the system.

5. $3x - 2y = 8$
$x = -3y$
$(3,-1)$

6. $x - 2y = 0$
$2x + y = 4$
$(2,1)$

7. $x + 2y = 3$
$y = 2x - 1$
$(1,1)$

Solve each system by graphing. Check your solutions.

8. $2x - y = 4$
$y = -2x$

9. $3y - 2x = 6$
$y = x + 1$

10. $2x + 3y = 6$
$y + 2 = 0$

Write a system of linear equations. Solve by graphing.

11. The sum of two numbers is 19. Their difference is 5.

12. The sum of two numbers is 10. Twice the larger decreased by three times the smaller is 5. Find the two numbers.

WRITTEN EXERCISES

Tell whether the ordered pair is a solution of the system.

1. $y = x + 2$
$x - 3y = 4$
$(-5,-3)$

2. $y = x - 1$
$x = 4y$
$\left(\frac{4}{3}, \frac{1}{3}\right)$

3. $x + y = 2$
$-x + y = -4$
$(3,1)$

Solve each system by graphing. Check your solutions.

4. $y = x + 5$
$2x + y = 8$

5. $x = y - 4$
$x + y = 6$

6. $2x - y = 2$
$2y = 4x - 4$

7. $x + 4y = 6$
$x - 2 = 0$

8. $x + y = 3$
$2x = 10 - 2y$

9. $x = y$
$x + y = 4$

10. $y = x - 8$
$y = 3x$

11. $y = x - 2$
$x + 3y = 6$

12. $2x + 3y = 6$
$2x + y + 2 = 0$

13. $x + y = 1$
$y = -x - 1$

14. $y = 2x - 4$
$4x - 2y = 8$

15. $y = 2x - 2$
$x = 3$

Write a system of linear equations. Solve by graphing.

16. The sum of two numbers is 120. Their difference is 20. Find the numbers.

17. The sum of two numbers is 55. Their difference is 15. Find the numbers.

18. The difference of two numbers is 5. The greater number decreased by twice the lesser number is 9. Find the numbers.

19. A 144-m rope is cut into 2 pieces. One piece is three times as long as the other. How long is each piece of rope?

MIXED REVIEW

Simplify.

1. $\frac{15x^3}{5x}$

2. $\frac{20x^2y^6}{8xy^3}$

Find the slope and y-intercept.

3. $x = y$

4. $2x + 3y = 12$

Solve each inequality.

5. $2x + 3 < 9$

6. $3 - (2x + 1) \leq 8$

Solve.

7. A coat regularly sells for $125. It is on sale for 40% off. What is the sale price?

20. Cliff is 6 years older than Claire. In two years, Cliff will be twice Claire's age. Find their present ages.

21. Questions on a 16-item test are worth either 5 points or 10 points each. There are a total of 100 points on the test. How many items of each point value appear on the test?

Describe the nature of each system of linear equations without graphing. Note that they are all written in the form $y = mx + b$.

22. $y = x + 2$
$y = -x + 2$

23. $y = -x + 2$
$y = -x + 5$

24. $y = x - 1$
$3y = 3x - 3$

25. *DATA FILE 8 (pp. 312–313)* In what year was the United States population approximately one fourth of the population in 1910?

26. The unit of distance a boat uses to navigate is called a *nautical mile.* One nautical mile is 6,076.1 ft. Saona Island and Mona Island are located in the Caribbean Sea. They are 45 mi apart from each other.

a. To the nearest tenth, how many nautical miles apart are Saona Island and Mona Island? *Hint:* 5,280 ft is 1 mi.

b. A boat measures its speed in knots. One knot is equal to one naut mi/h. If your boat is traveling at a rate of 12 naut mi/h, how long will it take, to the nearest hour, to go from Saona Island to Mona Island?

TEST YOURSELF

Find the x-intercept and the y-intercept for each equation.

1. $2x + 5y = 20$

2. $3y = 6 + 9x$

3. $5x + 15 - y = 5$

Find the slope of the line containing the given points.

4. $(7,-3)\ (7,4)$

5. $(-12,6)\ (4,-2)$

6. $(-5,-3)\ (6,-1)$

Write each equation in slope-intercept form. Name the slope and y-intercept. Sketch the graph of the equation.

7. $4x + 2y = 14$

8. $3y = -2$

9. $-4 + 6y = -2x$

Solve each system of linear equations by graphing.

10. $2x + y = 4$
$y = \dfrac{-1}{2}x + 7$

11. $2x - 3y = 12$
$4x - 24 = 6y$

12. $2x - 3y = 12$
$x - 3 = 0$

OBJECTIVE:
To solve linear
inequalities in two
variables.

8-7 Solving Linear Inequalities

▼ The radiator of a car requires a 40% solution of antifreeze to protect it to ‑24°F. You can write an equation in two variables to describe the amount of antifreeze needed for your car. Let x represent the capacity of your radiator and y represent the amount of antifreeze solution needed.

$$y = 0.4x$$

You may put more antifreeze in the radiator than is needed to be sure your car is protected. You can describe the situation with an inequality in two variables.

$$y \geq 0.4x$$

▼ An ordered pair that makes an inequality in two variables a true statement is a solution of the inequality.

Example 1 **Tell whether each ordered pair is a solution of the inequality $y \geq 0.4x$.**

   a. $(4,5)$ **b.** $(5,1)$ **c.** $(-5,-2)$

Solution

a. $y \geq 0.4x$
$5 \geq 0.4(4)$
$5 \geq 1.6$ ✓

True, so $(4,5)$ is a solution.

b. $y \geq 0.4x$
$1 \geq 0.4(5)$
$1 \geq 2$ ✗

False, so $(5,1)$ is not a solution.

c. $y \geq 0.4x$
$-2 \geq 0.4(-5)$
$-2 \geq -2$ ✓

True, so $(-5,-2)$ is a solution.

▼ You can find solutions for a linear inequality in two variables by solving for y in terms of x.

Example 2 **Find three solutions of the inequality $x - y > 1$.**

Solution Solve for y in terms of x.

$x - y > 1$
$x - y - x > 1 - x$ Subtract x from each side.
$-y > 1 - x$
$-1(-y) < -1(1 - x)$ Multiply each side by -1.
$y < -1 + x$
$y < x - 1$ Substitute a value, say 0, for x.
$y < 0 - 1$
$y < -1$

When x is 0, y can be any number less than ‑1. So, $(0,-2)$, $(0,-3)$, and $(0,-4)$ are three solutions of the inequality. There may be infinitely many solutions of an inequality.

FLASHBACK

When both sides of an inequality are multiplied by a negative number, the inequality sign is reversed.

▼ You can solve inequalities to find solutions for real world problems.

Example 3 William has $36. He wants to buy some tropical fish. Red Oscars are $6 each. Blue Acaras are $12 each. How many of each can William buy if he wants to buy at least one of each?

Solution
1. Write an inequality to describe the situation.

   Let x equal the number of Red Oscars.
   So, $6x$ equals the amount of money for Red Oscars.
   Let y equal the number of Blue Acaras.
   So, $12y$ equals the amount of money for Blue Acaras.
   The inequality $6x + 12y \leq 36$ describes William's situation.

2. Solve the inequality for y.

$$6x + 12y \leq 36$$
$$6x + 12y - 6x \leq 36 - 6x \qquad \text{Subtract 6x from each side.}$$
$$12y \leq 36 - 6x$$
$$\frac{12y}{12} \leq \frac{36 - 6x}{12} \qquad \text{Divide each side by 12.}$$
$$y \leq \frac{36}{12} - \frac{6x}{12}$$
$$\leq 3 - \frac{1}{2}x$$

3. Substitute values for x. Use a chart to organize the data.

x	y	(x,y)
0	3	(0,3)
1	2.5	(1,2.5)
2	2	(2,2)
3	1.5	(3,1.5)
4	1	(4,1)
5	0.5	(5,0.5)
6	0	(6,0)
7	-0.5	(7,-0.5)

4. Analyze the chart to make reasonable conclusions.

   The ordered pairs (2,2) and (4,1) are solutions. William can buy 2 Red Oscars and 2 Blue Acaras or 4 Red Oscars and 1 Blue Acara.

   The ordered pairs (0,3) and (6,0) are *not* solutions. William wants to buy *at least* one of each type.

   The ordered pairs (1,2.5), (3,1.5), and (5,0.5) are *not* solutions. William cannot buy a fraction of a fish.

   The ordered pair (7,-0.5) is *not* a solution. William can only buy positive numbers of items.

CLASS EXERCISES

Tell whether each ordered pair is a solution of the inequality.

1. $|x + y| > 3$; $(0,-5)$

2. $2x + y \leq -1$; $(2,3)$

3. $3x - 5y \geq 36$; $(7,-4)$

4. $|x| - |y| > 0$; $(-1,-11)$

Solve each inequality for y in terms of x. Write three ordered pairs that are solutions of the inequality.

5. $3x - 2y > -12$

6. $4x + 5y \geq 15$

7. $x \leq -3y$

8. $x - 2y < -1$

9. $-6x + 8y > 48$

10. $x - y < 1$

11. Students are selling tickets for a play. Student tickets cost $3. General admission tickets cost $5. How many of each kind must the students sell to raise at least $200 for costumes?

   a. Suppose only student tickets are sold. How many must the students sell to purchase costumes?

   b. Suppose only general admission tickets are sold. How many must the students sell to purchase costumes?

   c. Let x equal the number of student tickets sold and y equal the number of general admission tickets sold. Write an inequality that describes the situation.

   d. Find three solutions. Assume at least one of each type of ticket must be sold.

GENERAL ADMISSION $5

STUDENT $3

WRITTEN EXERCISES

Tell whether each ordered pair is a solution of the inequality.

1. $|x + y| > 3$; $(-2,1)$

2. $2x + 3y \leq 12$; $(-2,5)$

3. $x - 5y < 0$; $(7,-3)$

4. $|x| + |y| > |x + y|$; $(-4,10)$

CALCULATOR Tell whether each ordered pair is a solution of the inequality.

5. $|x| - 6.8y < -27.09$; $(-3.75,4.5)$

6. $2x - 9.4y \geq 3.7x$; $(8.96,-1.73)$

7. $3.2x + y < 0.35$; $(-1.25,4.5)$

8. $13.85x + 7.94y > 0$; $(3.91,-6.72)$

Solve each inequality for y in terms of x. Write three ordered pairs that are solutions of the inequality.

9. $5x - 2y < 10$

10. $x + 2y + 13 \geq 5x - y - 6$

THINK AND DISCUSS

1. List three ordered pairs that satisfy the inequality $y > 2x$.

2. Describe the solution set of the inequality $|x + y| < 0$.

3. Describe the solution set of the inequality $|x| + |y| \leq 0$.

11. $(x - 2y) > x + y + 1$　　**12.** $6 - (3x - y) \leq 12$

13. $|x| - y \geq 4$　　**14.** $11 - 2\left(x - \frac{1}{2}y\right) - 3y < 0$

15. $3 - y \geq x - 2$　　**16.** $-x > 3y - 5(2y - 3)$

Solve.

17. Ray bought five identical pencils and two identical pens. He spent not more than $2. What could be the cost of each item?

18. A collection of nickels and dimes is worth less than $1.70. Determine how many coins of each type are in the collection.

  a. Suppose the collection contains only nickels. How many nickels could there be?

  b. Suppose the collection contains only dimes. How many dimes could there be?

  c. Let x equal the number of nickels in the collection and y equal the number of dimes in the collection. Write an inequality that describes the problem situation.

  d. Find ten possible solutions. Assume there is at least one nickel and one dime in the collection.

19. Write a journal entry explaining how you know how many solutions each inequality has.

  a. $|x| + |y| \geq 0$　　　　**b.** $|x - y| < 0$

Critical Thinking

EXPLORING GRAPHING

▼ Classify each graph.

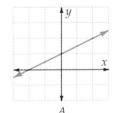 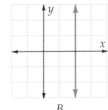 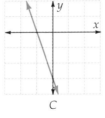 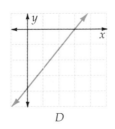

    A　　　　　　*B*　　　　　　*C*　　　　　　*D*

1. a. Which graphs have a positive slope?

  b. Which graphs have a negative slope?

2. a. Which graphs have a positive y-intercept?

  b. Which graphs have a negative x-intercept?

MIXED REVIEW

Write each fraction as a decimal and as a percent.

1. $\frac{3}{40}$　　　　**2.** $\frac{2}{9}$

Solve by graphing.

3. $4x - y = 3$
   $x + 2y = 3$

4. $y = x - 4$
   $x + 3y = 12$

Find each answer.

5. Graph the equation: $y = -x + 3$.

6. Is the point (0,0) above or below the graph of the equation $y = -x + 1$?

Solve.

7. The interest on an account of $2,500 for one year is $300. What is the rate of interest?

OBJECTIVE:
To graph a linear
inequality in two
variables and to
explore simple
systems of
inequalities.

8-8 Graphing Linear Inequalities

▼ You can use the graph of the
equation $x + y = 5$ to solve the
inequality $x + y \leq 5$.

The line shows the solutions
for $x + y = 5$.

The shaded region of the graph
shows the solutions for $x + y < 5$.

The line and the shaded region
show the solutions for $x + y \leq 5$.

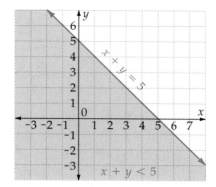

▼ Sometimes the line may include points that are not solutions to
the inequality.

Example 1 **Graph the inequality $2x - 3y > 6$.**

Solution   1. Substitute $=$ for $>$.

$$2x - 3y > 6$$
$$2x - 3y = 6$$

2. Solve the equation for y.

$$2x - 3y - 2x = 6 - 2x$$
$$-3y = 6 - 2x$$

$$\frac{-3y}{-3} = \frac{6 - 2x}{-3}$$

$$y = \frac{6}{-3} - \frac{2x}{-3}$$

$$y = -2 + \frac{2}{3}x$$

$$y = \frac{2}{3}x - 2$$

3. Graph the equation. The
inequality does not include
is equal to, so use a dotted
line to show that the line
itself is not part of the
solution set.

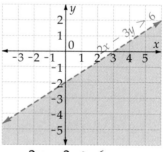

Check Choose any point above
or below the line. Determine if
the point is a solution. Try (0,0).

$$2x - 3y > 6$$
$$2(0) - 3(0) > 6$$
$$0 - 0 > 6$$
$$0 > 6 \text{ False}$$

Since (0,0) is not a solution, shade the area below the line.

Any point that is shaded is a solution of the inequality.

▼ When you graph linear inequalities in two variables, the line is part of the solution if the inequality symbol is ≤ or ≥. The line is not part of the solution if the inequality symbol is < or >.

Example 2 Write the equation of the line you would graph for each inequality. Tell whether the graph of the equation would be drawn as a solid or a dotted line.

   a. $y > 4x + 3$ **b.** $3x - 7y \leq -21$ **c.** $3x \geq 2y + 1$

Solution   **a.** Graph the equation $y = 4x + 3$. The graph is a dotted line.

   b. Graph the equation $3x - 7y = -21$. The graph is a solid line.

   c. Graph the equation $3x = 2y + 1$. The graph is a solid line.

▼ You can show the solution of a *system of linear inequalities* by graphing both inequalities on the same set of coordinate axes.

System of Linear Inequalities	A system of linear inequalities is two or more linear inequalities using the same variables.

Example 3 Solve the system of linear inequalities $y > x$ and $y \leq 2$.

Solution   **1.** Graph $y > x$. Shade the region above the dotted line.   **2.** Graph $y \leq 2$ on the same set of axes. Shade below the solid line.

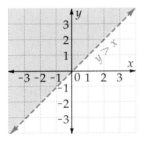   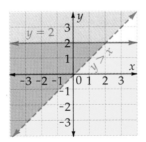

The graph of the solution is the part shaded in both colors.

▼

THINK AND DISCUSS

1. Is $(-2,-1)$ a solution of the inequality $y > x$?

2. If (p,q) is a solution of $y > x$, what must be true about $\frac{p}{q}$?

3. State whether $(0,0)$ is a solution.

   a. $4x - 11y \leq 15$

   b. $-x + y > -1.45$

   c. $x \geq -3$

CLASS EXERCISES

Write the equation of the line you would graph for each inequality. Tell whether the graph would be a solid or a dotted line.

1. $x + 2y > 5$ **2.** $3x - y \leq 1$ **3.** $x < 6$

4. $y + 2x \leq -1$ **5.** $x - 3y \geq 9$ **6.** $y > 7$

Tell whether the region containing the origin (0,0) would be shaded in the graph of each inequality.

7. $x + 2y > 5$
8. $3x - y \leq 1$
9. $x < 6$

Graph each inequality.

10. $x + 2y > 5$
11. $3x - y \leq 1$
12. $x < 6$

Write an inequality for each word sentence. Graph the inequality.

13. The sum of two numbers is greater than 3.
14. A number is greater than or equal to three times another.
15. The y-coordinate of a point is less than twice the x-coordinate.

Write two inequalities. Graph the system of inequalities.

16. Find two numbers such that one is greater than four times the other and their sum is greater than 14.
17. Find two numbers such that the sum is greater than 3 and the difference is less than 5.

MIXED REVIEW

Determine whether each system has one solution, no solution, or infinitely many solutions.

1. $4x - 2y = 6$
   $2x - y = 3$
2. $4x - 2y = 6$
   $2x - y = 1$
3. $4x - 2y = 6$
   $2x + y = 1$

Write three ordered pairs that are solutions of each inequality.

4. $4x - y \leq 6$
5. $5 - 2x - y > x$

Solve.

6. A student has $120 to spend on clothes. Shirts cost $15 and sweaters cost $24.
   a. What is the maximum number of shirts she can buy?
   b. What is the maximum number of sweaters she can buy?
   c. Assume she wants to buy at least one shirt and one sweater. How many of each can she buy?

WRITTEN EXERCISES

Write the equation of the line you would graph for each inequality. Tell whether the graph would be a solid or a dotted line.

1. $2x + y \geq 3$
2. $\frac{1}{2}x - y < 4$
3. $y \geq -2$
4. $-3x < 6$
5. $x - 4y > 1$
6. $3x + 2y > 4$
7. $5x - 3y < 2$
8. $2x - y \geq 7$
9. $x \geq 9$
10. $x - 2y \leq 4$
11. $3x + y < 2$
12. $x + 4y \leq 5$

Tell whether the region containing the origin would be shaded in the graph of each inequality.

13. $2x + y \geq 6$
14. $\frac{1}{2}x - 2y < 4$
15. $y \geq -4$
16. $-3x < 18$
17. $x > y$
18. $2x - 2y \leq 1$
19. $y > -2x - 1$
20. $x + 2y > 4$
21. $y > 3x + 1$

Graph each inequality.

22. $2x - y \geq -4$
23. $\frac{3}{4}x + 4y < -8$
24. $y \geq 2$
25. $-2x < 6$
26. $-1 \leq x - 3$
27. $10 - y \leq 1$
28. $y + 4 < 3x$
29. $y > x + 4$
30. $2x + 3y < 9$
31. $x + 6 < 3y$
32. $x - y \leq 4$
33. $2x - y \geq -2$
34. $x < 6$
35. $y > 0$
36. $3x > 4y$

Write an inequality for each word sentence. Graph the inequality.

37. Find two numbers whose difference is greater than 3.

38. Find two numbers where one is at least three times the other.

39. Timothy has a collection of nickels and dimes valued at less than $1. Let x equal the number of nickels and y equal the number of dimes.

40. A gift wrapper cut a ribbon so that one piece was more than twice as long as the other. Let x equal the shorter piece and y equal the longer piece.

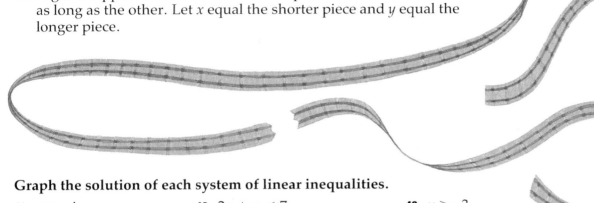

Graph the solution of each system of linear inequalities.

41. $x > -4$
   $y \leq 0$

42. $2x + y < 7$
   $x - y \leq 2$

43. $y > -3$
   $x < 5$

Use the system of linear inequalities $2x - y \geq 5$ and $\frac{1}{3}x + y < 2$ to find each point described.

44. a point which satisfies the first inequality but not the second

45. a point which satisfies the second inequality but not the first

Write two inequalities. Graph the system of inequalities.

46. Find two numbers where one is more than three times the other and their sum is greater than 12.

47. Find two numbers such that their sum is not more than 10 and the larger is greater than twice the smaller. Let y equal the larger number.

48. A student has a collection of more than 18 dimes and quarters. It is valued at more than $2.80. Let x equal the number of dimes and y equal the number of quarters.

49. *WRITE* two different situations that you could represent by the inequality $y \geq x + 3$.

50. *PROJECT* *Linear programming* is an interesting topic related to inequalities that has numerous real world applications. Research this topic and give some examples of situations where linear programming might be useful.

Practice

In which quadrant or on what axis does each point fall?

1. (4,5)
2. (-3,0)
3. (11,-7)
4. (-6,-2)

State the coordinates of each point described. Begin at the origin.

5. the point which is 4 units to the left of the y-axis and down 3 units from the x-axis

6. the point which is 3 units to the right of the y-axis and up 7 units from the x-axis.

Solve for y in terms of x. Find three solutions of each equation.

7. $3x + y = -10$
8. $2x + 4y = 8$
9. $4x + 2y - 8 = 0$

Find the x-intercept and y-intercept for each equation.

10. $3x - 4y = 12$
11. $y = 6x$
12. $\frac{4}{5}x - y = 20$

Graph each equation on a separate set of coordinate axes.

13. $x = 8$
14. $-4x + y = 16$
15. $2y + 6 = -4x$
16. $y = -\frac{1}{2}$
17. $2y = -6$
18. $|y| = 5$

Find the slope of the line containing the given points.

19. $(1,-1)(-1,1)$
20. $(2,-5)(2,4)$
21. $(2,-9)(12,3)$

Graph each line described.

22. the line having slope -5 and containing the point (-3,2)

23. the line having no slope and containing the point (6,-1)

Write each linear equation in slope-intercept form. Name the slope and y-intercept. Sketch the graph of each equation.

24. $6x + y = 24$
25. $x - 4y = 12$
26. $-x - y = -1$

Solve each system by graphing. Check your solutions.

27. $y = x + 2$
    $3x + 4y = 22$
28. $x = y - 8$
    $x - y = 2$
29. $2x + 3y = 8$
    $y = 2x$

Solve each inequality for y in terms of x. Write three ordered pairs that are solutions of each.

30. $7x - 2y < 20$
31. $4x + 5y > -6$
32. $12x + 2y - 8 > 0$

Graph each inequality.

33. $y > -x + 3$
34. $x - y \leq -6$
35. $2x + y \geq 1$

8-9 *Direct and Indirect Variation*

OBJECTIVE:
To solve problems involving direct and indirect variation.

FLASHBACK

Volume is the amount of space an object occupies.

■ The temperature and volume of a gas vary *directly*.

Direct Variation	Direct variation means that as one factor increases the other factor also increases. We represent direct variation by an equation in the form $y = kx$, where k is not zero. k is the constant of variation.

■ *Charles's law* states the relationship between the temperature in degrees Kelvin and volume of a gas.

NOTES & QUOTES

Jacques Charles (1746–1823) was a French scientist. He discovered the relationship between the temperature of a gas and its volume in the late 1700s.

Charles's Law	The volume of a fixed amount of gas varies directly with the temperature of the gas.

Example 1 A gas has a volume of 250 mL at 300°K. The temperature of the gas decreases to 240°K. What is its volume?

Solution Let x = temperature.
Let y = volume.

$$y = kx \qquad \text{Find } k, \text{ the constant of variation.}$$
$$250 = k(300)$$
$$\frac{250}{300} = k$$
$$\frac{5}{6} = k$$
$$y = \frac{5}{6}x \qquad \text{Rewrite the formula.}$$
$$= \frac{5}{6}(240) \qquad \text{Substitute 240 for } x.$$
$$= 200$$

The volume of the gas is 200 mL.

■ The volume and pressure of a gas vary *indirectly*.

NOTES & QUOTES

Robert Boyle (1627–1691) was an Irish scientist. In 1662, he reported the relationship between the pressure and volume of a gas. This is now known as Boyle's law.

Indirect Variation	In indirect variation, one factor increases as the other factor decreases. The equation $xy = k$ represents an indirect variation. k is the constant of variation.

■ *Boyle's law* states the relationship between the volume and pressure of a gas.

Boyle's Law	The volume of a fixed amount of gas varies indirectly with the pressure of the gas.

Example 2 The volume of a gas is 60 ft³ under 5 lb of pressure. What is the gas's volume under 10 lb of pressure?

Solution

Let x = pressure
Let y = volume

$$xy = k \qquad \text{Find } k, \text{ the constant of variation.}$$
$$5(60) = k$$
$$300 = k$$
$$xy = 300 \qquad \text{Rewrite the formula.}$$
$$10y = 300 \qquad \text{Substitute 10 for } y.$$
$$\frac{10y}{10} = \frac{300}{10}$$
$$y = 30$$

The volume of the gas is 30 ft³.

CLASS EXERCISES

State whether the data varies directly or indirectly. Write an equation to describe each variation. State the constant of variation.

1.	x	y
	2	4
	3	6
	4	8

2.	x	y
	6	3
	2	9
	1	18

3.	x	y
	40	120
	60	180
	80	240

■■■■■■ Decision Making ■ *DECISION MAKING* ■ Decision Making ■ Decision Making ■ Decision Making ■

DIRECT AND INDIRECT VARIATION

■ A product is packaged under pressure by inserting a gas into the container.

■ **COLLECT DATA**

1. Find five products that are packaged under pressure.

2. Read each warning label. Write a paragraph telling how the labels are similar to each other.

3. What does packaging a product under pressure allow the contents to do?

■ **ANALYZE DATA**

Support each answer using either Charles's law or Boyle's law.

4. What do you think will happen to a container that is stored above the recommended temperature?

5. When pressure is applied to the container, what will happen to the contents of the container?

WRITTEN EXERCISES

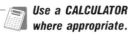 Use a **CALCULATOR** where appropriate.

State whether each equation is a direct or indirect variation. For each variation, state the constant of variation.

1. $y = 30x$ **2.** $xy = 58$ **3.** $8.5x = y$ **4.** $x = \dfrac{10}{y}$

Assume that y varies directly as x.

5. An object weighs 6 times more on Earth than it does on the moon. Ian weighs 165 lb on Earth. What would he weigh on the moon?

6. A gas has a volume of 150 mL at 320°K. The gas's temperature is increased to 360°K. What is its volume to the nearest tenth?

Assume that y varies indirectly as x.

7. A piano string 40 in. long vibrates at a frequency of 520 cycles/s. Find the frequency of the string if it were shortened to 18 in. Round to the nearest whole unit.

8. Pressure acting on 12 m³ of a gas is 20 atmospheres. The pressure is reduced until the volume is 15 m³. What is the new pressure acting on the gas?

9. Amy drove for 4 h at a rate of 40 mi/h. To the nearest hour, how long would it have taken Amy if she drove at 55 mi/h?

Dr. Maria Mayer (1906–1972), Nobel Prize winner in physics, wrote the classic textbook *Statistical Mechanics* along with her husband. They developed the book from their lectures on this branch of physics, which deals with the study of molecules and their atomic makeup.

■ *Decision Making* ■ *Decision Making* ■ *Decision Making* ■ *Decision Making* ■ *Decision Making* ■ *Decision Making* ■

6. Why do container labels suggest that you use pressurized products in well-ventilated areas?

7. Why do airlines recommend that you not bring contents that are under pressure on board a plane?

8. Do you think that there is a minimum temperature that pressurized products must be stored under? Explain.

■ **MAKE DECISIONS**

■ Some products that are packaged under pressure contain gases that are harmful to the environment.

9. What environmental concerns arise from the use of chlorofluorocarbons in a container stored under pressure?

10. What are alternative packaging methods that manufacturers could use?

11. What can we do as individuals to promote these alternatives?

Chapter 8 Review

Write *true* or *false*. If false, change the underlined word(s) to make a true statement.

1. A <u>coordinate</u> pair is a pair of numbers (x,y) assigned to a point on a coordinate plane.

2. A linear equation is an equation for which the graph is a <u>line</u>.

3. The x-intercept is the x-coordinate of the point at which the graph of a linear equation intersects the <u>y-axis</u>.

4. A linear equation in the form $y = mx + b$ is in slope-intercept form. The slope is <u>b</u>, and the y-intercept is <u>m</u>.

5. When you graph a linear inequality in two variables, the line <u>is part of</u> the solution if the inequality symbol is $<$ or $>$.

The Coordinate Plane   8-1

To locate $P(x,y)$ on the coordinate plane,

    1. Begin at the origin.

    2. Move x units along the x-axis.

    3. Move $|y|$ units up or down.

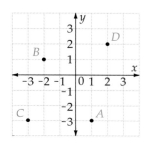

State the coordinates of each point.

6. A **7.** B **8.** C **9.** D

Solving Equations   8-2

To solve an equation in two variables, choose a value for x. Then substitute the x value into the equation to find the y value. Write the solution as an ordered pair.

Write the solution for the given value of x.

10. $2x + 5y = 12$; $x = 1$ **11.** $3x = -\frac{1}{2}y + 5$; $x = 2$ **12.** $3(x - 1) = 2y$; $x = 3$

Graphing Linear Equations   8-3

To graph a linear equation,

    1. Solve for y in terms of x.

    2. Find three solutions to the equation.

    3. Plot the points and draw a straight line.

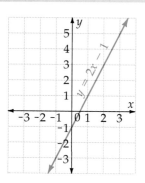

Determine whether each point is on the graph.

13. $(1,1)$ **14.** $(2,2)$ **15.** $(-1,-3)$ **16.** $(3,5)$

Slope and y-intercept

To find the slope of a line when you know the coordinates of any two points on the line, use the slope formula.

$$\text{slope} = \frac{\text{difference in } y\text{-coordinates}}{\text{difference in } x\text{-coordinates}}$$

An equation in the form $y = mx + b$ is in slope-intercept form. The slope is m and the y-intercept is b.

Find the slope of the line containing the given points.

17. $(1,3)(2,5)$ **18.** $(-1,0)(1,3)$ **19.** $(2,-2)(3,-3)$ **20.** $(-6,7)(4,7)$

Write each linear equation in slope-intercept form. Name the slope and y-intercept.

21. $y - 2x = 3$ **22.** $\frac{1}{2}x + y = -2$ **23.** $2x + 2y = 10$ **24.** $5 - 2y = 10x$

Problem Solving

To solve a word problem using a graph, write the given information as ordered pairs, plot the points, and draw a line. Find the missing information by reading the graph.

25. A car uses 10 L of gasoline to travel 90 km. How much gasoline will the car use to travel 198 km?

Solving Systems of Linear Equations

To solve a system of linear equations, graph both equations on the same coordinate plane. A solution is any ordered pair that satisfies all equations in the system.

Tell whether the ordered pair is a solution of the system.

26. $y = 2x - 1$
$3y + 2x = 13$
$(2,3)$

27. $3x - 2y = 10$
$x + y = 0$
$(-2,-8)$

28. $\frac{1}{3}x + 2y = 1$
$\frac{3}{4}x + \frac{1}{4}y = -2$
$(-3,1)$

Solving and Graphing Linear Inequalities

A solution of a linear inequality is an ordered pair that makes the inequality true.

To graph a linear inequality, graph the related equation. Determine if the line should be solid or dotted and whether the solutions are above or below the line. Shade in the appropriate region.

Graph each inequality. Give three ordered pair solutions.

29. $y \geq x + 2$ **30.** $y < x - 3$ **31.** $y > x + 3$ **32.** $y < x + 3$

Chapter 8   Test

In which quadrant or on which axis does each point fall?

1. $(-5,7)$ **2.** $(0,-4)$ **3.** $(-8,-6)$

Write an equation using two variables. Find three solutions.

4. Mrs. Jones bought eight cans of juice. Some were orange juice and some were apple juice. Let x = the number of cans of orange juice and let y = the number of cans of apple juice.

5. A collection of nickels and dimes is valued at $2.50. Let x = the number of nickels and y = the number of dimes.

Find the slope of the line containing the given points.

6. $(5,1)(8,-2)$ **7.** $(6,3)(-2,4)$ **8.** $(-4,3)(6,-5)$

Write each linear equation in slope-intercept form. Name the slope and y-intercept.

9. $x + \frac{1}{2}y = 4$ **10.** $6x - 3y = 6$ **11.** $3x = 4y + 1$

Graph each equation on a separate set of coordinate axes.

12. $3x + y = 4$ **13.** $2x - y = 1$ **14.** $y = 3x + 1$

Write a system of linear equations. Find the solution.

15. A piece of ribbon 30 in. long is cut into 2 pieces. One piece is 5 times as long as the other. How long is each piece of ribbon?

16. The sum of two numbers is 35. When the greater number is decreased by 3 times the lesser number, the result is 15.

Solve each system by graphing. Check your solutions.

17. $x + y = 3$ **18.** $x + 3y = 6$ **19.** $y = 2x + 3$
    $x - y = 1$ $x + 3y = 9$ $3y - 6x = 9$

Write an inequality. Find three solutions.

20. Find two numbers whose sum is less than 5.

Graph each inequality or system.

21. $x + y > 1$ **22.** $x - y < 2$ **23.** $y + 2 < x$
                                          $y - 3x > 2$

Choose the correct answer. Write A, B, C, or D.

1. In which quadrant does $\left(-1\frac{1}{2},2\right)$ fall?
   - **A.** I
   - **B.** II
   - **C.** III
   - **D.** not given

2. Find a solution of $2x + y = 3$.
   - **A.** $(-1,2)$
   - **B.** $(-1,1)$
   - **C.** $(2,-1)$
   - **D.** not given

3. State the inequality of which $(3,1)$ is a solution.
   - **A.** $2x - y \geq 5$
   - **B.** $2x - y < 5$
   - **C.** $2x - y > 5$
   - **D.** not given

4. Find the missing digit so that the resulting number is divisible by 9.

   $5,76\blacksquare,239$
   - **A.** 1
   - **B.** 9
   - **C.** 4
   - **D.** not given

5. Evaluate $\frac{3}{7} \div 1\frac{2}{5}$.
   - **A.** $\frac{3}{5}$
   - **B.** $3\frac{4}{5}$
   - **C.** $\frac{5}{7}$
   - **D.** not given

6. Compare $\frac{5}{8}$ ▨ $\frac{3}{5}$.
   - **A.** $>$
   - **B.** $<$
   - **C.** $=$
   - **D.** not given

7. 37.5% of a is 36. What is a?
   - **A.** 96
   - **B.** 48
   - **C.** 64
   - **D.** not given

8. Write the inequality.

   -3 -2 -1 0 1
   - **A.** $x < -2$
   - **B.** $x > -2$
   - **C.** $x \geq -2$
   - **D.** not given

9. Solve $-2(x - 1) \leq -6$.
   - **A.** $x \leq 3$
   - **B.** $x \leq -3$
   - **C.** $x \geq 3$
   - **D.** not given

10. Write 132% as a decimal.
    - **A.** 0.132
    - **B.** 13.2
    - **C.** 1.32
    - **D.** not given

11. Find the slope of the line containing the points $(3,2)$ and $(1,-2)$.
    - **A.** -2
    - **B.** 2
    - **C.** 1
    - **D.** not given

12. Write an inequality to describe the situation. A movie costs $5. A drink costs $1. Aaron did not spend more than $7.
    - **A.** $5x + 1y = 7$
    - **B.** $5x + 1y \leq 7$
    - **C.** $5x + 1y < 7$
    - **D.** not given

13. Write 0.28 as a fraction in lowest terms.
    - **A.** $\frac{28}{100}$
    - **B.** $\frac{7}{25}$
    - **C.** $\frac{2}{25}$
    - **D.** not given

14. Write 9.05×10^8 in standard notation.
    - **A.** 905,000,000
    - **B.** 90,500,000
    - **C.** 90,500,000,000
    - **D.** not given

15. Simplify $\frac{8a^2b^{-3}c}{24a^3bc^{-2}}$.
    - **A.** $\frac{c^3}{3ab^4}$
    - **B.** $3a^5b^{-2}c$
    - **C.** $\frac{b^{-2}}{3ac}$
    - **D.** not given

16. Find the y-intercept of the equation $x + 2y = -4$.
    - **A.** -4
    - **B.** -2
    - **C.** $-\frac{1}{2}$
    - **D.** not given

There are two different types of golf clubs—woods and irons. Woods have a bit more weight in the head and thus hit the ball farther. Irons are used for accuracy.

WOODS

10°	13°	16°	19°
No. 1 Driver	No. 2	No. 3	No. 4

IRONS

18°	20°	23°	27°	31°	35°
1 iron	2 iron	3 iron	4 iron	5 iron	6 iron

39°	42°	47°	54°	58°	0°
7 iron	8 iron	9 iron	pitching wedge	sand wedge	putter

The *loft* of a club is the angle at which a club is set from vertical. The height and distance a ball travels are a function of the loft.

47° loft

2°

sole angle

YD 100 110 120 130 140 150 160 170 180 190 200 210 220

IRONS Wedge 9 8 7 6 5 4 3 2 1

WOODS 4 3 2 1

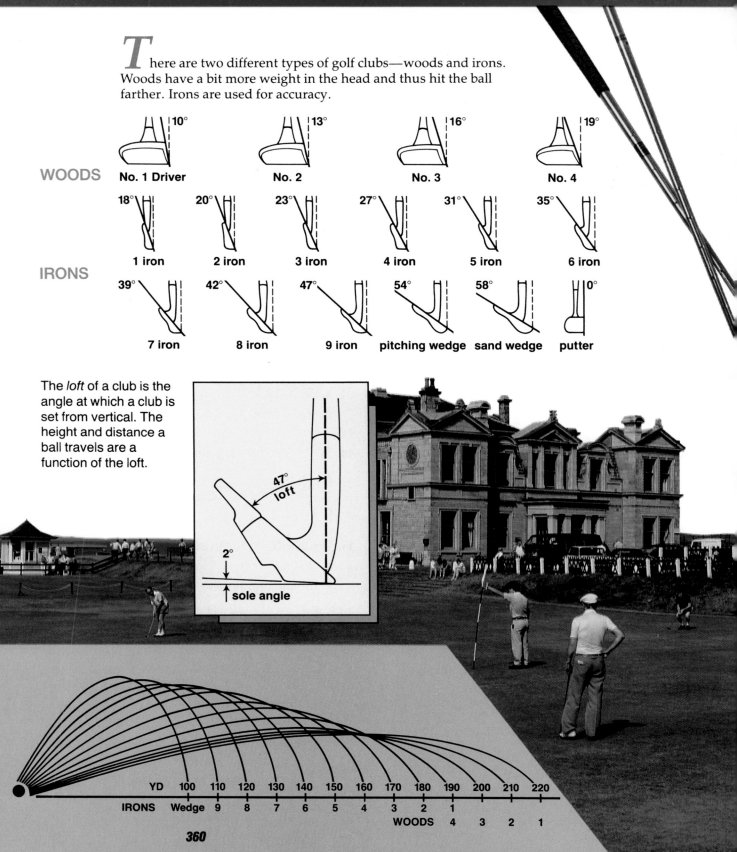

Algebra in Geometry and Measurement

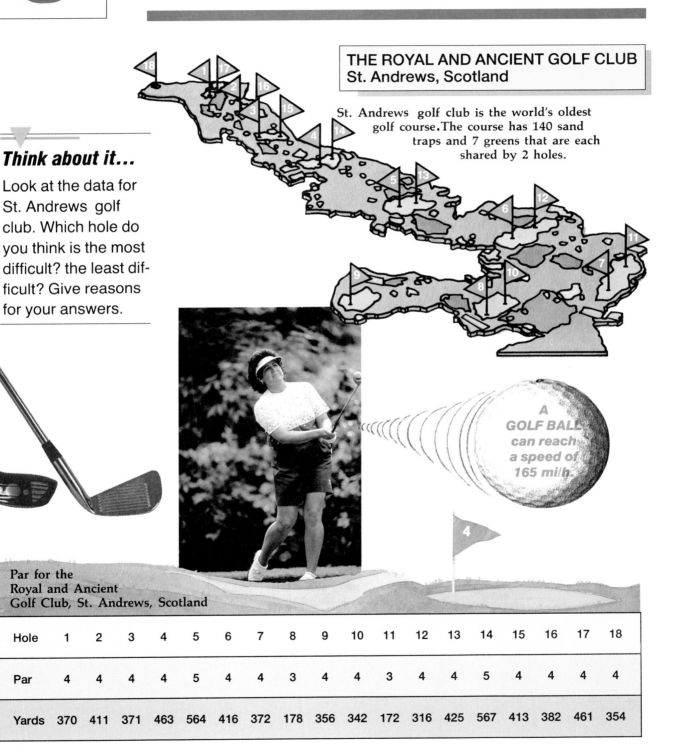

THE ROYAL AND ANCIENT GOLF CLUB
St. Andrews, Scotland

St. Andrews golf club is the world's oldest golf course. The course has 140 sand traps and 7 greens that are each shared by 2 holes.

Think about it...

Look at the data for St. Andrews golf club. Which hole do you think is the most difficult? the least difficult? Give reasons for your answers.

A **GOLF BALL** can reach a speed of 165 mi/h.

Par for the
Royal and Ancient
Golf Club, St. Andrews, Scotland

Hole	1	2	3	4	5	6	7	8	9	10	11	12	13	14	15	16	17	18
Par	4	4	4	4	5	4	4	3	4	4	3	4	4	5	4	4	4	4
Yards	370	411	371	463	564	416	372	178	356	342	172	316	425	567	413	382	461	354

9-1 Introduction to Geometry

▼ Geometric shapes are evident in many man-made and natural structures. The hexagonal design of the snowflake or honeycomb and the spiral design of the snail are but two examples of geometry in nature.

▼ The table illustrates some basic geometric figures.

Figure	Properties	Example	Symbol	Read as
Point	• represents a position in space	• A	A	point A
Line	• continues without end in opposite directions	A B	$\overleftrightarrow{AB}$	line AB
Plane	• is a flat surface with no thickness that continues without end in all directions	A B M D C	ABCD M	plane ABCD or plane M
Segment	• is part of a line with two endpoints	A B	$\overline{AB}$	segment AB
Ray	• is part of a line with only one endpoint • continues without end in one direction	A B	$\overrightarrow{AB}$	ray AB

▼ You can name a line by any two points on the line.

Example 1 **Use the figure at the right.**

a. Give three ways, other than line *AB*, to name the line.

b. Name three different segments.

c. Name three different rays.

d. Are there points other than *A*, *B*, *C*, and *X* on the line?

Solution a. $\overleftrightarrow{AC}$, $\overleftrightarrow{BA}$, and $\overleftrightarrow{BX}$ are three possible ways to name the line.

b. $\overline{AC}$, $\overline{BC}$, and $\overline{BX}$ are three different segments.

c. $\overrightarrow{AX}$, $\overrightarrow{BX}$, and $\overrightarrow{CA}$ are three possible rays.

d. Yes. There are an infinite number of points on the line.

▼ When lines, rays, and segments intersect, the intersection is a point. *Parallel lines* (∥ lines) are lines that are always the same distance apart and never intersect.

Parallel Lines	Two lines are parallel if they lie in the same plane and do not intersect.

Parallel Planes	Two planes are parallel if they do not intersect.

Skew Lines	Skew lines are lines that do not lie in the same plane and do not intersect.

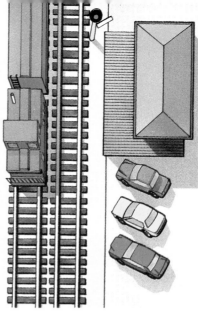

Railroad tracks are an example of parallel lines. Can you think of an example of parallel planes?

▼ Unless you are given other instructions, you will be judging the geometric properties of figures in this book by appearance.

Example 2 Use graph paper to draw and label a figure containing three lines. Make two of the lines parallel.

Solution

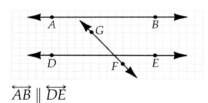

$\overleftrightarrow{AB} \parallel \overleftrightarrow{DE}$

CLASS EXERCISES

Use the figure at the right.

1. Name the line in three ways.
2. Name three different segments.
3. Name three rays.

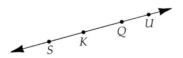

Use dot paper or graph paper to draw and label a figure to fit each description.

4. intersecting lines $\overleftrightarrow{AB}$ and $\overleftrightarrow{CD}$

5. parallel rays $\overrightarrow{MN}$ and $\overrightarrow{OP}$

6. point Q on $\overline{MN}$ and $\overline{XY}$

7. $\overleftrightarrow{CD}$ containing point X

8. **WRITE** a description of the streets in your neighborhood. Use the street names and the terms *parallel* and *intersecting* as appropriate. Could streets in a town form skew lines? Why or why not?

WRITTEN EXERCISES

1. Name all possible segments in the figure below using the points labeled.

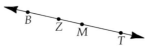

2. Name four different rays in the figure below.

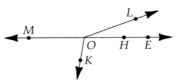

3. Points *A*, *B*, *C*, and *D* are collinear (all on a line) and in the same order. Name $\overrightarrow{DA}$ three different ways.

4. Draw a figure in which $\overleftrightarrow{ZR}$ contains *P* and $\overline{PQ}$ contains *R*.

   a. Is only one figure possible? If *no*, show an alternate figure.

   b. Is *R* between *Q* and *P*?

   c. Must $\overrightarrow{ZR}$ contain *P*?

   d. Could $\overrightarrow{ZR}$ contain *P*?

5. How many lines can you draw that contain a given point *Q*? that contain two given points *X* and *Y*?

6. a. Suppose a town installs a mailbox at point *M*. How many straight roads can the town build leading to *M*?

   b. Suppose a town installs mailboxes at points *M* and *A*. How many straight roads might the town build that pass by both mailboxes?

7. WRITE Remember to use complete sentences.

   a. Describe the intersection of two planes.

   b. Give a physical example of the intersection of two planes.

8. Planes *M* and *N* do not intersect. What can you conclude?

Write an equation and then find the length of each segment.

9.

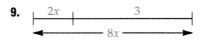

10.

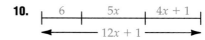

True or false?

11. Skew lines never intersect.

12. A ray has two endpoints.

13. A line has no endpoints.

14. A segment has two endpoints.

15. PROJECT Collect at least five pictures from magazines and catalogs that show geometry in the real world. **WRITE** a sentence for each picture to explain the connection.

MIXED REVIEW

1. Graph the points *A*(5,0), *B*(6,3), *C*(1,1). Connect *A* to *B* and *B* to *C*.

2. $a = \frac{b}{2} + c - 2$. Find *a* if *b* = 11 and *c* = 3.

3. What percent of 73 is 25?

4. A 12-oz can of juice costs 69¢. What would you expect to pay for a 16-oz can?

Solve.

5. $2x + 8 = 12$

6. $3 + \frac{a}{8} = 11$

7. How many three-digit numbers, greater than 500, can you form using the digits 2, 6, and 8 exactly once each?

9-2 Angles

▼ When lines or parts of lines intersect, they form angles. Different angles contribute to designs on quilts, tile floors, stained glass windows, and other forms of art and architecture.

▼ You can name an angle by the vertex and points on the sides, by a number, or by the vertex alone. When using three letters, the middle letter always names the vertex.

Angle	Two rays with a common endpoint form an angle.

Example 1 Name the angle shown in four different ways.

Solution ∠ABC, ∠1, ∠B, ∠CBA

▼ We classify angles by their measure in degrees (°). The notation $m\angle ABC$ means *the measure of angle ABC.*

acute
less than 90°
$m\angle 2 < 90°$

obtuse
between 90° and 180°
$90° < m\angle 3 < 180°$

right
equals 90°
$m\angle PQR = 90°$

straight
equals 180°
$m\angle AOR = 180°$

▼ We use a protractor to measure and draw angles.

Example 2 Use a protractor to measure ∠XYZ.

1. Place the center point of the protractor on Y, the vertex of the angle.

2. Position the protractor so that $\overrightarrow{YZ}$ passes through zero on the protractor scale. Estimate to decide which scale to read. Is ∠XYZ acute or obtuse?

3. Read the angle measure at the point where $\overrightarrow{YX}$ passes through the protractor scale.

Solution $m\angle XYZ = 29°$

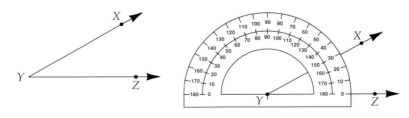

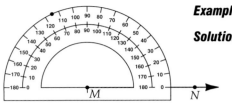

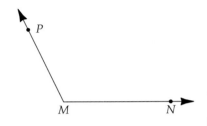

Example 3 Use a protractor to draw an angle with measure 115°.

Solution
1. Draw and label a ray.
2. Place the center point of the protractor on the endpoint of the ray. Line up the ray so that it passes through zero.
3. Mark a point at 115° on the protractor scale.
4. Remove the protractor. Draw a ray connecting the endpoint of the ray and the point marked at 115°.
5. $m\angle PMN = 115°$

▼ You can add or subtract the measures of *adjacent angles*.

Adjacent Angles	Two angles that have the same vertex and have a common side but no interior points in common form adjacent angles.	

Supplementary Angles	Two angles are supplementary angles if the sum of their measures is 180°.	

Complementary Angles	Two angles are complementary angles if the sum of their measures is 90°.	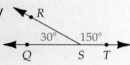

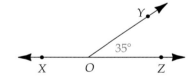

Example 4 $m\angle XOZ = 180°$. Find $m\angle YOX$.

Solution
$$35° + m\angle YOX = 180°$$
$$35° + m\angle YOX - 35° = 180° - 35°$$
$$m\angle YOX = 145°$$

$\angle XOY$ and $\angle YOZ$ are supplementary.
Subtract 35° from each side.

▼ When segments, rays, or lines intersect, they form vertical angles.

Vertical Angles	Two intersecting lines form two pairs of vertical angles. The measures of vertical angles are equal.

Example 5 Find the value of x and y.

Solution $x = 28$ $y = 152$

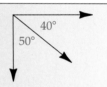

Example 6 Find the measure of each numbered angle.

Solution
$$m\angle 1 = 90° - 26° = 64°$$
$$m\angle 2 = 180° - 90° = 90°$$
$$m\angle 3 = 26°$$
$$m\angle 4 = m\angle 1 = 64°$$
$$m\angle 5 = m\angle 2 = 90°$$

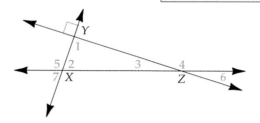

▼

THINK AND DISCUSS

1. Describe a real world example of vertical angles.

2. How can you measure an angle if one ray is not on the base line of the protractor?

3. Can a pair of vertical angles be adjacent? Why or why not?

CLASS EXERCISES

Refer to the figure at the right.

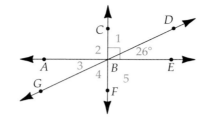

1. Give another name for $\angle 1$.

2. Find $m\angle 5 + m\angle 2$.

3. Name a pair of supplementary angles.

4. Name a pair of adjacent angles.

5. Is $\angle Y$ acute, obtuse, or right?

6. State the relationship between $\overleftrightarrow{XZ}$ and $\overleftrightarrow{ZY}$.

7. Name two pairs of vertical angles.

8. $m\angle 3 = t°$ and $m\angle 4 = 9t°$. Find the value of t.

WRITTEN EXERCISES

Classify each angle as acute, obtuse, right, or straight.

1.

2.

3.

4.

5.

6.

7. Under what conditions are two angles supplementary?

8. Use a drawing to illustrate vertical angles.

Name two pairs of vertical angles in each figure.

9.
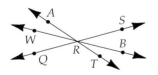

10.

Describe the angles in the photograph.

Find the measure of each indicated angle.

11. ∠ACD and ∠ACB

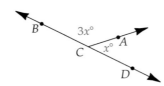

12. ∠QRT and ∠QRU

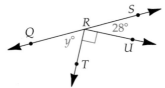

13. ∠TMX

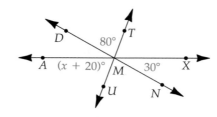

14. ∠AMT and ∠TMH

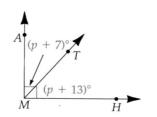

PROBLEM SOLVING HINT
Try guess and test.

15. Find an angle with a measure that is twice as great as a supplement.

16. Find a pair of supplementary angles such that the difference of their measures is 56°.

Use a protractor to measure each angle.

17.

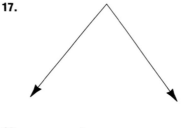

18.

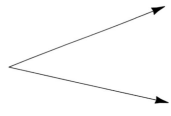

19.

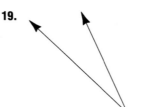

20.

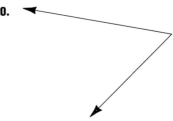

MIXED REVIEW

Solve for y in terms of x.

1. $x = 4y - 8$

2. $x - y + 12 = 2x$

3. Name one pair of parallel segments.

4. $\overline{CD}$ and $\overline{AB}$ are called ▨ segments.

5. The Jones' monthly mortgage payment is $1,237. There is a 2% penalty if the payment is late. How much is the penalty?

Tell whether each angle is acute, right, obtuse, or straight.

21. 65°   **22.** 45°   **23.** 90°   **24.** 180°

25. 125°   **26.** 27°   **27.** 21°   **28.** 108°

Find the measure of a complement and a supplement of each angle, if possible.

29. 90°   **30.** 18°   **31.** 115°   **32.** 89°

33. 43°   **34.** $x°$ **35.** $(y - 20)°$ **36.** $(3a)°$

OBJECTIVE:
To explore segments and angles using geoboards.

Exploring Segments and Angles

▼   You can use a geoboard to explore many geometric concepts. As you complete the activities that follow, think about the ideas of segments and angles. The geoboard at the right shows a segment *one unit in length.*

MATERIALS

- Geoboards and colored rubber bands or

- Dot paper and colored pencils

- Math journal to record work

---

1. Use your geoboard or dot paper to represent a segment of the given length.

   a. 2 units   **b.** 4 units   **c.** 5 units

2. What is the longest segment you can show? Explain how you know you have the longest possible segment.

▼   In geometry, the word *congruent* means *same size and same shape.*

3. **Model** the following on your geoboard or draw on dot paper.

   a. two or more congruent segments

   b. two intersecting segments that are not congruent
   Discuss the ways your segments might intersect.

   c. two parallel segments; three parallel segments
   Discuss the ways your segments might be parallel.

   d. two perpendicular segments
   Discuss the ways your segments might be perpendicular.

4. Show each figure below on your geoboard or on dot paper. **Classify** each angle as acute, obtuse, right, or straight.

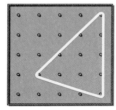 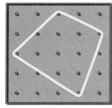 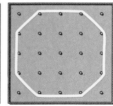 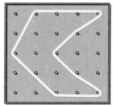

▼   Shapes you make with one rubber band in which edges do not cross or touch are called *polygons.* A place where the band turns a corner (or is hooked on a peg) is called a *vertex.* The segment joining two vertices is called a *side.*

5. Make several polygons on your geoboard or dot paper. Make each one a different color. State the number of vertices and sides for each polygon you made.

6. What are some limitations you experience when modeling figures on a geoboard?

Exploring Segments and Angles   **369**

9-3 Polygons and Quadrilaterals

▼ Many of the shapes you see in the world around you and in art are examples of *polygons*.

Describe the polygons you see in the picture of the pyramidal entrance to the Louvre Museum.

Polygon	A polygon is a closed plane figure such that no two segments with a common endpoint are collinear and segments intersect only at the endpoints.

Example 1 State whether or not each figure is a polygon.

a.   b.   c.

Solution   **a.** no (not closed)   **b.** no (not segments)   **c.** yes

▼ Polygons may be *convex* or *concave*.

Convex and Concave Polygons	A polygon is convex if all points on the diagonals are inside the polygon. Otherwise, the polygon is concave.

Example 2 Determine whether each polygon is convex or concave.

a.   b.   c.

Solution   **a.** convex   **b.** concave   **c.** convex

▼ A polygon is *regular* if the measures of all sides and all angles are equal.

Example 3 Decide if the polygon is regular.

a.

b.

c.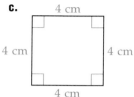
4 cm
4 cm   4 cm
4 cm

Solution   a. no   b. no   c. yes

▼ Some quadrilaterals have special names and properties.

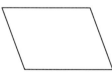

parallelogram
two pairs of opposite
parallel sides

rectangle
parallelogram with four
right angles

rhombus
parallelogram with all
sides equal

square
a parallelogram that is
both a rectangle and a
rhombus

trapezoid
exactly one pair of parallel
sides

FLASHBACK
We name polygons by
their number of sides.

Number of Sides	Polygon
3	triangle
4	quadrilateral
5	pentagon
6	hexagon
7	heptagon
8	octagon
9	nonagon
10	decagon
12	dodecagon
n	n-gon

THINK Is a trapezoid a
parallelogram?

CLASS EXERCISES

State whether or not the figure is a polygon.

1.

2.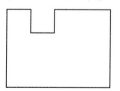

3.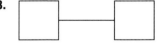

Give three correct names for each figure. Choose from polygon,
quadrilateral, parallelogram, rectangle, square, or trapezoid.

4.

5.

6.

THINK AND DISCUSS

1. Use a Venn diagram to
show the relationship
between quadrilaterals,
squares, parallelograms,
trapezoids, rhombuses, and
rectangles.

2. Can a regular polygon
be concave?

3. Which quadrilateral is a
regular polygon?

WRITTEN EXERCISES

True or false? Write *T* or *F*.

1. Every rhombus is a regular quadrilateral.

2. All quadrilaterals are parallelograms.

3. Some trapezoids are squares.

4. All squares are rectangles.

5. All rectangles are squares.

6. Some rectangles are rhombuses.

7. Some parallelograms are squares.

8. All parallelograms are quadrilaterals.

Give two other correct names for each figure.

9. square *ABCD*

10. parallelogram *BASE*

11. trapezoid *QRTS*

Determine whether the polygon is concave or convex. Then classify the polygon by the number of sides.

12.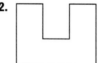

13.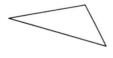

14.

Draw a figure to fit each description.

15. a convex quadrilateral

16. a concave hexagon

17. a pentagon

18. a rhombus

19. Look at convex hexagon *ABCDEF*. How many diagonals can you draw from vertex *A*? How many triangles are formed?

20. **PROJECT** Use or make a tangram.

    a. Classify the pieces in as many ways as possible.

    b. Use any number of pieces to form a square, a hexagon, a pentagon, a trapezoid, and a parallelogram.

    c. Record the number of pieces used to make each figure.

    d. Compare with a classmate. Did you both use the same pieces to make the figures? Is there more than one way to make each figure?

MATERIALS

- graph paper

- LOGO software and a computer (optional)

- Math journal to record work

LOGO COMMANDS

FD	forward
BK	back
RT	right turn
LT	left turn
PU	pen up
PD	pen down

Exploring with LOGO

■ You can use LOGO to draw segments, angles, and polygons.

1. a. Sketch what you think the following commands will produce. Then, if possible, try them on a computer.

FD 25
RT 45
FD 25
RT 45

b. Classify the angle from part(a).

c. What command determines the measure of the angle? What numbers would give an acute angle? an obtuse angle?

d. Suppose you change the second and fourth lines from RT to LT. Does this change your angle measure?

e. Write a procedure to make an animal from segments and angles. Use the commands at the left.

2. a. Sketch what you think the following commands will produce. Then, if possible, try them on a computer.

FD 65 RT 90 FD 65 RT 90
FD 65 RT 90 FD 65 RT 90

b. What would you change to make a larger square?

c. What would you change to draw a rectangle that is not a square?

d. What would you change to draw a rhombus?

■ You can use the REPEAT command to shorten your procedures.

3. Type in the following POLYGON procedure.

TO POLYGON :LENGTH :SIDES

REPEAT :SIDES [FD :LENGTH RT 360 / :SIDES]

END

a. Choose a value for LENGTH. Replace SIDES with 3 and then with 4. What types of polygons did you get?

b. What would SIDES be for a hexagon?

c. Try greater and greater values for SIDES. ***Describe*** what happens to your polygon.

OBJECTIVE:
To discover properties of triangles.

9-4 Triangles

▼ The framework of a geodesic dome is made up of triangles. Engineers use triangles to lend stability to bridges and other structures.

▼ We classify triangles by their angles or sides.

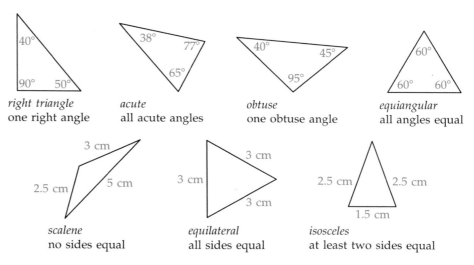

right triangle
one right angle

acute
all acute angles

obtuse
one obtuse angle

equiangular
all angles equal

scalene
no sides equal

equilateral
all sides equal

isosceles
at least two sides equal

THINK How could you use a protractor to find the sum of the measures of the interior angles of a triangle?

▼ You can do an experiment to show that the sum of the measures of the interior angles of a triangle is 180°.

a. Draw and label any triangle *ABC*. Tear off any two angles. (*B* and *C* for example)

b. Position *B* and *C* next to *A*, bringing vertices together. Notice that the angles form a straight angle.

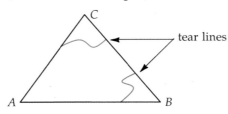

tear lines

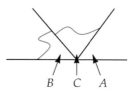

$m\angle A + m\angle B + m\angle C = 180°$

Example   Find $m\angle 1$.

Solution
$$m\angle 1 + 47° + 63° = 180°$$
$$m\angle 1 + 110° = 180°$$
$$m\angle 1 = 180° - 110°$$
$$= 70°$$

CLASS EXERCISES

Classify each triangle as acute, obtuse, or right.

1.   **2.**   **3.**

Draw a figure to fit each description.

4. right triangle *ABC*

6. isosceles triangle *TRI*

5. an obtuse scalene triangle

7. a regular triangle

WRITTEN EXERCISES

Classify each triangle by its angles or its sides.

1.   **2.**   **3.**

4.    **5.**    **6.**

True or false? Write *T* or *F*.

7. No equilateral triangles are scalene.

8. All right triangles are isosceles.

9. Some right triangles are isosceles.

10. Some right triangles are obtuse.

11. All triangles have three angles.

12. Some triangles are regular.

13. Some parallelograms are triangles.

14. All triangles are equilateral.

Draw a figure to fit each description.

15. a convex parallelogram   **16.** a trapezoid

17. an obtuse scalene triangle   **18.** a triangle with one obtuse angle

Find the measure of each numbered angle.

19.    **20.**   **21.**

CALCULATOR Find the measure of the third angle of a triangle that has two angles with the given measures.

22. 110°, 35°   **23.** 25°, 65°   **24.** 45°, 45°   **25.** 30°, 60°

26. 126°, 20°   **27.** 42°, 78°   **28.** $(2y)°$, 60°   **29.** $(x + 4)°$, 96°

Classify each triangle as acute, right, or obtuse.

30. △MNO with $m\angle M = 35°$, $m\angle N = 70°$, and $m\angle O = 75°$

31. △ABC with $m\angle A = 104°$, $m\angle B = 46°$, and $m\angle C = 30°$

Critical Thinking
EXPLORING INDUCTIVE REASONING

▼ You use *inductive reasoning* to draw conclusions based on specific examples.

1. Does the expression $n^2 + n + 5$ always produce a prime number when n is a positive integer?

a. Try several values of n.

b. A *counterexample* is an example that proves your conclusion is false. What value of n is a counterexample?

n	$n^2 + n + 5$
1	7
2	
3	
4	

Use inductive reasoning to tell whether the statement is true or false. If false, give a counterexample.

2. All squares are rectangles.

3. All rectangles are squares.

4. All equilateral triangles are equiangular.

5. **DISCUSS** How do you know when you have tried enough examples to make an inductive conclusion?

OBJECTIVE:
To discover the
properties of circles.

9-5 Circles

▼ Compact disks are shaped like circles. The circular shape allows the disk to store thousands of bits of information on a spiral track. If unraveled, the hair-thin track could stretch for several miles.

Circle	A circle (⊙) is the set of all points the same distance from a given point called the center.

▼ The table shows some parts of circles and their properties.

Term	Description
chord	a segment that has endpoints on the circle
diameter	a chord that passes through the center of the circle; The diameter (*d*) is the length of such a chord.
radius	a segment that has endpoints at the center of the circle and on the circle; The radius (*r*) is the length of such a segment.
central angle	an angle with vertex at the center of the circle

▼ We usually name a circle by its center.

Example 1   **Name all the radii, diameters, chords, and central angles shown in ⊙O.**

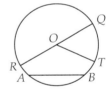

Solution   radii $\overline{OT}(\overline{TO}); \overline{OQ}(\overline{QO});$
                            and $\overline{OR}(\overline{RO})$

                diameter $\overline{RQ}(\overline{QR})$

                chord $\overline{AB}(\overline{BA}); \overline{RQ}(\overline{QR})$

                central angles $\angle TOQ(\angle QOT); \angle ROT(\angle TOR)$

▼ In any circle, the diameter *d* is twice the radius *r*.

Example 2   In a given circle, $\overline{YZ}$ and $\overline{XW}$ are diameters.

   a. If $OZ = 10$ cm, find YZ.

   b. If $WX = 25$ cm, find OX.

Solution   Draw a figure to show the given information.

   a. $YZ = 2(OZ)$
           $= 2(10) = 20$ cm

   b. $OX = \dfrac{WX}{2}$

           $= \dfrac{25}{2} = 12.5$ cm

Metals in Gold Jewelry

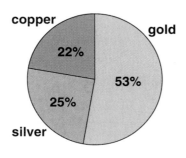

▼ There are 360° in any circle. You can use this fact to construct circle graphs.

Example 3 **Construct a circle graph for the data at the left.**

Solution

1. Write the data in decimal form.

$22\% = 0.22$
$25\% = 0.25$
$53\% = 0.53$

2. Multiply each decimal by 360 to determine the measure of each central angle. Round to the nearest degree. Make sure the total is 360.

$360 \ \boxed{\times} \ 0.22 \ \boxed{=} \ 79.2 \approx 79$
$360 \ \boxed{\times} \ 0.25 \ \boxed{=} \ 90$
$360 \ \boxed{\times} \ 0.53 \ \boxed{=} \ 190.8 \approx 191$

3. Draw a circle with a compass and any radius. Draw each angle with a protractor.

4. Label each section. Give your graph a title.

THINK AND DISCUSS

1. Is every chord a diameter? Explain.

2. How many chords, radii, and diameters does a circle have?

CLASS EXERCISES

1. Name all chords, radii, diameters, and central angles in the circle at the right.

2. If $PO = 15$ in., find PB.

3. If $LM = 37.5$ in., find OM.

4. $\angle MOP$ is $\frac{1}{5}$ of circle O. Find $m\angle MOP$.

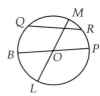

WRITTEN EXERCISES

True or false? Write *T* or *F*.

1. If a chord of a circle is 20 cm long, the radius is 10 cm.

2. The longest chord in any circle is the diameter.

3. All radii of a given circle are the same length.

4. All chords of a circle are the same length.

5. If two circles have the same radius, they have the same diameter.

MENTAL MATH **For each length, find the radius or the diameter.**

6. $r = 50$ cm
$d = $ ▨

7. $r = 42.5$ in.
$d = $ ▨

8. $d = 100$ cm
$r = $ ▨

9. $d = 70$ cm
$r = $ ▨

10. $r = 36$ ft
$d = $ ▨

11. $d = 500x$ ft
$r = $ ▨

CALCULATOR For each length, find the radius or the diameter.

12. $r = 32.2$ mm
$d = \blacksquare$

13. $r = 15.75$ in.
$d = \blacksquare$

14. $d = 17.09$ cm
$r = \blacksquare$

15. $d = 0.58$ cm
$r = \blacksquare$

16. $r = 7,832$ ft
$d = \blacksquare$

17. $d = 90,089$ mi
$r = \blacksquare$

18. Circle O has a diameter of 12 in. Point A is 6 in. from point O.

a. Is point A inside, outside, or on the circle?

b. Is $\overline{OA}$ a radius of $\odot O$?

c. Point B is on $\odot O$. Is $\overline{AB}$ a chord?

d. What must be true of $\overline{OB}$ for $\overline{AB}$ to be a diameter?

> **PROBLEM SOLVING HINT**
> Drawing a diagram may help.

19. Draw $\odot O$, with $r = 3$ cm. Label two points as C and D inside the circle.

a. Is $\overline{CD}$ a chord of $\odot O$?

b. Can $\overline{CD}$ be a diameter of $\odot O$? why or why not?

20. In $\odot O$ at the right, $\overline{OA}$ and $\overline{OB}$ are radii. What kind of triangle is $\triangle AOB$? How do you know?

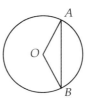

CALCULATOR Use the data to construct a circle graph.

21.

Recommended Diet Components	
Carbohydrates	48%
Refined sugars	10%
Saturated fats	10%
Monosaturated fats	10%
Polyunsaturated fats	10%
Protein	12%

22.

Teens' Career Choices	
Health care	16%
Trade	8%
Teacher	7%
Performer	6%
Sports	6%
Business/law	6%
Other	20%
Undecided	31%

23. CALCULATOR In a survey about favorite colors, 28% responded that blue was their favorite color. Another 56% chose red. All other respondents chose yellow. Draw a circle graph to display the results of the survey.

24. PROJECT Choose a topic from the list below, or one of your own. Collect data in your class and construct a circle graph to display the results.

a. career choice

b. favorite sport

c. favorite subject

d. own TV, camera, phone, computer

> **MIXED REVIEW**
> Solve.
> **1.** $\frac{6}{8} = \frac{n}{12}$ **2.** $\frac{a}{24} = \frac{30}{48}$
> Evaluate.
> **3.** $y^2 + 5$ for $y = 12$
> **4.** $5a^4 - a$ for $a = 10$
> **5.** Find $m\angle 1$ and $m\angle 2$.
>
>
>
> Use the formula $d = rt$.
> **6.** A satellite orbiting Earth travels at a rate of 28,000 km/h. How far will it travel in 24 h?

9-6 Congruence and Symmetry

▼ Two figures with the same size and shape are *congruent*. We use the symbol ≅ to mean *is congruent to*. When two figures are congruent their *corresponding* parts are equal. The symbol ↔ means *corresponds to*.

▼ Think of sliding one figure on top of the other. You can see the following correspondences.

$S \leftrightarrow T$ $\angle S \leftrightarrow \angle T$
$L \leftrightarrow I$ $\angle L \leftrightarrow \angle I$
$O \leftrightarrow M$ $\angle O \leftrightarrow \angle M$
$W \leftrightarrow E$ $\angle W \leftrightarrow \angle E$

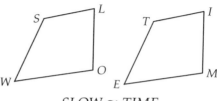

$SLOW \cong TIME$

Describe figures in the kaleidoscope picture that appear to be congruent.

▼ The definition of congruent figures follows.

Congruent Polygons	Two polygons are congruent if there is a correspondence between their vertices such that the corresponding sides and corresponding angles are congruent.

Example 1   Do the figures appear to be congruent? Explain.

a.   b.    c.

Solution   **a.** no; not the same size

       b. yes; same size and same shape

       c. no; not the same shape

FLASHBACK

We use hatch marks and arcs on figures to indicate congruent parts.

Example 2 $\triangle ABC \cong \triangle XYZ$. **Write congruence statements for corresponding parts.**

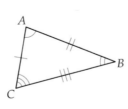   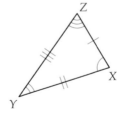

Solution $\overline{AB} \cong \overline{XY}$ $\angle A \cong \angle X$
            $\overline{BC} \cong \overline{YZ}$ $\angle B \cong \angle Y$
            $\overline{CA} \cong \overline{ZX}$ $\angle C \cong \angle Z$

▼ If you can draw a line through a figure so that one side is a reflection of the other, the figure is said to have *line symmetry*. Some figures have more than one line of symmetry. Some figures have no lines of symmetry.

Example 3 Is each dotted line a line of symmetry?

a. 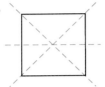 b.   c.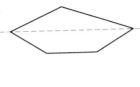

Solution **a.** yes **b.** yes **c.** no

CLASS EXERCISES

Write congruence statements for corresponding parts.

1. 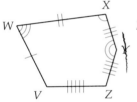 **2.**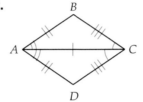

Trace each figure and draw all lines of symmetry.

3. 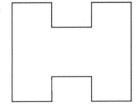 **4.**

5. WRITE Why would it be important for machines to produce congruent parts?

THINK AND DISCUSS

1. Do congruent figures have to be polygons? Can segments, angles, circles, curves, or shapes from nature be congruent?

2. Are all right angles congruent? all acute angles?

3. How many lines of symmetry does a circle have?

WRITTEN EXERCISES

1. Which figure appears not to be congruent to the other three?

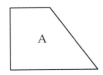 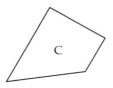 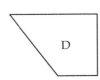

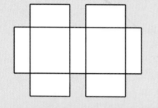
Write congruence statements for corresponding parts.

2.

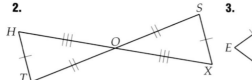

3.

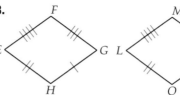

$\triangle XYZ \cong \triangle ABC$. **Write each angle measure or segment length.**

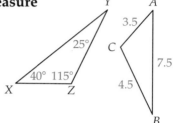

4. $\angle C$ **5.** $\angle A$ **6.** $\angle B$

7. XZ **8.** XY **9.** YZ

Suppose $RSTU \cong WXYZ$. **Which congruence statements must be true?**

10. $\angle R \cong \angle W$ **11.** $\overline{ST} \cong \overline{XY}$ **12.** $\angle R \cong \angle Z$

13. $\overline{UT} \cong \overline{ZY}$ **14.** $\overline{RS} \cong \overline{XY}$ **15.** $\angle T \cong \angle W$

Find the measure of each numbered angle.

16. $\triangle ABC \cong \triangle XYZ$

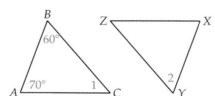

17. $\triangle PQR \cong \triangle MNO$

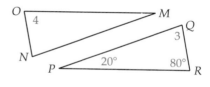

Trace each pair of symmetric figures. Fold to find the line of symmetry.

18.

19.

The dotted line is a line of symmetry for each figure. Trace the figure and complete the drawing.

20.

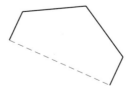

21.

Which figures have line symmetry?

22.

23.

24.

25. Fold a plain sheet of paper in half lengthwise. Write your name along the fold. Turn the paper over and trace your name through the paper. Is the fold a line of symmetry? Are the two names congruent?

26. Which letters of the alphabet have only one line of symmetry when written in capital block form? Sketch your responses with the symmetry lines.

27. PROJECT Carpenters and artisans use a tool called a level to insure that a surface is flat. You can make a level that uses the properties of congruent triangles.

Cut three congruent rectangles out of oak tag. Join the rectangles at the short edges to form a triangle. Mark the midpoint of the triangle's base. Attach a string weighted with a button to the vertex at the top of the triangle. When you stand the level on a flat surface, $\triangle FLT \cong \triangle ALT$. Rest the triangle on a non-level surface. Do you still see congruent triangles? Explain.

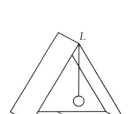

TEST YOURSELF

1. Name three lines, three rays, three segments, and three angles in the figure at the right.

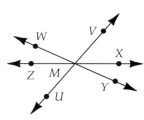

Use the figure at the right.

2. Classify *ABCD* as a square, a rectangle, or a parallelogram.

3. Classify $\triangle ABD$ as *acute*, *obtuse*, or *right*.

4. Write a congruence statement for corresponding parts in $\triangle ABD$ and $\triangle CDB$.

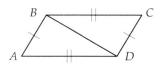

For each given length, find the radius or diameter.

5. $r = 26$ ft
$d = $ ▓

6. $d = 60$ in.
$r = $ ▓

7. $r = 15.5$ m
$d = $ ▓

8. $d = 22.2$ cm
$r = $ ▓

OBJECTIVE:
To determine
correspondences in
similar figures and to
find missing
measures in similar
figures.

9-7 Similar Figures

▼ Designers often make scale models of new products. The models are the same shape but not the same size as the final product. We say the models and the real product are *similar*.

FLASHBACK

A proportion is an equation stating that two ratios are equal.

Similar Figures	Two figures are similar (∼) if corresponding angles are congruent and corresponding sides are in proportion.

Example 1   Do the pairs of figures appear to be similar?

a.

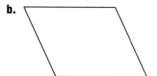

b.

Solution   **a.** yes   **b.** no; not the same shape

▼ In similar figures, the lengths of the sides may change but the measures of the angles remain the same. You can use proportions to find an unknown length when two figures are similar.

Example 2 $ABCDE \sim VWXYZ$. **Find AB.**

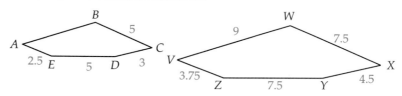

Solution   Since the figures are similar, corresponding sides are in proportion.

$\dfrac{AB}{VW} = \dfrac{BC}{WX}$ Write a proportion.

$\dfrac{AB}{9} = \dfrac{5}{7.5}$ Substitute values.

$AB = \dfrac{5}{7.5} \cdot 9$ Solve.

$= 5 \div 7.5 \times 9 = 6$

$AB = 6$

▼ When you know the measures of the angles, you can determine whether or not two triangles are similar.

| **Similar Triangles** | Two triangles are similar if two angles of one are congruent to two angles of another. |

Example 3   Determine whether or not the triangles are similar. If *yes*, write a similarity statement.

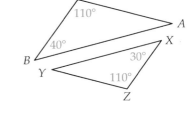

Solution $m\angle Y = 180° - (110° + 30°)$ since $m\angle B = m\angle Y$
$= 40°$ and $m\angle C = m\angle Z$
$\triangle ABC \sim \triangle XYZ$

Two angles of one triangle are congruent to two angles of the other. The triangles are similar.

▼ You can use similar triangles to measure distances that you would be unable to measure directly.

Example 4   A 6-ft tall man, standing near a tree, casts a shadow 14 ft long. The tree casts a shadow 40 ft long. Use similar triangles to find the height of the tree to the nearest tenth of a foot.

Solution   Draw a sketch to display the information in the problem.

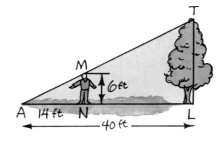

$m\angle N = m\angle L$ Right angles are congruent.
$m\angle A = m\angle A$ An angle is congruent
$\triangle TAL \sim \triangle MAN$ to itself.
$\dfrac{AL}{AN} = \dfrac{TL}{MN}$

$\dfrac{40}{14} = \dfrac{TL}{6}$

$40 \cdot 6 = 14 \cdot TL$ Cross multiply to solve.
$240 \div 14 = 17.142 \ldots$
$TL \approx 17.1$ ft   Round to the nearest tenth.

CLASS EXERCISES

1. Draw three different equilateral triangles. Are all your triangles similar?

2. In similar figures, what ratios are always equal?

HGFE ~ MNOP.

3. Find *EF*.

4. Find *MN*.

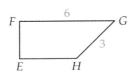
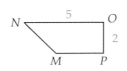

WRITTEN EXERCISES

Use graph paper to sketch a figure similar to, but not congruent to, each figure.

1.

2.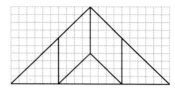

3. $MORE \sim TRYS$. Name four equal ratios.

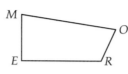

4. $\triangle HOT \sim \triangle PIE$. Name three equal ratios.

Assume each pair of triangles is similar. Find the missing length.

5.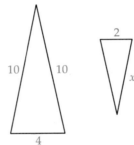

6.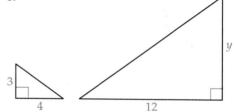

7.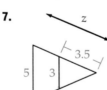

8.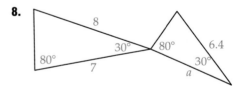

Is each pair of triangles similar? If _yes,_ identify three pairs of corresponding sides.

9.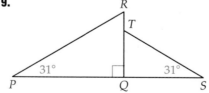

10.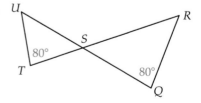

11. Suppose you wish to make a mailbox which is a model of your home. **WRITE** a paragraph which describes your plan. Include as many details as possible.

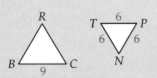

Solve.

12. A tree casts a shadow 10 ft long. A 5-ft tall person casts a shadow 3 ft long. How tall is the tree?

PROBLEM SOLVING HINT
Draw a diagram.

13. A photographic slide is 35 mm wide and 22 mm high. The projected image is 85 cm wide. How high is the image?

14. **PROJECT** Use similar triangles to measure the height of your school, flagpole, or a tall tree.

15. **DATA FILE 3 (pp. 96–97)** Find the dimensions of a dollar bill. What are the possible dimensions for a sheet of bills?

Check Your Proportions

What do paintings by Leonardo DaVinci, buildings of ancient Greece, and your physical proportions have in common? They all reflect the *Golden ratio*. The golden ratio (calculated as approximately 1.61) is the ratio of the length to the width of a golden rectangle, which is thought to be the most pleasing to the eye. Examples of the golden ratio are found in art, architecture, nature, and in the human skeleton. An American researcher found that the ratio of a person's height to the distance from the ground to his waist approaches the golden ratio. How do you measure up?

16. Use the article above. Measure, then compute each ratio. Do your ratios approach the golden ratio?

a. $\dfrac{\text{head to ground}}{\text{waist to ground}}$ b. $\dfrac{\text{shoulder to finger tips}}{\text{elbow to finger tips}}$

Critical Thinking
EXPLORING DEDUCTIVE REASONING

▼ When you reach conclusions after reasoning from accepted information, you are using *deductive reasoning*.

1. Each card has either a triangle, circle, or square on the back. Use the given information to decide the figure on each card.

   a. The figure on card 1 is not a quadrilateral.

   b. The figure on the even-numbered card is not a polygon.

2. **WRITE** a problem of your own that requires deductive reasoning. Give it to a classmate to solve.

Practice

Find the measure of each indicated angle.

1. ∠PNM

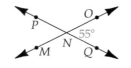

2. ∠CBD

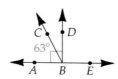

3. ∠UEN

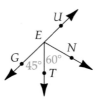

Find the measure of a complement and a supplement of each angle, if possible.

4. 12°   **5.** 57°   **6.** 101°   **7.** 43°

8. 128°   **9.** 16°   **10.** 92°   **11.** 179°

Find the measure of the third angle of a triangle that has two angles with the given measures.

12. 55°, 65°   **13.** 45°, 45°   **14.** 60°, 70°   **15.** 80°, 28°

16. 58°, 65°   **17.** 110°, 25°   **18.** 78°, 19°   **19.** 103°, 33°

For each length, find the radius or the diameter.

20. $r = 17$ in.
$d = \blacksquare$

21. $r = 56.8$ m
$d = \blacksquare$

22. $d = 85.5$ cm
$r = \blacksquare$

23. $d = 0.38$ km
$r = \blacksquare$

24. $r = 28.6$ mi
$d = \blacksquare$

25. $r = 67{,}385$ mi
$d = \blacksquare$

Name all chords, diameters, radii, and central angles shown in each circle.

26.

27.

28.

Write congruence statements for the corresponding parts of each pair of polygons.

29.

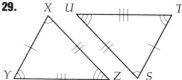

30.

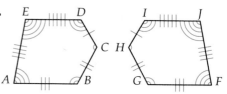

OBJECTIVE:
To explore pi as a ratio.

MATERIALS

- String and a measuring stick or a measuring tape

- Several circular objects (cans, records, CDs, etc.)

- Large grid paper

- Coin or other marker

- Calculator

- Math journal to record work

Exploring Pi

▼   Pi (π) is a fascinating ratio. You may use it in many calculations with circles. The activities that follow will help you discover pi.

1. Choose at least five circular objects. Complete steps (a–c) and record your data in a chart.

  a. Measure the circumference of each object.

  b. Measure the diameter of each object.

Object	Circumference (C)	Diameter (d)	$\frac{C}{d}$

  c. Use a calculator to find the ratio $\frac{C}{d}$ for each object. What is the approximate value for the ratio?

▼   Here is another experiment that approximates pi.

2. Use a penny and a large grid like the one below. Toss the coin so that it lands on the grid. Count only tosses that land completely on the grid.

  a. Make a 10 × 10 chart to record your tosses. Count a hit when the coin touches or covers a dot. Make an *h* in a box on your chart. When the coin misses, mark an *m* on your chart. Continue filling in your grid for 100 tosses.

  b. Use your data from (a) to complete a chart like the one at the left.

  c. Combine your data with data from other groups. Use your data to complete the formula $\frac{4h}{t} = $ ■ .

3. Is your result close to 3.1416? Do you think more tosses will result in a closer approximation of π?

Tosses						
1–10	h	m	m	h	h	h
11–20						

	h	t	$\frac{4h}{t}$
20 tosses		20	
40 tosses		40	
60 tosses			
80 tosses			
100 tosses			

Exploring Pi   **389**

OBJECTIVE:
To find the perimeter
or circumference of a
figure.

9-8 *Perimeter and Circumference*

▼ A seamstress buying lace for the bottom of a dress needs to know the *perimeter* of the hem.

Perimeter	Perimeter is the distance around a figure.

▼ You may need to find the perimeter of a common shape.

Example 1 A homeowner wants to buy a wallpaper border for a rectangular room. The room is 9 ft 2 in. long and 12 ft 3 in. wide. There is a 3-ft wide doorway. Borders are sold in 11-yd lengths. How many rolls of border does the homeowner need?

Solution

1. Find the perimeter. $P = 2l + 2w$
$$P = 2(9 \text{ ft } 2 \text{ in.}) + 2(12 \text{ ft } 3 \text{ in.})$$
$$= 42 \text{ ft } 10 \text{ in.}$$

2. Subtract the width   42 ft 10 in. $-$ 3 ft = 39 ft 10 in.
of the doorway.

3. Round to the   39 ft 10 in. $\approx$ 40 ft
nearest foot.

4. Compare.   11 yd = 33 ft

Since one roll is not enough, the homeowner must purchase two rolls of border paper.

▼ We call the distance around a circular figure *circumference*. The ratio of the circumference to the diameter is pi (π).

Circumference	The circumference (C) is the distance around a circle. Use the formula $C = \pi d$ to compute circumference.

Example 2 Find each circumference.

a.
10 m

b.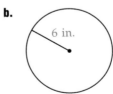
6 in.

c.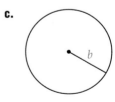
b

Solution

a. $C = \pi d$
$= 10\pi$ m

b. $C = \pi d$
$= \pi(2r)$
$= \pi(2 \cdot 6)$
$= 12\pi$ in.

c. $C = \pi d$
$= \pi(2r)$
$= \pi(2b)$
$= 2b\pi$ units

▼ If you know the circumference of a circle, you can find the radius and diameter.

Example 3 **The circumference of a circle is 43π ft. Find the diameter and the radius.**

Solution

$$C = \pi d$$
$$43\pi = \pi d$$

$$\frac{43\pi}{\pi} = \frac{\pi d}{\pi} \qquad \text{Divide both sides by } \pi.$$
$$43 = d$$
$$d = 2r$$
$$43 = 2r \qquad \text{Substitute 43 for } d.$$
$$43 \boxed{\div} 2 \boxed{=} r \qquad \text{Divide both sides by 2.}$$
$$21.5 = r$$

▼ We frequently use 3.14 or $\frac{22}{7}$ as approximations for π. Unless you are asked to approximate your answer, or given a value for π, leave answers in terms of π.

Example 4 **Find the circumference of a circle with the given radius or diameter. Round measures to the nearest tenth.**

a. $d = 12$ mi (Use 3.14 for π.)

b. $r \approx 7$ ft $\left(\text{Use } \frac{22}{7} \text{ for } \pi.\right)$

Solution

a. $C = \pi d$
$\approx (3.14)(12)$
$= 37.68$
≈ 37.7 mi

b. $C = \pi \, 2r$
$\approx \frac{22}{7}(2)(7)$
$= \frac{22}{7}(14)$
$= 2(22)$
$= 44$ ft

NOTES & QUOTES
Using only paper and pencil, William Shanks (1812–1882) spent 20 years calculating π to 707 decimal places. In 1945 it was discovered that Mr. Shanks had made an error in the 528th place. Today, supercomputers can calculate the value of π to millions of places in seconds.

THINK AND DISCUSS

1. Describe a method for finding the perimeter of some irregularly shaped objects such as a leaf or an oil spill.

2. Suppose you are asked to find the perimeter of your math book. Would you rather measure in inches or feet? Explain your choice.

CLASS EXERCISES

1. Choose five objects or areas in the classroom. Estimate and then measure the perimeter of each object. Choose an appropriate unit for measuring each item. Record your results in a table like the one below.

Item	Unit	Estimate	Measure	Difference	% Error

Estimate the circumference of each circle in centimeters. Then measure each diameter and compute the circumference. Use 3.14 for π.

2.

3.

WRITTEN EXERCISES

Find the perimeter of each figure.

1. a square with side 9 ft

2. an equilateral triangle with side 5 yd

3. a trapezoid with bases 3 ft and 3 yd, and sides 5 ft

4. a regular hexagon with side 3.7 in.

Find the perimeter of each polygon.

5. 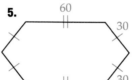 **6.** **7.**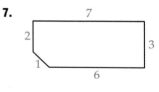

Find the amount of tape needed to wrap each figure. Use 3.14 for π.

8. **9.** **10.** 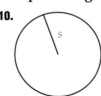 **11.**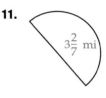

Find the diameter and the radius of a circle with the given circumference.

12. $C = 15\pi$ m   **13.** $C = 5a\pi$ yd   **14.** $C \approx 19$ in.   **15.** $C \approx 2.5x$ units

CALCULATOR Find the circumference to the nearest tenth of a unit. Use 3.14 for π.

16. $r = 5$ **17.** $r = 3.5$ **18.** $d = 17.8$ **19.** $d = 0.625$

Find the circumference. Use $\frac{22}{7}$ for π.

20. $r = \frac{1}{4}$ **21.** $r = \frac{3}{11}$ **22.** $d = 49$ **23.** $d = 181$

Find the unknown length.

24. $P = 75$

25. $P = 91$

26. $P = 10$

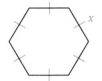

27. $P = 37$

Write an expression for the perimeter of each polygon.

28.

29.

30.

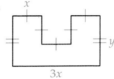

Use graph paper to draw a polygon that fits each description.

31. a rectangle with a perimeter of 12 units

32. a square with a perimeter of 60 units

33. a hexagon with a perimeter of 8 units

34. *DATA FILE 3 (pp. 96–97)* Find two possible perimeters for a sheet of dollar bills.

NOTES & QUOTES

In about 200 B.C., using only his knowledge of geometry, Eratosthenes estimated Earth's circumference as 46,250 km. In 1700, the French mathematician, Jean Picard used a telescope to refine the estimate to 40,040 km. Today's technology uses the orbits of satellites to measure Earth's circumference to an accuracy of 0.5 m. Modern instruments show that Earth is pear-shaped with the diameter from North Pole to South Pole about 43 km less than at the equator.

TEST YOURSELF

1. Find BC. $\triangle ABC \sim \triangle DEF$.

Find the perimeter or circumference. Use 3.14 for π.

2.

3.

9-9 *Draw a Diagram*

OBJECTIVE:
To solve problems by
drawing a diagram.

■ For many geometric problems it helps to draw a diagram to represent the given information.

PROBLEM

The wheels of a bicycle have a diameter of 60 cm. How many revolutions do the wheels make during a 4,000 m race?

SOLUTION

READ ▶ What information do you have?

The wheels have a diameter of 60 cm.
The race is 4,000 m long.

What do you want to find?

How many revolutions (turns) do the wheels make in a race?

PLAN ▶ Decide on a strategy.

Draw a picture to represent the information.

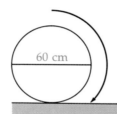

60 cm

What is a complete turn?

the circumference of the wheel

What units will you use?

Find the circumference in centimeters. Then write the circumference in meters.

SOLVE ▶ Use the formula $C = \pi d$. Use 3.14 for π.

$C = \pi d$
$\approx 3.14(60)$
$= 188.4$ cm
$= 1.884$ m

Divide the total distance by the distance of one revolution. Round to the nearest whole number.

$4,000 \div 1.884$

$= 2,123.142 \ldots$
$\approx 2,123$

LOOK BACK ▶ Estimate to check your answer.

Each revolution was 1.8 m or about 2 m. The race was 4,000 m, so each wheel turned about 2,000 times.

The answer of 2,123 turns is reasonable.

CLASS EXERCISES

Refer to the problem on page 394. Use 3.14 for π.

1. Suppose the race was 6,000 m long. Estimate the number of revolutions for the tires.

2. Suppose a race car has tires with diameter of 34 in.

   a. How far would the tires turn in one complete revolution?

   b. How many revolutions would the tires make in a 500 mi race?

WRITTEN EXERCISES

 Use a CALCULATOR where appropriate.

Solve using a picture. Use 3.14 for π. Round to the nearest whole number.

1. How many laps must you run on the track pictured at the right to cover 1 mi? *Hint:* 5,280 ft = 1 mi

2. Sam is building a circular table for eight people. Each person needs 2 ft of table edge. What is the diameter of the table?

3. Two intersecting circles can form two or three regions. Three intersecting circles can form from three to seven regions. What is the greatest number of regions you can form with four intersecting circles?

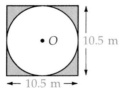

Solve using any strategy.

4. Find the circumference of circle O. Use 3.14 for π.

5. Suppose you want to make a scale model of Earth, the sun, and the moon. Use the **DATA** at the right to determine the dimensions of the model. Assume that Earth will have a diameter of 3 in.

   a. What will be the diameter of the sun and the moon?

   b. In the model, how far from Earth must each be?

	d (mi)	distance from Earth (mi)
Earth	8,000	0
Sun	864,000	93,000,000
Moon	2,200	240,000

6. The figures shown are all composed of equal size squares. Figure A has a perimeter of 36. Find the perimeter of each figure.

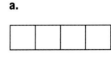 **a.**

 b.

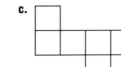 **c.**

Problem Solving Practice

PROBLEM SOLVING STRATEGIES

Look for a Pattern
Guess and Test
Simplify the Problem
Account for All Possibilities
Make an Organized List
Work Backwards
Make a Table
Write an Equation
Solve by Graphing
Draw a Diagram
Make a Model
Simulate the Problem

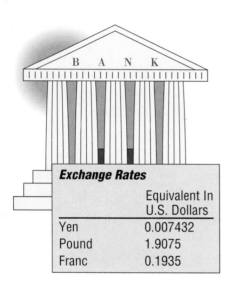

Exchange Rates

	Equivalent In U.S. Dollars
Yen	0.007432
Pound	1.9075
Franc	0.1935

Solve. The list at the left shows some strategies you might use.

1. The scores in a game were -7, 8, 7, 15, -6, 12, and -6. Was the final score positive or negative?

2. State sales tax on new car purchases is 5%. Find the sales tax on a car costing $22,489.

3. The Blazers lost 35% of the 20 games they played this season. How many games did they win?

4. You open a book and the product of the page numbers is 16,002. To what pages have you opened?

5. Two buses leave a terminal at the same time and travel in opposite directions. One bus travels at 55 mi/h. The other travels at 48 mi/h. How far apart will the buses be in 3 h?

6. Sabrina can run 5 km in 1 h. In the same time, Lucy can run a 3-km distance. How much of a head start does Lucy need for both girls to finish an 8-km course at the same time?

7. A stamp collector has 53 rare stamps. This is 12 less than 5 times the number he had a year ago. How many stamps did the collector have a year ago?

8. Suppose you want to find the thickness of one sheet of paper. Describe a method that uses a ruler.

9. **DATA** Use the data at the left. How many yen would you get for $100? how many pounds? how many francs?

10. At a track meet, finishers received 5 points for blue ribbons and 3 points for red ribbons. How many and what color ribbons were won for the following points?

    a. 12   **b.** 14   **c.** 18   **d.** 15

11. A real estate agent earns a 6% commission on the sale of a house. Find the commission on a $289,000 house.

12. **DATA FILE 10 (pp. 404–405)** Find the circumference of the circular home range for a snowshoe hare.

13. Two friends rented a canoe for 10 days. One friend used the canoe for 6 days. The other friend used the canoe for 4 days. How much of the $150 rental fee should each friend pay?

14. José bought two posters for $9. The posters were on sale at one for full price and the second at half price. How much was the full price poster?

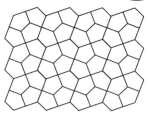

9-10 Tessellations

OBJECTIVE:
To understand and
create tessellations.

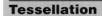

NOTES & QUOTES

"All my works are games.
Serious games."

M. C. Escher

Maurice Cornelius Escher
(1898–1972), a Dutch
artist, used tessellations in
many of his sketches. He
created at least 150
different tessellations
without ever having any
formal mathematics
training.

■ The *tessellation* at the right is made
from congruent pentagons. You could
see this tessellation in the street tiling
of portions of Cairo, Egypt. When a
tessellation uses only one shape, we call
it a *pure tessellation.*

Tessellation	A tessellation is a design that covers a plane with no gaps and no overlaps.

■ You can determine if a figure forms a pure tessellation by using
graph paper to represent a plane.

Example 1 Determine whether the figure at the right
forms a pure tessellation.

Solution

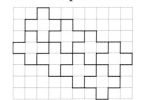

Yes, the figure forms a pure tessellation.

■ Tiled floors often use a pattern in which two figures tessellate.
The patterns are *semiregular tessellations.* You can use a pattern to
determine whether two figures form a semiregular tessellation.

Semiregular Tessellation	A semiregular tessellation is a design that covers a plane using more than one shape.

Example 2 Determine whether the figures at the
right form a semiregular tessellation.

Solution

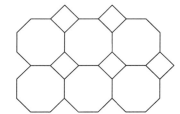

Yes, the figures form a semiregular tessellation.

■ You can create a tessellating figure by beginning with a shape that is known to tessellate.

THINK What are four shapes that will tessellate?

Example 3 **Create a tessellating figure using a square.**

Solution
1. Begin with a square.

2. Cut a shape out of one side. Slide the shape to the opposite side. Tape the shape in place.

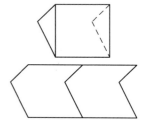

3. Use the new shape as a pattern. Trace the shape in different places to form a tessellation.

THINK The Greeks proved that only three *regular* polygons will tessellate a plane. Which regular polygons tessellate?

CLASS EXERCISES

Use graph paper to determine whether each figure forms a pure tessellation.

1.

2.

3.

■■■■■■ Decision Making ■ **DECISION MAKING** ■ Decision Making ■ Decision Making ■ Decision Making ■

TESSELLATIONS

Tessellations are frequently found in nature. Architects and designers often use nature as a model for their work.

■ **COLLECT DATA**

1. List three places in nature where tessellations occur.

2. List three places where you see man-made tessellations in your home and community.

3. Visit a store that sells floor tiles. In what shapes do the tiles come? Write down the cost of each tile.

■ **ANALYZE DATA**

4. **a.** Why do you think bees use a hexagon shape for their honeycombs instead of an octagon?

WRITTEN EXERCISES

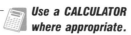
Use a pattern to determine whether the figures form a pure tessellation.

1.

2.

3.

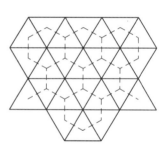
THINK Some patterns will tessellate around a sphere rather than a plane. What shapes tessellate on a soccer ball?

4. A triangle tessellates six times around point P. What must be the size of each angle around point P?

5. Create a pure tessellation on graph paper.

Use a pattern to determine whether the figures form a semiregular tessellation.

6.

7.

8. Create a semiregular tessellation on graph paper.

9. PROJECT A tessellation of equilateral triangles is shown at the right. You can form another tessellation when you connect the center of each triangle across the common sides of the tessellating triangles. The new tessellation is called a *dual*. Every tessellation of regular polygons has a dual. Create a dual using any regular polygon. Describe your results.

■ Decision Making ■ Decision Making ■ Decision Making ■ Decision Making ■ Decision Making ■ Decision Making ■

b. Each hexagon in a honeycomb can be broken down into smaller regular polygons. What kind of regular polygons are they?

5. What is the sum of the measures of all the angles that come together at a point in a pure tessellation? in a semiregular tessellation?

6. Why do you think architects frequently use a triangular truss to build bridges?

■ **MAKE DECISIONS**

7. A customer wants you to design a tiling pattern for a rectangular foyer. The foyer is 15 ft by 15 ft. Create two designs on graph paper. Make the first a pure tessellation and the second a semiregular tessellation. For each design, determine how many of each shape tile the customer will need. Then find the total cost of each design.

Chapter 9 Review

1. Classify the following words. Use the categories basic geometric figures, angles, triangles, quadrilaterals, polygons, or circles. Some words belong in more than one category.

acute	diameter	obtuse	ray	square
adjacent	equiangular	parallelogram	rectangle	straight
chord	equilateral	pentagon	rhombus	supplementary
circumference	hexagon	plane	right	triangle
complementary	isosceles	point	scalene	trapezoid
convex	line	radius	segment	vertical

Introduction to Geometry   9-1

The basic geometric figures include point, line ($\overleftrightarrow{AB}$), segment ($\overline{AB}$), ray ($\overrightarrow{AB}$), and plane.

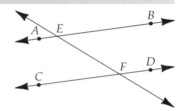

Refer to the figure at the right.

2. Name two parallel lines.

3. Name three lines.

4. Name five different segments.

5. Name eight different rays.

Angles   9-2

We classify angles by their measures. Acute angles have measures greater than 0° and less than 90°. Obtuse angles have measures greater than 90° and less than 180°. Right angles measure 90°.

Two angles are supplementary if the sum of their measures is 180. Two angles are complementary if the sum of their measures is 90.

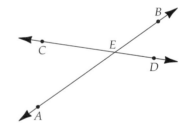

Refer to the figure at the right.

6. ∠AEC is an ▨ angle.

7. ∠AEC and ∠BEC are ▨ angles.

8. ∠AEC ▨ ∠BED.

9. If $m\angle CEB = 120°$, $m\angle AED = $ ▨.

10. If $m\angle BED = 55°$, $m\angle AED = $ ▨.

Polygons and Quadrilaterals   9-3

Some quadrilaterals have special names and special properties.

True or *false*? **Write *T* or *F*.**

11. A trapezoid is a parallelogram.

12. All squares are rhombuses.

13. A rhombus is a rectangle.

14. Some rhombuses are rectangles.

15. All rectangles are parallelograms.

16. A rhombus can be a square.

Triangles

We classify triangles by angles and by sides. The sum of the measures of the interior angles of a triangle is 180°.

Classify each triangle by its angles.

17. 30°, 60°, and 90°   **18.** 40°, 37°, and 103°   **19.** 55°, 55°, and 70°

20. A triangle has two angles with measures of 50° and 70°. What is the measure of the third angle?

Circles

In any circle, the diameter d is twice the radius r.

For each length, find the radius or the diameter.

21. $r = 25$ cm
$d = $ ▨

22. $d = 40$ cm
$r = $ ▨

23. $r = 3\frac{1}{2}$ in.
$d = $ ▨

24. $r = 4.2$ cm
$d = $ ▨

25. $d = 30$ ft
$r = $ ▨

26. $d = 9$ ft
$r = $ ▨

Congruent Figures

Two figures are congruent if their corresponding angles and corresponding sides are congruent.

27. $ABCD \cong WXYZ$. Write congruence statements for corresponding parts.

Similar Figures

Two figures are similar if the corresponding angles are congruent and the corresponding sides are in proportion.

Assume each pair of triangles is similar. Find the missing length.

28.

29.

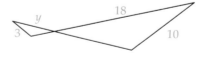

Perimeter and Circumference

To find the perimeter of a polygon, add the lengths of the sides.

To find the circumference of a circle, use the formula $C = \pi d$.

Find the perimeter or the circumference. Use 3.14 for π.

30. rectangle with sides 24 in. and 18 in.   **31.** circle with $d = 150$ cm

Use the figure at the right.

1. Name $\overleftrightarrow{AB}$ in three ways.

2. Name three different segments on $\overleftrightarrow{CD}$.

3. Name three rays on $\overleftrightarrow{GH}$.

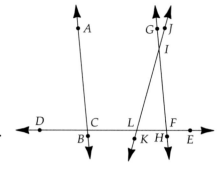

Complete each sentence.

4. $\angle ACL$ is an ▊ angle.

5. $\angle ACD$ and $\angle LCB$ are ▊ angles.

6. $m\angle GIL$ ▊ $m\angle JIF$.

7. $\overleftrightarrow{AB}$ is ▊ to $\overleftrightarrow{GH}$.

8. $\angle JLF$ is an ▊ angle.

9. $m\angle GFL = 85°$, $m\angle GFE = $ ▊.

10. **WRITE** Describe the intersection of two lines.

Draw a figure to fit each description.

11. a regular quadrilateral   12. a hexagon   13. an acute triangle

Find the measure of each numbered angle. Then classify each triangle by its angles and its sides.

14.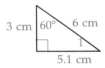

15.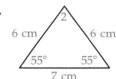

16.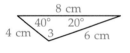

Find the radius or diameter for each given length.

17. $r = 12$ in.

$d = $ ▊

18. $d = 15$ cm

$r = $ ▊

19. $r = 30$ mm

$d = $ ▊

20. Which figure appears *not* to be congruent to the other three?

a.   b.   c.   d.

Each pair of triangles is similar. Find the missing length.

21.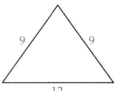

22.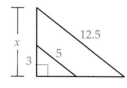

Find each perimeter or circumference. Use 3.14 for π.

23. a rectangle with length 12 in. and width 8 in.   24. a circle with radius 0.5 cm

25. an isosceles triangle with side 60 mm and base 30 mm

Chapters 1–9   Cumulative Review

Choose the correct answer. Write A, B, C, or D.

1. Order $\frac{1}{2}, \frac{5}{6}, \frac{2}{3}, \frac{3}{8}$ from least to greatest.

  A. $\frac{1}{2}, \frac{2}{3}, \frac{3}{8}, \frac{5}{6}$ **B.** $\frac{3}{8}, \frac{2}{3}, \frac{1}{2}, \frac{5}{6}$

  C. $\frac{3}{8}, \frac{1}{2}, \frac{2}{3}, \frac{5}{6}$ **D.** not given

2. Write $\frac{5}{8}$ as a decimal.

  A. 0.58   **B.** 0.625

  C. 0.875   **D.** not given

3. Solve.

  A. 3   **B.** -4

  C. -2   **D.** not given

4. $d = 4.5$. What is the radius?

  A. 9   **B.** 2.25

  C. 3.14   **D.** not given

5. $|-0.5| - |1.5| = $ ▨

  A. -1   **B.** 2

  C. -2   **D.** not given

6. $b(2b + 3) - b^2 = $ ▨

  A. $5b - b^2$ **B.** $2b^2 + 3b - b^2$

  C. $3b^2 + 3b$ **D.** not given

7. Describe the solution to the system.
$2y - x = 3; 3y = \frac{3}{2}x + 9$

  A. no solution   **B.** one solution

  C. infinite   **D.** not given

8. Classify the triangle.

  A. obtuse isosceles

  B. right scalene

  C. acute isosceles

  D. not given

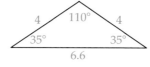

9. Write $1\frac{2}{3}$ as a percent.

  A. $16\frac{2}{3}\%$ **B.** 123%

  C. $166\frac{2}{3}\%$ **D.** not given

10. 3,256,134 is divisible by ▨ .

  A. 8   **B.** 2, 3

  C. 2, 3, 6   **D.** not given

11. Name the figure.

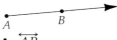

  A. $\overleftrightarrow{AB}$ **B.** $\overrightarrow{AB}$

  C. $\overline{AB}$ **D.** not given

12. $3x - 2y = 8$. What is the slope?

  A. 3   **B.** $\frac{3}{2}$

  C. -2   **D.** not given

13. $ABCD \sim EFGH$. Find x.

  A. 8   **B.** 10

  C. 4   **D.** not given

14. What percent of 80 is 20?

  A. 20%   **B.** 80%

  C. 60%   **D.** not given

15. The 6 members of a chess club play each other once. How many games are played?

  A. 6   **B.** 12

  C. 15   **D.** not given

16. A plane climbs to 30,000 ft then descends 5,000 ft. The plane then climbs another 7,000 ft. What is the plane's altitude?

  A. 6,000 ft   **B.** 32,000 ft

  C. 28,000 ft   **D.** not given

EARTH'S TROPICAL RAIN FORESTS AND OCEANS

Costa Rica's Diminishing Rain Forests

1940   1985

Tropical rain forests cover only about 2% of the earth's surface and yet are home to half the world's wild plant and animal life. Though many of the rain forest's plants are vital to medical research, the rain forests are being cut down at the rate of 50 acres per minute.

Corcovado, Costa Rica Rain Forest

area	163 mi^2
average rainfall	220 in./y
species of trees	500
species of mammals	140
species of insects	6,000
species of butterflies	123

EARTH'S OCEANS

OCEAN	AREA (mi^2)	GREATEST WIDTH (mi)	GREATEST KNOWN DEPTH (ft)	AVERAGE DEPTH (ft)
Arctic	5,105,700	2,630	17,880	4,360
Indian	28,350,500	6,200	25,344	12,780
Atlantic	31,820,000	4,150	28,374	14,000
Pacific	63,820,000	11,000	36,198	14,050

CHAPTER

10

Area and Volume Formulas

WILDLIFE HOME RANGES ▪ An

animal's home range is the amount of space the animal needs to fulfill its requirements for food, breeding, and so forth. Home range can be expressed in acres or by the radius of a circular area.

Home Ranges for Mammals in Oregon and Washington

MAMMAL	HOME RANGE (Acres)	CIRCULAR HOME RANGE (Radius in Meters)
Black bear	4,382.4	2,370
Cougar	123,753	12,600
Gray wolf (pack of five)	380,970	22,100
Grizzly bear	938,730	34,600
Mule deer	1,045.8	1,160
Northern flying squirrel	0.082	32
Otter	7,494.9	3,100
Porcupine	86.9	333
Red fox	154.38	718
Snowshoe hare	6.35	90
Striped skunk	251.49	567

▼
Think about it...

Look at the home range data. Do you think there is a relationship between the size of an animal and the size of its home range?

405

10-1 Area of Rectangles and Parallelograms

▼ Geoboards and dot paper are helpful models for understanding area. Each figure at the left takes up 12 square units of area.

1 square unit

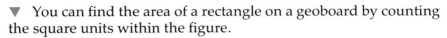

| **Area** | Area is the amount of surface inside a region. |

▼ You can find the area of a rectangle on a geoboard by counting the square units within the figure.

Example 1 Find the area of each rectangle.

a.

b.

Solution **a.** The area is 12 square units.

b. The area is 4 square units.

▼ You can find the area of a rectangle by multiplying the base length (b) by the height (h). Either side may be the base or the height.

| **Area of a Rectangle** | The area (A) of a rectangle equals the product of its base length (b) and its height (h). |
| | $A = bh$ |

Example 2 Find the area of each rectangle.

a.

b.

Solution **a.** $A = bh$
$= 4 \cdot 5$
$= 20$

The area is 20 square units.

b. $A = bh$
$= 9 \cdot 3$
$= 27$

The area is 27 cm^2.

▼
THINK How many rectangles can you form that have an area of 48 ft^2?

Example 3 Use the area formula to find the missing information.
a. b is x and h is $5x$. Find A.
b. A is 21 cm^2 and h is 7 cm. Find b.

Solution **a.** $A = bh$
$= x \cdot 5x$
$= 5x^2$

The area is $5x^2$ square units.

b. $A = bh$
$21 = b \cdot 7$
$b = 3$

The base is 3 cm.

▼ A rectangle is a special kind of parallelogram. You can make a parallelogram into a rectangle by rearranging the pieces.

Example 4 **Use a geoboard or dot paper. Show that a parallelogram and a rectangle with height 3 and base length 7 have the same area.**

Solution

Copy the triangle formed on the left. Place the same shape on the right.

$A = bh$ Find the area of the rectangle.
$= 7 \cdot 3$
$= 21$ square units

The parallelogram and rectangle each have an area of 21 square units.

▼ Example 4 illustrates that you find the area of a parallelogram the same way you find the area of a rectangle.

Area of a Parallelogram	The area of a parallelogram equals the product of its base length (*b*) and its height (*h*). $A = bh$

THINK When is the height of a parallelogram equal to the length of each of the sides?

▼ The height of a parallelogram is the length of an *altitude*.

Altitude	An altitude is a segment from one vertex perpendicular to the line containing the opposite side, called the base.

Example 5 **State the height and the measure of the base. Find the area.**

a.

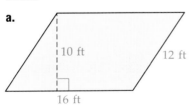

10 ft
12 ft
16 ft

b.

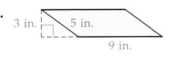

3 in.   5 in.
9 in.

Solution **a.** $h = 10$ ft,
$b = 16$ ft
$A = bh$
$= 16 \cdot 10$
$= 160$ ft^2

b. $h = 3$ in.
$b = 9$ in.
$A = bh$
$= 9 \cdot 3$
$= 27$ in.^{2}

10-1 Area of Rectangles and Parallelograms   **407**

THINK AND DISCUSS

1. We use a unit square as the basic unit for measuring area. Why is this a better choice than a unit circle?

2. Choose mm², cm², or m² as the most appropriate unit of area measure for each.

a. textbook cover
b. thumbprint
c. classroom floor
d. pan pizza
e. football field
f. postage stamp

CARPET SALE $9.99 per square yard, including pad. Buy today and we will install tomorrow.

CLASS EXERCISES

Find the area of each figure.

1. 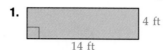 14 ft, 4 ft

2. 6 m, 4 m

3. 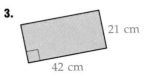 42 cm, 21 cm

State the height and the measure of the base. Find the area.

4. 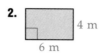 24 m, 18 m, 19.6 m

5. 10 cm, 12 cm

6. 12 in., 10 in., 8 in.

Complete.

7. parallelogram, Area = 8 m², $b = 3$ m, $h = $ ▧

8. rectangle, Area = $75x^2$, $h = 15x$, $b = $ ▧

9. parallelogram, Area = 525 cm², $b = 25$ cm, $h = $ ▧

10. Use the advertisement at the left. What would it cost for both carpet and pad for your classroom?

WRITTEN EXERCISES

Name something you would measure with the given unit.

1. 1 square centimeter
2. 1 square foot
3. 1 square meter
4. 1 square millimeter
5. 1 square inch
6. 1 square mile

CALCULATOR Find the area of each figure.

7. 3.9 cm, 1.8 cm
8. 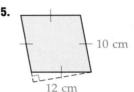 23 ft, 17.3 ft, 13.8 ft
9. 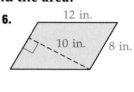 15.4 in.

10. 22.4 in., 8.4 in., 5.7 in.
11. 17.2 cm, 10.5 cm, 9 cm
12. 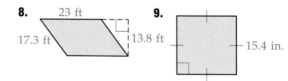 18.2 m, 33.4 m

Complete.

13. rectangle, $A = 22$ cm², $b = 4$ cm, $h = $ ▧

14. parallelogram, $A = 24.8$ ft², $h = 16$ ft, $b = $ ▧

15. parallelogram, $A = 120x^2$, $b = 8x$, $h = $ ▧

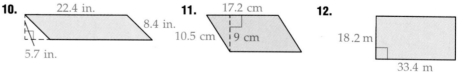

CALCULATOR Find the area of each parallelogram with the given base and height. Round to the nearest hundredth.

16. $b = 8.2$ cm, $h = 11.4$ cm

17. $b = 15$ ft, $h = 36$ ft

18. $b = 7.4$ m, $h = 0.008$ m

19. $b = 5.879$ km, $h = 10$ km

20. $b = 29.9$ in., $h = 32.67$ in.

21. $b = 55$ cm, $h = 10.5$ cm

22. $b = 3x + 7$, $h = 3x$

23. $b = 6x$, $h = 7x$

24. Find the area of each parallelogram.

a.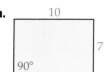

b.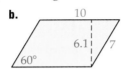

c.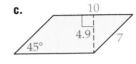

d. Does the angle measure affect the area measure?

e. Two parallelograms have sides of lengths 10 and 7. The parallelograms have altitudes to the same base. One height is 5 and the other is 4.99. Without calculating, which parallelogram has the greater area?

25. The area of a square is 64 ft². What is its perimeter?

26. The area of a square is $144x^2$ m². What is its perimeter?

27. The perimeter of a square is 28 cm. What is its area?

28. The area of a parallelogram is 36 ft². Its height is 4 ft. Find its perimeter.

29. The base length of a rectangle is 5 times as great as its height. The area is 320 ft². What is the perimeter of the rectangle?

30. The area of a rectangle is 56 cm². Name three different dimensions that the rectangle could have.

31. How many square feet are in a square yard? Draw a diagram to illustrate your answer.

32. **PROJECT** Cut the label from any cylindrical can. Make sure the cut is perpendicular to the ends. Tape the label to your paper and find the area to the nearest square centimeter.

Use the article at the right.

33. You wish to erect a political sign that is 6 ft high. What is the greatest width it can be?

34. Draw and label the dimensions for three different political signs that use the maximum possible area.

35. **PROJECT** Research the sign laws in your community. Design a political campaign sign for a candidate of your choice.

MIXED REVIEW

1. **DATA FILE 1 (pp. 2–3)** Write the freezing point of salt in scientific notation.

2. Simplify $2^2 \cdot 3^{-4}$.

3. $3^4 \blacksquare 4^3$.

4. Between what two integers is the square root of 41?

5. Find the circumference of a circle with $r = 8$.

6. What is the sum of the measures of the angles of a triangle?

7. A 3-ft tall child casts an 8-ft long shadow. How high is the tree next to the child if the tree's shadow is 60 ft?

Sign Regs for Politicos

The city council issued the following regulations for political signs:

1. Only one sign may be posted on a single parcel of land.

2. Signs may not exceed 32 ft².

3. Detached signs cannot be more than 6 ft high.

4. All signs must be removed within 15 days after the election.

10-2 Area of Triangles and Trapezoids

▼ You can form two congruent triangles by drawing a diagonal in any parallelogram.

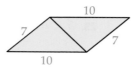 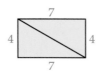

The figures suggest that the area of a triangle is half the area of a parallelogram.

THINK Why are the
triangles formed by the
diagonal of a parallelogram
congruent?

Example 1 **Find the area of the parallelogram. Then find the area of each triangle formed by the diagonal.**

Solution $A = bh$
$= 9 \cdot 4$
$= 36$

4 in.

9 in.

The area of the parallelogram is 36 in.².
The area of each triangle is $\frac{1}{2} \cdot 36$ or 18 in.².

Area of a Triangle	The area of a triangle equals half the product of the base length (*b*) and the height (*h*). $$A = \tfrac{1}{2}bh$$

▼ The height (*h*) of a triangle is the measure of an altitude. You can draw an altitude from each vertex of a triangle. An altitude may be inside, outside, or on the triangle.

Example 2 **State the height and the measure of the base. Find the area.**

a.

$11x$ $8x$ $16x$
$20x$

b.

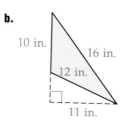

10 in. 16 in.
12 in.
11 in.

Solution **a.** $h = 8x; b = 20x$

$A = \frac{1}{2}bh$

$= \frac{1}{2} \cdot 20x \cdot 8x$

$= 80x^2$ square units

b. $h = 11$ in.; $b = 10$ in.

$A = \frac{1}{2}bh$

$= \frac{1}{2} \cdot 10 \cdot 11$

$= 55$ in.²

▼ A diagonal through a trapezoid forms two triangles having different areas.

Example 3 **Find the area of each triangle and of the trapezoid.**

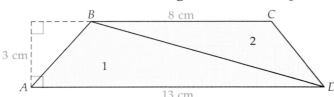

THINK Why is the height of both triangles the same?

Solution

Area of $\triangle ABD$

$A = \frac{1}{2}bh$

$= \frac{1}{2} \cdot 13 \cdot 3$

$= 19.5 \text{ cm}^2$

Area of $\triangle BCD$

$A = \frac{1}{2}bh$

$= \frac{1}{2} \cdot 8 \cdot 3$

$= 12 \text{ cm}^2$

The area of the trapezoid is $19.5 + 12 = 31.5 \text{ cm}^2$.

▼ The area of a trapezoid is the sum of the areas of the two triangles formed by a diagonal. In a trapezoid, we label the bases (the parallel sides) as b_1 and b_2.

$$A = \frac{1}{2}b_1 h$$

$$+ \ A = \frac{1}{2}b_2 h$$

Area of trapezoid $\quad = \frac{1}{2}b_1 h + \frac{1}{2}b_2 h$

$$= \frac{1}{2}h(b_1 + b_2)$$

Area of a Trapezoid	The area of a trapezoid equals half the product of the height (h) and the sum of the bases (b_1 and b_2). $$A = \frac{1}{2}h(b_1 + b_2)$$

Example 4 **Use the formulas to find the missing information.**

a. triangle, $h = 9$ mm, $A = 67.5 \text{ mm}^2$ Find b.

b. trapezoid, $b_1 = 12$ cm, $b_2 = 16$ cm, $A = 112 \text{ cm}^2$ Find h.

Solution **a.** $A = \frac{1}{2}bh$

$67.5 = \frac{1}{2}b \cdot 9$

$67.5 = 4.5b$

$b = 15$ mm

b. $A = \frac{1}{2}h(b_1 + b_2)$

$112 = \frac{1}{2}h(12 + 16)$

$112 = \frac{1}{2}h \cdot 28$

$112 = 14h$

$h = 8$ cm

▼ When you find the area of a figure, all units must be the same.

Example 5 Find the area of a trapezoid with $b_1 = 5$ mm, $b_2 = 1$ cm, and $h = 4$ mm.

Solution $b_2 = 1$ cm $= 10$ mm   Write 1 cm as 10 mm so the bases are in the same units.

$$A = \frac{1}{2}h(b_1 + b_2)$$

$$= \frac{1}{2} \cdot 4(5 + 10)$$

$$= 30 \text{ mm}^2$$

THINK AND DISCUSS

1. Are $\left(\frac{1}{2} \cdot 3\right) \cdot 8$ and $3 \cdot \left(\frac{1}{2} \cdot 8\right)$ equal? How can this help in finding the area of a triangle?

2. Find the area pictured. Is there more than one method?

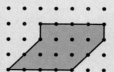

3. Why can the sides be the altitude and base in a right triangle?

CLASS EXERCISES

Find the area of a triangle with the given base and height.

1. $b = 12$ cm
$h = 7$ cm

2. $h = 3$ in.
$b = 1$ ft

3. $b = 2.5$ mm
$h = 5$ mm

4.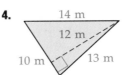

5.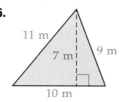

6.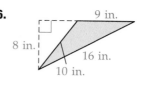

Find the area of a trapezoid with the given base lengths and height.

7. $b_1 = 6$ cm
$b_2 = 10$ cm
$h = 5$ cm

8. $b_1 = 6$
$b_2 = 2$
$h = 5$

9. $h = 3$
$b_1 = x$
$b_2 = x + 2$

10.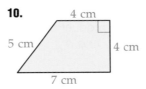

11.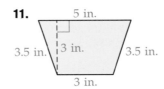

12.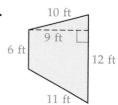

WRITTEN EXERCISES

CALCULATOR Find the area of a triangle with the given base and height.

1. $b = 8.2$ m
$h = 9.6$ m

2. $h = 35$ mm
$b = 20$ mm

3. $b = 49$ in.
$h = 18$ in.

4.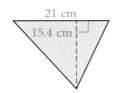
3.6 in.
3.3 in.
4.8 in.

5.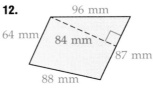
21 cm
15.4 cm

6.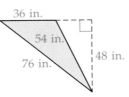
36 in.
54 in.
76 in.
48 in.

CALCULATOR Find the area of a trapezoid with the given base lengths and height.

7. $b_1 = 40$ cm
$b_2 = 35$ cm
$h = 20$ cm

8. $b_1 = 54$ m
$b_2 = 80$ m
$h = 15$ m

9. $h = 62.4$ ft
$b_1 = 30.5$ ft
$b_2 = 14.2$ ft

10.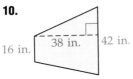
16 in. 38 in. 42 in.

11.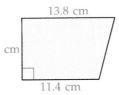
13.8 cm
9.5 cm
11.4 cm

12.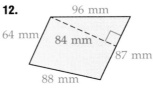
96 mm
64 mm 84 mm
87 mm
88 mm

Measure each figure to the nearest tenth of a centimeter and find the area.

13.

14.

15.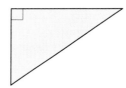

Find the missing values.

	Figure	h	b_1	b_2	A
16.	triangle	0.1 m	4 cm	—	
17.	square	9x	—	—	
18.	trapezoid		8 ft	2 ft	15 ft²
19.	parallelogram		10 ft	10 ft	15 ft²

20. Find the area of the yellow square tile at the right.

True or false? Write T or F.

21. A triangle has three altitudes.

22. A square is always a parallelogram.

23. A trapezoid and a parallelogram can never have the same area.

24. A square crossed by two diagonals will form four congruent triangles.

25. An altitude is always perpendicular to a side of a triangle.

26. Two rectangles with the same perimeter always have the same area.

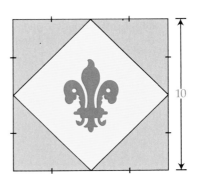

10-3 Area of Circles

▼ Notice what happens when you cut a circle into several equal size pieces and then rearrange the pieces.

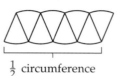

$\frac{1}{2}$ circumference

$\frac{1}{2}$ circumference

The new shape closely resembles a parallelogram where the height, h, is about the same as the radius of the circle. The base length, b, is about half the circumference (C) of the circle. You can use the formula for the area of a parallelogram to find the formula for the area of a circle.

$b = \frac{1}{2}C$ Substitute the formula for circumference.

$\quad = \frac{1}{2}2\pi r$

$\quad = \pi r$

$A = bh$ Substitute πr for b and r for h.

$\quad = \pi r \cdot r$

$\quad = \pi r^2$ Simplify.

Area of a Circle	The area of a circle equals the product of π and the square of the radius (r). $$A = \pi r^2$$

Example 1   Find the area of a circle with diameter 12 cm. Give both an exact and an approximate answer. Use 3.14 for π.

Solution $d = 12, r = 6$ The radius is half the
$\qquad\quad A = \pi r^2$ diameter.
$\qquad\qquad = \pi(6)^2$
$\qquad\qquad = 36\pi$ cm^2, exact answer
$\qquad\qquad \approx 36 \cdot 3.14$ Substitute 3.14 for π.
$\qquad\qquad = 113.04$ cm^2

THINK Why does substituting 3.14 for π give you an approximate answer?

▼ If you know the area of a circle, you can find the radius.

Example 2   Find the radius of a circle with area 452.16 cm^2. Use 3.14 for π.

Solution $A = \pi r^2$
$\qquad\qquad 452.16 = 3.14 \cdot r^2$ Divide each side by 3.14.
$\qquad\qquad\quad 144 = r^2$ Find the square root of 144.
$\qquad\qquad\qquad r = 12$ cm

CLASS EXERCISES

Find the area of each circle. Give an exact answer and an approximate answer. Use 3.14 for π.

1. $r = 3$ ft

2. $d = 10$ m

3. $r = 20$ cm

4.
16 m

5.
12 ft

6.
60 cm

Find the radius of a circle with the given area. Use 3.14 for π.

7. 49π cm^2

8. 254.34 yd^2

9. $225x^2\pi$ square units

THINK AND DISCUSS

1. Name two real world situations where area of a circle is important.

2. Suppose you didn't know the formula for the area of a circle. How could you approximate the number of square units in a circle?

WRITTEN EXERCISES

Find the area of each circle. Give an exact answer and an approximate answer. Use 3.14 for π. Round to nearest hundredth.

1. $r = 11$ mi

2. $r = \frac{1}{2}$ m

3. $d = 1.2$ in.

4. $d = 12$ in.

5. $d = 3.2$ ft

6. $d = 8.4$ mm

7. $r = 5x$

8. $d = 6\sqrt{2}$

9. $d = 4.2x$

Match the item listed with the most reasonable area.

	Item	Area
10.	dinner plate	**a.** 3.14 cm^2
11.	quarter	**b.** 113.04 in.^{2}
12.	circle on basketball floor	**c.** 28.26 cm^2
13.	jar lid	**d.** 36π ft^2
14.	shirt button	**e.** 452.16 mm^2
15.	12-in. pizza	**f.** 78.5 in.^{2}

16. Which has a greater area, a circle with a radius of 2 or a square with side of length 2? Explain your answer.

17. Which has a greater area, four circles with the radius of 1 or one circle with the radius of 4? Explain your answer.

18. Write a formula for the area of a circle that uses the diameter instead of the radius.

19. What is the area of the largest circle that will fit in a square with area 64 cm^2?

20. *DATA FILE 10 (pp. 404–405)* Find the approximate area of the circular home range for each animal. Use 3.14 for π.

    a. cougar   **b.** red fox   **c.** Northern flying squirrel

21. Copy and complete the table at the left. Round to the nearest tenth. Use 3.14 for π.

    a. Graph the results. Use the *x*-axis for radius and the *y*-axis for area.

    b. Predict the radius of a circle with area 125 square units.

r (units)	*A* (square units)
1	■
3	■
5	■
7	■

Find the radius of a circle with the given area. Use 3.14 for π.

22. 81π cm²   **23.** 803.84 in.²   **24.** 7.065 mm²

Find the circumference and area of each circle. Use 3.14 for π. Round to the nearest tenth.

25. $r = 5.2$ cm   **26.** $d = 7.8$ in.   **27.** $r = 18.6$ m

28. $r = \frac{3}{4}$ cm   **29.** $r = 8.7$ m   **30.** $d = 15xy$

Find the area of each shaded portion. Use 3.14 for π.

31.

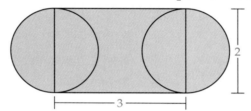

32.

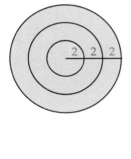

33. Find the area of the outer ring of the figure at the left.

34. Manufacturers of tin cans stamp the lids from rectangular sheets of tin.

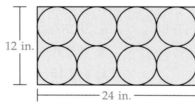

    a. What is the radius of each lid?

    b. What is the total area used by the lids?

    c. How much of the sheet of tin is wasted?

35. You wish to carpet the border of the pool at the left.

    a. How many square feet do you need for the border?

    b. Carpets are sold by the square yard. How many square feet are in a square yard?

    c. How many square yards of carpet should you purchase?

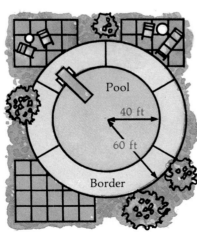

36. **a.** What is the area of each pizza pictured below?

b. What is the price per square inch?

c. Is the largest pizza always the best buy?

10 in.
$6.50

12 in.
$8.50

14 in.
$10.50

37. COMPUTER Use a spreadsheet to compare the radius, circumference, and area of different circles. Use the format shown below.

	A	B	C
1	Radius	Circumference	Area
2	1	=2*A2*3.14	=3.14*A2^2
3	2	=2*A3*3.14	=3.14*A3^2
4	3	=2*A4*3.14	=3.14*A4^2
5			

Complete cells A2 to A10 for radii from 1 to 9.

a. What happens to the circumference of a circle if the radius is doubled? if the radius is tripled?

b. If you double the radius of a circle, do you double the area?

TEST YOURSELF

State the formula for the area of each figure.

1. circle   **2.** triangle   **3.** rectangle

4. trapezoid   **5.** parallelogram

Find the area of each figure. Use 3.14 for π.

6.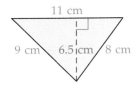
11 cm
9 cm   6.5 cm   8 cm

7.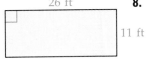
26 ft
11 ft

8.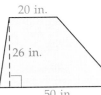
20 in.
26 in.
50 in.

9.
35 mm

10.
2.8 ft   3.9 ft

11.
24 ft

OBJECTIVE:
To develop Pick's
theorem using
geoboards.

MATERIALS

- Geoboards and colored rubber bands or
- Dot paper and colored pencils
- Math journal to record work

Exploring Pick's Theorem

▼ You can use a geoboard to develop a formula or rule about area. Each square on the geoboard represents 1 square unit of area. Use dot paper to copy the shapes shown.

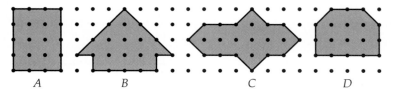

A   B   C   D

1. Find the area of each shape.

2. Copy and complete the chart for each shape. Interior dots are those inside the shape. Boundary dots are those on the side or at corners of the shape.

	Boundary Dots	Interior Dots	Area
A	14	6	
B			
C			
D			

3. **Describe** the relationship between the number of interior dots, the number of boundary dots, and the area.

4. **Model** several figures with five boundary dots and up to four interior dots. Find the area of each figure. **Discuss** how the dots are related to the area.

5. Copy the shapes below on a geoboard or dot paper.

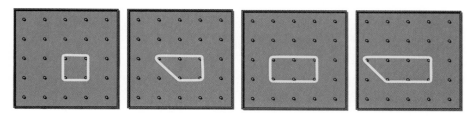

a. Copy and complete the chart.

Boundary Dots	Interior Dots	Area
4	0	
5	0	
6	0	
7	0	

b. Which rule relates boundary dots (B) to area when the number of interior dots is zero?

I. $\dfrac{B}{2} + 1$ **II.** $\dfrac{B}{2}$ **III.** $\dfrac{B}{2} - 1$

6. Copy the shapes below on a geoboard or dot paper.

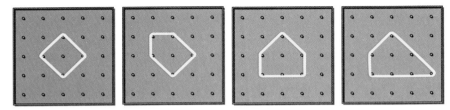

    a. Complete a chart for one interior dot.

    b. *Predict* the area of a shape with 12 boundary dots and one interior dot.

    c. *Write* a rule that relates boundary dots to area when there is one interior dot.

7. Copy the shapes below on a geoboard or dot paper.

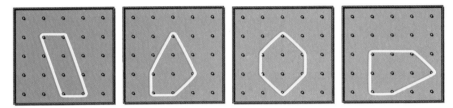

    a. Complete a chart for two interior dots.

    b. *Predict* the area of a shape with 12 boundary dots and two interior dots.

    c. *Write* a rule that relates boundary dots to area when there are two interior dots.

8. *Write* a rule for finding area for each number of dots.

    a. three interior dots   **b.** four interior dots   **c.** n interior dots

9. Test your rule. Find the area of each figure using area formulas. Then use your rule.

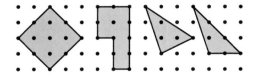

10. Use Pick's theorem to find the area of each shaded region.

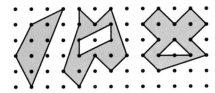

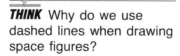

10-4   Space Figures

▼   An interior designer must be aware of the interplay of shapes in a room. Three-dimensional or space figures interact to produce different effects.

▼   *Prisms* are a type of *polyhedron*. An unsharpened six-sided pencil is in the shape of a prism. The diagram shows some of the terms we use to describe the parts of a prism.

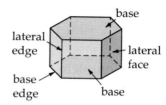

Polyhedron	A polyhedron is a space figure in which all faces are polygons.

Prism	A prism is a polyhedron with two parallel bases that are congruent polygons and sides that are parallelograms.

We name a prism by the shape of its bases.

Example 1

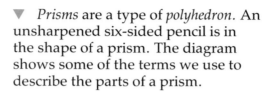

triangular prism   trapezoidal prism   hexagonal prism

▼   *Pyramids* are a type of polyhedron. The ancient Egyptians built pyramids for tombs. You can also find a pyramid on a dollar bill. The diagram at the left shows the parts of a pyramid.

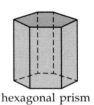

Pyramid	A pyramid is a polyhedron with triangular sides that meet at a vertex. The base of a pyramid is a polygon.

We name a pyramid by the shape of its base.

Example 2

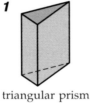   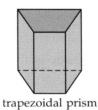

square pyramid   triangular pyramid   hexagonal pyramid

THINK Why do we use dashed lines when drawing space figures?

▼ Cylinders, cones, and spheres are space figures that contain circles.

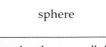

cylinder   cone   sphere

| **Cylinder** | A cylinder is a space figure with two circular, parallel, and congruent bases. |

| **Cone** | A cone is a space figure with one circular base and one vertex. |

| **Sphere** | A sphere is the set of all points in space that are the same distance from a given point called the center. |

▼

THINK How is the definition of a sphere similar to the definition of a circle?

▼ A *net* is a pattern you can fold into a space figure.

Example 3   **Name the space figure you can form from each net.**

a.

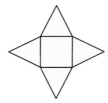

b.

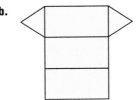

Solution   **a.** square pyramid   **b.** triangular prism

CLASS EXERCISES

1. Give another name for a cube.
2. What polyhedron is a cone most like?
3. What polyhedron is a cylinder most like?
4. How many faces of a regular hexagonal pyramid are congruent? What is the name of the shape of a face?
5. Draw a net for a pentagonal pyramid.
6. Draw a net for a hexagonal prism.
7. Draw a net for a cylinder.

▼

THINK AND DISCUSS

1. How many nets can you draw for a cube? Draw them.

2. How do the bases of a cylinder look when they are drawn? Draw a cylinder and a cone.

3. What is a mathematical name for a brick?

1. Find the area of a circle with diameter 6*a* units.

2. Find the area of a parallelogram with base 2*x* and height 4.

3. Find the area of a circle with radius 5 in.

4. Find the area of a triangle with *b* = 7 cm and *h* = 10 cm.

Solve.

5. $2x + 7 = -19$

6. $-3x + 8 = 29$

7. $\frac{5}{8}x - \frac{1}{2} = \frac{3}{8}$

8. *DATA FILE 7 (pp. 272–273)* Suppose it is 11:00 A.M. in Rio de Janeiro, Brazil. What time is it in Fairbanks, Alaska?

9. Two angles of a triangle measure 74° and 86°. Find the measure of the third angle and classify the triangle by its angles.

WRITTEN EXERCISES

Name each polyhedron.

1.   **2.**   **3.**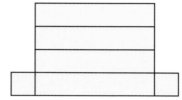

Name the space figure you can form from each net.

4.    **5.**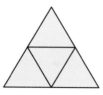

Draw a net for each space figure named.

6. hexagonal pyramid   **7.** octagonal prism

True or false? Write T or F.

8. A cone has two bases.

9. A square pyramid has four triangles.

10. The lateral faces of a prism are parallelograms.

11. A cylinder is an example of a polyhedron.

12. The lateral faces of a regular pyramid are isosceles triangles.

13. A pyramid can have a circular base.

Complete each statement.

14. A triangular prism has ▦ triangles.

15. An octagonal prism has 8 ▦ and 2 ▦.

16. A hexagonal prism has ▦ lateral edges.

17. A square pyramid has ▦ base edges.

18. A cone has ▦ vertex.

19. A ▦ has 5 parallelograms for faces and 2 ▦ for bases.

Write the mathematical name for each object.

20. soup can   **21.** shoe box   **22.** tepee   **23.** basketball

24. *WRITE* Examine a soccer ball. Describe it using mathematical names.

25. *PROJECT* A tetrahedron, octahedron, hexahedron, dodecahedron, and icosahedron are regular polyhedra.

  a. Find out how many faces each regular polyhedron has and what polygons make the faces.

  b. These shapes are often called Platonic solids. Research what each solid represented for Plato.

Copy each of the figures below on graph paper and write the mathematical name for each.

26. 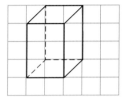   **27.**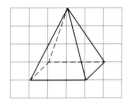

28. *PROJECT* Draw the nets for four polyhedra on heavy paper or cardboard. Fold to form the polyhedron and label with the mathematical name.

Critical Thinking

EXPLORING VISUALIZATION

      A   *B*   *C*   *D*

1. Guess the pattern for *D*.

2. Name each shape in pattern *A* in order from greatest area to least. Do this for pattern *B* and pattern *C*.

3. Predict the pattern for *D* and draw it.

4. Select the pattern that best completes the series below.

                                        A   *B*   *C*

Exploring Patterns in a Cube

MATERIALS

- Graph paper
- Math journal to record work

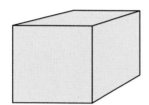

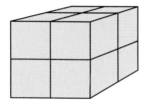

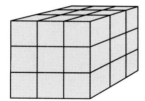

■ You can explore the characteristics of three-dimensional objects by thinking about how they appear and by sketching them.

1. Consider a cube.

   a. How many faces does it have?

   b. You tie a string to the cube and dip it into paint. How many faces have you painted?

2. Suppose you cut the painted cube in half vertically and horizontally to make smaller cubes. Each edge is half the length of the original cube.

   a. How many smaller cubes do you have?

   b. How many cube faces have painted surfaces?

   c. How many faces of each of the smaller cubes would be painted?

3. Complete the chart and extend it for a cube cut into smaller cubes of equal size.

Number of Segments on Each Edge	Total Number of Cubes	Total Expressed as a Number Cubed	Number of Cubes with the Given Number of Sides Painted			
			0	1	2	3
2	8	2^3	0	0	0	8
3	■	■	■	■	■	■
4	■	■	■	■	■	■
5	■	■	■	■	■	■
6	■	■	■	■	■	■

4. **Discuss** the patterns you find in each column of the chart.

5. **Predict** the total number of cubes if there are 12 smaller cubes on each edge.

6. There are 100 cubes on each edge. How many will be painted on three sides?

7. **Predict** the number that have two sides painted if there are 10 cubes on each edge. How many will have no paint at all?

8. **Analyze** Suppose you could paint only the sides of the cube that you can see without moving it. How many sides of the original cube would be painted? How will this change all of your results?

9. **Write** Was it necessary to draw a sketch of each cube? Explain when you were able to anticipate the results of the next row.

OBJECTIVE:
To solve problems by
making a model.

10-5 Make a Model

■ Sometimes solving a problem is made simpler by a model.

PROBLEM

A delivery person is unloading drums of oil along a ramp. In order to prevent the drums from being damaged, the ramp is not too steep. The more slowly a moving drum rolls, the less likely it is that it will be damaged. What kind of drum is better to use, one with a large or small radius?

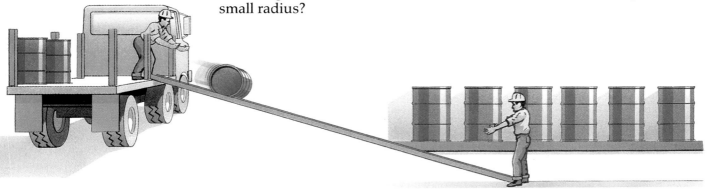

SOLUTION

READM ▸ What do you want to find?   which size of cylindrically shaped drum travels more slowly down an inclined plane

PLAN ▸ Use a wooden plank as an inclined plane.
Take some cylinders such as an oatmeal box or the cardboard center from paper towels. Make sure that the cylinders have different radii but the same height. Roll the object down the inclined plane. Determine which cylinder takes longer to roll down the plane.

SOLVE ▸ What do you notice?   Cylinders with a greater radius take longer to travel down the plane.

LOOK BACK ▸ What can you conclude?   Cylindrical drums with a greater radius should be used because they travel down a ramp more slowly.

CLASS EXERCISES

Answer each question.

1. How might the area touching the ramp affect the speed at which a cylinder rolls down the ramp?

2. How can you find the area of the part of the cylinder that touches the ramp?

3. Use cylinders with the same radii but with different lengths. What affect does length have on the rate a cylinder travels down a ramp?

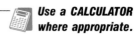 Use a **CALCULATOR** where appropriate.

WRITTEN EXERCISES

Explain how a model could be made for each situation.

1. You wish to find out the effect the length of a pendulum has on the amount of time the pendulum will swing.

2. You must decide which bridge design will be the strongest for a new bridge across Niagara Falls.

Use any strategy to solve each problem.

3. The junior class sold tickets for a pancake breakfast. One hundred twenty people came to the breakfast. This amount accounted for 60% of the tickets sold. How many tickets were sold?

4. The length of a rectangle is twice the width. The perimeter of the rectangle is 42 cm. What are the length and width?

5. *DATA FILE 2 (pp. 52–53)* A treasure hunter must determine the depth of a sunken ship. She sends a sonar wave towards the location of the ship. It takes 9.2 s for the sound to return. How far beneath the ocean is the sunken ship?

6. The difference between two numbers is 18. The sum of the two numbers is 34. What are the two numbers?

7. Eight teams are in a soccer tournament. When a team wins, it goes on to play another team. A team that loses is out of the tournament. How many games must be played in this tournament?

8. You fill a container $\frac{3}{4}$ full of water. The amount of water now in the container is 6 quarts. How much can the container hold?

9. A number n is multiplied by $\frac{5}{8}$. Then the result is subtracted from $\frac{2}{3}$. The answer is $\frac{7}{12}$. What is n?

10. Sara rented a car for two days. The rate was $22.50 per day and $.32 per mile. Sara traveled 150 mi. How much was she charged?

11. Troy is digging post holes for his ranch. He has a triangular plot that is 100 yd by 300 yd by 250 yd. He digs a hole every 10 yd. How many holes must he dig?

OBJECTIVE:
To use a model to
find surface area of
prisms and cylinders.

10-6 Surface Area—Prisms and Cylinders

▼ The packages for most food items are prisms and cylinders. The cost of the package is part of the price of the item. Manufacturers consider the surface area of a package when calculating the price.

Surface Area	Surface area (*SA*) is the sum of the areas of the base(s) and the side(s).

▼ You can use a net to help you find the surface area.

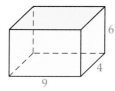

Example 1 **Find the surface area of the rectangular prism at the left using a net.**

Solution

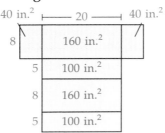

Draw and label a net.

Write the area of each rectangle on the net.

$$40 + 40 + 160 + 100 + 160 + 100 = 600 \quad \text{Add the areas.}$$

The surface area is 600 in^2.

▼ You can use formulas to find the surface area.

Lateral Area of a Prism	The lateral area (*LA*) of a prism is the product of the perimeter of the base (*P*) and the height of the prism (*h*). $A = Ph$

Example 2 **Find the surface area of the rectangular prism at the left using formulas.**

Solution

1. State each dimension. $b = 4, h = 6$
   height of prism $= 9$
2. Find the perimeter. $P = 2(b + h) = 2(4 + 6) = 20$
3. Find the lateral area. $LA = Ph = 20 \cdot 9 = 180$
4. Find the base area. $A = bh = 4 \cdot 6 = 24$
5. Find the sum of the two base areas and the lateral area. $SA = 2 \cdot 24 + 180 = 228$

The surface area is 228 square units.

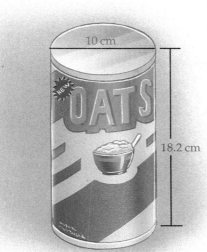

▼ You can cut a label from a can of soup to see that it is a rectangle. The height of the rectangle is the height of the can. The base length of the rectangle is the circumference of the can. The area of the rectangle is the *lateral area* of the can.

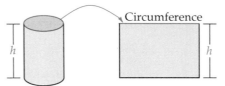

Lateral Area of a Cylinder	The lateral area (*LA*) of a cylinder is the product of the circumference of the base (*C*) and the height of the cylinder (*h*). $A = Ch$

Example 3   **Find the surface area of the oatmeal box at the left to the nearest square centimeter. Use 3.14 for π.**

Solution

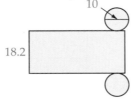

Draw and label a net.

$$\begin{aligned} \text{Area of bases} &= 2(\pi r^2) = 2(\pi \cdot 5^2) \approx 50(3.14) &&= 157 \\ LA \qquad\qquad &= Ch = \pi \cdot 10 \cdot 18.2 \approx 182(3.14) &&= 571.48 \\ \hline \text{Total} &&&= 728.48 \end{aligned}$$

The surface area of the oatmeal box is about 728 cm².

CLASS EXERCISES

1. Find the surface area of a cube that is 10 ft on each edge.

2. Draw and label a net for a hexagonal prism with base edge 7 and height 13.

3. Draw and label a net and find the surface area for a cylinder with radius 8 and height 12. Use 3.14 for π.

4. Draw and label a net and find the surface area of a rectangular prism. The base is 3 in. × 5 in. and the height is 11 in.

5. Draw and label a net and find the surface area of a cylindrical water tank with radius 20 ft and height 30 ft. Use 3.14 for π.

6. Use formulas to find the surface area of a square prism with base edge 7 m and height 15 m.

WRITTEN EXERCISES

Find the surface area of the space figure shown in each net.

1.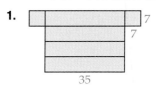

2.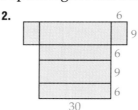

3.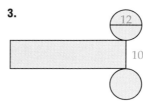

MIXED REVIEW

1. $(x)(2x)(3x)$

2. $a(4a + 7)$

3. Solve for x. $\frac{3x}{4} = \frac{5}{6}$

4. $\sqrt[2]{144}$

5. 16^2

Find the area.

6. circle, $r = 12$

7. parallelogram, $b = 8$ and $h = 14$

8. *DATA FILE 2 (pp. 52–53)* Express the sound intensity of a rocket launch in bels.

9. The wheels of a racing bike are about 70 cm in diameter. What is the circumference of a wheel?

CALCULATOR Find the surface area of each space figure.

4.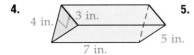

5.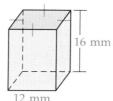

6.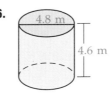

Find the surface area.

7. a triangular prism with all base edges 9 cm, base height 7.8 cm, and height of the prism 15 cm

8. a cylinder with radius 8 cm and height 10 cm; Use 3.14 for π.

9. Use cubes of base 1, 2, and 3 units to answer the following questions.

   a. Find the surface area of each cube.

   b. If the length of the cube is doubled, the surface area is ▓.
   If the length is tripled, the surface area is ▓.

10. The neighborhood swimming pool needs to be resurfaced. The pool is 40 ft by 60 ft. The depth of the pool is 6 ft.

   a. How many sides need to be resurfaced? how many bases?

   b. What is the total number of square feet to be resurfaced?

   c. The materials for resurfacing the pool cost $1.75/ft². What is the cost of resurfacing the pool?

11. A cylindrical storage tank needs painting. The radius of the tank is 18 ft and its height is 30 ft. The paint covers 350 ft²/gal. How many gallons of paint are needed? Use 3.14 for π.

12. Which cylinder at the right will be the more expensive to paint? Explain your answer.

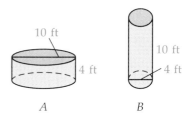

13. *PROJECT* Draw and label a net and find the number of square feet in the surface area of a room in your home.

10-7 *Surface Area—Pyramids, Cones, Spheres*

▼ To find the surface area of pyramids and cones, you must use the height of a face, called the *slant height* (*l*), to find the area of the lateral faces.

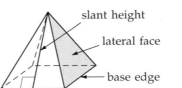

slant height

lateral face

base edge

slant height

▼ You can draw a net to help find the surface area of a pyramid.

Example 1 A pyramid has a base edge of 720 ft. The slant height is 584 ft. Find the surface area.

Solution

584

720

Draw and label a net.

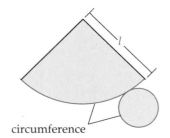

$$\text{Area of lateral faces} = 4\left(\tfrac{1}{2}bl\right)$$

$$= 4\left(\tfrac{1}{2} \cdot 720 \cdot 584\right) = 840{,}960 \text{ ft}^2$$

$$\text{Area of base} = (bh) = \quad (720 \cdot 720) \quad = 518{,}400 \text{ ft}^2$$

$$\text{Total} \qquad\qquad\qquad\qquad = 1{,}359{,}360 \text{ ft}^2$$

The surface area is 1,359,360 ft².

▼ The curved surface of a cone is its *lateral area*. A cone that is cut and flattened may remind you of a triangle with the height of *l* and the base equal to the circumference of the circular base. If you substitute *C* for *b* and *l* for *h* in the triangle area formula, the result is the formula for the lateral area of a cone.

circumference

l

$$\text{Triangle Area} = \tfrac{1}{2}bh$$

$$\text{Lateral Area} = \tfrac{1}{2}Cl$$

Lateral Area of a Cone	The lateral area (*LA*) of a cone equals half the product of the circumference (*C*) and slant height (*l*).
	$$LA = \tfrac{1}{2}Cl$$

Example 2 Find the surface area of the cone. Use 3.14 for π.

Solution Draw and label a net.

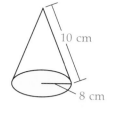

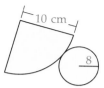

Lateral area $= \frac{1}{2}Cl = \frac{1}{2} \cdot 16\pi \cdot 10 \approx 80(3.14) = 251.2$

Base area $= \pi r^2 = \pi \cdot 8^2 \approx 64(3.14) = 200.96$

Total $= 452.16$ cm^2

The total surface area of the cone is about 452.16 cm^2.

▼ Many sports, including basketball, tennis, soccer, and golf rely on spheres.

Surface Area of a Sphere	The surface area of a sphere equals the product of 4π and the square of the radius (r). $$A = 4\pi r^2$$

Example 3 Calculate the surface area of a basketball. Use 3.14 for π.

Solution $A = 4\pi r^2$
$= 4\pi(12)^2$
$\approx 576(3.14)$
$= 1{,}808.64$

The surface area of a basketball is about 1,808.64 cm^2.

CLASS EXERCISES

Draw and label a net and find the surface area. Use 3.14 for π.

1.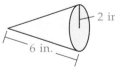

2.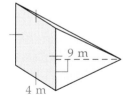

3.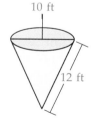

4. Find the surface area of a cone with radius 3 and slant height 8. Use 3.14 for π.

5. Find the surface area of a square pyramid with base 5 and slant height 8.

6. Which has the greater surface area, a cylinder with radius 2 and height 2 or a sphere with radius 2?

7. Which has the greater surface area, a square prism with base edge 4 and height 5 or a square pyramid with base edge 4 and slant height 5?

8. Find the surface area of a tennis ball with diameter of 2.5 in.

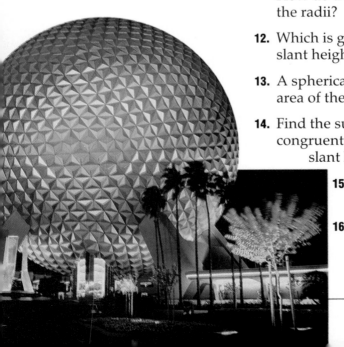

MIXED REVIEW

Solve.

1. $2x - 5 = 39$

2. $18 - 3x = 42$

3. *DATA FILE 5 (pp. 180–181)* The list price on a CD is $11.97. How much will the artist receive in royalties, to the nearest cent, on each CD sold?

4. $\frac{x}{12} = \frac{4}{15}$

Find the perimeter.

5. a regular hexagon with side 13.2 cm

6. an equilateral triangle with side 8.6 in.

7. Use scientific notation to find $(3.2 \times 10^4)(3.2 \times 10^4)$.

8. Explain how a hexagonal pyramid and a hexagonal prism are alike and how they are different.

WRITTEN EXERCISES

Draw and label a net and find the surface area. Use 3.14 for π.

1.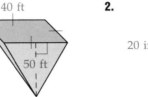
40 ft
50 ft

2.
20 in.
30 in.

3.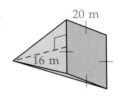
20 m
16 m

4. square pyramid,
$s = 35$ in.
$l = 42$ in.

5. cone,
$r = 14$ m
$l = 25$ m

6. cone,
$d = 22$ cm
$l = 34$ cm

CALCULATOR **Find the surface area. Use 3.14 for π.**

7. a sphere with radius 15 in.   **8.** a sphere with diameter 18 m

9. a hemisphere (half of a sphere) with radius 27 m

10. a hemisphere with diameter 42 cm

11. Find the surface areas of a sphere, $r = 2$, and a sphere, $r = 5$. How do the ratios of the surface areas compare with the ratios of the radii?

12. Which is greater, the surface area of a cone with radius 5 and slant height 10 or the surface area of a sphere with radius 5?

13. A spherical satellite is 3 m in diameter. What is the approximate area of the material covering its surface?

14. Find the surface area of a triangular pyramid that has a base congruent to the lateral faces. The base edge is 24 cm and the slant height is 16 cm.

15. *PROJECT* Research the radius of both Earth and the moon. Calculate the surface area of each.

16. Spaceship Earth at Epcot Center in Florida is a 180-ft geosphere. Estimate the approximate surface area by assuming it is a sphere with diameter 180 ft.

OBJECTIVE:
To use area formulas
to plan parade floats.

10-8 Parade Floats

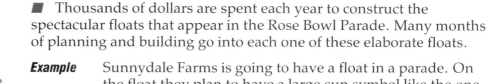

■ Thousands of dollars are spent each year to construct the spectacular floats that appear in the Rose Bowl Parade. Many months of planning and building go into each one of these elaborate floats.

Example Sunnydale Farms is going to have a float in a parade. On the float they plan to have a large sun symbol like the one at the left. The interior circle will have a diameter of 4 ft. Each triangle will have a height of 4 ft. The base will be 1.25 ft. What will be the total area of the sun symbol?

Solution Use the formulas for the area of a circle and the area of a triangle to find the total area of the sun symbol. Use 3.14 for π.

$$A = \pi r^2 \qquad \text{Find the area of a circle.}$$
$$\approx 3.14 \cdot 2^2$$
$$= 3.14 \cdot 4$$
$$= 12.56 \text{ ft}^2$$

$$A = \tfrac{1}{2}bh \qquad \text{Find the area of a triangle.}$$
$$= \tfrac{1}{2} \cdot 1.25 \cdot 4$$
$$= 2.5 \text{ ft}^2$$
$$2.5 \cdot 10 = 25 \text{ ft}^2 \qquad \text{Find the area of 10 triangles.}$$
$$12.56 + 25 = 37.56 \text{ ft}^2 \qquad \text{Find the total area.}$$

The total area of the sun symbol is 37.56 ft².

CLASS EXERCISE

Use the *DATA* in the figure at the left to solve.

1. A float will have a child holding a large arrow. All parts of the arrow will be made from heavy cardboard.

   a. What is the area of the head of the arrow?

   b. What is the area of the shaft of the arrow?

   c. What is the area of each section of feathers in the arrow?

   d. What is the total area of the arrow?

   e. The cardboard costs $.27/ft². What is the cost to build the arrow?

   f. Covering the arrow with flowers will cost $3.60/ft². What is the cost of the flowers? What is the total cost?

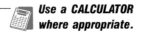

WRITTEN EXERCISES

Use the *DATA* below to solve.

1. A float will have a large heart made of plywood. To make the heart, builders will take a circle with a diameter of 5 ft and cut it in half. They will then attach both pieces to one side of an equilateral triangle. The triangle has height 8.6 ft and side 10 ft. The builders will cover the heart with red roses. To control expenses, they do not want the area covered to exceed 275 ft^2.

    a. Make a sketch of the way the heart will look when it has been constructed as described. Include measurements in your sketch.

    b. How many square feet of plywood will have to be covered with roses if both sides are covered? Will this be within the limit of 275 ft^2?

    c. The cost of covering the float with red roses is $10/ft^2. What is the cost for covering one side of the heart with flowers? both sides?

▪▪▪▪▪▪ Decision Making ▪ **DECISION MAKING** ▪ Decision Making ▪ Decision Making ▪ Decision Making ▪

PARADE FLOATS

■ **COLLECT DATA**

1. You are on the committee to design a float for your school's homecoming parade. You want an imaginative design that is simple to build. You also want to use real flowers.

    a. Decide what kind of float platform you will use. Find the dimensions of the platform.

    b. Sketch several figures that you could build for the float.

    c. Find the cost of a square foot of building materials.

    d. Survey local florists. Find the cost of various flowers. Determine which flowers will stay fresh the longest. Record your results in a chart like the one below.

Types of Flowers	Number of Blossoms to Cover 1 ft^2	Life Expectancy of Flowers
Roses		
Daisies		
Carnations		

Use the *DATA* below to solve.

2. Every year near the end of November, Chicago has a parade. A department store plans to build a large gift box for the middle of its float. The gift box will measure 6 ft by 9 ft by 5 ft. The platform of the float will be the bottom of the box. This will save the cost of materials for one side of the box.

   a. Make a sketch of the gift box that the store plans to build. Include measurements.

   b. To save as much building material as possible, which side of the box should be the bottom? Give its length, width, and area.

   c. What will be the total area of the sides that need to be decorated?

   d. Building materials cost $.55/ft^2. What is the cost of building the box?

   e. The cost of decorations is $2.25/ft^2. What is the cost of decorating the gift box?

   f. What is the total cost of the gift box?

■ *Decision Making* ■ *Decision Making* ■ *Decision Making* ■

■ **ANALYZE DATA**

2. Calculate the areas of the shapes you plan to build. Find the cost of the building materials.

3. Calculate the areas of the shapes you plan to cover with each type of flower.

4. Calculate the cost of flowers for each part of the float you are designing.

5. Find the total cost of the design.

■ **MAKE DECISIONS**

6. What is the cost of decorating your float? What changes can you make to lower the cost?

7. Suppose you have an unlimited budget. What design would you use for your float? What would be the total cost?

Practice

Find each area. Round to the nearest tenth.

1. trapezoid: $b_1 = 2.5$ m; $b_2 = 3.4$ m; $h = 9.9$ m
2. triangle: $b = 5$ in.; $h = 7.2$ in.
3. rectangle: $b = 3\frac{1}{2}$ ft; $h = 8\frac{3}{4}$ ft
4. square: $s = 87\frac{7}{8}$ cm
5. parallelogram: $b = 4.8$ yd; $h = 9.2$ yd
6. circle: $d = 6.5$ cm
7. trapezoid: $b_1 = 3.8$ m; $b_2 = 5.2$ m; $h = 2,800$ cm
8. circle: $r = 3.25$ cm

9.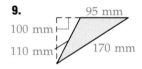
100 mm 95 mm 110 mm 170 mm

10.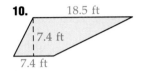
18.5 ft 7.4 ft 7.4 ft

11.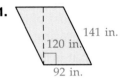
141 in. 120 in. 92 in.

Name the space figure that each net can form.

12.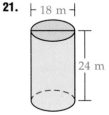

13.

14.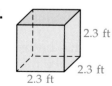

Find each surface area. Use 3.14 for π.

15.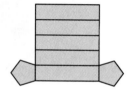
2 ft 3 ft 4 ft

16.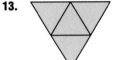
9 cm

17.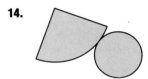
22 cm 10 cm 14 cm

18.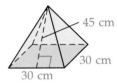
45 cm 30 cm 30 cm

19.
20 m 30 m

20.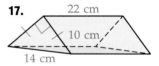
4 cm 10 cm

21.
18 m 24 m

22.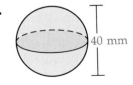
2.3 ft 2.3 ft 2.3 ft

23.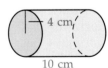
40 mm

Volume—Prisms and Cylinders

OBJECTIVE:
To find the volume of prisms and cylinders.

▼ A gallon and a liter are liquid measures, but they also measure volume. A gallon of milk occupies 231 in.^{3} of space. A liter of milk occupies 1,000 cm^3 of space.

THINK Why do scientists prefer to use metric measure?

Volume	Volume is the measure of the space inside a space figure. We measure volume in cubic units.

▼ The figure below shows a rectangular prism. The base is covered by 12 cubes. The height is 2, allowing for 2 layers of 12 cubes. The volume of the prism is 24 cubic units.

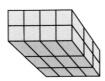

This example suggests the following formula.

THINK To find the volume of a rectangular prism you can multiply length × width × height. How is this the same as $V = Bh$?

Volume of a Prism or Cylinder	The volume (V) of a prism or a cylinder is base area (B) times the height (h). $$V = Bh$$

▼ In formulas for volume, B represents the base area, while b is the length of the base edge.

Example 1 **Find the volume of the triangular prism.**

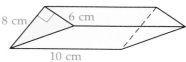

THINK Why is $h = 6$ used to find base area and $h = 10$ used to find volume?

Solution

$B = \frac{1}{2}bh$ Find the area of the base.

$= \frac{1}{2}(8 \times 6)$ Substitute 8 for b and 6 for h. Simplify.

$= 24$

$V = Bh$ Find the volume.

$= (24)10$ Substitute 24 for B and 10 for h.

$= 240$ Simplify.

The volume is 240 cm^3.

3 cm

12.5 cm

fruit Juice

355 ml

▼ Finding the volume of a cylinder is similar to finding the volume of a prism.

Example 2   Find the volume of a juice can in centimeters. Use 3.14 for π.

Solution $B = \pi r^2$ Find the area of the base.
$\quad\quad = \pi \cdot 3^2$
$\quad\quad = 9\pi$

$V = Bh$ Use the formula for volume.
$\quad\quad = 9\pi \cdot 12.5$
$\quad\quad = 112.5\pi$
$\quad\quad \approx 3.14 \times 112.5$
$\quad\quad = 353.25 \text{ cm}^3$

The volume is about 353.25 cm^3.

THINK AND DISCUSS

1. Why is volume usually labeled in gallons or liters rather than cubic inches or cubic centimeters?

2. In metric units, volume and mass are easily changed from one unit to another. For water, $1 \text{ ml} = \blacksquare \text{ cm}^3 = \blacksquare \text{ g}$.

3. When finding the volume of a rectangular prism with dimensions $5 \times 8 \times 9$, does it matter which two dimensions represent the base of the figure?

4. Name at least one prism and one cylinder where you need to know the volume.

CLASS EXERCISES

MENTAL MATH Calculate the volume of each rectangular prism.

1.

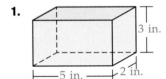

3 in.

5 in.   2 in.

2.

8 cm

12 cm   5 cm

Find the volume of each prism.

3.

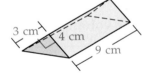

3 cm   4 cm

9 cm

4.

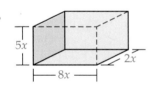

5x

8x   2x

Find the volume of each cylinder. Use 3.14 for π.

5.

60 m

8 m

6.

10 ft

8 ft

Complete.

7. $1 \text{ ft}^2 = \blacksquare \text{ in.}^2$

8. $1 \text{ yd}^2 = \blacksquare \text{ ft}^2$

9. $1 \text{ cm}^2 = \blacksquare \text{ mm}^2$

10. $1 \text{ m}^2 = \blacksquare \text{ cm}^2$

11. $1 \text{ ft}^3 = \blacksquare \text{ in.}^3$

12. $1 \text{ yd}^3 = \blacksquare \text{ ft}^3$

13. $1 \text{ cm}^3 = \blacksquare \text{ mm}^3$

14. $1 \text{ m}^3 = \blacksquare \text{ cm}^3$

WRITTEN EXERCISES

Find the volume of a prism with the given dimensions.

1. square base:
7 in. by 7 in.
height: 13 in.

2. rectangular base:
9 ft by 5 ft
height: 36 in.

3. cube:
sides: $3a$

4.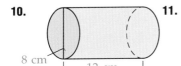

5.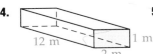

6.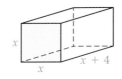

CALCULATOR **Find the volume of a cylinder with the given dimensions to the nearest hundredth. Use 3.14 for π.**

7. radius: 12 ft
height: 15 ft

8. diameter: 3.8 m
height: 18 m

9. radius: 7.6 cm
height: 32 cm

10.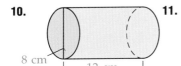

11.

12.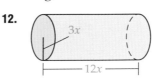

13. Wood for wood-burning stoves is sold by the cord. A cord is 8 ft × 4 ft × 4 ft. How many cubic feet is a cord?

14. When purchasing concrete, the price quoted is *per yard*, which means per cubic yard. Concrete costs $52 a yard. How much would it cost to pour a 14 ft × 16 ft × 6 in. slab for a patio?

15. Cylinder A has radius 1 and height 3. Cylinder B has radius 1 and height 6. What is the ratio of the volumes of the two cylinders? How does doubling the height affect the volume?

16. Cylinder A has radius 1 and height 3. Cylinder B has radius 2 and height 3. What is the ratio of the volumes of the two cylinders? How does doubling the radius affect the volume?

17. How much juice can a drinking straw hold? A straw has a diameter of 6 mm and a length of 208 mm.

18. Write a formula for the volume of a cube that has side x.

19. Write a formula for the volume of a cylinder with radius x and height x.

20. **PROJECT** Pop half a cup of popcorn.

  a. How many cups of popped corn do you have?

  b. What is the ratio of popped to raw popcorn?

Sailing Across the Prairie

American pioneers traveled west of the Mississippi in prairie schooners, or covered wagons. For two thousand miles and several months, the wagon was home for the pioneer family. A prairie schooner was about 4 ft wide and 10 ft long. Most wagons were about 8 ft high. In this small space, pioneer families carried all of the supplies needed to survive the trip and to start new lives.

Use the article at the left to answer each question.

21. What is the volume of a rectangular prism the dimensions of a prairie schooner?

22. A wagon wheel is about 4 ft in diameter.

   a. What is its circumference? Use 3.14 for π.

   b. A mile is 5,280 ft. About how many turns would a wheel make in a mile? in 2,000 mi?

TEST YOURSELF

Find the surface area of each figure.

1. 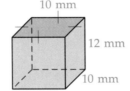 10 mm, 12 mm, 10 mm

2. 8 m, 15 m

3. 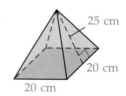 25 cm, 20 cm, 20 cm

Find the volume of each figure.

4. 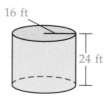 16 ft, 24 ft

5. 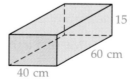 15 cm, 60 cm, 40 cm

6.  10 in., 12 in., 20 in.

7. 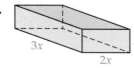 3x, 2x

8. 2x, x, 4x

9. $5x^2$, 10x

OBJECTIVE:
To find the volume of
pyramids, cones, and
spheres.

10-10 Volume—Pyramids, Cones, and Spheres

▼ You can fill three cones
with water and pour the
contents into a cylinder
with the same height and
radius. The cylinder will
be completely filled.

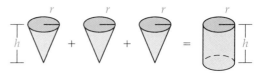

The volume of the cone is $\frac{1}{3}$ the volume of the cylinder. The same
relationship is true of a pyramid and a prism with the same base and
height.

FLASHBACK

The formula for the
volume of a prism and
a cylinder is *Bh*.

Volume of a Cone and a Pyramid	The formula for the volume of a cone and pyramid is $\frac{1}{3}$ the base area (*B*) times the height (*h*). $$V = \frac{1}{3}Bh$$

▼ The height of a regular pyramid or cone is the measure of the
altitude from the vertex to the center of the base.

Example 1   Find the volume of each figure.

a.

10 ft
3 ft

b.

10 ft
6 ft

Solution   a. $B = \pi r^2$

$= \pi \cdot 3^2$

$= 9\pi$

$V = \frac{1}{3}Bh$

$= \frac{1}{3} \cdot 9\pi \cdot 10$

$= 30\pi$

$\approx 30 \cdot 3.14$

$= 94.2$

b. $B = bh$

$= 6 \cdot 6$

$= 36$

$V = \frac{1}{3}Bh$

$= \frac{1}{3} \cdot 36 \cdot 10$

$= 120$

The volume of the cone is about 94.2 ft³.
The volume of the square pyramid is 120 ft³.

THINK Why is the volume of
the cone less than the
volume of the pyramid?

▼ Below is the formula for the volume of a sphere.

Volume of a Sphere	The volume (*V*) of a sphere with radius *r* is $$V = \frac{4}{3}\pi r^3.$$

Example 2 Find the volume of a spherical scoop of ice cream with radius 3 cm.

Solution
$$V = \frac{4}{3}\pi r^3$$

$$\approx \frac{4}{3} \cdot 3.14 \cdot 3^3 \qquad \text{Use 3.14 for } \pi.$$

$$= \frac{4}{3} \cdot 3.14 \cdot 27$$

$$= 113.04 \text{ cm}^3$$

The volume is about 113.04 cm³.

THINK AND DISCUSS

1. Does $\frac{1}{3}Bh = \frac{1}{3}hB = \frac{Bh}{3}$? How can this help in finding volume of a pyramid or a cone?

2. Compare the formula for the surface area of a sphere to the formula for the volume of a sphere. How are they alike? How are they different?

3. In a sphere, if the radius is doubled, how is the volume changed?

CLASS EXERCISES

Find the volume of each figure. Use 3.14 for π.

1.
6 yd
2 yd

2.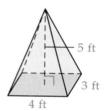
5 ft
3 ft
4 ft

3.
9 m

4. A cone has a radius 1 and height 1. What is the exact volume of the cone?

5. The volume of a pyramid is 25 m³. What is the volume of a prism with the same base and same height?

Complete each analogy.

6. square : cube : : circle : ▦

7. pyramid : cone : : polygonal base : ▦

8. volume : cubic units : : area : ▦

9. cylinder : prism : : cone : ▦

10. perimeter : area : volume : : cm : ▦ : ▦

11. Cone A has $h = 5$ and $r = 3$. Cone B has $h = 5$ and $r = 6$. What is the ratio of the volumes? How does doubling the radius affect the volume?

12. Cone A has $h = 5$ and $r = 3$. Cone B has $h = 10$ and $r = 3$. What is the ratio of the volumes? How does doubling the height affect the volume?

13. How many cones of radius 1 and height 1 equal the volume of a sphere with radius 1?

WRITTEN EXERCISES

CALCULATOR Find the volume. Use 3.14 for π.

1. sphere,
  $r = 6$ cm

2. square-based
  pyramid,
  $s = 12$ m, $h = 15$ m

3. cone,
  $r = 9$ ft, $h = 10$ ft

4.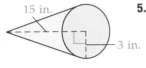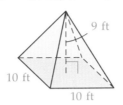

5.

6.

7. Theater A sells popcorn in prism-shaped boxes. Theater B sells popcorn in pyramid-shaped boxes. The base and height of both popcorn boxes are the same. Which box holds more popcorn? How much more?

8. Find the volume of a square-based pyramid with base edge 9 in. and height 1 ft.

Find the radius of a sphere for each volume.

9. $\frac{256}{3}\pi$ m^3

10. $\frac{4}{3}\pi$ cm^3

11. $\frac{500}{3}\pi$ ft^3

12. CALCULATOR The diameter of Earth is about 7,926.6 mi.

  a. Find the surface area.

  b. Find the volume of Earth. You may need to use scientific notation.

  c. Find the surface area and volume of Earth in the encyclopedia. Compare your answers.

13. Tennis balls with a diameter of 2.5 in. are sold in cans of three. The can is a cylinder. What is the volume of the space in the can not occupied by tennis balls? Assume the balls touch the can on the sides, top, and bottom.

14. You place a steel ball with diameter 4 cm, in a water-filled cylinder that is 5 cm in diameter and 10 cm high. How much water will spill?

15. The diameter of the world's largest ball of string is 12 ft 9 in. Francis A. Johnson of Darwin, Minnesota, collected the ball of string between 1950 and 1978.

  a. What is the circumference of the ball of string?

  b. What is the surface area?

  c. What is the volume?

16. **WRITE** Which is the better buy on oranges? Explain how you made your selection.

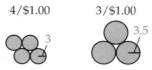

4/$1.00   3/$1.00

17. A pyramid is 460 ft high. It is 760 ft on each side of its square base. What is the volume of the pyramid?

18. You want to fill the top half of an hourglass $\frac{2}{3}$ full of salt. The height of the hourglass is 12 cm and the radius is 3 cm. Find the volume of salt needed.

Critical Thinking
EXPLORING A HYPOTHESIS

A hypothesis is an educated guess. To find if a hypothesis is true, you must test it.

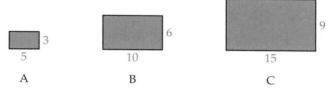

A   B   C

1. Write a hypothesis about the ratio of the perimeters and areas of two similar figures.

2. Make a table with entries for base, height, perimeter, and area and find this information for similar figures A, B, and C.

3. Use the information in your chart for figures B and C to answer the following questions. Write all fractions in lowest terms.
   a. What is the ratio of the heights?
   b. What is the ratio of the bases?
   c. What is the ratio of the perimeters?
   d. What is the ratio of the areas?

4. Do you need to revise your hypothesis? Do so, if necessary. Test it on figures A and C.

5. Predict the ratio of the perimeters and areas of two triangles if the ratio of their heights is $\frac{5}{8}$.

Problem Solving Practice

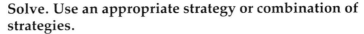

PROBLEM SOLVING STRATEGIES

Look for a Pattern
Guess and Test
Simplify the Problem
Account for All Possibilities
Make an Organized List
Work Backwards
Make a Table
Write an Equation
Solve by Graphing
Draw a Diagram
Make a Model
Simulate the Problem

Solve. Use an appropriate strategy or combination of strategies.

1. A rectangular piece of tin measures 26 in. × 20 in. A square measuring 2 in. × 2 in. is cut out of each corner and the sides are folded to form a box. What is the volume of the box?

2. Susan and Karen are in a marathon race. Susan's average speed is 5 mi/h and Karen's is 8 mi/h. If they start at 10 A.M., when will they be $4\frac{1}{2}$ mi apart?

3. Frank Goodshot usually hits his mark when throwing free throws. However, in the last few games he has made only 15 shots out of 24. How many consecutive free throws must Frank make to raise his record to 80%?

4. A 12-m by 15-m rectangular garden has a walk 1 m wide around it. What is the area of the walk?

5. Three boys, Jack, Jim, and Jay, planned to share a bag of apples equally. Jack found the bag on the doorstep first and took his share. Jim came along later and took what he thought was his share. Later yet, Jay arrived, taking what he thought was his share. He left 8 apples. How many apples were there to start with?

6. Five economically minded girls decided to share wardrobes. Each bought a different three-piece outfit, a skirt, a blouse, and a vest. Then they traded pieces around. How many different outfits can they make?

7. Juan and his younger brother Kimo picked apples. The average of what they picked was 10 bushels. Juan picked three times as many apples as Kimo. How many bushels did each pick?

8. **DATA (p. 128)** Use the formula for cricket chirps and temperature. How many chirps does a cricket make per minute when the temperature is 56°?

9. Six girls ran a 100-yd race. Fran beat Clara by 8 yd. Clara finished 12 yd behind Teresa. Marie finished 16 yd behind Fran but 2 yd ahead of Cindy. Vivian finished exactly between the first and last runner. In what order did the girls finish the race?

10. **DATA FILE 10 (pp. 404–405)** About how many Arctic Oceans could fit into the Pacific Ocean? Consider the volume of water in each, based on the average depth.

11. A rectangle is 8 ft longer than it is wide. The area of the rectangle is 240 ft². What are the dimensions?

Chapter 10 Review

Complete each statement. Use the vocabulary words given.

1. The ▪ is the amount of surface inside a region.
2. A polyhedron is a space figure that has ▪ for all faces.
3. The sides of a pyramid are ▪ that meet at a common point.
4. The sides of a ▪ are parallelograms.
5. A ▪ has two circular bases that are parallel and congruent.
6. A ▪ has one circular base and one ▪.
7. A ▪ is the set of all points in space that are the same distance from a given point called the ▪.
8. Surface area is the sum of the area of the ▪.
9. The ▪ ▪ is the height of a face.
10. ▪ is the measure of the space inside a space figure.

VOCABULARY

area
cone
volume
cylinder
sphere
polygons
prism
faces
slant height
vertex
triangles
center

Finding Areas of Polygons   10-1, 10-2

To find the area of a polygon, use the appropriate formula.

parallelogram	triangle	trapezoid
$A = bh$	$A = \frac{1}{2}bh$	$A = \frac{1}{2}(b_1 + b_2)h$

Find the area of each figure.

11.

7 cm

12.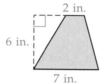

2 in.
6 in.
7 in.

13.

5 ft
6 ft

14.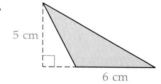

5 cm
6 cm

Finding the Area of a Circle   10-3

To find the area of a circle, multiply π by the square of the radius.
$A = \pi r^2$.

Find the area of each figure. Use 3.14 for π.

15.

10 m

16.

8 mm

17.

12 m

18.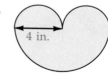

4 in.

We name pyramids and prisms by the shape of their bases.

Name the space figure that each net can form.

19.

20.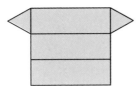

21.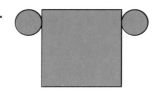

Problem Solving   **10-5**

To solve some problems, make a model.

22. What are the dimensions of a rectangular sheet of wrapping paper that will cover a 6 in. $\times$ 6 in. $\times$ 6 in. gift box with no more than a $\frac{1}{2}$ in. overlap?

Finding Surface Area   **10-6, 10-7**

To find the surface area of a prism or a cylinder, add the areas of the base(s) and the side(s).

To find the surface area of a cone or a pyramid, use the slant height. The surface area is the sum of the lateral area and the base area.

The surface area of a sphere is $A = 4\pi r^2$.

Find the surface area. Use 3.14 for π.

23.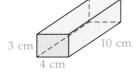

24.

25.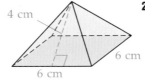

26.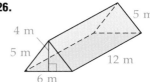

Finding Volume   **10-9, 10-10**

To find the volume of a space figure, use the appropriate formula.

prisms and cylinders	pyramids and cones	spheres
$V = Bh$	$V = \frac{1}{3}Bh$	$V = \frac{4}{3}\pi r^3$

Find the volume. Use 3.14 for π.

27.

28.

29.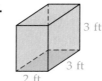

30.

Chapter 10   Test

Find the area of each figure. Use 3.14 for π.

1.
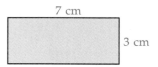
7 cm
3 cm

2.
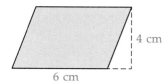
4 cm
6 cm

3.
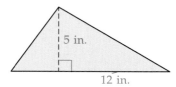
5 in.
12 in.

4.

10 ft

5.
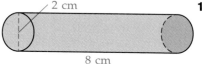
6 yd
3 yd
8 yd

6.
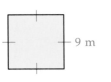
9 m

Find the missing measures.

7. a square
  $A = 121$ m²
  $b = $ ▨

8. a triangle
  $A = 28$ m²
  $b = 7$ m
  $h = $ ▨

9. a circle
  $A = 64\pi$ cm²
  $r = $ ▨

10. a parallelogram
  $A = 48$ in.²
  $b = 16$ in.
  $h = $ ▨

Find the surface area of each figure. Use 3.14 for π.

11.
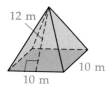
2 cm
8 cm

12.
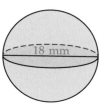
12 m
10 m
10 m

13.
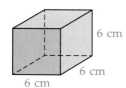
6 cm
6 cm
6 cm

Find the volume of each figure. Use 3.14 for π.

14.
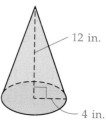
12 in.
4 in.

15.
18 mm

16.
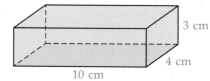
3 cm
4 cm
10 cm

Solve.

17. The height of a rectangle is doubled. How does this affect the area?

18. What is the surface area of a sphere with radius 5 ft?

19. How much greater is the volume of a cone with radius 6 ft and height 10 ft than the volume of a square pyramid with base edge 6 ft and height 10 ft? Use 3.14 for π.

20. **WRITE** How is the formula for the volume of a prism or cylinder the same as the formula for volume of a pyramid or cone? How are they different?

Chapters 1–10   Cumulative Review

Choose the correct answer. Write A, B, C, or D.

1. What is the volume?

A. 30   **B.** 10

C. 15   **D.** not given

2. $\triangle ABC \sim \triangle DBE$. Find x.

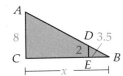

A. 14   **B.** 5

C. 12.5   **D.** not given

3. $\triangle ABC \cong \triangle DEF$. Which is not true?

A. $\angle A \cong \angle D$ **B.** $\overline{AC} \cong \overline{FD}$

C. $\angle B \cong \angle F$ **D.** not given

4. Simplify $\frac{3x^5y^3z^{-2}}{24x^6y^2z}$.

A. $\frac{y}{8xz^3}$ **B.** $8xyz^{-3}$

C. $\frac{y^5}{8xz^3}$ **D.** not given

5. What is the prime factorization of 84?

A. $2^3 \cdot 7$ **B.** $2 \cdot 3^2 \cdot 7$

C. $2 \cdot 3 \cdot 7$ **D.** not given

6. A $250 coat was on sale for $200. What was the percent decrease?

A. 25%   **B.** 80%

C. 20%   **D.** not given

7. Marcia has 13 dimes and quarters worth $2.80. How many of each does she have?

A. 10 d, 3 q **B.** 6 d, 7 q

C. 3 d, 10 q **D.** not given

8. Find the area of the shaded region.

A. 32   **B.** 64

C. 16   **D.** not given

9. Name the space figure the net will form.

A. prism   **B.** pyramid

C. cylinder   **D.** not given

10. Solve $5 - 3x > 17$.

A. $x < 4$ **B.** $x > \text{-}4$

C. $x < \text{-}4$ **D.** not given

11. What percent of 23 is 4.6?

A. 80%   **B.** 20%

C. 46%   **D.** not given

12. Find the LCM of 18 and 24.

A. 6   **B.** 72

C. 42   **D.** not given

13. What is the equation for a line having slope -2 and y-intercept 3?

A. $2x + y = 3$ **B.** $y - 2x = 3$

C. $3x + y = -2$ **D.** not given

14. Which point lies on the line $2y - 3x = 14$?

A. (-4,1)   **B.** (1,-4)

C. (0,-7)   **D.** not given

PARACHUTING TERMS

TERM	DEFINITION
HOLDING	facing canopy into the wind to minimize ground speed
FREE FALL	a jump in which the parachute is activated manually
TARGET	the landing area
TERMINAL VELOCITY	the greatest speed at which a body falls through the air; about 176 ft/s which a jumper reaches after 12 s of free fall
WIND DRIFT INDICATOR	determines the strength and direction of the wind; usually a windsock that is 19.5 ft long with a diameter that varies from 36.25 in. to 12 in.
RUNNING	directing the canopy downwind to maximize ground speed

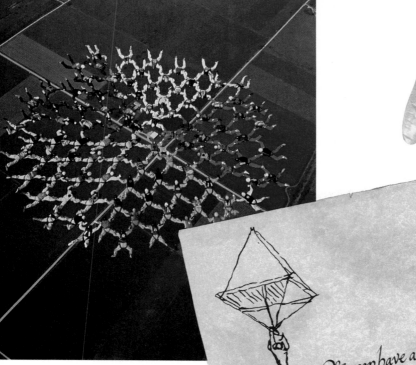

"If a man have a tent made of linen of which the apertures have all been stopped up, and it be twelve braccia across and twelve in depth, he will be able to throw himself down from any great height without sustaining any injury."

Leonardo daVinci

designed a parachute, called a *tent roof* in 1495. Today, parachuting is a popular sport in the United States and Europe. The first sport parachute championships were held in 1951.

Right Triangles in Algebra

IF A PARACHUTIST descends at a rate of 10 ft/s, and travels 2,460 ft straight down, it takes 4.1 min to reach the ground.

You can use right triangles to determine the angle the parachutist makes with the ground, the distance traveled in the jump, and the time it takes to reach the ground.

Up, up, and away

You can use the tangent ratio and the table of trigonometric ratios on page 580 to find the angle the jumper makes with the ground.

$$\tan x = \frac{2,460}{5,280} \approx .46591$$
$$x \approx 25°$$

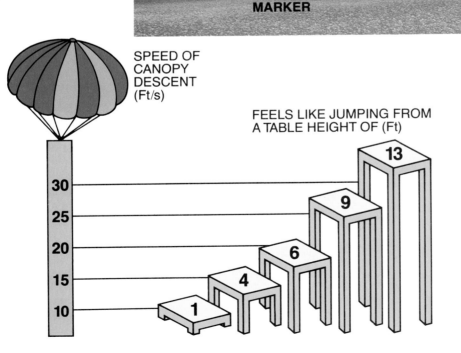

2,460 ft

Holding all the way

Running all the way

1 mi   **GROUND MARKER**   1 mi   **TARGET**   1 mi   1 mi

SPEED OF CANOPY DESCENT (Ft/s)

FEELS LIKE JUMPING FROM A TABLE HEIGHT OF (Ft)

13

9

6

4

1

30
25
20
15
10

Think about it...

Do you think the size and shape of the parachute canopy affect the rate at which a parachute descends? Describe an experiment to test your hypothesis.

OBJECTIVE:
To explore square roots using several methods.

MATERIALS

- Algebra tiles or graph paper

- Standard calculator

- Math journal to record work

Exploring Square Roots

▼ Suppose you build a square having length of 5 tiles.

1. *Model* the square using algebra tiles.

2. How many tiles make up the length of each side of the square?

3. How many tiles do you need to build the square?

4. a. *Write* an equation using an exponent to describe the relationship between the number of tiles on each side of the square and the total number in the square.

   b. *Model* other squares using algebra tiles. Write an equation for each square as you did in (a).

5. What part of the equation corresponds to the number of tiles on each side of the square?

6. *Discuss* how you can determine the number of tiles in a square, given the number of tiles on each side.

▼ The opposite of squaring a number is finding its *square root*. We refer to the number of tiles on each side of the square as the square root of the total number of tiles in the square.

7. a. *Model* a square with 9 tiles.

   b. How many tiles are on each side?

   c. What is the square root of 9?

$4^2 = 16$
4 is a square root of 16

8. *Model* the square represented by each equation using graph paper. Shade in the square root. State the square root of the product.

   a. $6^2 = 36$ **b.** $49 = 7^2$ **c.** $1^2 = 1$ **d.** $3.5^2 = 12.25$

   e. *Describe* the position in each equation of the square root of the product.

   f. *Write* a sentence relating your answers in (5) and (8e).

5 is a square root of 25
$\sqrt{25} = 5$

▼ We say *five is a square root of twenty-five* and write $\sqrt{25} = 5$. The notation $\sqrt{25}$ means to find a positive number that when squared is equal to 25. We call the symbol $\sqrt{}$ the square root sign.

9. a. Is there a number other than positive five, that when squared gives you twenty-five?

   b. *Explain* why this number is not a correct value of $\sqrt{25}$.

10. Find each square root.

   a. $\sqrt{81}$ **b.** $\sqrt{100}$ **c.** $\sqrt{144}$ **d.** $\sqrt{20.25}$

▼ Suppose you are given 21 tiles with which to build a square.

11. a. _Model_ the square. Describe your results.

    b. Does 21 have a whole number square root? Explain.

12. Complete each statement.

    a. If I could eliminate ▨ tiles, I would have a ▨ × ▨ square.

    b. If I could add ▨ more tiles, I would have a ▨ × ▨ square.

13. a. Between what two positive integers does the $\sqrt{21}$ lie?

    b. To what integer is $\sqrt{21}$ closer? Base your answer on the number of squares you need to add or subtract.

14. Each square root lies between what two integers? Circle the integer to which it is closer.

    a. $\sqrt{5}$ **b.** $\sqrt{76}$ **c.** $\sqrt{147}$

▼ You can use a standard calculator to estimate a square root.

Estimate the value of $\sqrt{76}$ to the nearest tenth. You already know that $\sqrt{76}$ lies between the integers 8 and 9.

Try 8.3	8.3	✕	8.3	=	68.89	too low
Try 8.6	8.6	✕	8.6	=	73.96	too low
Try 8.7	8.7	✕	8.7	=	75.69	very close

So, to the nearest tenth, $\sqrt{76}$ is approximately 8.7.

15. Use a calculator to find an approximate value, to the nearest tenth, for each square root. Do not use the square root key.

    a. $\sqrt{75}$ **b.** $\sqrt{29}$ **c.** $\sqrt{94}$ **d.** $\sqrt{186}$

16. a. _Describe_ a method for finding an approximate value of a square root to the nearest hundredth.

    b. Find the value of $\sqrt{131}$ to the nearest hundredth.

▼ You can also use a square root key on a calculator.

17. _Explore_ how to find the square root of a number using a square root key. Start with a square root you already know, such as $\sqrt{9}$.

18. Use a calculator to find the value of each square root.

    a. $\sqrt{25}$ **b.** $\sqrt{19}$ **c.** $\sqrt{0}$ **d.** $\sqrt{-36}$

19. a. _Describe_ the result when you took the square root of -36.

    b. Is it possible to take the square root of a negative number?

OBJECTIVE:
Finding square roots
of numbers and
expressions.

11-1 Finding Square Roots

▼ Each of the quadrilaterals in the puzzle is a square, except the surrounding quadrilateral. Here are two possible ways to find the length of a side of the shaded square if its area is 81.

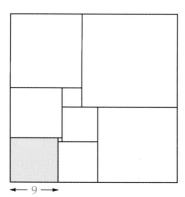

1. Think, *What number squared gives me 81?* Use guess and test with several numbers until you arrive at the correct answer, which is 9.

2. Think, *What is the square root of 81?* The result is also 9.

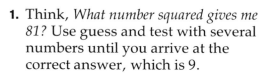

▼ The inverse of squaring a number is finding its *square root*.

Square Root	The square root of a number, n, is a if $a^2 = n$.

Example 1 Find the square root of 64.

Solution   **a.** $(-8)^2 = 64$, so -8 is a square root.

        b. $8^2 = 64$, so 8 is also a square root.

▼ We use the symbol $\sqrt{}$ to denote the positive square root or *principal square root* of a number.

Principal Square Root	The principal square root of a number is its positive square root. The principal square root is denoted by the symbol $\sqrt{}$.

Example 2 Find the principal square root of each expression.
      a. 10,000   **b.** $121x^2$

Solution   **a.** $100^2 = 10{,}000$, so the principal square root is 100.

        b. $(11x)^2 = 121x^2$, so the principal square root is $11x$.

Example 3 Evaluate.
      a. $\sqrt{196}$ **b.** $\sqrt{225p^6}$

Solution   **a.** $14^2 = 196$, so 14 is the value of the expression.

        b. $(15p^3)^2 = 225p^6$, so $15p^3$ is the value of the expression.

▼ Rational numbers such as 144, 64, and 1 are all perfect squares. They have whole number square roots of 12, 8, and 1, respectively. Rational numbers such as 27 and 65 are not perfect squares. They do not have whole number square roots. We call the square roots of these numbers *irrational numbers.* The set of *real numbers* is made up of the rational numbers and the irrational numbers.

Irrational Numbers	Irrational numbers are numbers which we cannot express as either terminating or repeating decimals.

Example 4 **Determine whether each number is rational or irrational. Use a calculator, if necessary.**

  a. 15   **b.** 0.1212 . . .   **c.** π **d.** $\sqrt{1.21}$

Solution   **a.** rational; 15 terminates

  b. rational; the decimal has a repeating pattern

  c. π 3.1415927 . . . ; irrational; the decimal does not terminate or repeat

  d. 1.21 ☑ 1.1; rational; 1.1 terminates

▼ You can use a table of square roots to find an approximate value for irrational square roots.

Example 5 **Find the approximate value of $\sqrt{29}$. Use the table on p. 579.**

Solution $\sqrt{29} \approx 5.385$

THINK Why does a table of square roots only show approximate values?

CLASS EXERCISES

Complete.

1. The name for the mathematical symbol $\sqrt{}$ is ▨.

2. *The square root of forty-nine* can be written using mathematical symbols as ▨.

3. A ▨ number is implied by the symbol $\sqrt{}$.

4. The set of real numbers is made up of ▨ and ▨ numbers.

5. A repeating decimal is a(n) ▨ number.

6. If a square has an area of 49 in.², each side has length of ▨.

7. The two square roots of 100 are ▨ and ▨. The principal square root is ▨.

8. $\sqrt{92}$ is between the integers ▨ and ▨.

9. The decimal 0.121231234 . . . is a(n) ▨ number.

THINK AND DISCUSS

1. Are the solutions for $x^2 = 16$ and $x = \sqrt{16}$ different? Why?

2. Do the expressions $\sqrt{25}$ and $-\sqrt{25}$ have the same value? Explain.

3. Rewrite the equation $3^2 + {}^-4^2 = 5^2$ to make it true.

4. What number results when you square a square root?

Find each square root. Use the square root table on p. 579 or a calculator, if necessary. Round answers to the nearest thousandth.

10. $\sqrt{100}$ **11.** $\sqrt{1}$ **12.** $\sqrt{13}$ **13.** $\sqrt{50}$

14. $\sqrt{\frac{4}{9}}$ **15.** $\sqrt{12.25}$ **16.** $\sqrt{15^2}$ **17.** $\sqrt{m^2}$

State whether each number is rational or irrational. Use a calculator, if necessary.

18. $\sqrt{0}$ **19.** $\sqrt{87}$ **20.** $-\sqrt{16}$ **21.** $4.1010010001\ldots$

WRITTEN EXERCISES

True or false.

1. All real numbers are integers.

2. All integers are real numbers.

3. The principal square roots of 36 are -6 and 6.

4. $\sqrt{36} + \sqrt{64} = 14$

5. $\sqrt{36 + 64} = \sqrt{100} = 10$

6. $\sqrt{79}$ is between 8 and 9.

7. If a square has an area of 225 cm², the side is 15 cm.

8. An approximation for $\sqrt{3}$ is 1.723.

MENTAL MATH Square each term.

9. 16   **10.** -8 **11.** $\frac{2}{3}$ **12.** 11

13. $5x^3$ **14.** $\sqrt{2}$ **15.** $\sqrt{9^2}$ **16.** $\sqrt{2x}$

MENTAL MATH Evaluate.

17. $\sqrt{10,000}$ **18.** $\sqrt{169}$ **19.** $\sqrt{59 + 5}$ **20.** $\sqrt{p^2}$

Find each square root. If necessary, use your calculator. Round decimal answers to the nearest thousandth.

21. $\sqrt{49}$ **22.** $\sqrt{81}$ **23.** $\sqrt{\frac{16}{25}}$ **24.** $\sqrt{(r + 3)^2}$

25. $\sqrt{49.49}$ **26.** $\sqrt{196x^6}$ **27.** $\sqrt{8y^5 \cdot 2y^5}$ **28.** $\sqrt{3 \cdot 12x^{16}}$

29. $\sqrt{256}$ **30.** $\sqrt{7y^4}$ **31.** $\sqrt{100 \div 5}$ **32.** $\sqrt{a^4b^6c^8}$

Between what two integers does each square root lie? Circle the integer to which the square root is closer.

33. $\sqrt{51}$ **34.** $\sqrt{93}$ **35.** $\sqrt{5}$ **36.** $-\sqrt{22}$

37. $-\sqrt{5}$ **38.** $\sqrt{132}$ **39.** $\sqrt{7 + 11}$ **40.** $\sqrt{99}$

State whether each term is rational or irrational. Use a calculator, if necessary.

41. $\sqrt{625}$ **42.** $-\sqrt{36}$ **43.** $\sqrt{32}$ **44.** $\sqrt{0}$

45. 198.94762 **46.** $\sqrt{53}$ **47.** $4.33333\ldots$ **48.** $\sqrt{5} + 11$

Use the square root table on p. 579 to approximate each value.

49. $\sqrt{50}$ **50.** $\sqrt{77}$ **51.** $\sqrt{99}$ **52.** $\sqrt{2}$

53. $\sqrt{43}$ **54.** $\sqrt{17}$ **55.** $\sqrt{54}$ **56.** $\sqrt{87}$

Critical Thinking

EXPLORING PATTERNS

Sir Isaac Newton devised a method for finding a square root. It is often referred to as the *divide and average method.*

Problem   Approximate the value of $\sqrt{47}$.

Solution   Use the *divide and average method:*

1. Trap between two integers.	$6 < \sqrt{47} < 7$
2. Identify the closer integer.	$\sqrt{47}$ is closer to 7
3. Estimate to the nearest tenth.	6.8
4. Divide the number that you are taking the square root of by the estimate. Carry to whatever place accuracy is desired in the answer.	$47 \div 6.8 \approx 6.91$
5. Find the mean average of the quotient and the divisor.	$(6.8 + 6.91) \div 2 \approx 6.86$
6. Use the mean as the new divisor.	$47 \div 6.86 \approx 6.85$

7. If necessary, repeat Steps 4, 5, and 6 until the divisor is very close to the quotient.

You can use a BASIC program to simulate Newton's method.

```
10 PRINT "Square root of
what number";
20 INPUT A
30 PRINT "How many
averages";
40 INPUT B
50 PRINT "What is your first
estimate";
60 INPUT C
70 FOR X = 1 to B
80 PRINT (A/C + C)/2
90 NEXT X
```

1. Continue this pattern for $\sqrt{47}$. Explain your results. How can you get the answer?

2. Use Newton's method to find the approximate value of $\sqrt{19}$.

3. Why do you think people no longer use Newton's method?

4. *PROJECT* Use the computer program shown at the right to find the square roots of various numbers.

11-2 *Simulating a Problem*

OBJECTIVE:
To solve a problem
by simulation.

■ Sometimes when solving a problem, it is helpful to act out or *simulate* the problem.

PROBLEM

A class of 25 seated students counted off by ones beginning with the number one. Each student who counted a multiple of four stood up. Then the students who were still seated counted off by ones again. Each student who counted a multiple of four stood up. This process was repeated one more time. How many students were standing after the third counting?

SOLUTION

READbar➤ What do you want to find?   The number of students standing after the third counting

PLAN ➤ Start out with 25 students. Act out each step of the problem.

SOLVE ➤ Have 25 students sit in their seats.

Students Sitting	Students Standing
👤👤👤👤👤👤👤👤👤👤👤👤👤 👤👤👤👤👤👤👤👤👤👤👤👤	None

First Counting
1. All students count off by ones.
2. All students who counted a multiple of four stand up.

Students Sitting	Students Standing
👤👤👤👤👤👤👤👤👤👤👤👤👤 👤👤👤👤👤👤	👤👤👤👤👤👤

Second Counting
1. All students seated count off by ones.
2. All students who counted a multiple of four stand up.

Students Sitting	Students Standing
👤👤👤👤👤👤👤👤👤👤👤👤👤👤	👤👤👤👤👤👤👤👤👤👤

Third Counting
1. All students seated count off by ones.
2. All students who counted a multiple of four stand up.

Students Sitting	Students Standing
👤👤👤👤👤👤👤👤👤👤👤👤	👤👤👤👤👤👤👤👤👤👤👤👤👤

LOOK BACK ➤ There will be 13 students standing after the third counting.

CLASS EXERCISES

Refer to the problem on page 458.

1. How many students will be standing after the fifth counting?

2. After how many countings will three students be sitting?

Use a **CALCULATOR** where appropriate.

WRITTEN EXERCISES

Solve by simulating the problem.

1. Suppose you purchase a rare coin for $15, sell it for $23, and then buy it back for $31. How much money did you make or lose in selling and repurchasing this coin?

2. Jim is hosting a dinner party. Jim greets the first guest and they shake hands. The second guest arrives and shakes hands with Jim and the first guest. The third guest arrives and shakes hands with Jim, the first guest, and the second guest. This pattern continues. How many handshakes have taken place after the ninth guest arrives?

Solve. Use any strategy.

3. Sandy and Toby are 18 mi apart. They begin to walk toward one another. Sandy walks at 3 mi/h and Toby walks at 2 mi/h. After 1 h of walking Toby decides to rest for 1 h. In how many hours will they meet? How far will Sandy have walked? Toby?

4. Jon's bicycle license is a three digit number. The product of the digits is 140. The sum of the digits is 16. The numbers appear in descending order. What is Jon's license number?

5. Chris was thinking of a number. He added 4, multiplied the sum by -5, then subtracted 12. He then doubled the result to get -34. Of what number was Chris thinking?

6. There are 180 children standing around a parachute (assume this is a circle). The children are spaced evenly and numbered consecutively from 1 to 180. Ann is number 7. Tara is standing directly opposite Ann. What is Tara's number?

7. A hot air balloon is 2,200 ft in the air. It is scheduled to land at 3:22 P.M. The balloon descends at a rate of 110 ft/min. At what time should the descent begin?

8. **DATA FILE 12 (pp. 486–487)** Milwaukee, WI, has an altitude of 635 ft. Boston, MA, has an altitude of 21 ft. About how much farther will an average home run travel in Milwaukee than in Boston?

OBJECTIVE:
To explore properties of right triangles.

Exploring Right Triangles

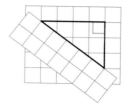

▪ Look at the right triangle shown. We call the side opposite the right angle the *hypotenuse*. We call the other two sides *legs*.

1. How many units long is each leg?

2. **a.** How many units long is the hypotenuse?

   b. **Explain** how the length of the hypotenuse was determined using graph paper.

MATERIALS

• Graph paper

• Math journal to record work

▪ A square is drawn on each side of the right triangle.

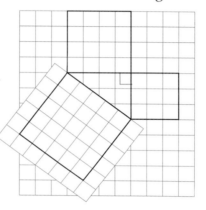

Egyptian rope stretchers used right triangles to relocate property lines after the annual flooding of the Nile river.

3. What is the length of a side on each square? **Describe** what it means to square a side of a triangle.

4. **a.** What are the areas of the squares on each leg?

   b. What is the area of the square on the hypotenuse?

   c. **Explain** how to draw the square on the hypotenuse.

   d. **Discuss** the relationship between your findings in (a) and (b).

▪ A right triangle has side lengths 6, 8, and 10.

5. **Model** the right triangle and square each side.

6. **a.** What are the areas of the squares on each leg?

   b. What is the area of the square on the hypotenuse?

   c. **Discuss** the relationship between your findings in (a) and (b).

▪ The sides of a right triangle share a special relationship.

7. **Describe** the relationship between the sides of any right triangle.

OBJECTIVE:
To use the rule of
Pythagoras to verify
right triangles and to
find missing values of
right triangles.

11-3 *Pythagorean Theorem*

NOTES & QUOTES

Pythagoras was a Greek
mathematician born about
500 B.C. He founded a
school to promote the
study of philosophy,
mathematics, and natural
science.

▼ Pythagoras is most famous for discovering the relationship between the lengths of the sides of a right triangle. This relationship is known as the *Pythagorean theorem.*

Pythagorean Theorem	In any right triangle with legs *a* and *b*, and hypotenuse *c*, $a^2 + b^2 = c^2$.

▼ You can model the Pythagorean theorem using graph paper. The sum of the squares on each side equals the number of squares on the hypotenuse.

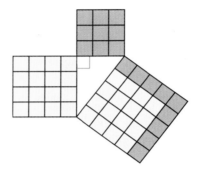

▼ You can use the Pythagorean theorem to find unknown lengths of a triangle.

Example 1 **Find *c*, the length of the hypotenuse.**

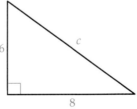

Solution

$$a^2 + b^2 = c^2 \qquad \text{Write the theorem.}$$
$$6^2 + 8^2 = c^2 \qquad \text{Substitute values for the variables.}$$
$$36 + 64 = c^2$$
$$100 = c^2$$
$$\sqrt{100} = \sqrt{c^2} \qquad \text{Find the square root of each side.}$$
$$10 = c$$

The hypotenuse, *c*, has length 10.

Check $\quad a^2 + b^2 = c^2 \qquad$ Substitute values.
$$6^2 + 8^2 = 10^2$$
$$36 + 64 = 100$$
$$100 = 100\checkmark$$

▼ The converse of the Pythagorean theorem is also true.

Converse of Pythagorean Theorem	If $a^2 + b^2 = c^2$, then the triangle with sides a, b, and c is a right triangle.

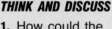

THINK When given three side lengths of a right triangle, how do you know which one is the length of the hypotenuse?

Example 2 **Determine if the triangle with the given side lengths is a right triangle.**

a. 12, 16, 20   **b.** 7, 8, 9

Solution

a. $12^2 + 16^2 = 20^2$
   $144 + 256 = 400$
   $400 = 400$ ✓
This is a right triangle.

b. $7^2 + 8^2 = 9^2$
   $49 + 64 = 81$
   $113 = 81$ ✗
This is not a right triangle.

We say that a set of integers such as 12, 16, 20 is a *Pythagorean triple*.

▼ You can use the Pythagorean theorem to help solve a problem.

Example 3 **Find the area of *ABCED*.**

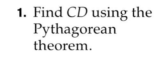

Solution

1. Find *CD* using the Pythagorean theorem.

   $6^2 + 8^2 = CD^2$
   $36 + 64 = CD^2$
   $100 = CD^2$
   $\sqrt{100} = \sqrt{CD^2}$
   $10 = CD$

2. Find the area of the triangle.

   $A = \frac{1}{2}bh$

   $24 = \frac{1}{2}(6)(8)$

3. Find the area of the rectangle.

   $A = lw$
   $80 = (10)(8)$

4. Find the total area. Add areas together.

   $24 + 80 = 104$

The area of *ABCED* is 104 square units.

THINK AND DISCUSS

1. How could the Pythagorean theorem be used to find the altitude of an equilateral triangle with side length 12?

2. Is it possible for all three numbers in a Pythagorean triple to be even? odd?

3. A cube has a side length of 5. Find the length of the diagonal on one of the faces to the nearest hundredth.

CLASS EXERCISES

Name the legs and the hypotenuse.

1.

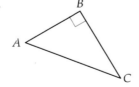

2.

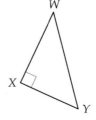

Write an equation. Solve for x.

3. 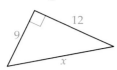 9, 12, x

4. 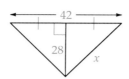 42, 28, x

5.  $\sqrt{53}$, x, 7

6. Is 1, 1, $\sqrt{2}$ a Pythagorean triple?

7. Two hikers started their trip from base camp by walking 15 m due east. They then turned due north, walking 17 m to a large pond. How far is the pond from base camp to the nearest tenth of a meter?

WRITTEN EXERCISES

MENTAL MATH **Simplify.**

1. $\sqrt{5}^2$

2. $\sqrt{144}$

3. $\left(\frac{3}{5}\right)^2$

4. $(2\sqrt{3})^2$

CALCULATOR **Find each value to the nearest thousandth.**

5. $\sqrt{63}$

6. $\sqrt{12}$

7. $\sqrt{32}$

8. $\sqrt{95}$

Name the legs and the hypotenuse.

9.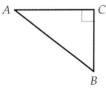

10.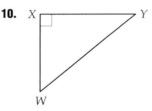

State which value is the length of the hypotenuse.

11. 10, 6, 8

12. $\sqrt{9}, \sqrt{25}, \sqrt{16}$

13. 5, $\sqrt{56}$, 9

Write an equation. Solve for x. Round to the nearest hundredth.

14. 3, x, 5

15. 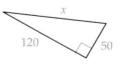 x, 120, 50

16. 9, x, 12

17. $6\sqrt{5}$, 18, x

18. 26, x, 26, 20

19. 11, $\sqrt{202}$, x

Write an equation. Solve for x. Round to the nearest hundredth.

20.

21.

22.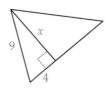

Determine whether each is a Pythagorean triple.

23. 7, 24, 25

24. 5, 12, 13

25. $1, 2, 2\sqrt{3}$

26. 1, 0.24, 0.26

27. 4, 5, 6

28. $1\frac{3}{5}, 1\frac{1}{5}, 2$

29. $3p, 4p, 5p$

30. $\sqrt{5}, \sqrt{3}, \sqrt{2}$

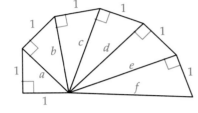

31. Find the lengths of the sides, a, b, c, d, e, f. Your answer may contain radical signs.

32. A carpenter was building a square deck. He measured the sides and the diagonal of the deck and got measures of 8 ft, 9 ft, and 12 ft. Did the carpenter fulfill his contract?

33. The recommended dimensions for a basketball court are 94 ft long and 50 ft wide. To the nearest foot, how long is the diagonal of the basketball court?

34. **CALCULATOR** A desk top is 75 cm wide and 130 cm long. How long is the diagonal of the desk top to the nearest hundredth?

35. Each side of a square is 15 in. long. Find the length of the diagonal to the nearest hundredth.

36. You are working for a landscaping company and you must plant and stake a tree. The stakes must be 2 ft from the base of the tree and the wires must extend 5 ft up the trunk. How long will the wires be to the nearest tenth?

37. Each side of a cube is 10 ft long. Find the length of the diagonal on one of the faces to the nearest tenth.

38. A ladder is 6 ft away from the base of a building. The ladder is 18 ft long. How many feet above the ground is the top of the ladder to the nearest hundredth?

39. The base of a pyramid is square. Each side of the base is 8 in. The slant height of the pyramid is 22 in.

   a. Find the height of the pyramid to the nearest hundredth.

   b. Find the volume of the pyramid to the nearest hundredth.

40. A cone has a diameter of 10 in. and a slant height of 16 in.

   a. Find the height of the cone to the nearest thousandth.

   b. Find the volume of the cone to the nearest thousandth. Use 3.14 for π.

OBJECTIVE:
To use parts of
similar triangles in
problem solving.

11-4 *Similar Right Triangles*

▼ Jack plans to cut down a tree. Since he does not want the tree to land on his house, pool, or shed, he must fell the tree towards the fence. To make sure the tree does not damage the fence, which is 49 ft away, Jack must know the height of the tree. Jack is 6 ft tall and casts a shadow 17 ft long. The tree casts a shadow 102 ft long. Using these measures and his knowledge of similar triangles, Jack finds the height of the tree.

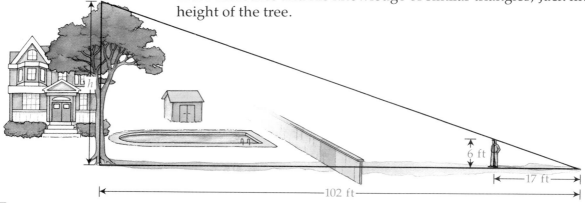

THINK What would be the proportion if Jack's height were 5 ft 9 in?

You can use similar triangles to set up a proportion.

$$\frac{\text{height of tree } (h)}{\text{length of tree shadow}} = \frac{\text{Jack's height}}{\text{length of Jack's shadow}}$$

Solve the proportion for h.

$$\frac{h}{102} = \frac{6}{17} \qquad \text{Substitute values.}$$

$$17h = 6(102) \qquad \text{Cross multiply.}$$

$$17h = 612$$

$$\frac{17h}{17} = \frac{612}{17} \qquad \text{Divide each side by 17.}$$

$$h = 36$$

The tree is 36 ft tall. Since $36 < 49$, the fence will not be damaged.

▼ There is often more than one way to solve a problem.

Example 1 **Find x using two different methods. The right triangles are similar.**

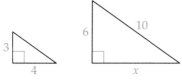

Solution **Method 1**   Use the Pythagorean theorem.

$$a^2 + b^2 = c^2 \qquad \text{Write the theorem.}$$

$$6^2 + x^2 = 10^2 \qquad \text{Substitute values.}$$

$$36 + x^2 = 100$$

$$36 + x^2 - 36 = 100 - 36$$

$$x^2 = 64$$

$$\sqrt{x^2} = \sqrt{64} \qquad \text{Take each square root.}$$

$$x = 8$$

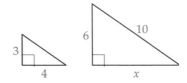

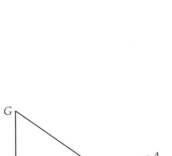

Method 2   Use similar triangles.

$$\frac{3}{4} = \frac{6}{x}$$ Write a proportion.

$$24 = 3x$$ Cross multiply.

$$\frac{24}{3} = \frac{3x}{3}$$ Divide each side by 3.

$$8 = x$$

The value of x is 8 no matter what method you use.

▼ You may need to use both methods to solve a problem.

Example 2   Find FB. $\overline{FC}$ and $\overline{CB}$ are altitudes of the triangles.

Solution

1. Find CB using the Pythagorean theorem.

$$a^2 + b^2 = c^2$$ Write the theorem.

$$3^2 + CB^2 = 5^2$$ Substitute values.

$$9 + CB^2 = 25$$

$$9 + CB^2 - 9 = 25 - 9$$ Subtract 9 from each side.

$$CB^2 = 16$$

$$\sqrt{CB^2} = \sqrt{16}$$ Find each square root.

$$CB = 4$$

2. Find FC using similar triangles.

$$\frac{9}{3} = \frac{FC}{4}$$ Write a proportion.

$$4 \cdot \frac{9}{3} = \frac{FC}{4} \cdot 4$$ Multiply each side by 4.

$$\frac{36}{3} = FC$$

$$12 = FC$$

3. $FB = CB + FC$

$$= 4 + 12$$

$$= 16$$

THINK AND DISCUSS

1. How are the acute angles of a right triangle related?

2. If one acute angle of a right triangle has measure $x°$, how would you express the measure of the other acute angle?

3. In a triangle, if two pairs of corresponding angles are congruent, are three pairs of corresponding angles congruent? Explain.

CLASS EXERCISES

Solve for x.

1. $\dfrac{x}{5} = \dfrac{12}{30}$ **2.** $\dfrac{2.5}{x} = \dfrac{7}{6}$ **3.** $\dfrac{9}{22} = \dfrac{x}{154}$ **4.** $\dfrac{a}{b} = \dfrac{x}{y}$

Complete each proportion. $\triangle ABC \sim \triangle DEC$.

5. $\dfrac{BC}{EC} = \dfrac{AC}{\blacksquare}$ **6.** $\dfrac{\blacksquare}{CB} = \dfrac{DC}{AC}$ **7.** $\dfrac{EC}{BC} = \dfrac{\blacksquare}{AB}$

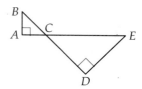

8. a. Find x using the Pythagorean theorem.

b. Find y using the Pythagorean theorem.

c. $\triangle ABC \sim$ ▨ $\sim$ ▨

d. $\triangle DBC \sim$ ▨ $\sim$ ▨

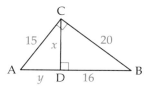

WRITTEN EXERCISES

MENTAL MATH Solve for variable x.

1. $\dfrac{4}{9} = \dfrac{12}{x}$

2. $\dfrac{x}{9} = \dfrac{7}{6}$

3. $\dfrac{1.5}{4} = \dfrac{x}{8}$

4. $\dfrac{y}{x} = \dfrac{a}{b}$

Solve for x using the Pythagorean theorem. Use the square root table on p. 579 to find the length to the nearest thousandth.

5.

6.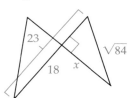

7.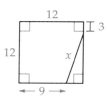

Solve for x using similar triangles. Each pair of triangles is similar.

8.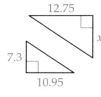

9.

10.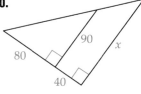

CALCULATOR Solve for x and y. Round to the nearest hundredth.

11.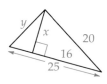

12.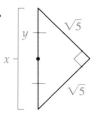

13.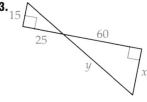

Solve.

14. A ladder is leaning against a building in such a way that the ladder touches the top of an 8-ft fence. The bottom of the ladder is 4 ft from the base of the fence. The fence is 8 ft from the building. How high up the building is the top of the ladder?

MIXED REVIEW

Determine if each is a Pythagorean triple.

1. 16, 30, 34

2. 16, 12, 15.5

Write in scientific notation.

3. 8,960,000,000,000

Find the GCF.

4. 18,48   **5.** 76,38

Write an equation and solve.

6. Four divided by twice x equals one-eighth of 12.

7. Half the product of 6 and x is four greater than x.

8. Pat missed 2% of the 50 balls pitched. How many did he miss?

PROBLEM SOLVING HINT

Draw a diagram to help visualize the problem.

15. A radio tower is 25 ft high and casts a shadow of 40 ft. At the same time, a taller tower casts a shadow of 70 ft. What is the height of the taller radio tower?

16. Ian is 160 cm tall. His image on the film of a camera is 1.6 cm. Suppose the film is 2 cm from the camera lens. How far is Ian from the camera?

Use the article at the left to answer each question.

17. a. Determine the slant height of the faces of the pyramid to the nearest hundredth.

b. Find the area of the base of the pyramid.

c. *PROJECT* Research the gromma. Tell how Egyptians used this instrument to construct right angles.

TEST YOURSELF

Solve for variable x. Round to the nearest tenth.

1.

2.

3.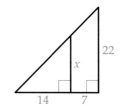

4. A rectangular box has a square base with area 16 cm². The height of the box is 7 cm. Find the length of the diagonal of a rectangular side. Use the square root table on p. 579.

5. A 42-ft tree casts a shadow of 63 ft. How long is the shadow cast by a 5-ft tall girl?

OBJECTIVE:
To discover and use
the properties of
45°-45°-90° and
30°-60°-90° right
triangles.

11-5 Special Right Triangles

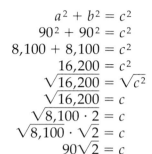

▼ A baseball diamond is a square. The distance between the bases is 90 ft. How long is a throw from home plate to second base? You can use a special right triangle and the Pythagorean theorem to find the distance.

$$a^2 + b^2 = c^2$$ Write the theorem.
$$90^2 + 90^2 = c^2$$ Substitute values.
$$8,100 + 8,100 = c^2$$
$$16,200 = c^2$$
$$\sqrt{16,200} = \sqrt{c^2}$$ Take each square root.
$$\sqrt{16,200} = c$$ Simplify the right side.
$$\sqrt{8,100 \cdot 2} = c$$
$$\sqrt{8,100} \cdot \sqrt{2} = c$$
$$90\sqrt{2} = c$$

A throw from home plate to second base is $90\sqrt{2}$ ft long.

▼ The triangle formed by the diagonal of a square is an *isosceles right triangle*. Each base angle has a measure of 45°.

45°-45°-90° Triangle	In a 45°-45°-90° right triangle, the lengths of the sides have the following relationships.
	hypotenuse = $\sqrt{2} \cdot$ leg
	leg = $\frac{\text{hypotenuse} \cdot \sqrt{2}}{2}$

▼ You can use the properties of a 45°-45°-90° triangle to determine missing lengths.

Example 1 Find x. The answer may contain a square root sign.

a.

b.

Solution

a. hypotenuse = $\sqrt{2} \cdot$ leg
$$7\sqrt{2} = x\sqrt{2}$$
$$\frac{7\sqrt{2}}{\sqrt{2}} = \frac{x\sqrt{2}}{\sqrt{2}}$$ Divide each side by $\sqrt{2}$.
$$7 = x$$

b. leg = $\frac{\text{hypotenuse} \cdot \sqrt{2}}{2}$
$$x = \frac{1}{2}(16)(\sqrt{2})$$
$$x = 8\sqrt{2}$$

▼ The 30°-60°-90° right triangle is another special right triangle.

THINK In a 30°-60°-90° right triangle, how do you know which leg is longer?

30°-60°-90° Triangle	In a 30°-60°-90° triangle, the lengths of the sides have the following relationships. hypotenuse = 2(shorter leg) longer leg = shorter leg($\sqrt{3}$)

You can use these relationships to determine missing lengths.

Example 2   **Find x and y. The answer may have a square root sign.**

a.

b.

Solution   **a.** hypotenuse = 2(shorter leg)   **Solve for x.**
$$x = 2(5)$$
$$x = 10$$

longer leg = shorter leg($\sqrt{3}$)   **Solve for y.**
$$y = \text{shorter leg}(\sqrt{3})$$
$$y = 5\sqrt{3}$$

b. longer leg = shorter leg($\sqrt{3}$)   **Solve for x.**
$$6\sqrt{3} = (x)(\sqrt{3})$$
$$\frac{6\sqrt{3}}{\sqrt{3}} = \frac{\sqrt{3}x}{\sqrt{3}}$$
$$6 = x$$

hypotenuse = 2(shorter leg)   **Solve for y.**
$$y = 2(6)$$
$$y = 12$$

THINK AND DISCUSS

1. In a 45°-45°-90° triangle, by what do you multiply each leg to get the length of the hypotenuse?

2. In a 30°-60°-90° triangle, what operation do you perform on the hypotenuse to get the length of the side opposite the 30° angle?

3. In a 30°-60°-90° triangle, what operation do you perform on the side opposite the 60° angle to get the length of the side opposite the 30° angle?

CLASS EXERCISES

Use the triangle at the right.

1. Which side is opposite $\angle A$?

2. Which side is opposite $\angle B$?

3. Which side is opposite $\angle C$?

4. Which side is the hypotenuse?

5. Which sides are the legs?

6. Which side of the triangle is the longest?

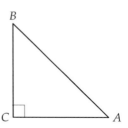

Tell whether a triangle with sides of the given lengths is 45°-45°-90°, 30°-60°-90°, or neither.

7. 6, 8, 10 **8.** 5, 5, 5√2 **9.** 15, 7.5√3, 7.5

Find each value. Answers may contain square root signs.

10. **11.** 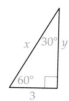 **12.**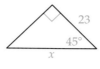

WRITTEN EXERCISES

The length of one side of the triangle is given. Find the missing measures. Answers may contain square root signs.

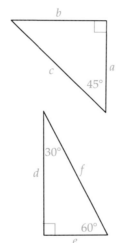

	a	*b*	*c*
1.	9		
2.		5.4	
3.			4√2
4.			3

	d	*e*	*f*
5.		2	
6.			10
7.		7	
8.	8√3		

Find each value. Answers may contain square root signs.

9. **10.** 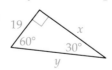 **11.**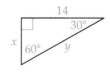

12. MENTAL MATH A square has a diagonal 6√2 in. long.

   a. Find the length of a side of the square.

   b. Find the perimeter of the square.

13. Each face on a cube has a diagonal 12 in. long.

   a. Find the length of a side of the cube to the nearest tenth.

   b. Find the surface area of the cube to the nearest hundredth.

11-5 Special Right Triangles **471**

MIXED REVIEW

Solve and check.

1. $\frac{x}{4} - 2 = 7 + x$

2. $-3.5x - 4x + 85 = x$

Solve the proportion.

3. $\frac{9.5}{x} = \frac{1.5}{0.75}$

4. Simplify $-(4x^3)^2$.

5. $-12 - (-18)$

6. A polygon with five sides is a ▨.

7. DATA FILE 6 (pp. 230–231) What percent of teens study for 2 or more hours each night?

8. All books are on sale for 40% off. Judy paid $19.99 for the new best seller. What was the original price?

14. The base of a cone has a diameter of 8. The cone slants on a 60° angle and has a slant height of 8. Find the height of the cone to the nearest thousandth. Use the square root table.

15. △ABC is equilateral. Each side has a length of 52 in. Find the altitude. The answer may contain a square root sign.

16. The length of the hypotenuse of a 30°-60°-90° triangle is 20*a*. What is the length of the shorter leg? What is the length of the longer leg? Your answers may contain square root signs.

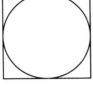

17. Use the diagram at the left. The diameter of the circle is 16 cm. How much larger is the area of the square than the area of the circle? Use 3.14 for *π*.

18. *CALCULATOR* A 15-ft ladder is leaning against a wall at a 45° angle. To the nearest tenth, how high above the ground is the ladder touching the wall?

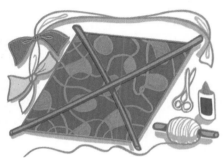

19. Janet is building a kite in the shape of a square. Each side of the square is 18 in. To the nearest inch, how much wood does Janet need to make the diagonals?

20. *DATA FILE 11 (pp. 450–451)* A skydiver jumps out of a plane at 2,750 ft. He wants to hit a marker 1.25 mi away. He falls at a rate of 10 ft/s. To the nearest tenth of a minute, how long will it take the jumper to hit the marker?

Critical Thinking
EXPLORING LOGIC

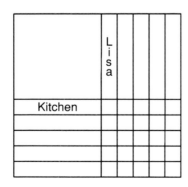

▼ To solve a logic problem, organize the information in a chart like the one at the left. Each of Mrs. Stephan's five children cleans one room each week. The rooms cleaned are the living room, family room, kitchen, bathroom, and a bedroom. Who cleans each room?

Copy and complete the chart to solve.

1. Lisa does not have to scrub the kitchen floor.

2. Nicole never makes her bed.

3. Robert and Eric always vacuum under the couches.

4. The family room joins the kitchen. Eric and Jo Ann enjoy talking to each other while they clean.

5. Only the living room and family room contain couches.

11-6 Trigonometric Ratios

▼ *Trigonometry* means triangle measurement. A *trigonometric ratio* is a ratio of the measures of two sides of a right triangle.

Example 1 Find each ratio.

a. $\dfrac{CA}{CB}$ **b.** $\dfrac{CA}{AB}$ **c.** $\dfrac{CB}{AB}$

Solution   **a.** $\dfrac{3}{4}$ **b.** $\dfrac{3}{5}$ **c.** $\dfrac{4}{5}$

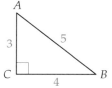

▼ Trigonometric ratios have special names.

Trigonometric Ratios	
	tangent of $\angle A = \dfrac{\text{length of side opposite } \angle A}{\text{length of side adjacent to } \angle A}$
	sine of $\angle A = \dfrac{\text{length of side opposite } \angle A}{\text{hypotenuse}}$
	cosine of $\angle A = \dfrac{\text{length of side adjacent to } \angle A}{\text{hypotenuse}}$

You can write the terms tangent, sine, and cosine using the abbreviations *tan, sin,* and *cos.* A shorter version of the trigonometric ratios follows.

$$\tan = \frac{\text{opposite}}{\text{adjacent}} \qquad \sin = \frac{\text{opposite}}{\text{hypotenuse}} \qquad \cos = \frac{\text{adjacent}}{\text{hypotenuse}}$$

Example 2 Find each trigonometric ratio.

　　　　a. $\tan Y$　　　　　　**b.** $\cos X$

Solution　　**a.** $\tan Y = \dfrac{\text{opposite}}{\text{adjacent}} = \dfrac{12}{5}$

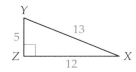

　　　　　　　b. $\cos X = \dfrac{\text{adjacent}}{\text{hypotenuse}} = \dfrac{12}{13}$

▼ If you know the measure of an acute angle of a right triangle, you can use a table of trigonometric ratios to approximate values of the tangent, sine, and cosine of the angle.

Example 3 Find the tangent, sine, and cosine of 42° using the table on p. 580.

Solution　　$\tan 42° \approx 0.9004$　　　$\sin 42° \approx 0.6691$　　　$\cos 42° \approx 0.7431$

Angle	Sin	Cos	Tan
51°	.7771	.6293	1.2349
52°	.7880	.6157	1.2799
53°	.7986	.6018	1.3270
54°	.8090	.5878	1.3764
55°	.8192	.5736	1.4281

▼ You can use a table of trigonometric ratios to approximate the measure of an angle when you know the sine, cosine, or tangent.

Example 4 Sin A = .7986. Find $m\angle A$.

Solution　　Use the table. Find .7986 in the sin column.
　　　　　　　$m\angle A = 53°$.

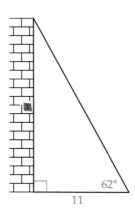

Example 5 A carpenter needs a ladder to do repair work on a building. The base of the ladder is 11 ft away from the building and forms a 62° angle with the ground. To the nearest foot, how high up on the building must the ladder rest?

Solution Draw a diagram.

$$\tan 62° = \frac{x}{11}$$ Use the tangent ratio.

$$1.8807 \approx \frac{x}{11}$$

$$11(1.8807) = \left(\frac{x}{11}\right)(11)$$ Multiply each side by 11.

$$20.6877 = x$$

$$21 \approx x$$ Round to the nearest whole number.

The ladder must rest about 21 ft up on the building.

▼ You may need to use more than one trigonometric ratio to find measures in a triangle.

Example 6 Use the triangle at the left. Find x, y, and z in $\triangle ABC$. Round to the nearest hundredth.

Solution **1.** Find x.

$$x = 90 - 38$$ $\angle A$ and $\angle B$ are

$$= 52$$ complementary.

2. Find y.

$$\sin 38° = \frac{y}{33}$$ $\sin = \frac{\text{opposite}}{\text{hypotenuse}}$

$$0.6157 \approx \frac{y}{33}$$ Substitute the value from the table.

$$33(0.6157) \approx \left(\frac{y}{33}\right)(33)$$ Multiply each side by 33.

$$20.3181 \approx y$$ Round.

$$20.32 \approx y$$

3. Find z.

$$\tan 38° = \frac{20.3181}{z}$$ $\tan = \frac{\text{opposite}}{\text{adjacent}}$

$$0.7813 \approx \frac{20.3181}{z}$$ Substitute the value from the table.

$$z(0.7813) = \left(\frac{20.3181}{z}\right)(z)$$ Multiply each side by z.

$$0.7813\, z = 20.3181$$

$$\frac{0.7813\, z}{0.7813} = \frac{20.3181}{0.7813}$$ Divide each side by 0.7813.

$$z = 26.005504$$

$$\approx 26.01$$ Round.

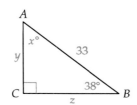

Angle	Sin	Cos	Tan
36°	.5878	.8090	.7265
37°	.6018	.7986	.7536
38°	.6157	.7880	.7813
39°	.6293	.7771	.8098
40°	.6428	.7660	.8391

CLASS EXERCISES

Use the table of trigonometric ratios on p. 580 to find each value.

1. sin 86° **2.** cos 16° **3.** tan 53°

Find $m\angle A$.

4. sin $A = 0.8480$ **5.** tan $A = 3.7321$ **6.** cos $A = 0.5$

State a trigonometric equation using the given values.

7.   **8.**  **9.**

Find x, y, and z for each triangle. Round to the nearest hundredth. Use the table of trigonometric ratios on p. 580.

10. 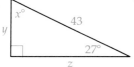 **11.**   **12.**

WRITTEN EXERCISES

Use the table of trigonometric ratios on p. 580 to find each value.

1. sin 10° **2.** cos 80° **3.** tan 15°

4. tan 55° **5.** sin 78° **6.** cos 60°

Find $m\angle B$. Use the table of trigonometric ratios on p. 580.

7. sin $B = 0.9945$ **8.** cos $B = 0.7660$ **9.** tan $B = 1.9626$

MENTAL MATH Use 45°-45°-90° and 30°-60°-90° right triangles to find each value. Your answer may contain a square root sign.

10. tan 45° **11.** tan 60° **12.** sin 30°

State a trigonometric equation using the given values.

13.   **14.** 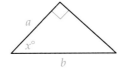 **15.**

Find x, y, and z for each triangle. Round to the nearest hundredth. Use the table of trigonometric ratios on p. 580.

16.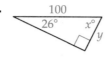

17.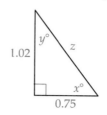

18.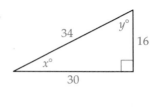

19.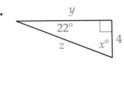

20.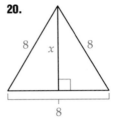

21.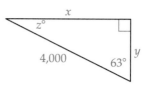

22. A navigator brings you a map charting a ship's course. She wants to know how far it is, to the nearest mile, from the island to the mainland port. Use the diagram at the left.

23. A Boeing 747 climbs continuously at a 30° angle to a height of 35,000 ft. To the nearest tenth of a mile, how far has the plane traveled to reach that elevation? *Hint:* 5,280 ft = 1 mi.

24. *DATA FILE 11 (pp. 450–451)* A skydiver jumps from 22,500 ft. He hits a marker 10,224 ft away. To the nearest degree, what angle does the skydiver make with the ground?

25. A man 6 ft tall paces 75 ft from the base of a tree. He uses a protractor to approximate the angle from his eye to the top of the tree. He finds that this angle is about 25°. Find the height of the tree to the nearest foot.

TEST YOURSELF

Tell whether a triangle with sides of the given lengths is 45°-45°-90°, 30°-60°-90°, or neither.

1. 10, 5, $5\sqrt{3}$　　　**2.** 8, $8\sqrt{2}$, 8　　　**3.** 6, 8, 10

Find x, y, and z for each triangle. Round to the nearest hundredth.

4.

5.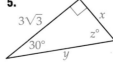

6.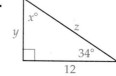

OBJECTIVE:
To apply right triangle concepts and trigonometric ratios to precision drawings.

11-7 *Precision Drawing*

■ Architects and designers often require accurate plans and drawings. Professionals frequently use computers with graphic capability to help them with their work. Even so, there are many occasions when precision drawing must be done by hand.

▼

THINK What are some professions that require precision drawing?

■ You can draw an angle accurately using a compass and a ruler.

Example 1 **Draw a right angle using a ruler and a compass.**

Solution A triangle whose sides measure 3 units, 4 units, and 5 units is a right triangle. Draw a right triangle with these dimensions.

1. Draw $\overline{AB}$, 3 cm long. $A \bullet\!\!-\!\!-\!\!-\!\!-\!\!-\!\!-\!\!\bullet B$

2. Use a compass with a radius of 4 cm. With center at B, draw an arc above B.

$A \bullet\!\!-\!\!-\!\!-\!\!-\!\!-\!\!-\!\!-\!\!\bullet B$

3. Use a compass with a radius of 5 cm. With center at A, draw an arc that crosses the arc above B. Label the point of intersection as C.

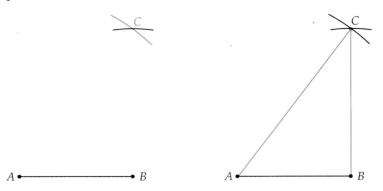

Connect the three points to form $\triangle ABC$. By the converse of the Pythagorean theorem, $\triangle ABC$ is a right triangle. Therefore, $\angle ABC$ is a right angle.

■ You can draw any angle by finding the tangent of the angle and by predetermining the length of the adjacent side.

Example 2 Draw a 23° angle. Use a protractor, a ruler, and the table of trigonometric ratios on p. 580.

Solution

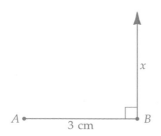

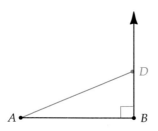

1. Choose a length, say 3 cm, for the side adjacent to the 23° angle. Draw $\overline{AB}$ with length 3 cm. Use a protractor to draw ∠B with measure 90°. Let x represent the unknown length.

2. Solve for x to determine the length of the side opposite the 23° angle.

$$\tan = \frac{\text{opposite}}{\text{adjacent}}$$ Use the tangent ratio.

$$\tan 23° = \frac{x}{3}$$ Substitute values.

$$0.4245 = \frac{x}{3}$$ Find tan 23° in the table.

$$3(0.4245) = \frac{x}{3}(3)$$ Multiply each side by 3.

$$1.2735 = x$$ Round to the nearest tenth.

$$x \approx 1.3$$

3. Mark a point 1.3 cm from B. Label the point as D. Then draw $\overline{AD}$.

$$∠A \approx 23°.$$

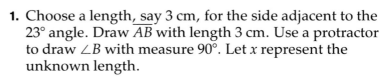

■■■■■■ Decision Making ■ **DECISION MAKING** ■ Decision Making ■ Decision Making ■ Decision Making ■

PRECISION DRAWING

■ **COLLECT DATA**

1. Visit a store that sells drafting supplies. Take along the compass, ruler, and protractor that you use in school.

   a. Do the inch and centimeter marks on your ruler perfectly match those on the best quality ruler found in the store?

   b. Is your protractor the same size as the best one in the store?

■ **ANALYZE DATA**

2. Can the quality of the instruments you use affect the accuracy of the drawings you make? Explain.

3. Can the width of the markings on a ruler or compass affect the accuracy of a drawing? Explain.

4. Can the fineness of your pencil point affect the accuracy of a drawing? Explain.

CLASS EXERCISES

Find the tangent of each angle. Use the table of trigonometric ratios on p. 580.

1. $87°$ **2.** $15°$ **3.** $72°$

Solve for x. Use the table of trigonometric ratios on p. 580.

4. $\tan 47° = \frac{x}{4}$ **5.** $\tan 63° = \frac{x}{7}$ **6.** $\frac{x}{5} = \tan 36°$

WRITTEN EXERCISES

 Use a CALCULATOR where appropriate.

Use a compass, a ruler, and the table of trigonometric ratios to draw an angle with the given measure. Check using a protractor.

1. $20°$ **2.** $25°$ **3.** $85°$ **4.** $50°$ **5.** $76°$
6. $35°$ **7.** $145°$ **8.** $176°$ **9.** $138°$ **10.** $121°$

11. Use a compass and a ruler to draw a right triangle with sides of measure 5 units, 12 units, and 13 units.

  a. Label the triangle as shown. Use the table of trigonometric ratios on p. 580 to find $m\angle A$ and $m\angle B$.

  b. Check your results using a protractor.

■ *Decision Making* ■ *Decision Making* ■ *Decision Making* ■ *Decision Making* ■ *Decision Making* ■ *Decision Making* ■

5. Would inaccuracies in angles and lengths in a drawing be more easily detected in small or in large drawings? Explain.

■ **MAKE DECISIONS**

6. Do you think it would be more accurate to draw a right triangle using a compass and ruler with the measurements in the ratio $3 : 4 : 5$, $6 : 8 : 10$, or $9 : 12 : 15$? Explain.

7. Suppose you are using a compass, ruler, and trigonometric ratios to draw angles. Would a table that expresses the ratios to hundredths or one that rounds ratios to the nearest tenth help you make a more accurate drawing? Explain.

Practice

Find each square root.

1. $\sqrt{169}$
2. $\sqrt{4x \cdot 4x}$
3. $\sqrt{\dfrac{81}{4}}$
4. $\sqrt{a^2 b^2}$
5. $\sqrt{\dfrac{x^2}{y^2}}$
6. $\sqrt{625x^{10}y^8}$
7. $\sqrt{400x^6}$
8. $\sqrt{529c^2}$
9. $\sqrt{121c^4}$
10. $\sqrt{2{,}500}$

Approximate each square root to the nearest integer.

11. $\sqrt{2}$
12. $-\sqrt{5}$
13. $\sqrt{10}$
14. $\sqrt{47}$
15. $\sqrt{96}$

State whether each number is rational or irrational.

16. $\sqrt{11}$
17. $-\sqrt{9}$
18. $4.1472\ldots$
19. $\sqrt{0.04}$
20. $\sqrt{81}$

Determine whether each is a Pythagorean triple.

21. 10, 11, 12
22. 2, 3, 4
23. 1.2, 0.5, 1.3
24. 30, 40, 50
25. $\sqrt{16}, \sqrt{25}, \sqrt{36}$
26. 5, 12, 13
27. 17, 8, 15
28. 1, 3, 5

Identify each triangle as 45°-45°-90°, 30°-60°-90°, or neither.

29. 5.2, $5.2\sqrt{2}$, 5.2
30. 8, 4, $4\sqrt{3}$
31. 15, 20, 25

Use the Pythagorean theorem to find x.

32.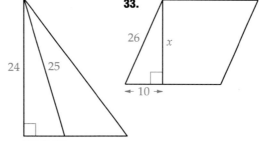

33.

34.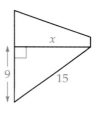

Use similar triangles to find y.

35.

36.

37.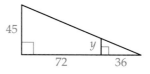

Find each missing length. Answers may contain square root signs.

38.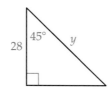

39.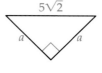

40.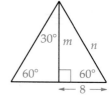

Problem Solving Practice

Solve. Use an appropriate strategy or a combination of strategies.

PROBLEM SOLVING STRATEGIES

Look for a Pattern
Guess and Test
Simplify the Problem
Make an Organized List
Work Backwards
Account for All Possibilities
Make a Table
Write an Equation
Solve by Graphing
Draw a Diagram
Make a Model
Solve Another Way
Simulate the Problem

1. A car manufacturer offers exterior colors of white, blue, red, black, and silver. The manufacturer offers the same colors, plus tweed, for the interior. The manufacturer offers pinstripes, but only for cars with black or silver exteriors. How many different styles are there to choose from?

2. *The Battle of Gettysburg* is the largest painting in the world. The painting is 410 ft. long and 70 ft. wide. A tennis court is 78 ft. by 27 ft. How many tennis courts can fit inside the world's largest painting?

3. In $\triangle XYZ$, $m\angle X$ is 29° less than $m\angle Y$, and $m\angle Z$ is 52° less than $m\angle Y$. Find the measure of each angle.

4. Mt. Vesuvius is a volcano in Italy. Its crater is 7,920 ft in diameter. What is the area of the crater?

5. **CALCULATOR** The length of the Golden Gate Bridge in San Francisco, California, is 4,200 ft. How long, to the nearest hundredth of a minute, would it take a car driving at a continuous rate of 35 mi/h to cross the bridge? *Hint:* 5,280 ft = 1 mi.

6. **DATA FILE 10 (pp. 404–405)** How much more circular area, to the nearest square meter, does a snowshoe hare require than a Northern flying squirrel requires? Use 3.14 for π.

7. First-class letters cost $.29 for the first ounce and $.23 for each additional ounce. Warren spent $2.82 to send a first-class letter. How many ounces did his letter weigh?

8. I am a number less than 100. I am the product of two prime numbers. If you reverse my digits I am prime. The sum of my digits is a one-digit prime. One of my digits is a square number. What number am I?

9. Each face of cube A has a diagonal of $10\sqrt{2}$ cm. Each face of cube B has a diagonal of $7\sqrt{2}$ cm. How much more liquid will cube A hold than cube B?

10. Madison Square Garden in New York City is built in the shape of a circle. Its diameter is 404 ft. The stadium accommodates 20,234 spectators. To the nearest hundredth square foot, how much area does this allow for each person? Use 3.14 for π.

11. Three integers have a sum of 48. The greater integer is four more than the middle integer. The least integer is ten less than the middle integer. Find the integers.

Chapter 11 Review

Match each word with the example that illustrates its meaning.

1. square root symbol
2. principal square root
3. irrational number
4. Pythagorean theorem
5. in a 45°-45°-90° triangle
6. in a 30°-60°-90° triangle
7. tangent A
8. cosine A
9. sine A

a. hypotenuse = $\sqrt{2}$(length of leg)
b. $a^2 + b^2 = c^2$
c. $\dfrac{\text{opposite}}{\text{adjacent}}$
d. $\sqrt{4} = +2$
e. $\dfrac{\text{opposite}}{\text{hypotenuse}}$
f. 2.6457513 . . .
g. $\sqrt{}$
h. hypotenuse = 2(shorter side)
i. $\dfrac{\text{adjacent}}{\text{hypotenuse}}$

Finding Square Roots   11-1

To find the square root, think of the squares. You can also use a calculator or a table of squares.

Find each square root. Use the square root table on p. 579.

10. $\sqrt{196}$ 11. $\sqrt{64p^2}$ 12. $\sqrt{3}$ 13. $\sqrt{(x-2)^2}$ 14. $\sqrt{625}$ 15. $\sqrt{31+5}$

Problem Solving   11-2

To solve a problem, sometimes it is helpful to act it out.

16. A class of 31 students counted off by 1s beginning with the number one. Each student who counted a multiple of 5 stood up. This process was repeated. Those who were standing were skipped. After the fourth counting, how many students were standing?

Pythagorean Theorem   11-3

To use the Pythagorean theorem to find unknown parts of a right triangle, substitute the known values in the formula $a^2 + b^2 = c^2$, and solve for the unknown.

Write an equation. Solve for x.

17.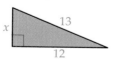

18.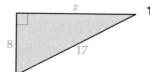

19.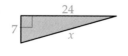

20.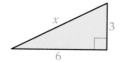

To find values in similar right triangles, you can use the Pythagorean theorem or write a proportion. Sometimes you will use both.

Solve for x. Each pair of triangles is similar.

21.

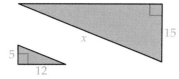

22.

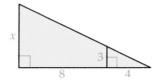

23.

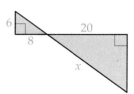

To find missing lengths in a 45°-45°-90° triangle, use the relationships

$$\text{hypotenuse} = \sqrt{2} \cdot \text{leg} \qquad \text{leg} = \frac{\text{hypotenuse} \cdot \sqrt{2}}{2}.$$

To find missing lengths in a 30°-60°-90° triangle, use the relationships

$$\text{hypotenuse} = 2(\text{shorter leg}) \qquad \text{longer leg} = \text{shorter leg} \, (\sqrt{3}).$$

Find each value. Answers may contain square root signs.

24.

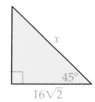

25.

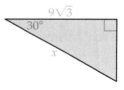

26.

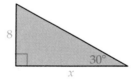

27.

To find measures in a right triangle, use a trigonometric ratio.

$$\tan A = \frac{\text{opposite}}{\text{adjacent}} \qquad \cos A = \frac{\text{adjacent}}{\text{hypotenuse}} \qquad \sin A = \frac{\text{opposite}}{\text{hypotenuse}}$$

Find each missing length or angle measure. Round to the nearest thousandth. Use the table of trigonometric ratios on p. 580.

28.

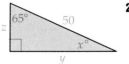

29.

30.

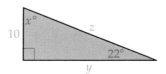

31.

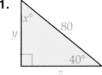

32. A ladder is 8 ft away from a building and forms a 54° angle with the ground. What is the length of the ladder?

33. A train in the mountains rises 8 ft for every 200 ft it moves along the track. Find the angle of elevation of the tracks.

Find each square root.

1. $\sqrt{64}$ **2.** $\sqrt{169}$ **3.** $\sqrt{\dfrac{36}{49}}$ **4.** $\sqrt{(x+5)^2}$

Solve for x. Calculate each length to the nearest hundredth.

5.   **6.** 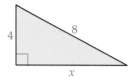 **7.** 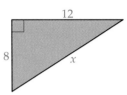 **8.**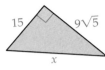

Determine if the lengths can be the sides of a right triangle.

9. 9, 12, 14 **10.** 1.1, 6.0, 6.1 **11.** $\dfrac{3}{5}, \dfrac{4}{5}, 1$ **12.** 8.1, 15.2, 18.6

Solve for x. Answers may contain square root signs.

13.   **14.**   **15.** 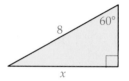 **16.**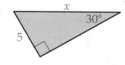

Use the table of trigonometric ratios on p. 580 to find each value.

17. $\cos 25°$ **18.** $\tan 40°$ **19.** $\sin 73°$ **20.** $\tan 88°$

Find each missing length or angle measure. Round angles to the nearest whole number and lengths to the nearest thousandth. Use the table of trigonometric ratios on p. 580.

21. 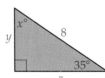 **22.** 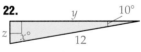 **23.** 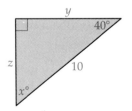 **24.**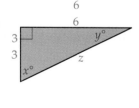

Solve.

25. A square is 6 in. on each side. What is the measure of the diagonal of the square?

26. The captain of a ship sights a lighthouse. The angle of elevation is 12°. The captain knows that the lighthouse is 24 m above sea level. What is the distance from the ship to the lighthouse?

Choose the correct answer. Write A, B, C, or D.

1. Solve $\frac{2}{3}x - 5 = 3x + 9 - \frac{1}{3}x$.
   A. -7
   B. 7
   C. $3\frac{1}{2}$
   D. not given

2. Solve.

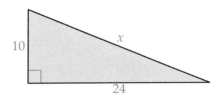

   A. 17
   B. 26
   C. 28
   D. not given

3. Find the y-intercept.
   $2x + 3y = 12$
   A. 2
   B. 12
   C. 3
   D. not given

4. Solve.

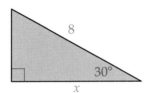

   A. 4
   B. $4\sqrt{3}$
   C. $8\sqrt{3}$
   D. not given

5. $\angle ABC$ and $\angle CBD$ are complementary angles. $m\angle ABC = 73°$. Find $m\angle CBD$.
   A. 107°
   B. 17°
   C. 27°
   D. not given

6. Simplify $\sqrt{32x^3 \cdot 2x^5}$.
   A. $64x^8$
   B. $16x^2\sqrt{2}$
   C. $8x^4$
   D. not given

7. Solve $\frac{a}{16} = \frac{15}{48}$.
   A. 5
   B. 10
   C. 24
   D. not given

8. Find the area.

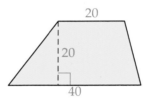

   A. 400 sq. units
   B. 300 sq. units
   C. 600 sq. units
   D. not given

9. The area of a triangle is 20 cm². The height is 5 cm. What is the base?
   A. 4 cm
   B. 8 cm
   C. 10 cm
   D. not given

10. Solve.

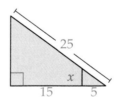

   A. 3.75
   B. 5
   C. 8.5
   D. not given

11. Name the inequality for the model.

   A. $x < 1$
   B. $x \geq 1$
   C. $x \leq 1$
   D. not given

12. Determine the slope of the line containing $(-2,3)$ and $(5,-1)$.
   A. $\frac{5}{6}$
   B. $-\frac{4}{7}$
   C. 2
   D. not given

BASEBALL STADIUMS

TEAM	STADIUM	SEATING CAPACITY
ATLANTA BRAVES	Atlanta–Fulton County Stadium	52,003
BALTIMORE ORIOLES	Memorial Stadium	54,017
BOSTON RED SOX	Fenway Park	34,182
CALIFORNIA ANGELS	Anaheim Stadium	64,593
CHICAGO CUBS	Wrigley Field	39,600
CHICAGO WHITE SOX	Comiskey Park	44,087
CINCINNATI REDS	Riverfront Stadium	52,392
CLEVELAND INDIANS	Cleveland Stadium	74,483
DETROIT TIGERS	Tiger Stadium	52,416
HOUSTON ASTROS	Astrodome	45,000
KANSAS CITY ROYALS	Royals Stadium	40,625
LOS ANGELES DODGERS	Dodger Stadium	56,000
MILWAUKEE BREWERS	Milwaukee County Stadium	53,192
MINNESOTA TWINS	Hubert H. Humphrey Metrodome	55,883
MONTREAL EXPOS	Olympic Stadium	59,149
NEW YORK METS	Shea Stadium	55,300
NEW YORK YANKEES	Yankee Stadium	57,545
OAKLAND A's	Oakland Coliseum	49,219
PHILADELPHIA PHILLIES	Veterans Stadium	64,538
PITTSBURGH PIRATES	Three Rivers Stadium	58,727
SAN DIEGO PADRES	Jack Murphy Stadium	58,433
SAN FRANCISCO GIANTS	Candlestick Park	58,000
SEATTLE MARINERS	Kingdome	58,150
ST. LOUIS CARDINALS	Busch Stadium	54,224
TEXAS RANGERS	Arlington Stadium	43,508
TORONTO BLUE JAYS	Skydome	53,000

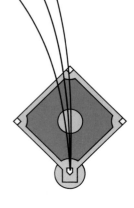

+ 2 ft

+275 ft Altitude

+ 2 ft

+275 ft Altitude

At higher altitudes where the air is thinner, a baseball faces less resistance. A 275-ft rise in altitude adds about 2 ft to the distance an average home run will travel.

There is a 30% chance that a base runner will be caught if trying to steal a base.

Statistics and Probability

CHAPTER 12

YEAR	1928	1932	1936	1948	1952	1956	1960	1964	1968	1972	1976	1980	1984	1988	1992
MALE	5:01.6	4:48.4	4:44.5	4:41.0	4:30.7	4:27.3	4:18.3	4:12.2	4:09.0	4:00.27	3:51.93	3:51.31	3:51.23	3:46.25	3:45
FEMALE	5:42.8	5:28.5	5:26.4	5:17.8	5:12.1	4:54.6	4:50.6	4:43.3	4:31.8	4:19.44	4:09.89	4:08.76	4:07.10	4:03.85	4:07.18

OLYMPIC RECORD TIMES FOR 400-m FREESTYLE SWIMMING (min.)

Think about it...

Look at the data for the Olympic records in the 400-m freestyle swimming competition. Why do you think the times for this Olympic event have gone down since 1928? Do you think the times will continue to go down?

USA

1988 WINTER OLYMPICS

Brian Boitano's scores for Technical Merit in Men's Figure Skating:

5.9
5.9
5.9
5.9
5.9
5.8
5.8
5.8
5.8

OBJECTIVE:
To calculate the
measures of central
tendency and select
the most appropriate
measure for a given
situation.

12-1 Mean, Median, and Mode

▼ A company's employees stated that average weekly wages were $200. Owners argued that wages averaged $300. The personnel department insisted that wages were $250. Each group is correct.

In statistics we use three *measures of central tendency* to describe data characteristics: *mean, median,* and *mode*. The company's weekly salary data are shown below.

Employee Wages (in dollars)	200, 200, 200, 200, 200, 200, 200, 200, 200 250, 250, 250, 250, 250, 250 350, 350 500, 500 1,000

▼ To find the mode, group all wages of the same amount together. Wages of $200 appear most often. The mode is 200. The employees used the mode as the average.

THINK Why does it help to group wages of the same amount together?

Mode	The mode is the data item that occurs most often.

▼ The owners divided the total wages by the total number of employees, $6,000 \div 20 = 300$, to get the mean.

▼ To find the median, order the wages for all the employees. Find the middle number. If there is an even number of data items, add the two middle numbers. Then divide by 2 to find the midpoint. The median is 250. Personnel used the median as the average.

THINK The best average in a situation is the one that best reflects what is most typical. Which average reflects a typical salary? Why?

Median	The median is the middle value in a set of data.

▼ Some data have more than one mode. Some data have no mode.

Example 1 Find the mode for each set of data.

a. 2 5 3 3 4 5 6 5 3 4 2 7

b. 6 3 2 5 6 4 4 2 3 5

Solution **a.** 7 6 5 5 5 4 4 3 3 3 2 2   Group like numbers.

Bimodal data have two modes. The modes of these data are 5 and 3.

b. 6 6 5 5 4 4 3 3 2 2   Group like numbers.

There is no mode.   All numbers are listed the same number of times.

▼ You can use the measures of central tendency to describe various situations.

Example 2 **Is the mean, median, or mode the best average for each situation? Explain.**

    a. the favorite rock group of the Freshman class

    b. the time it takes each student to get to school

    c. the cost of houses in your community

Solution   **a.** Mode; The mode is useful in determining the most frequently chosen category. Mode is the preferred statistic when the data are not numerical.

    b. Mean; The mean is useful in situations that do not use unusually large or small numbers that distort the results.

    c. Median; This measure tells that half the data items are above and half below the average. The median is used when extreme measures distort the mean.

▼ *Range* is a measure of data dispersion.

Range	The range of a set of data is the difference between the greatest and least values in the set.

Example 3 **Find the range in the following set of data.**

    car prices: $8,750; $24,560; $16,230; $26,990; $12,400

Solution $26,990 - $8,750 = $18,240   Subtract the least value from the greatest.

CLASS EXERCISES

Find the mean, median, mode, and range of each of the following.

1. 1 1 2 2 3 3 4 4 4 4 5 5 6 7 8

2. 10   13   15   15   16   16

3. 50   50   50   50   60   70   70   70   90   90   100   100   100   100

4. 3   3   3   3

5. 59   63   48   50   85

What is the best average for each situation? Explain.

6. the average height of the students in the class

7. the average scores of candidates on a scholarship examination

8. the average scores of candidates on a driver's education test

9. the average earnings of 14-year-old students

WRITTEN EXERCISES

Find the mean, median, mode, and range for each set of data.

1. golf scores   5 5 5 6 3 3 4 7

2. diving scores   9.7 9.8 9.2 9.9 8.9 8.7 8.8

3. miles per gallon   17.8 22.5 27.0 23.5 18.9 16.7 24.8 19.0 23.0

4. allowance   3.50 5.50 2.00 5.00 2.75 3.00 4.00 4.50 3.00 3.50

MENTAL MATH **Find the mean, median, mode, and range for each set of data.**

5. 0 0 1 1 2 2 2 3 3 4 4

6. 1 1 2 2 3 3 3 4 5 6

7. 2 2 2 3 4 5 6 6 7 8

8. 1 3 3 4 6 6 6 8 8

CALCULATOR **Find the mean, median, mode, and range for each set of data.**

9. 76 84 88 90 78 80 84 88 92 80 86 84

10. 135 170 165 170 185 165 170 175 160 150 145

11. 98 97 101 104 105 102 103 100 101 99

Solve.

12. A student timed the length of telephone calls made over one weekend.

    Minutes of calls   10   2   11   4   20   12   16   9   14   2
                             16   13   35   5   18   4

    a. Find the mean, median, and mode for the length of the calls.

    b. Which average best reflects the typical phone call? Explain.

    c. Find the range of the length of the calls.

13. A basketball player made the following points per game.
    10 5 8 15 7 9 3 30 3

    a. Find the mean, the median, and the mode.

    b. Which average best reflects a typical game? Explain.

MIXED REVIEW

Find each answer.

1. Find the area of a circle with a diameter of 6.5 in.

2. Find the surface area of a rectangular prism that is 3 ft × 6 ft × 18 ft.

3. Find sin *A*.

4. Find tan *B*.

Use the table for Questions 5 and 6.

Rainfall (in.)	1	1	3	3	2
Day	1	2	3	4	5

5. On which day or days did the most rain fall?

6. On which day or days did the least rain fall?

7. The cost of taking a taxi is $1 plus $.11 per $\frac{1}{10}$ mi. What is the cost of a trip that is $5\frac{3}{5}$ mi?

14. In a classroom experiment each student estimated when one minute had elapsed. The results of their estimates, in seconds, are listed below.

57 59 56 54 61 60 63 55 59 51 65 58 69 62 63
57 54 64 58 55 64 61 63 60

  a. Find the mean, the median, and the mode.

  b. Which average best reflects a typical estimate? Explain.

Would you use the mean, the median, or the mode for each situation? Explain.

15. the heights of the members of the basketball team

16. the distance members of your class live from the school

17. the rainfall for the month of August in your community

18. the number of times each class member went to a mall last week

19. the cost of new cars

20. the amount of TV each student watches each week

21. the amount of time spent doing homework by the members of your class

22. *WRITE* a paragraph describing three situations in which the mode, the mean, and the median would each be the most appropriate measure of central tendency.

23. *PROJECT* Record the age of each member of your class in years and months. Find the mean, the median, and the mode. Which measure is the most representative?

24. *DATA FILE 12 (pp. 486–487)* Use the score for Brian Boitano to calculate each of the following.

  a. Find the mean, the median, and the mode of his scores.

  b. Which average best reflects a typical score? Explain.

25. A student had the following scores on exams in her history class: 83, 76, 92, 76, 93.

  a. The teacher allows the student to decide which measure of central tendency to use as an average. Which measure do you recommend? Explain.

  b. There is one more exam. What score must the student make to raise her average to 85 if using median as the average?

  c. What score must the student make to raise the average to 85 if using the mean as the average?

  d. *WRITE* a paragraph explaining which measure of central tendency you consider the most representative of the student's grades. What measure would you choose for your grades?

OBJECTIVE:
To arrange data into
line plots and
frequency tables.

12-2 Line Plots and Frequency Tables

THINK What does more
than one x in a column
represent?

▼ In a survey, 25 students were stopped in the hallway and asked how many books they were carrying. Their responses were:
2, 0, 4, 1, 2, 3, 1, 0, 1, 6, 4, 1, 0, 2, 5, 1, 4, 3, 1, 6, 2, 5, 4, 3, 1.

The *line plot* shows the data.
An × represents one student.

The greatest number of ×s
are above the number 1. The
mode is 1.

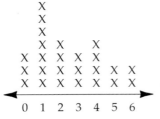

```
                    X
                    X
                    X
              X  X     X
           X  X  X  X
           X  X  X  X  X  X  X
           X  X  X  X  X  X
        <------------------------>
           0  1  2  3  4  5  6
```

Line Plot	A line plot shows data on a number line. You place an x for each response above the category of the response.

NOTES & QUOTES

*Statistical thinking will one
day be as necessary for
efficient citizenship as the
ability to read and write.*
–H. G. Wells (1866–1946)

▼ A *frequency distribution* is another way to organize data. Instead of the ×s of the line plot, you write the frequency of a particular response to correspond to the type of response.

The table shows the frequency distribution for the book survey.

Number of books	n	0	1	2	3	4	5	6
Number of students	f	3	7	4	3	4	2	2

You can see that three students carried no books, seven carried 1 book, and so on. The greatest frequency is seven, so 1 is the mode.

Frequency Distribution	A frequency distribution is a listing of data that pairs each data item with the number of times it occurs.

▼ You can construct a frequency table from a tally.

Example 1 **Arrange the data in a frequency table.**

7 2 5 4 1 6 5 2 5 1
3 6 2 3 4 5 2 6 3 4

Solution 1. Determine the values for *n*. Then prepare a tally chart.

2. Count the tally marks for each value. Record that number as the frequency.

n	1	2	3	4	5	6	7
Tally	//	////	///	///	////	///	/
f	2	4	3	3	4	3	1

▼ Sometimes you need to find the mean, median, and mode from a frequency distribution.

Example 2 Find the mean, median, and mode.

n	0	1	2	3	4
f	2	3	5	4	1

Solution **a.** To find the mean, multiply the number (n) times the frequency (f) for all n. Add the products. Divide by the total of the f.

$$\frac{2(0) + 3(1) + 5(2) + 4(3) + 1(4)}{2 + 3 + 5 + 4 + 1} = \frac{29}{15} = 1.9\overline{3}$$

The mean is $1.9\overline{3}$.

b. To find the median, list each number (n) f times. Then find the middle number.

0 0 1 1 1 2 2 2 2 2 3 3 3 3 4

There are 15 items. The eighth one is in the middle. The median is 2.

c. The mode is 2, the number with the highest frequency.

CLASS EXERCISES

Draw a line plot for each set of data. Find the mean, median, and mode.

1. 7 11 10 10 8 11 9 7 9 8 11 11

2. 5 0 2 1 4 3 4 0 2 5 4 3 2 0 4

Find the mean, median, and mode for each.

3.	x	f		4.	x	f		5.	x	f		6.	x	f
	0	3			16	2			2	1			1	1
	1	2			17	5			4	3			2	2
	2	2			18	4			6	2			3	2
	3	1			19	2			8	3			4	2
	4	2			20	1			10	1			5	2
									12	3			6	1

Make a frequency table for each set of data. Determine the mode of each distribution, if one exists.

7. 25 29 28 28 30 25 26 28 27 29 26 30

8. 10 30 20 30 50 10 40 30 50 40 30 50

9. 1 4 0 3 0 1 3 2 2 4

10. 6 2 8 7 9 3 5 4 8 2 4 6 4 1

▼

THINK AND DISCUSS

1. Would you expect a set of exam scores to have more than one mode? Explain.

2. Describe the line plot of a distribution with no mode.

Draw a line plot for each frequency distribution. Find the median and the mode.

1.

x	1	2	3	4	5	6
f	2	5	7	8	4	3

2.

x	1	2	3	4	5	6
f	1	3	5	8	8	5

3.

x	1	2	3	4	5	6
f	7	5	3	2	6	7

4.

x	1	2	3	4	5	6
f	5	5	5	5	5	5

5.

x	1	2	3	4	5	6
f	1	8	6	7	5	3

6.

x	1	2	3	4	5	6
f	1	2	9	8	9	1

Make a frequency table for each set of data. Find the mean, the median, and the mode.

7. baseball scores   9 6 6 7 10 6 8 6 8 7

8. the ages of club members   14 16 14 16 14 16 13 12 15 16 12 12 15 14 15 15

9. the heights of test plants   25 25 20 25 20 25 30 25 31 26 28 30

10. a class set of test scores   100 90 70 60 95 65 85 70 70 75 80 85 75 70 100 90

Construct the frequency table from each line plot. Find the median and the mode.

11.

```
                X
            X   X       X
    X       X   X   X   X
 ◄─────────────────────────►
    1   2   3   4   5   6
```

12.

```
    X                       X
    X           X   X   X
    X       X   X   X   X
 ◄─────────────────────────►
    1   2   3   4   5   6
```

13.

```
    X                       X
    X       X           X   X
    X   X   X   X   X   X
    X   X   X   X   X   X
 ◄─────────────────────────────►
   15  16  17  18  19  20
```

14.

```
    X           X           X
    X   X   X   X   X   X
    X   X   X   X   X   X
    X   X   X   X   X   X
 ◄─────────────────────────────►
   70  75  80  85  90  95
```

15. The number of letters in each of the first twenty-five words in a given passage of text are shown below.

2 7 6 3 1 2 7 6 3 2 2 6 9
5 3 2 2 4 5 4 3 2 3 2 11

a. Draw the line plot for the data.

b. Make a frequency table.

c. Find the mean, the median, and the mode for the data.

16. The following figures represent the weekly earnings in dollars of the employees at Yanktown Industrial Enterprise.

160 160 160 200 200 200 200 200
200 240 240 240 360 360 360 520

a. Draw a line plot.

b. Draw a frequency table.

c. Find the mean, median, mode, and range.

17. Use the **DATA** at the right.

a. Draw a frequency table.

b. Find the mean, median, and mode.

c. Which measure of central tendency best reflects the average number of gold medals won? Explain your choice.

18. Babe Ruth's home runs from 1920 to 1934 are shown below.

54 59 35 41 46 25 47 60 54
46 49 46 41 34 22

a. Draw a frequency table.

b. Find the mean, median, and mode.

c. Which average best reflects a typical year? Explain your choice.

19. PROJECT Select a 50-word passage from a reading of your choice.

a. Tally the number of times each letter of the alphabet is used.

b. Draw a frequency table.

c. Find the mean, the median, and the mode of the distribution.

d. *E* is the most frequently used letter in English. Is this true of your data?

20. PROJECT Survey car usage. Count the number of people in each vehicle that passes a given point for a half-hour each weekday. Repeat at the same time on a weekend day. Construct two frequency tables. Are the results the same during the weekend as they are during the week? How could you use this information to determine the need for a traffic light?

21. Use the **DATA** at the right.

a. What age has the highest frequency for each group?

b. **ANALYZE** How would you find the median age for a large set of data? Find the median for men and women.

22. DATA FILE 12 (pp. 486–487) Round the seating capacity for each baseball stadium to the nearest thousand. Use the rounded data to draw a frequency table and to find the median and the mode of the data.

Distribution of Gold Medals 1988 Winter Games

Country	Medals
Soviet Union	11
East Germany	9
Switzerland	5
Austria	3
West Germany	2
Finland	4
Netherlands	3
Sweden	4
United States	2
Italy	2
Norway	0
Canada	0
Yugoslavia	0
Czechoslovakia	0
France	1
Japan	0
Liechtenstein	0

1990 Boston Marathon

Age	Number Entered	
	Male	Female
Under 20	19	3
20–24	251	96
25–29	828	330
30–34	1,318	396
35–39	1,533	371
40–44	1,681	297
45–49	1,026	147
50–54	605	76
55–59	266	16
60 & over	140	11

OBJECTIVE:
To draw valid conclusions from statistical data.

Exploring Misuse of Statistics

▼ Statistics is a powerful tool when used to influence the way a person perceives a situation. You might cite statistics to influence a friend's opinion. In a similar manner, companies often use statistics to present their best image. Advertisers also use statistics to influence you to select their product.

▼ When you use statistics, you must analyze the problem before choosing the data that meet your needs.

1. A toy manufacturer wants to sell more toys. The manufacturer decides to advertise on the most frequently watched television program. Using data collected by a rating company, the manufacturer determines that an adult comedy program is the most popular.

   a. **Analyze** Did the manufacturer find the group of people that might want to own the toy (the target market)?

   b. **Discuss** What factors need to be considered when deciding where to advertise?

   c. **Decide** Who is in the target market? What types of shows would reach more people in the target market?

▼ The most accurate way to collect data is to get everyone's opinion. This is usually impractical. A *sample* of the target group can often provide sufficient information from which to make decisions.

2. Suppose you want to find the number of boys in your school who watch football on Sunday.

   a. **Describe** the group about which you want information.

   b. Suppose your sample includes all the boys in your class. Does your sample represent the boys in the school? **Explain.**

   c. **Discuss** What might be a better sample? Do you think the size of the sample has any effect on the outcome? Would ten boys be enough? **Explain.**

   d. **Discuss** Where would you take the survey? When would be a good time to take the survey?

   e. **Discuss** methods of sampling. Would an interview survey be as accurate as a written survey? How would you word your survey?

   f. Would the time of year in which you took the survey make a difference? the part of the country? **Explain.**

   g. What other factors could influence your results?

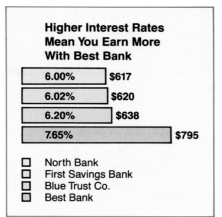

**Higher Interest Rates
Mean You Earn More
With Best Bank**

6.00%	$617
6.02%	$620
6.20%	$638
7.65%	$795

☐ North Bank
☐ First Savings Bank
☐ Blue Trust Co.
☐ Best Bank

Explain how the graph is misleading.

▼ Sometimes people present accurate data in a misleading manner to encourage the conclusions they support.

3. **Compare** and analyze the data in the graphs below.

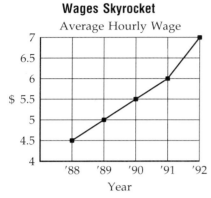

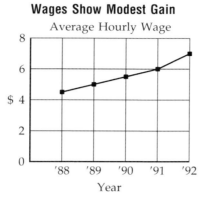

a. **Discuss** What is the difference in the way the vertical scales are used?

b. Do you think the information was presented accurately by each graph? **Explain.**

c. **Write** a short paragraph telling which graph you think was prepared by the personnel department of the company and which was prepared by the workers. Support your viewpoint.

4. An ad stated that 3 out of 4 dentists recommend *Smile* toothpaste.

a. **Decide** Do you need to know how many dentists were included in the sample?

b. **Decide** How could the city where the survey was taken affect the validity of the sample?

c. **Discuss** whether the dentists also recommend other brands. **Explain** why this might affect your opinion of the data.

5. **PROJECT** Find examples in a newspaper or a magazine where statistical data is used.

a. **Explain** Does the collection of data appear to be accurate?

b. Is the information presented in a distorted manner?

c. **Discuss** How could you present the data more fairly?

6. **PROJECT** Write a survey question.

a. **Decide** What is your target market?

b. Can you survey the entire target market or is it more practical to take a sample? Take the survey.

c. **Analyze** How can you accurately present the survey results? Make a presentation with a graph.

OBJECTIVE:
*To present statistical
data in the form of
stem and leaf plots.*

12-3 Stem and Leaf Plots

▼ The table at the left gives the fat content in one serving of various foods. How does the fat content for a cheese pizza compare with other items in the list?

It is difficult to compare the fat content from the table. You can reorganize the data by constructing a *stem and leaf plot*.

Choose the value for the *stem* by finding the least value and the greatest value for the fat content totals. The least value is 10. The greatest value is 33. Both numbers have two digits. The tens' digits will become the stem. Therefore, the stems for this data will be the digits 1 through 3.

Write the digits from 1 to 3 in a column. Draw a line to their right.

```
1 |
2 |
3 |
```

The *leaves* are the ones' digits associated with the tens' values. For a cheeseburger with the fat content of 17 g, the stem is 1 and the leaf is 7. For an apple turnover with fat content of 24 g, the stem is 2 and the leaf is 4. Record each food's fat content to obtain the plot below.

```
1 | 0 7 5 2 2
2 | 2 6 1 6 6 4
3 | 3
```

Arrange the leaves on each stem in order from least to greatest.

```
1 | 0 2 2 5 7
2 | 1 2 4 6 6 6
3 | 3
```

The mode is the greatest number of repeated leaves. For this data the mode is 26. Since the data are in order, the median is the midpoint of the twelve items. The median is the average of the sixth item, 21, and the seventh item, 22. The median is 21.5.

Now it is easier to evaluate the data. A cheese pizza, with fat content of 12 g for a serving, is below the median and the mode for fat content of the foods listed.

▼ In summary, to make a stem and leaf plot:

1. Choose a stem.

2. Write all values between and including the least stem and the greatest stem in order in a column. Draw a line to their right.

3. Write the leaf values to the right of the stem values.

4. Rewrite the plot, putting the values in order.

Fat Content in One Serving

Food	Fat Content in Grams
Deluxe, large hamburger	33
Plain, small hamburger	10
Cheeseburger	17
Roast beef sandwich	15
Beef and cheese sandwich	22
Fish sandwich	26
Fried chicken pieces	21
Deluxe pizza	26
Cheese pizza	12
Taco	26
Apple turnover	24
French fries	12

▼ The stem may be more than one digit. It can be any number that will provide a useful way to organize the data.

Example 1 Use the table at the right to construct a stem and leaf plot to compare the Olympic times for the 80-m hurdles from 1932–1968. Then find the mode.

Solution The stem will be the whole number of seconds. The leaves will be the tenths of a second.

$$
\begin{array}{c|ccccc}
10 & 3 & 5 & 7 & 8 & 9 \\
11 & 2 & 7 & 7 \\
\end{array}
$$

The mode is 11.7 s.

▼ A back-to-back stem and leaf plot records two sets of data. The side-by-side display makes the data easier to compare.

Example 2 Draw a back-to-back stem and leaf plot for the times in the 100-m dash in the Olympic Games from 1928–1968. Find each median and mode.

Solution Use seconds for the stem and tenths of seconds for the leaves.

Men's Time (tenths of seconds)	Stem (seconds)	Women's Time (tenths of seconds)
9	9	
8 5 4 3 3 3 2 0	10	
	11	0 0 4 5 5 5 9 9
	12	2

Men's Scores		Women's Scores
10.3 s	Median	11.5 s
10.3 s	Mode	11.5 s

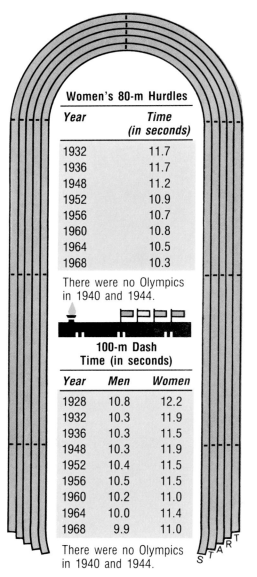

Women's 80-m Hurdles

Year	Time (in seconds)
1932	11.7
1936	11.7
1948	11.2
1952	10.9
1956	10.7
1960	10.8
1964	10.5
1968	10.3

There were no Olympics in 1940 and 1944.

100-m Dash Time (in seconds)

Year	Men	Women
1928	10.8	12.2
1932	10.3	11.9
1936	10.3	11.5
1948	10.3	11.9
1952	10.4	11.5
1956	10.5	11.5
1960	10.2	11.0
1964	10.0	11.4
1968	9.9	11.0

There were no Olympics in 1940 and 1944.

CLASS EXERCISES

Use the stem and leaf plot below to answer each question.

$$
\begin{array}{c|cccccc}
6 & 1 & 1 & 3 & 5 & 5 \\
7 & 0 & 2 & 2 & 4 \\
8 & 4 & 5 & 8 & 9 \\
9 & 3 & 6 & 7 & 9 & 9 & 9 \\
\end{array}
$$

1. What numbers make up the stem?

2. What numbers make up the leaves for the first stem?

3. What is the mode?

4. What is the median?

5. **WRITE** Describe a situation for which the data in the stem and leaf plot might apply.

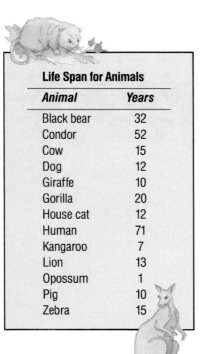

THINK AND DISCUSS

1. Is the stem and leaf plot a useful method of organizing data if you only want to find the mean? Explain.

2. A set of data contains numbers in the 20s, 30s, and 50s only. Is it necessary to put a 4 on the stem in a stem and leaf plot? Explain.

3. In a stem and leaf plot, can a leaf have no stem? Explain.

Make a stem and leaf plot from each set of data. Then find the median and the mode.

6. 15, 22, 25, 10, 36, 15, 28, 35, 18

7. 105, 115, 95, 97, 86, 89, 102, 107, 114, 113, 113, 113

8. 786, 789, 791, 777, 771, 781, 796, 797, 800, 801, 781

Make a back-to-back stem and leaf plot from each of the sets of data. Then find the median and the mode for each set of data.

9. Set A: 25, 23, 33, 36, 42, 44   Set B: 19, 16, 23, 34, 26

10. Set C: 236, 237, 241, 250, 242   Set D: 262, 251, 248, 243, 257

11. Set E: 9.1, 8.2, 7.3, 6.4, 7.3, 8.5   Set F: 7.6, 9.2, 8.2, 8.3, 9.7, 7.6

WRITTEN EXERCISES

Make a stem and leaf plot for each set of data. Then find the median and the mode.

1. 785, 785, 776, 772, 792, 788, 761, 768, 768, 750

2. 4.5, 4.3, 0.8, 3.5, 2.6, 1.4, 0.2, 0.8, 4.3, 6.0

3. 89, 70, 102, 82, 74, 74, 78, 105, 108, 107, 75

4. 47, 41, 60, 75, 85, 53, 57, 76, 79, 81, 84, 86

5. 11.5, 11.8, 10.6, 10.4, 9.5, 12.2, 11.8, 11.8, 11.8, 10.6

6. 225, 220, 221, 222, 231, 231, 219, 219, 215, 229, 236

Make a back-to-back stem and leaf plot for each set of data. Then find the median and the mode.

7. Set A: 63, 62, 63, 52, 58, 63   Set B: 45, 48, 53, 57, 61, 58, 65

8. Set C: 156, 158, 142, 142, 147   Set D: 141, 145, 148, 156, 157

9. Set E: 5.2, 5.8, 6.7, 6.3, 5.9, 4.1   Set F: 7.1, 6.4, 6.5, 6.8, 5.1, 5.2

10. Set G: 206, 205, 210, 215, 222   Set H: 218, 219, 228, 208, 209

Life Span for Animals

Animal	Years
Black bear	32
Condor	52
Cow	15
Dog	12
Giraffe	10
Gorilla	20
House cat	12
Human	71
Kangaroo	7
Lion	13
Opossum	1
Pig	10
Zebra	15

11. Use the **DATA** at the left to solve.

  a. What number will make up the stem for the kangaroo and the opossum?

  b. Construct a stem and leaf plot.

  c. Find the mode.

  d. Find the median.

12. **DATA FILE 7 (pp. 272–273)** Draw a stem and leaf plot for the passenger boardings in 2000. Find the median.

Use the stem and leaf plot below to answer each question. The plot is for the length of time, in minutes, two classes spent on homework.

Class A		Class B
7 4 3	6	1 1 3 5 5
9 9 8 5 4 4	7	0 2 2 4
5 2 1 0	8	4 5 8 9
7 6 6 4 2	9	3 6 7 9 9 9

13. What numbers make up the stem?

14. What is the lowest time for each set of data?

15. What is the median and the mode for each set of data?

MIXED REVIEW

Solve.

1. $2x^2 = 72$

2. Find the surface area of a cube with sides that measure 2.5 in.

Use the frequency table to find each answer.

x	1	2	3	4
f	6	7	4	2

3. Find the median.

4. Find the mode.

Find $\frac{1}{2}$, $\frac{1}{4}$, and $\frac{3}{4}$ of each number.

5. 36   **6.** 92

7. *DATA FILE 13 (pp. 534–535)* Find the mean, median, and mode of the global carbon emissions. Your answer will be in millions of tons.

Critical Thinking

EXPLORING HISTOGRAMS

▼ A *histogram* uses rectangles to show frequency data. You can make a histogram from a stem and leaf plot. The horizontal axis corresponds to the stem. The vertical axis reflects the number of items in the leaf (the frequency).

4	8 9
5	2 5 6 7
6	3
7	4 5

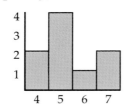

▼ You can divide the information on the horizontal scale of the histogram into smaller groupings.

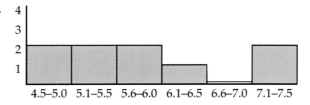

1. How does a change in the horizontal scale of a histogram affect the vertical scale?

2. How can the change in scales affect how people understand the information on the histogram?

3. Draw two histograms with different horizontal scales for the data at the right. Which scale more accurately reflects the information? Explain.

Record High Temperatures in Western States (°F)

State	Temperature
Alaska	100
Arizona	127
California	134
Colorado	118
Hawaii	100
Idaho	118
Montana	117
Nevada	122
Oregon	119
Utah	116
Washington	118
Wyoming	114

12-4 Box and Whisker Plots

▼ The chart at the left shows the top sixteen scorers for the Boston Bruins during a recent hockey season. You can make a *box and whisker plot* to show the data. A box and whisker plot is especially useful in showing the distribution of data in each *quartile*, that is, in each 25% of the data.

SCORE	
HOME	2
VISITORS	1

Boston Bruins Scorers' points for year

Bourque	61
Brickley	35
Burridge	61
Carpenter	40
Carter	22
Crowder	33
Galley	29
Hawgood	40
Janney	62
Johnston	21
Joyce	49
Linseman	72
Neely	75
Sweeney	28
Thelven	21
Wesley	54

1. Arrange the data in order from least to greatest. Then find the median. For these data, the median is 40.

2. Separate the data into four groups. Find the medians of the lower and upper halves. The median of the lower half is 28.5, and the median of the upper half is 61. These values are the first and third quartiles.

3. Draw a number line to display the data. Mark the number line with the quartile values.

4. Draw a box that extends from the first to the third quartiles. Mark the median with a vertical line across the box. Then draw whiskers from the box to the highest and lowest scores.

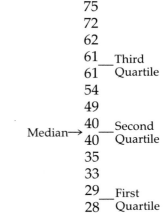

75	
72	
62	
61	Third
61	Quartile
54	
49	
Median→ 40	Second
40	Quartile
35	
33	
29	First
28	Quartile
22	
21	
21	

THINK Why aren't the quartiles marked at $\frac{1}{4}$ of the distance on the number line?

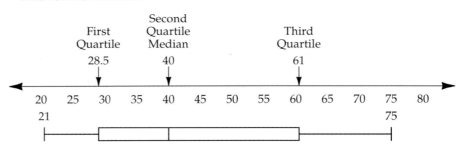

▼ Some trends are easy to recognize in a box and whisker plot.

Example 1 Describe the data in the plot below.

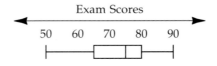

Solution The highest score is 90 and the lowest is 50. Of the scores, 25% are greater than 80 and 25% are less than 65. The plot has a small box indicating that half of the scores are clustered around the median, which is 75.

▼ You can use a box and whisker plot to compare two sets of data, such as scores for teams or individual players.

Example 2 Use the box and whisker plots to compare the leading scores for the Los Angeles Kings and the New York Islanders. What conclusions can you draw?

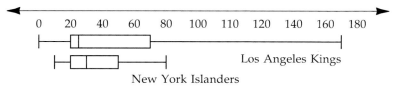

Los Angeles Kings

New York Islanders

Solution The first and second groups for both teams look fairly similar. The New York Islanders have a slightly higher median score. The top half is very different. The Kings have 25% of their scores between 70 and 170. The top 25% for the Islanders is between 50 and 80. The top group shows that the Kings outscore the Islanders by a large margin.

CLASS EXERCISES

Make a box and whisker plot for each set of data.

1. 16, 18, 59, 75, 29, 34, 25, 49, 27, 16, 21, 58, 71, 19, 31, 50

2. 138, 149, 200, 101, 128, 196, 186, 150, 129, 176, 192, 190, 107, 175, 171, 163

Use the box and whisker plot below to answer each question

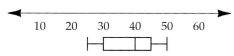

3. What is the median?

4. What percent of the numbers are contained in the box?

5. Are the data evenly distributed? Explain.

Make a box and whisker plot for each set of data. Use a single number line.

6. 1st set: 12, 16, 62, 48, 16, 59, 43, 39
   2nd set: 34, 92, 73, 71, 59, 68, 49, 84

7. 1st set: 36, 9, 4, 3, 12, 29, 50, 16, 25, 21
   2nd set: 18, 22, 7, 4, 11, 16, 40, 18, 33, 9

THINK AND DISCUSS

1. Explain how you can find the quartiles for a set of data.

2. Describe a set of data that has a long box and short whiskers.

3. How is a box and whisker plot like a stem and leaf plot? How is it different?

4. Can you tell what the mean, median, and mode of a set of data would be by looking at a box and whisker plot? Explain.

1. $29\frac{1}{2}\%$ of 400 is what number?

2. What percent of 48 is 18?

Use the set of test scores: 92, 84, 76, 68, 90, 67, 82, 71, 79, 85, 79.

3. Find the median and range.

4. Find the mean.

5. Find the mode.

6. Make a stem and leaf plot.

Solve.

7. Find $5 \cdot 4 \cdot 3 \cdot 2 \cdot 1$

8. **DATA FILE 12 (pp. 486–487)** Draw a back-to-back stem and leaf plot for the Olympic records for 400-m freestyle swimming. Round the time to the nearest second.

Maximum Speed of Animals for a Quarter Mile (mi/h)

Cheetah	70
Lion	50
Quarter horse	47.5
Coyote	43
Hyena	40
Rabbit	35
Giraffe	32
Grizzly bear	30
Cat (domestic)	30
Man	27.89
Elephant	25
Squirrel	12

WRITTEN EXERCISES

Make a box and whisker plot for each set of data.

1. 4, 6, 9, 4, 5, 12, 16, 21, 38, 5, 2, 27

2. 4, 5, 3, 2, 1, 6, 7, 8, 4, 5, 5, 6, 2, 1, 9, 3

3. 38, 49, 16, 21, 48, 36, 29, 52, 31, 25, 49, 36

4. 47, 19, 98, 16, 25, 38, 55, 49, 86, 79, 15, 91, 57

Use the box and whisker plot to answer each question.

Prices of 20 Walk-around Stereos

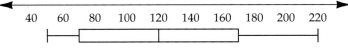

40   60   80   100   120   140   160   180   200   220

5. What are the highest and lowest prices for stereos?

6. What is a median price for a stereo?

7. What percent of prices are greater than $70?

8. What percent of stereos cost more than $170?

9. Are the data evenly distributed?

WRITE Make a box and whisker plot for each set of data. Use a single number line. Then write a comparison.

10. 1st Set: 3, 7, 9, 12, 2, 1, 6, 5, 4, 3, 7, 10, 13, 8, 1, 9
    2nd Set: 9, 8, 1, 7, 6, 3, 7, 9, 8, 6, 4, 7, 8, 9, 10, 10

11. 1st Set: 34, 25, 19, 38, 49, 16, 38, 49, 56, 24, 42, 36
    2nd Set: 38, 49, 52, 39, 50, 55, 46, 45, 40, 39, 51, 42

12. Use the data at the left to make a box and whisker plot for the maximum speed of animals.

13. **PROJECT** Measure the heights of the students in your class. Make a box and whisker plot of the data, by gender, to compare the heights of male and female students.

14. **WRITE** Make a box and whisker plot for each set of data on a single number line. Compare. Then write your conclusions.

National Hockey League High Scorers

Buffalo Sabres	18, 88, 57, 44, 1, 18, 70, 28, 6, 60, 16, 41, 18, 52, 49, 52, 20, 43, 44, 17
St. Louis Blues	7, 67, 13, 70, 84, 34, 29, 26, 45, 17, 52, 55, 23, 24, 25, 26, 19, 43, 42, 20

15. **DATA FILE 13 (pp. 534–535)** Make a box and whisker plot for the global carbon emissions per person.

16. _PROJECT_ Find scores for your two favorite teams for the past season. Make a box and whisker plot for each set of scores on a single number line. Compare. Then write your conclusions about the data.

Use the article below and the chart at the right.

Earthquakes in Stable Areas	
Place	**M**
New Madrid, 1812	8.3
New Madrid, 1811	8.2
New Madrid, 1812	8.1
Kutch, 1819	7.8
Baffin Bay, 1933	7.7
Taiwan Straits, 1604	7.7
South Carolina, 1886	7.6
Nanai, 1918	7.4
Grand Banks, 1929	7.4
Basel, 1356	7.4

Earthquake!

A scientific journal recently reported that earthquakes can occur even in areas considered stable, far away from the edges of the earth's rigid plates. Stable regions make up about two-thirds of the continental crust.

The journal reported that the most reliable gauge of an earthquake's size is the moment-magnitude scale (M). The moment-magnitude scale is based directly on the physical process in the center of an earthquake.

17. What is the mean, median, and mode of the magnitude of the earthquake? Which measure is the most representative?

18. Draw a line plot for the information in the chart.

19. Make a frequency table of the information in the chart.

20. Explain why a box and whisker plot is not helpful in understanding the information in the chart.

TEST YOURSELF

Use the data below for Exercises 1–3.

Average Monthly Temperatures(°F) for Washington, DC

44, 45, 55, 65, 75, 83, 86, 84, 78, 67, 56, 45

1. Find the mean, median, mode, and range.

2. Draw a stem and leaf plot.

3. Draw a box and whisker plot.

Use the data below for each exercise.

3, 2, 5, 7, 2, 4, 3, 1, 2, 5, 3, 4

4. Draw a line plot.   **5.** Make a frequency table.

OBJECTIVE:
To explore whether a game is fair or unfair.

MATERIALS

- Number cubes
- Spinners
- Counters
- Coins
- Math journal to record work

Exploring Fair and Unfair Games

▼ Playing a game is fun if the game is fair. It helps to analyze the rules of a game to see if each player has an equally likely chance of winning. Read the rules of the game below.

The Good Times and the Bad Times

Players:	Player A and Player B
Materials:	Two number cubes
Rules:	• Players take turns tossing the number cubes and then finding the product of the numbers on the two cubes.
	• If the product of the numbers is even, Player A scores a point. If the product of the numbers is odd, Player B scores a point.
	• The player with the most points at the end of 20 rounds is the winner. A round consists of each player tossing the number cubes once.

1. ***Discuss*** Is one player more likely to win the game than the other player? ***Explain***.

2. Choose a partner and play the game four times. Record your results.

3. ***Discuss*** Which player won more games? Based on your results, do you think each player has an equal chance of winning?

4. Make a list or draw a diagram to find all possible outcomes.
   a. How many possible outcomes are there?
   b. In how many ways can a player toss a product that is even? a product that is odd?

5. ***Analyze*** Is the game fair or unfair? ***Explain***.

6. ***Discuss*** How could you change the game to make it fair? Use lists or diagrams to support your conclusions.

7. ***Discuss*** How do other factors, such as the age and experience of the players, contribute to making a contest fair or unfair? Is a game of basketball fair as long as all players play by the same rules? Is a spelling bee always fair?

8. *Analyze* each game. Make a conjecture about whether the game is fair or unfair. Explain your reasoning. Then play each game.

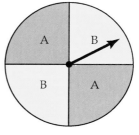

Match or Not

Players: Player A and Player B

Materials: Two counters. One counter with both sides labeled **X** and the other with one side labeled **X** and the other side labeled **Y**.

Rules:
- Each player takes turns tossing the counters.
- If both counters match, Player A gets one point. If the counters do not match, Player B gets the point.
- The first player to get 20 points wins.

Spin Around

Players: Player A and Player B

Materials: Spinner

Rules:
- Each player spins the spinner twice.
- Player A scores if the spinner lands on the same letter both times. Player B scores if the spinner lands on different letters each time.
- The player with the most points after each player has had 50 spins is the winner.

A Lucky Trio of Coins

Players: Player A and Player B

Materials: Three coins

Rules:
- Each player takes turns tossing three coins.
- If all three coins show tails or all three coins show heads, Player A gets one point. If not, Player B gets the point.
- The player with the most points after 20 tosses is the winner.

9. *Summarize* Which of the three games is the most fair? the most unfair? ***Explain***. Support your conclusions with lists or diagrams.

10. *PROJECT* Make up a fair game and an unfair game. Use number cubes, coins, or spinners. Trade with a partner. ***Analyze*** the rules of each game. Decide which is fair and which is unfair. Play the games to test your conjectures.

OBJECTIVE:
To calculate the
number of outcomes
generated by a given
event.

12-5 *Counting Principle*

▼ Suppose you can fulfill your English requirement by taking Literature (L), Poetry (P), or Drama (D) first semester and Composition (C), Speech (S), Grammar (G), or Creative Writing (W) second semester. How many different ways can you choose?

You can draw a tree diagram to display the possible choices.

THINK How could you make a tree diagram with the branches spreading down rather than across?

1st Semester	2nd Semester	Possible Choices
L	C	LC
	G	LG
	S	LS
	W	LW
P	C	PC
	G	PG
	S	PS
	W	PW
D	C	DC
	G	DG
	S	DS
	W	DW

▼ You can also use the *counting principle*.

Number of Choices First Semester		Number of Choices Second Semester		Possible Choices
3	×	4	=	12

THINK Could you use the counting principle for more than two events? Explain.

Counting Principle	The number of outcomes for an event with two or more stages equals the product of the number of outcomes at each stage.

▼ You can use the counting principle when you must make choices in an ordered arrangement.

Example 1 Four Olympic gold medalists will pose together for a promotional photograph. How many different ways can they stand side-by-side in the photo?

Solution

1st Position		2nd Position		3rd Position		4th Position
4 choices		3 choices		2 choices		1 choice
4	×	3	×	2	×	1 = 24

▼ *Factorials* are a mathematical shorthand for situations such as finding the product of numbers in an ordered arrangement.

Example 2 **Find the value of 6 factorial.**

Solution $6! = 6 \times 5 \times 4 \times 3 \times 2 \times 1 = 720$

Factorial	A factorial is the product of all whole numbers from n to 1. We write this as $n!$.

▼
THINK Will 10^n be greater than or less than $n!$?

▼ You can use factorial expressions for products of all whole numbers from n to m, where m is a whole number less than n. Algebraically, this is $n(n-1)(n-2)(n-3) \ldots (m)$.

Example 3 **Express $9 \cdot 8 \cdot 7 \cdot 6 \cdot 5$ as a factorial.**

Solution
$$\frac{9 \times 8 \times 7 \times 6 \times 5}{1}$$ Express as a fraction.

$$\frac{9 \times 8 \times 7 \times 6 \times 5 \times 4 \times 3 \times 2 \times 1}{4 \times 3 \times 2 \times 1} = \frac{9!}{4!}$$ Multiply numerator and denominator by $4 \cdot 3 \cdot 2 \cdot 1$.

$$9 \cdot 8 \cdot 7 \cdot 6 \cdot 5 = \frac{9!}{4!}$$

Example 4 **Evaluate $\frac{10!}{6!}$.**

Solution
$$\frac{10!}{6!} = \frac{10 \times 9 \times 8 \times 7 \times 6 \times 5 \times 4 \times 3 \times 2 \times 1}{6 \times 5 \times 4 \times 3 \times 2 \times 1}$$ Divide common terms.

$$\frac{10!}{6!} = \frac{10 \times 9 \times 8 \times 7}{1}$$ Simplify.

$$\frac{10!}{6!} = 5,040$$

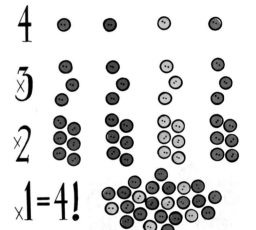

CLASS EXERCISES

Find the value of each factorial.

1. $4!$ **2.** $8!$ **3.** $\frac{11!}{8!}$ **4.** $\frac{22!}{17!}$

Write each expression as a factorial.

5. $5 \cdot 4 \cdot 3 \cdot 2 \cdot 1$ **6.** $12 \cdot 11 \cdot 10 \cdot 9 \cdot 8 \cdot 7$

7. $15 \cdot 14 \cdot 13 \cdot 12$ **8.** $8 \cdot 7 \cdot 6$

Solve. Make a tree diagram to check your answer.

9. There are 6 roads leading from Seymour to Clarksville and 3 roads leading from Clarksville to Belleview. How many possible routes are there from Seymour to Belleview through Clarksville?

▼
THINK AND DISCUSS

1. When is it impractical to make a tree diagram?

2. How is using factorials a modification of the counting principle?

3. Does $6! - 2! = 4!$?

10. A student has 4 blouses and 5 skirts. How many different blouse skirt combinations can she wear?

MIXED REVIEW

Write using scientific notation.

1. 100,000,000,000

2. 0.0001

Use the data to solve the problem: 11, 15, 18, 19, 22, 27, 30, 8, 45.

3. Find the median.

4. Draw a box and whiskers plot for the data.

Simplify.

5. $\frac{9}{27}$ 6. $\frac{40}{88}$

Solve.

7. A storekeeper marks a $38 sweater 25% off. What is the new price?

WRITTEN EXERCISES

Find the value of each factorial.

1. 5!   2. 7!   3. 10!   4. 2!

5. $\frac{5!}{2!}$ 6. $\frac{6!}{3!}$ 7. $\frac{10!}{5!}$ 8. $\frac{13!}{7!}$

CALCULATOR Find the value of each factorial.

9. 12!   10. 8! × 3!   11. $\frac{15!}{10!}$ 12. 9! · 9

MENTAL MATH Find the value of each factorial.

13. $\frac{6!}{5!}$ 14. $\frac{100!}{99!}$ 15. $\frac{10!}{8!}$ 16. 3!

Tell whether each is true or false. If it is false, explain why.

17. 5! × 2! = 5! + 5!   18. 5! × 2! = 10!

19. $\frac{12!}{4!}$ = 3!   20. $\frac{5!}{4!}$ = 5

Solve using a tree diagram.

21. There are 3 ways of performing Task A. There are 4 ways of performing Task B. How many ways are there of performing Task A and then Task B?

22. There are 8 roads leading from Marsh to Taft and 5 roads leading from Taft to Polk. How many possible routes are there to take from Marsh to Polk through Taft?

Solve using the counting principle.

23. A student has 5 pairs of pants, 8 shirts, and 2 ties. How many different outfits does he have to choose from? Each pant/shirt/tie combination is considered a different outfit.

24. You can buy a pizza with thin crust or thick crust. You have a choice of six toppings. How many different combinations can you make if you choose one type of crust and one type of topping for your pizza?

25. An automobile manufacturer makes 4 different car styles. Each style comes in 11 different colors. Each car can have 5 different interior styles and automatic or standard transmission. Jamal wishes to order one of each kind of car for his car lot. How many cars must Jamal order?

JAMAL'S AUTO WORLD

26. You wish to have your picture taken with 5 friends. In how many ways can you line up for the photograph?

27. There are seven people eligible for three different positions on the student council. Their names have been placed in a paper bag.

   a. How many people are eligible for the first position?

   b. How many people are eligible for the second position once the first has been selected?

   c. How many people are eligible for the third position once the first two have been selected?

   d. In how many ways can three people out of seven be selected for three positions on the student council?

28. *WRITE* a paragraph defining the counting principle. Give an example of a situation that uses the principle to solve a problem.

Use the *DATA* at the right to determine how many different costumes each character could wear in the class play.

29. A hobo must wear a hat, a jacket, and carry a suitcase.

30. A scarecrow must wear a hat, a scarf, and a jacket.

31. The mystery person must wear a hat, a scarf, and carry a suitcase.

Costume Props	
hat	*scarf*
straw	knit
baseball	kerchief
derby	
Jacket	*Suitcase*
denim	satchel
plaid	briefcase
striped	duffel bag
leather	

Critical Thinking
EXPLORING VISUAL THINKING

1. Look at the three views of a number cube shown below. What number is opposite the number 6?

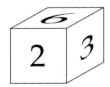 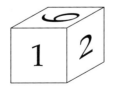 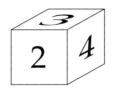

2. Look at the cube below. Side A is red, side B is blue, side C is green, and side D is yellow. What color is opposite side A?

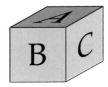  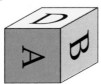

PROBLEM SOLVING HINT
1. Draw a net.
2. A number may be repeated.

OBJECTIVE:
To calculate the
probability of
occurrence of a
given event.

12-6 Probability

▼ Car owners pay insurance premiums to protect against loss or damage. If there is an accident, the insurance company pays damages. Usually the premium is less than the value of the car.

To set the fee, mathematicians use *probability* theory to review past claims payouts and estimate future payouts. Then they use the expected payout to determine insurance rates.

Probability	Probability is the likelihood that a certain *event*, or set of outcomes, will occur. $$P(E) = \frac{\text{number of favorable outcomes}}{\text{total number of possible outcomes}}$$

Sample Space	The set of possible outcomes is the sample space.

THINK How many favorable
outcomes are there for the
event of tossing an even
number?

Example 1 When tossing a number cube, there are six possible outcomes, 1, 2, 3, 4, 5, and 6.

▼ Probability relies on events occurring *randomly*. All outcomes must be equally likely to occur for the calculations to be valid.

Example 2 What is the probability that a letter chosen at random from the word **MISSISSIPPI** is the letter I?

Solution
1. Find the size of the sample space.   Number of letters → 11
2. Find the number of favorable outcomes.   Number of I's → 4
3. Find the probability. $P(I) = \frac{\text{Number of I's}}{\text{Number of letters}} = \frac{4}{11}$

The probability of choosing the letter I is $\frac{4}{11}$.

NOTES & QUOTES

In the small number of things we are able to know with any certainty, the principal means of ascertaining truth are based on probabilities.
 —Pierre Simon de Laplace
  (1749–1827)

▼ You can find the probability for more than one favorable outcome.

Example 3 You draw a card at random from a hat containing cards numbered 1–6. Find the probability that the card is even.

Solution
1. Find the size of the sample space.   Cards → 6
2. Find the favorable outcomes for the event.   Even cards, (2, 4, 6) → 3.
3. Find the probability. $P(\text{even}) = \frac{\text{Even cards}}{\text{All cards}} = \frac{3}{6} = \frac{1}{2}$.

The probability of drawing an even card is $\frac{1}{2}$.

▼ You can determine the probability of an event *not* occurring.

Example 4 There are 3 blue marbles, 2 yellow marbles, and 4 red marbles in a bag. What is the probability that a marble chosen at random is *not* a red marble?

Solution
1. Find the size of the sample space.   Number of marbles → 9

2. Find the favorable outcomes.   Number of not red marbles → 5

3. Find the probability. $P(\text{not red}) = \dfrac{\text{not red}}{\text{all marbles}} = \dfrac{5}{9}$

The probability of *not* drawing a red marble is $\frac{5}{9}$.

> **THINK** The probability of getting a red marble is $\frac{4}{9}$. Why is
> $P(\text{not red}) = 1 - P(\text{red})$?

CLASS EXERCISES

Use the word ARKANSAS to answer each question.

1. You wish to know the probability of selecting the letter A.

  a. What is the number of possible outcomes in the sample space for selecting the letter A?

  b. What is the number of favorable outcomes for the event of selecting the letter A?

  c. What is the probability of selecting the letter A?

  d. What is the probability of *not* selecting the letter A?

2. What is the probability of selecting a vowel?

3. What is the probability of selecting the letter C?

Find each sample space.

4. choosing a Monday from all the days of the week

5. choosing the letter X from all the letters in the alphabet

Find each probability.

6. What is the probability that a digit selected at random from the number 364,892 is a multiple of 3?

7. A math class has 10 boys and 15 girls. What is the probability that a student chosen at random is a girl?

8. In a class of 24 students, 8 are saving to buy a camera. What is the probability that a randomly selected student is *not* saving to buy a camera?

9. Find the probability that a student chosen at random from your math class has blue eyes.

> **THINK AND DISCUSS**
>
> 1. What is the probability of an event that is certain to occur? Give an example of such an event.
>
> 2. What is the probability of an event that is impossible? Give an example of such an event.
>
> 3. Can a probability be greater than 1? Explain.
>
> 4. Can a probability be less than 0? Explain.

WRITTEN EXERCISES

Find the probability of each event.

1. that a digit selected at random from the number 164,743 is a multiple of 2

2. that a randomly chosen month has 30 days

Find each probability when a letter is chosen at random from the word MATHEMATICS.

3. choosing a consonant

4. choosing the letter M

5. choosing a letter that occurs more than once

6. choosing the letter K.

Find each probability.

7. What is the probability that a state selected at random from a list of the 50 United States begins with the letter M?

8. A lab class has 8 boys and 10 girls. What is the probability that a student chosen at random is a boy?

9. Students in a class were asked to name their preferred type of motor vehicle. Eight students preferred a pickup, 12 preferred a sports car, and eight preferred a convertible. What is the probability that a randomly selected student preferred a sports car?

10. What is the probability that any letter of the alphabet is not included in the sentence *"The quick brown fox jumps over the lazy dog"*?

11. There are 14 boys and 12 girls in a math class. There are 60 boys and 65 girls in the freshman class. In the school there are 375 boys and 360 girls. Find the probability that a female student is chosen at random.

    a. from the math class

    b. from the freshman class

    c. from the school

    d. Are the answers for (a), (b), and (c) different? Why or why not?

12. Find the probability of each event when a day of the week is chosen at random.

    a. a day of the week has six letters

    b. the day of the week has more than six letters

    c. What is the sum of the answers to parts (a) and (b)? Explain.

MIXED REVIEW

Give each number.

1. opposite of -9

2. |-5|

Find the factorial.

3. 6!   4. $\frac{7!}{3!}$

Use the data for the questions below: 8, 9, 5, 12, 4, 6, 4, 10.

5. Find the mean.

6. Draw a box and whisker plot.

Write an equation. Then solve.

7. Students paid $850 for tickets to the Spring Fling. Each ticket cost $5. How many tickets did the students purchase?

13. Find the probability of each event when a prime number less than 100 is chosen.

  a. It has one digit.　　　　　　**b.** It has more than one digit.

  c. Why is the sum of parts (a) and (b) equal to 1?

14. The figure at the right illustrates a pattern of floor tiling. You drop a coin onto this portion of the floor tile. Find the probability for each event.

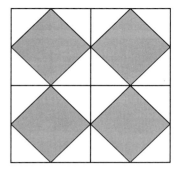

  a. The coin lands on a red tile.　**b.** The coin lands on a white tile.

15. A group of students was polled to find out their favorite sports. Four of the students chose skiing, eight chose baseball, ten chose basketball, four chose football, and two chose track. Find the probability of a randomly chosen student preferring each event.

  a. skiing　　　　**b.** baseball　　　**c.** basketball

  d. football　　　**e.** track

  f. What is the sum of the five probabilities? Explain.

16. A set of flash cards is numbered from 1 to 36. A card is chosen at random. Find the probability for each event.

  a. an even number　　　　　**b.** a multiple of 3

  c. a multiple of both 2 and 3　**d.** a multiple of 2 or 3

  e. a prime number　　　　　　**f.** a square number

17. A number is chosen at random. Find the probability of the last digit of its square being each number listed below.

  a. 1　　　**b.** 4　　　**c.** 5　　　**d.** 6　　　**e.** 9

  f. Why is the sum of these answers not equal to 1?

18. **PROJECT** What is the probability that a coin will land with the head face up? Record your answer.

  a. Toss a coin 100 times. Record the number of times the coin lands face up. Find the probability of the coin landing face up.

  b. Do the results of tossing the coin agree with the probability you expected? Why do you think there might be a difference?

Use the *DATA* at the right to solve.

19. What is the size of the sample space if each style comes in each color?

20. What is the probability of choosing a blue sweater at random?

21. What is the probability of choosing a sweater vest at random?

22. **WRITE** Suppose you have a bag containing an equal number of nickels, dimes, and quarters. Suppose you reach into the bag and choose a coin. Is it equally likely that you will pick a dime or a quarter? Explain.

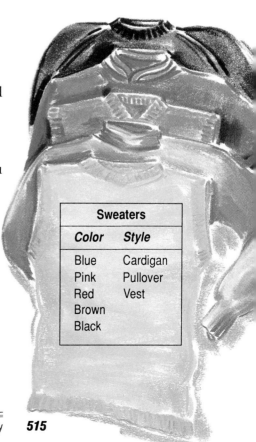

Sweaters	
Color	*Style*
Blue	Cardigan
Pink	Pullover
Red	Vest
Brown	
Black	

OBJECTIVE:
To explore probabilities using Pascal's triangle.

MATERIALS

- Coins

- Math journal to record work

Exploring Pascal's Triangle

■ In probability problems where the underlying experiment has two equally likely outcomes, you can often find solutions using Pascal's triangle.

Problem If three fair coins are tossed, what is the probability of obtaining exactly two heads?

Plan You need to list all possible outcomes and count them to find the denominator. You need to identify the successful outcomes and count them to find the numerator. Then put these numbers into a fraction to write the probability.

$$P = \frac{\text{number of successful outcomes}}{\text{total number of outcomes}}$$

■ Suppose you have a penny, a nickel, and a dime. How can you list all possible outcomes?

1. List the set of all possible outcomes as ordered triples (a, b, c) where a is the outcome of the penny, b the nickel, and c the dime.

   (H,H,H), (H,H,T), (H,T,H), (H,T,T), (T,H,H), (T,H,T), (T,T,H), (T,T,T)

   There are eight possible outcomes.

2. Make a tree diagram in which you consider the outcomes one coin at a time.

Penny	Nickel	Dime	Outcome
H	H	H	HHH
		T	HHT
	T	H	HTH
		T	HTT
T	H	H	THH
		T	THT
	T	H	TTH
		T	TTT

3. Identify the successful outcomes: HHT, HTH, THH.

4. Write the probability: $P(\text{two heads}) = \frac{3}{8}$.

5. Compare Row 3 in Pascal's triangle with the results of the coin tossing problem.

Row 0					1				
Row 1				1		1			
Row 2			1		2		1		
Row 3		1		3		3		1	
Row 4	1		4		6		4		1

6. Find the sum of the numbers in Row 3.

7. How does the sum compare with the total number of outcomes in the coin-tossing problem?

8. Look back at the list of outcomes for tossing three coins. In how many outcomes were there exactly zero heads? Notice that the first number in Row 3 is 1.

9. Look at the list of outcomes for tossing three coins. In how many outcomes were there exactly 1 head? Notice that the second number in Row 3 is 3. We know that there were 3 outcomes with exactly 2 heads. The third number in Row 3 is 3.

10. In how many outcomes were there exactly 3 heads? The fourth number in Row 3 is 1.

■ The numbers in Row 3 of Pascal's triangle tell how many of the possible outcomes in tossing three coins represent exactly 0, 1, 2, or 3 heads.

Use Row 4 of Pascal's triangle to answer each question. Check your results by listing the possible outcomes of the experiment.

11. How many possible outcomes are there for the experiment consisting of tossing four different coins?

12. In how many ways can you obtain exactly 0, 1, 2, 3, or 4 heads?

13. What is the probability of obtaining exactly 2 heads when tossing four coins?

14. What is the probability of obtaining exactly 3 heads when tossing four coins?

15. What is the probability of obtaining exactly 3 tails when tossing four coins?

16. In a family of four children, what is the probability that all four children are girls? *Hint:* There are two equally likely outcomes at the birth of each child, so the situation has the same mathematical structure as flipping a coin.

17. In a family of five children, what is the probability that exactly two of the children are boys?

18. *Write* a similar problem. Trade with a classmate and solve each other's problem.

PROBLEM SOLVING HINT
Extend Pascal's triangle to Row 5.

Exploring Pascal's Triangle   **517**

12-7 Simulate the Problem

OBJECTIVE:
To solve problems
using simulation.

Dr. Grace Yang is
a statistics professor
at the University of
Maryland. She
received her Ph.D.
degree in 1966
from the University
of California at Berkeley.
Dr. Yang believes it is
important for girls to do
well in mathematics. "If
young women don't
continue taking math
courses in high school, by
the time they enter college
their choice of fields will be
very much restricted."

■ You can solve many probability problems using a *Monte Carlo simulation*. Monte Carlo methods make it possible to model a situation for which a test is impractical and probability formulas are cumbersome. Use the steps below to develop a model.

1. Assign success to one outcome and failure to another.
2. Choose a random device, such as number cubes or a spinner.
3. Determine the probability of the outcome of one trial.
4. Decide the definition of a trial.
5. Perform a sufficient number of trials.
6. Compute the simulated probability $\frac{\text{number of successful trials}}{\text{number of trials}}$.

PROBLEM

You have been given a quiz written in ancient Sanskrit. You are expected to match five words with their definitions. What is the probability that you will get 1 out of 5 answers correct?

SOLUTION

READ ▶ What do you want to find?

the probability that you will get 1 out of 5 answers correct

PLAN ▶ Decide on a strategy.

Use a Monte Carlo simulation.

What random device can you use to simulate the problem?

Use a set of cards with the letters a, b, c, d, and e to represent the words. Use a second set of cards with A, B, C, D, and E to represent the definitions.

What is a *successful* outcome?

obtaining two or more correct answers by matching upper and lowercase letters

What is the probability of a match on each draw?

Each probability is $\frac{1}{5}$.

What will represent one *trial*?

drawing five pairs of cards, one card from each pile

SOLVE ▶ How many trials are sufficient?

at least 100 trials

Tally the results.

One student completed 19 successes out of 100 trials.

Give the expected probability.

$\frac{19}{100} = \frac{\text{number of successes}}{\text{number of trials}}$

LOOK BACK ▶ Did you solve the problem?

The probability is estimated to be $\frac{19}{100}$.

CLASS EXERCISES

1. Perform the experiment.

   a. Compare your results with those in the example.

   b. Why do you think the results of your experiment might differ from those of the student in the example?

2. Repeat the experiment to find the probability of getting two correct answers for each of these matching quizzes in Sanskrit.

   a. a 4-word quiz   **b.** a 6-word quiz

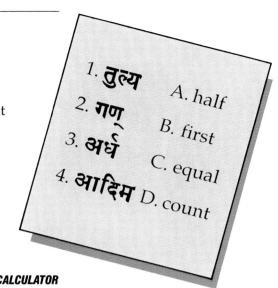

1. तुल्य   A. half
2. गण्   B. first
3. अर्ध   C. equal
4. आदिम D. count

WRITTEN EXERCISES

 Use a CALCULATOR where appropriate.

Solve by simulating the problem.

1. Suppose you take a true-false test. You don't know the answers to any of the ten questions. What is the probability you will get 7 out of 10 correct?

   a. Model the situation using a coin. Let heads represent a true statement and tails represent a false statement.

   b. Let another student prepare an *answer key* by tossing the coin ten times and recording each *correct answer*.

   c. A trial occurs when you toss the coin ten times to represent the ten questions on the quiz. A successful trial occurs when you get seven or more answers that match the *answer key*.

   d. You need to try about 100 trials.

   e. Write the probability: $\frac{\text{number of successful trials}}{\text{number of trials}}$.

2. Suppose you take a ten-question multiple-choice test. Each question has four choices. You don't know any of the answers.

   a. What is the probability you will get 7 out of 10 correct? Model the situation using a spinner with four equal sections.

   b. Compare your answer with Exercise 1. Explain why it is different.

   c. What is the probability you will get 4 out of 10 correct?

Solve using any strategy.

3. What is the probability that exactly three children in a family of five children will be boys?

4. What is the probability that exactly two children in a family of six children will be girls?

5. Thirteen of 25 students are going on a field trip. Six students are traveling in a van. What is the probability that a student chosen at random is *not* traveling in a van?

6. What is the probability that a student will draw a card at random showing A or B from these cards?

| P | R | O | B | A | B | I | L | I | T | Y |

7. A student is going to choose a date from the month of January at random. What is the probability that the student will choose January 1?

8. Suppose you toss three coins. What is the probability that all the coins will land heads up?

9. A student has a mean of 92 for two quizzes. What grade does the student need on the next quiz to have a mean of 94?

10. A student tells you that she receives an average salary of $3.50/h. Her manager tells you he pays an average of $4/h. The chain they work for says the pay averages $4.75/h. Explain how they could all be telling the truth.

11. A store advertises a jacket for $72. During a sale the store reduces the jacket price by 25%. After the sale, the store raises the jacket price by 25%. What is the price of the jacket after the sale?

12. The sum of five consecutive numbers is 380. What are the numbers?

13. Double a number minus half the number is five minus the number. What is the number?

14. A student uses 24 yd of fencing to make a rectangular pen. The pen is 6 yd longer than it is wide. What are the dimensions of the pen?

15. The circumference of the peg below is 3 in. Will the peg go through the hole? Explain.

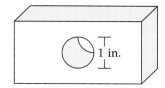

1 in.

16. The average American generates 3.5 lb of waste per day. Of all waste, about 6.5% is plastic. About how much plastic waste does the average American generate each day? each year?

17. In a recent year, the number of major trash composting projects in the United States rose from 42 to 75. Find the percent of change.

Practice

Find the mean, median, mode, and range for each set of data.

1. 6, 7, 8, 7, 6, 15, 24, 36, 28, 26, 18, 11
2. 1, 2, 5, 6, 7, 3, 8, 9, 1, 1, 2, 9, 8, 7, 6
3. 2, 5, 6, 5, 4, 2, 1, 4, 4, 7, 2, 4, 3, 7

Draw a line plot and make a frequency table for each set of data. Find the mean, the median, and the mode.

4. 11, 12, 13, 15, 11, 12, 14, 10, 28
5. 6, 5, 6, 5, 6, 2, 8, 0, 0, 0, 1, 6
6. 20, 30, 40, 50, 20, 30, 20, 50, 60, 10, 20

Make a back-to-back stem and leaf plot for each set of data. Find the median and the mode.

7. Set A: 23, 24, 25, 26, 23, 22   Set B: 19, 22, 25, 26, 17, 23, 21
8. Set C: 45, 46, 50, 51, 48, 49   Set D: 52, 53, 52, 54, 50, 51, 52

Make a box and whisker plot for each set of data. Use a single number line. Then compare.

9. Set A: 2, 4, 6, 1, 2, 3, 4, 12, 15, 10, 10, 8
   Set B: 8, 9, 10, 7, 10, 8, 8, 7, 10, 9, 11, 11
10. Set C: 30, 40, 50, 20, 30, 70, 80, 100, 60, 50, 50, 60
    Set D: 15, 25, 75, 75, 15, 35, 45, 65, 75, 25, 25, 45

Write each expression as a factorial.

11. $4 \cdot 3 \cdot 2 \cdot 1$
12. $9 \cdot 8 \cdot 7 \cdot 6$
13. $25 \cdot 24 \cdot 23$
14. $100 \cdot 99 \cdot 98 \cdot 97$

Evaluate.

15. $\frac{10!}{7!}$
16. $\frac{7!}{4!}$
17. $\frac{50!}{48!}$

Use the counting principle to solve.

18. A student has 3 clean shirts, 4 clean pairs of socks, and 2 clean pairs of pants. How many different outfits can he wear?

Find the probability of each event when a letter is chosen at random from the word BEEKEEPER.

19. selecting the letter K
20. selecting the letter E
21. selecting a consonant
22. selecting a vowel
23. selecting a letter of the English alphabet
24. selecting a number.

12-8 Independent and Dependent Events

▼ Some events are a combination of two or more single events. A trip from New York to Seattle via Chicago is actually a combination of two trips: one from New York to Chicago and one from Chicago to Seattle. We call this a *compound event*.

Compound Event	A compound event is a combination of two or more events.

▼ A compound event can be a combination of *independent events*.

Independent Events	Independent events are events in which the outcome of one has no effect on the outcome of the other.
	For two independent events A and B,
	$P(\text{A and B}) = P(\text{A}) \cdot P(\text{B})$.

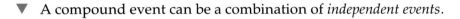

FLASHBACK

You can use a tree diagram to find a sample space.

Example 1 A student can walk, take the bus, or ride to school with a friend. After school, he can walk or ride with a friend to the library. The student is equally likely to make any of these choices. What is the probability that he will walk to school and then ride with a friend to the library after school?

Solution *Method 1.* Find the probability of two independent events using the counting principle.

Ways to School   Ways to Library   Possible Outcomes
     3   ×   2   =   6

Favorable outcome, write the probability as:

$\dfrac{\text{favorable outcome}}{\text{possible outcomes}} = \dfrac{1}{6}.$

Method 2. Find the probability of two independent events using the formula.

$P(\text{Walk}) = \dfrac{1}{3} \qquad P(\text{Car}) = \dfrac{1}{2}$

$P(\text{Walk, Car}) = \dfrac{1}{3} \times \dfrac{1}{2}$

$\qquad\qquad = \dfrac{1}{6}$

The probability of walking to school and then riding to the library with a friend after school is $\frac{1}{6}$.

▼ A compound event can be a combination of *dependent events.*

Dependent Events	Dependent events are events in which the outcome of one depends on the outcome of the other.
	For two dependent events A and B, where B is dependent on A,
	$$P(A \text{ and } B) = P(A) \cdot P(B, \text{ given } A).$$

THINK How are dependent events different from independent events?

Example 2   Three girls and two boys are running for class president and vice president. Slips of paper with the five names are put into a bag. The first name drawn from the bag will be president. The second will be vice president. What is the probability that both officers will be girls?

Solution $P(\text{Girl}) = \frac{3}{5}$ First draw.

$P(\text{Girl}) = \frac{2}{4} = \frac{1}{2}$ Second draw. Assume a girl has been chosen on the first draw. There are 4 names left, so 4 is the number of possible outcomes.

$\frac{3}{5} \times \frac{1}{2} = \frac{3}{10}$ Multiply the probabilities.

The probability that both officers will be girls is $\frac{3}{10}$.

CLASS EXERCISES

Are the events independent or dependent? Explain.

1. You select a card. Without putting the card back, you select a second card.

2. You select a card. After putting it back, you select a second card.

3. You roll a number cube. You roll it again.

4. Cards numbered 5, 5, 3, 7, and 4 are placed face down on a table.

   a. What is the probability that you select a 5 at random?

   b. You do not replace the 5. What is the probability that your next selection is a 4?

   c. You put the cards back on the table before making a second selection. What is the probability of selecting a 5, then a 4?

5. A student has 5 blue socks and 4 orange socks. Find the probability that she will randomly select these items.

   a. a blue sock, then an orange sock   **b.** two blue socks

   c. an orange sock, then a blue sock   **d.** two orange socks

THINK AND DISCUSS

1. Explain why you can multiply probabilities for two independent or two dependent events.

2. When computing the probability of dependent events, how does the probability of the second event show that the events are dependent?

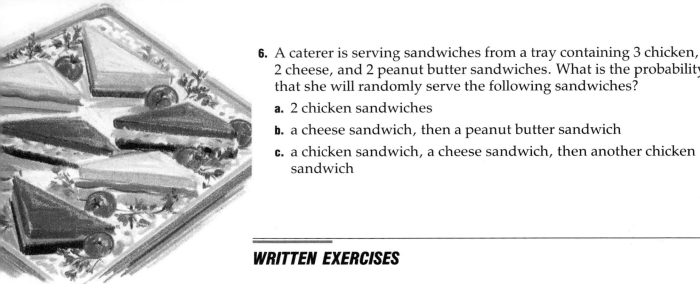

6. A caterer is serving sandwiches from a tray containing 3 chicken, 2 cheese, and 2 peanut butter sandwiches. What is the probability that she will randomly serve the following sandwiches?

   a. 2 chicken sandwiches

   b. a cheese sandwich, then a peanut butter sandwich

   c. a chicken sandwich, a cheese sandwich, then another chicken sandwich

WRITTEN EXERCISES

Are the events independent or dependent? Explain.

1. Two number cubes are thrown. The result on one is 3 and on the other is 5.

2. It has rained for the last three Saturdays. Rain is forecast for next Saturday.

3. You exercise daily. You make the tennis team.

4. You choose a white marble from a bag and do not put it back. You choose again and get another white marble.

For each exercise, assume that events A and B are independent. Then find P(A and B).

5. $P(A) = \frac{1}{2}$, and $P(B) = \frac{1}{5}$.

6. $P(A) = \frac{1}{3}$, and $P(B) = \frac{2}{7}$.

7. $P(A) = \frac{2}{9}$, and $P(B) = \frac{3}{8}$.

8. $P(A) = \frac{7}{16}$, and $P(B) = \frac{8}{35}$.

Tell whether each problem involves dependent or independent events. Then find the probability.

9. A refrigerator contains 12 orange drinks, 4 grape drinks, and 25 apple drinks. Ann is first in line. Mark is second. What is the probability that Ann gets an apple drink and Mark a grape drink if they choose their drinks at random?

10. Suppose you roll a number cube twice. What is the probability that you will roll each of the following pairs of numbers?

    a. 6, then 5   b. 6, then 6   c. 4, then 3, then 1

11. A student's wallet contains three one-dollar bills, two five-dollar bills, and three ten-dollar bills. The student selects two bills from her wallet at random. What is the probability that the student selects these bills?

    a. a one-dollar bill, then a ten-dollar bill

    b. a ten-dollar bill, then a five-dollar bill

12. Suppose you spin a spinner like the one at the right. What is the probability that you get each outcome?

a. C, then A   **b.** B, then C, then A

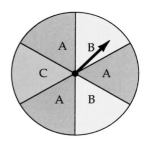

Use the DATA at the right.

13. How many students were in the survey? Would a sample be an appropriate way to measure preference in this case? Why or why not?

14. What is the probability that a student selected at random from the class prefers pizza?

15. What is the probability that a boy prefers pizza?

16. What is the probability that a girl does not prefer pizza?

17. PROJECT Choose a topic from the list below or one of your own and conduct an opinion poll. Survey at least 30 people.

- quality of cafeteria food
- curfew times for 9th graders
- study habits

a. Record the frequency of each response in a table.

b. Find the probability for each response (outcome).

c. WRITE three problems based on your poll. Trade with a friend. Solve each other's problem.

Votes for Class Party

	Barbecue	Pizza	Total
Boys	6	4	10
Girls	9	5	14

TEST YOURSELF

Make a stem and leaf plot for the data. Find the mean, median, and mode.

1. 33, 35, 32, 28, 28, 21, 27, 35, 39, 40, 22, 24

Solve.

2. From Compt there are 4 ways to get to Murch. From Murch there are 5 ways to get to Toll. How many ways are there from Compt to Toll through Murch?

3. You roll a number cube. What is the probability of rolling a 4 and then rolling another 4?

4. You have 12 socks in a drawer and choose 2 at random. Five socks are blue, three brown, and four black. What is the probability that you choose a black sock and then choose a brown one?

Problem Solving Practice

READ
PLAN
LOOK
BACK
SOLVE

PROBLEM SOLVING STRATEGIES

Look for a Pattern
Guess and Test
Simplify the Problem
Account for All Possibilities
Make an Organized List
Work Backwards
Make a Table
Write an Equation
Solve by Graphing
Draw a Diagram
Make a Model
Simulate the Problem

Solve. Use an appropriate strategy or combination of strategies.

1. A slope of $\frac{1}{10}$ is suitable for a ramp to allow wheelchair access to a building. How far from a doorway will a ramp extend if the doorway is $10\frac{1}{2}$ ft above the ground?

2. The sales tax on an item costing $23.50 is $1.88. What is the sales tax on an item costing $47?

3. A student has a coordinated wardrobe consisting of four blouses, two sweaters, and three skirts. How many three-piece outfits can she make?

4. In a collection of dimes and nickels, there are 9 more nickels than dimes. The collection is worth $1.65. How many nickels and dimes are there?

5. A classroom is 15 ft high. Its floor has an area of 642 ft². Each student needs 300 ft³ of air. How many students can be assigned to the room?

6. The number of calls to a weather information number for fifteen consecutive days was 79, 75, 84, 103, 129, 95, 89, 114, 128, 112, 115, 105, 120, 127, and 101.
   a. Find the median number of calls.
   b. Draw a stem and leaf plot.
   c. What must the number of calls be for the next day to change the median to 107?

7. The sum of two numbers is 11. Twice the greater subtracted from 3 times the lesser equals 3. What are the numbers?

8. A couple pays a babysitter $4.75/h plus $5 taxi fare and expenses. What is the greatest whole number of hours the babysitter can work and still receive less than $25?

9. The mean score of four bowlers is 140. Three scores are the same. The third is twice that of the fourth. Find the scores.

10. Two salespeople drove a distance of 600 mi in one day. The first salesperson drove at least 40 mi more than twice the distance driven by the second. What is the greatest distance that the second salesperson might have driven?

11. A band director wished to arrange the band members in pairs for a marching pattern. He found that he was one person short. He tried to arrange by fives and sevens and was still one person short. What is the least number of people in the marching band?

12-9 *Making Predictions*

OBJECTIVE:
To apply capture/ recapture methods to wildlife management.

Many species of wildlife in the United States have become extinct, including the North Carolina parakeet, the passenger pigeon, and the California grizzly bear. The increased number of wildlife in danger of becoming extinct is a concern for environmentalists.

Capture/recapture is a method for estimating a total population from a sample. Researchers capture, tag, and set free animals of a certain type. At a later time, animals in the same species are recaptured. You can use the following formula to estimate the number of animals in the total population.

$$\frac{\text{tagged animals}}{\text{total population}} = \frac{\text{tagged animals recaptured}}{\text{total animals recaptured}}$$

Example National park rangers wish to know the number of coyotes in a certain section of the Yellowstone National Park. Park rangers capture, tag, and set free 24 coyotes. Two weeks later, rangers capture 38 coyotes. Eight of the coyotes have tags. Estimate the number of coyotes in the section of the park surveyed.

Solution $\frac{\text{tagged animals}}{\text{total population}} = \frac{\text{tagged animals recaptured}}{\text{total animals recaptured}}$

$\frac{24}{n} = \frac{8}{38}$ Substitute values in the formula.

$8n = 912$ Write cross products.
$n = 114$

The estimated number of coyotes is 114.

CLASS EXERCISES

Solve.

1. A naturalist and his assistants capture, tag, and set free 32 spotted deer. A week later the scientists capture 45 deer. Twelve have tags.

   a. What is the ratio of tagged animals originally captured to the number of animals in the total population (n)?

   b. What is the ratio of tagged animals recaptured to the total number of animals recaptured?

   c. Estimate the total population of spotted deer.

WRITTEN EXERCISES

Use a **CALCULATOR** where appropriate.

Solve.

1. In a study of catfish in Beaver Lake, workers for the state extension service caught, tagged, and set free 124 catfish. A few weeks later the workers caught 140 catfish. Thirty-five had tags. Estimate the number of catfish in the lake.

2. There are an unknown number of marbles in a bag. You take 10 marbles out and mark them. You put the marked marbles back into the bag and mix the contents well. You take out 25 marbles. Five of them are marked. Estimate the number of marbles in the bag.

3. You are in a large city. You wish to estimate the number of yellow cabs. You count 75 yellow cabs and you keep track of their license numbers. The next day you count 84 cabs, 20 of which are repeats. Estimate the number of yellow cabs.

4. The ecology class is helping the local conservation society to determine the number of raccoons in a nearby forest. In early October, the students and society members captured, tagged, and set free 68 raccoons. Three weeks later, 84 raccoons were captured, and 16 had tags. Estimate the number of raccoons in the forest.

■■■■■■■ Decision Making ■ **DECISION MAKING** ■ Decision Making ■ Decision Making ■ Decision Making ■

MAKING PREDICTIONS

■ COLLECT DATA

The school bookstore plans to stock sweatshirts, hats, and jackets. It is important not to overstock. The store manager asks you to determine the number, color, and size of each item to order.

1. Write a survey questionnaire to find out student interest. Design the questionnaire so that you can estimate the sales by color and size of each item.

2. Who will you survey? Will a random survey suit your purposes or will selecting survey groups from each grade level be a more accurate method of determining your market?

3. Where will you conduct the survey? Will verbal responses be as helpful as written responses?

4. Conduct the survey.

Use the DATA below and at the right to solve.

5. The ecology class designed a T-shirt to sell to students as a fund-raiser. The profits are to go to the local conservation society. To determine the number of shirts to order, the class conducted a marketing survey. The results are on the chart at the right. The formula the class used to determine the expected sales is

$$\frac{\text{expected sales}}{\text{total in target group}} = \frac{\text{number of yes responses}}{\text{number of students surveyed}}.$$

One hundred fifty students were surveyed. The target group was the entire school population of 2,000 students.

a. What are the expected sales for the small T-shirt?

b. What are the expected sales for the medium T-shirt?

c. What are the expected sales for the large T-shirt?

d. The class did not want to order more T-shirts than they could actually sell. The group decided to order only 80% of the expected sales found in the survey. How many T-shirts in each size did the ecology class order?

e. The amount of money the club makes on each shirt is $1.25. How much money will the ecology club give to the conservation society if the club sells all of the T-shirts ordered?

Yes Responses to Marketing Survey for T-shirts	
small	18
medium	30
large	45

■ *Decision Making* ■ *Decision Making* ■ *Decision Making* ■ *Decision Making* ■ *Decision Making* ■ *Decision Making* ■

■ **ANALYZE DATA**

5. Calculate the number of expected sales for each item by color and size.

6. In collecting data, was interest expressed in items not on your list? Do you need to expand your choices and do another survey?

■ **MAKE DECISIONS**

7. Decide if you will order exactly the number of items you have found to be your expected sales. Should you order more? less? Explain your decision.

8. Contact a supplier to find the wholesale cost of each item. Determine what price you will set for each item.

9. Present your results to the school bookstore or to some other group for a fund-raising project.

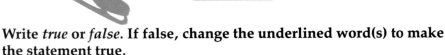

Chapter 12 Review

Write *true* or *false*. If false, change the underlined word(s) to make the statement true.

1. The <u>median</u> is the number that occurs most often in a set of data.

2. A <u>box and whisker plot</u> is useful in showing the distribution of data by quartiles.

3. A <u>line plot</u> shows data on a number line.

4. <u>Dependent</u> events are events in which the outcome of one has no effect on the outcome of the other.

5. A <u>multiple</u>, written as $n!$, is the product of all whole numbers from n to 1.

Finding Mean, Median, and Mode   12-1

In a set of data,

The *mode* is the number that occurs most often.

The *mean* is the sum of n numbers divided by n.

The *median* is the middle value.

To find the *range,* subtract the least value from the greatest value.

Find the mean, median, mode, and range of each of the following.

6. 5, 7, 9, 6, 7, 8, 6, 8, 9, 7, 8, 9, 8   7. 128, 111, 102, 107, 115, 125, 98, 135, 119

Making Line Plots and Frequency Tables   12-2

To make a line plot, use a number line.

To make a frequency distribution, make a table.

Data: 1, 0, 3, 3, 2, 1, 4, 4, 5, 7, 2, 3

```
              X
    X X X X
X X X X X X      X
◄───────────────────►
 0 1 2 3 4 5 6 7
```

n	0	1	2	3	4	5	6	7
f	1	2	2	3	2	1	0	1

Line plot   Frequency distribution

Draw a line plot and a frequency distribution for the following.

8. 8, 4, 5, 1, 8, 4, 7, 9, 10, 5, 0, 5, 3, 4, 2

Making a Stem and Leaf Plot and a Box and Whisker Plot 12-3, 12-4

To make a stem and leaf plot, arrange the data along a stem using any reasonable choice of place value.

To make a box and whisker plot, separate the data into four groups by finding the median and the medians of the upper and lower sections of data. Draw a box to extend from the first to the third quartiles. Draw whiskers from the box to the highest and lowest scores.

Data: 70, 65, 72, 83, 85, 78, 85, 78, 82, 74, 68, 76

```
6 | 5 8
7 | 0 2 4 6 8 8
8 | 2 3 5 5
```

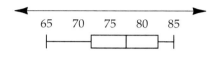

Stem and Leaf Plot   Box and Whisker Plot

Make a stem and leaf plot and a box and whisker plot for the following.

9. 75, 70, 80, 85, 85, 55, 60, 60, 65, 85, 75, 95, 50, 55, 75, 80, 65, 75

Using the Counting Principle 12-6

Use the counting principle to find the number of outcomes for two or more events. Find the product of the outcomes for each event.

Use factorials when the number of outcomes must be in an ordered arrangement.

$$\text{five factorial} \rightarrow 5! = 5 \cdot 4 \cdot 3 \cdot 2 \cdot 1$$

Find the value of each factorial.

10. $3!$ **11.** $7!$ **12.** $\frac{4!}{2!}$ **13.** $\frac{8!}{4!}$

Solve.

14. Jan has 5 pairs of pants and 7 shirts. How many different pant/shirt combinations are there for him to wear?

Using Probability and Finding the Probability of Independent and Dependent Events 12-7, 12-8

To determine probability, divide the number of favorable outcomes by the total number of possible outcomes.

To find the probability of independent and dependent events, multiply the probability of each event. For dependent events, the probability of the second event is affected by the first event.

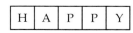

Find the probability of each event if a card is drawn at random.

15. selecting an H **16.** selecting a P **17.** selecting an A **18.** not selecting an H

19. selecting a Y, replacing it, and then selecting a P

20. selecting a Y, not replacing it, and then selecting a P

Chapter 12   Test

Find the mean, median, mode, and range of the following.

1. 15, 18, 23, 22, 19, 15, 17, 22, 29, 20   **2.** 42, 40, 39, 45, 41, 43

Draw a line plot for the following frequency distributions.

3.

x	1	2	3	4	5	6
f	0	4	2	1	3	2

4.

x	12	13	14	15	16	17
f	4	7	3	1	2	5

Arrange the set of data into a frequency table.

5. the weight of school children   98, 101, 105, 95, 108, 92, 95, 100, 101, 98, 97, 105, 92, 92, 100

Make a stem and leaf plot for the following.

6. 17, 25, 32, 18, 22, 31, 27, 16, 19, 22, 35, 28, 25, 24

7. Make a back-to-back stem and leaf plot for the data below.

200-Meter Dash Time (in seconds)	Year	1960	1964	1968	1972	1976	1980	1984	1988
	Men	20.5	20.3	19.83	20.00	20.23	20.19	19.80	19.75
	Women	24.0	23.0	22.5	22.4	22.37	22.03	21.81	21.34

Make a box and whisker plot for the following.

8. 12, 8, 5, 9, 7, 12, 6, 8, 7, 9, 10, 12   **9.** 58, 63, 45, 82, 55, 79, 59, 77, 54, 83, 58

Find the value of each factorial.

10. 4!   **11.** 5!   **12.** $\frac{9!}{3!}$ **13.** $\frac{7!}{2!}$

Solve.

14. At the school picnic the children had a choice of a hot dog or a hamburger. They had a choice of one of three toppings. How many choices did they have in all?

15. You and three friends want to have your picture made together. If you line up shoulder to shoulder, in how many ways can the picture be made?

You pick one marble at random from a bag with 4 red marbles, 3 green marbles, and 5 blue marbles. Find each probability.

16. selecting a red marble   **17.** selecting a yellow marble   **18.** selecting a green marble

19. selecting a red marble, replacing it, and then selecting another red marble

20. selecting a red marble, not replacing it, and then selecting another red marble

Chapters 1–12   Cumulative Review

Choose the correct answer. Write A, B, C, or D.

1. Name the opposite of $|-3 + (-2)^3|$.
   - **A.** 11
   - **B.** -11
   - **C.** 5
   - **D.** not given

2. The square root of a number cubed is 8. What is the number?
   - **A.** 8
   - **B.** 2
   - **C.** 4
   - **D.** not given

3. Find a decimal between $(-0.1)^2$ and 0.05.
   - **A.** 0.03
   - **B.** 0.2
   - **C.** 0.3
   - **D.** not given

4. Simplify $\frac{x^3y^4}{(x^2y^3)^2}$.
   - **A.** xy^2
   - **B.** $\frac{x}{y^2}$
   - **C.** $x^{-1}y^{-2}$
   - **D.** not given

5. Find the median.

1	6
2	5 7
3	4 4 4 6 6
4	1 2 8 9
5	4

   - **A.** 36.6
   - **B.** 36
   - **C.** 34
   - **D.** not given

6. Find the mean.

   250, 280, 240, 230, 270, 240, 270, 240, 230, 250
   - **A.** 250
   - **B.** 245
   - **C.** 240
   - **D.** not given

7. Evaluate $\frac{a^5b^3c}{a^6b^2}$ for $a = 2$, $b = -3$, and $c = -4$.
   - **A.** 12
   - **B.** 6
   - **C.** -6
   - **D.** not given

8. Find the slope for $2x - 3y = 15$.
   - **A.** 2
   - **B.** -2
   - **C.** -3
   - **D.** not given

9. In $\triangle ABC$, $\angle A = 55°$, $\angle C = 15°$. Name the triangle by angles.
   - **A.** acute
   - **B.** obtuse
   - **C.** right
   - **D.** not given

10. 25% of r is 200. What is r?
    - **A.** 25
    - **B.** 50
    - **C.** 800
    - **D.** not given

11. $3\frac{1}{5} \cdot 1\frac{1}{4} \div 2\frac{2}{3}$
    - **A.** $1\frac{1}{2}$
    - **B.** 4
    - **C.** $4\frac{4}{5}$
    - **D.** not given

12. Find the area of $\triangle CDE$.

    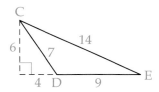

    - **A.** 27
    - **B.** 36
    - **C.** 12
    - **D.** not given

13. You have 10 red cards, 5 yellow cards, and 3 green cards. What is the probability of picking a yellow card?
    - **A.** $\frac{5}{18}$
    - **B.** $\frac{3}{18}$
    - **C.** $\frac{5}{10}$
    - **D.** not given

14. Write an inequality for *the number t is at least 35*.
    - **A.** $t > 35$
    - **B.** $t < 35$
    - **C.** $t \geq 35$
    - **D.** not given

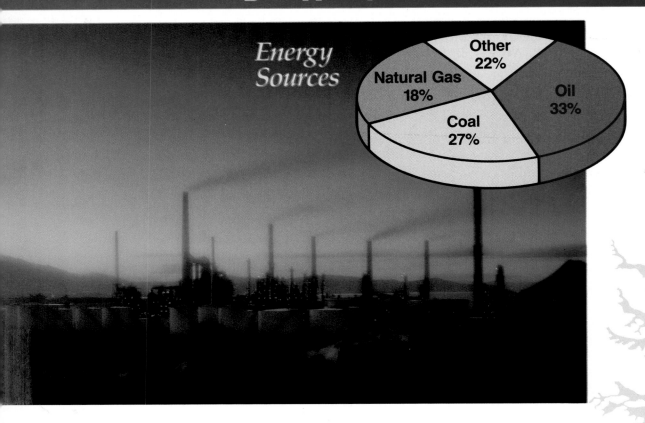

Energy Sources

Other 22%

Natural Gas 18%

Oil 33%

Coal 27%

COAL, OIL, AND NATURAL GAS are *fossil fuels.* They are formed from plants and animals that lived millions of years ago. *Carbon avoidance* is the comparative cost of a coal-fired electrical plant. The fuel and operating costs of a coal plant are about $.02/kW·h. Pollution costs are about $.015/kW·h. Thus, anything greater than $.035/kW·h is a carbon avoidance cost.

Fossil Fuel Alternative	Carbon Reduction	Carbon Avoidance Cost (per ton)
Improving Energy Efficiency	100 %	$0–19
Wind Power	100 %	$107
Geothermal Energy	99 %	$123
Wood Power	100 %	$141
Steam-injected Gas Turbine	61 %	$109–200
Solar with Gas	7.9 %	$216
Nuclear	86 %	$535

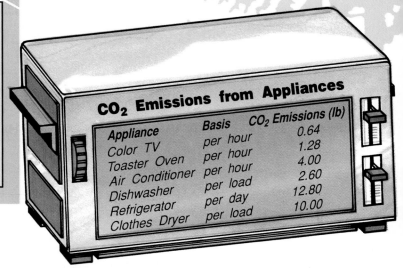

CO$_2$ Emissions from Appliances

Appliance	Basis	CO$_2$ Emissions (lb)
Color TV	per hour	0.64
Toaster Oven	per hour	1.28
Air Conditioner	per hour	4.00
Dishwasher	per load	2.60
Refrigerator	per day	12.80
Clothes Dryer	per load	10.00

Polynomials

1988 GLOBAL CARBON EMISSIONS

AREA	CARBON (millions of tons)	PER PERSON (tons)
North America	1,379	5.07
USSR	1,428	3.55
Latin America	910	2.09
W. Europe	774	2.03
Middle East	187	1.14
Africa	534	0.86
Central Asia	774	0.66
Far East Asia	833	0.55

GLOBAL WARMING ▪ Burning fossil fuels created 5.66 billion t of carbon waste in 1988, more than one ton for every person on the planet. Burning 1 t of carbon releases 3.7 t of carbon dioxide (CO_2). Carbon dioxide is a chief contributor to global warming. Some scientists believe that Earth's average temperature could rise 3°F to 9°F by the year 2050. This could result in the oceans rising, in coastal flooding, and the loss of farm land due to too much salt water.

CARBON DATA

An actively growing tree absorbs up to 26 lb of CO_2 per year.

One mature tree absorbs about 13 lb of CO_2 per year.

About $\frac{1}{2}$ the weight of any tree is carbon.

▼ Think about it...

Look at the Global Carbon Emissions data. Why do you think North America has greater carbon emissions per person than any other part of the world?

OBJECTIVE:
To explore polynomials using models.

MATERIALS

- Algebra tiles or colored paper to represent integers, variables, and a variable squared

- Math journal to record work

Exploring Polynomials

▼ You know you can use algebra tiles to represent algebraic expressions such as $4x$, $x + 3$, and $2x + 1$. You can also use algebra tiles to represent expressions such as $x^2 + 2$ and $2x^2 + 3x$.

1. *Compare* the models.

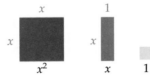

a. *Describe* the area of each model.

b. *Discuss* how the area describes the value of each model.

2. *Write* the expression represented by each model.

a.   **b.**

c.    **d.**

3. *Model* each expression.

    a. $3x^2 + 2$ **b.** $2x + 3$ **c.** $4x^2 + 3x$

    d. $x^2 + x + 4$ **e.** $3x^2 + x + 2$ **f.** $5x^2 + 4x$

▼ You can use models to help you combine like terms.

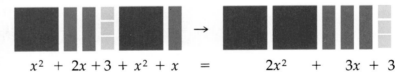

$$x^2 + 2x + 3 + x^2 + x = 2x^2 + 3x + 3$$

4. Use a model to represent each expression. Then use the model to combine like terms. Write the resulting expression.

    a. $2x^2 + 5 + 3x + x^2$

    b. $4x + 3x^2 + 5 + x^2$

    c. $7 + 3x^2 + 4x + 3 + 2x$

    d. $5x + x^2 + 2x + 6$

    e. $3x^2 + 2 + 2x + x^2 + 5$

    f. $12 + 3x^2 + 5x + 2 + x^2 + 4x$

    g. $7 + 2x^2 + 4x + 2 + 2x^2 + 3x$

Jaime Escalante proved to his students that with dedication and hard work, "there are no limits. You can become whatever you want to be." In the first year of his calculus class, all 18 students passed the Advanced Placement exam in college calculus.

5. **Describe** how you can use what you know about pairing like terms to find $(2x^2 + 3x + 4) + (x^2 + x + 3)$.

6. Use models to find each sum.

   a. $(3x^2 + 2x - 7) + (2x^2 + 4x + 2)$

   b. $(2x^2 + 3x) + (5x^2 + 8x + 12)$

   c. $(x^2 + 2) + (3x^2 + x)$

   d. $(x^2 + 3x + 2) + (2x^2 + x + 3)$

7. **Summarize** Write a rule for finding the sum of two algebraic expressions.

▼ You can use algebra tiles to help you find the difference of two algebraic expressions.

8. **Explore** what happens when you subtract $x^2 + x + 3$ from $3x^2 + 2x + 5$.

   a. Model $3x^2 + 2x + 5$.

   b. Remove tiles that represent $x^2 + x + 3$.

   c. The remaining tiles represent the difference which is $2x^2 + x + 2$.

9. **Write** the subtraction expression for each model.

   a.

   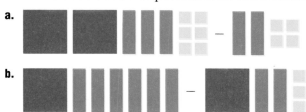

   b.

10. **Model** each difference. Write the resulting expression.

    a. $(4x^2 + 3x + 5) - (2x^2 + x + 3)$

    b. $(5x^2 + 2x + 1) - (4x^2 + 2x + 1)$

    c. $(3x^2 + 6x + 8) - (x^2 + 2x + 6)$

    d. $(6x^2 + 4x + 7) - (6x^2 + 3x + 7)$

    e. $(4x^2 + 2x + 7) - (x^2 + 2x + 3)$

    f. $(x^2 + 3x + 2) - (x^2 + 2x + 1)$

    g. $(5x^2 + 5x + 5) - (4x^2 + 4x + 4)$

13-1 Polynomials

▼ Mathematicians use algebraic expressions to represent real world situations. The expression $4.8s^2$ represents the distance in meters that an object falls in s seconds. The expression $4.8s^2$ is a *monomial*.

Monomial	A monomial is a real number, a variable, or the product of a real number and one or more variables.

A monomial cannot contain any operation other than multiplication and cannot have a variable as an exponent.

Example 1 **Tell which expressions are monomials.**

    a. $3x^2y$ **b.** 8   **c.** $8 + a$ **d.** $\frac{a}{7y}$

Solution **a.** monomial; It is the product of a real number (3) and one or more variables (x, x, y).

    b. monomial; It is a real number.

    c. not a monomial; It is the sum of a real number and a variable.

    d. not a monomial; The denominator cannot contain a variable.

▼ Some algebraic expressions that include monomials are *polynomials*.

Polynomial	A polynomial is a monomial or a sum or difference of monomials.

Example 2 **Tell which expressions are polynomials.**

    a. $x + 3y$ **b.** $\frac{7}{8}a^2 - 2b^2$ **c.** $\frac{7}{a^2} - 2b^2$

Solution **a.** polynomial; It is the sum of two monomials.

    b. polynomial; It is the difference of two monomials.

    c. not a polynomial; The expression $\frac{7}{a^2}$ is *not* a monomial because the denominator contains a variable.

FLASHBACK

Terms are the parts of an expression that are separated by addition and subtraction symbols.

▼ We call the monomials that make up a polynomial its *terms*.

Example 3 **How many terms does each polynomial have?**

    a. $3x^2y$ **b.** $2x - 4y$ **c.** $4a^2 + 2ab - 5b^2$

Solution **a.** one   **b.** two   **c.** three

▼ Some polynomials have special names that identify the number of terms in the polynomial.

Polynomial	Terms	Examples
monomial	one	$0.08x$, mn
binomial	two	$a - 3b$, $x^2y + 4$
trinomial	three	$2a - 4 + 6b$, $xy^3 - 0.2xy + 1.55y^4$

Example 4 Identify each expression as a monomial, binomial, or trinomial.

a. $3x - 2y$ **b.** $8x^3yz$ **c.** $7x^5y + 8y + 18$ **d.** $12 - n$

Solution   **a.** binomial   **b.** monomial   **c.** trinomial   **d.** binomial

▼ You can write a polynomial for a model.

Example 5 Write the polynomial represented by the model.

Solution $2x^2$ + $4x$ + 3

▼ You can model a given polynomial.

Example 6 Show a model for $3x^2 + x + 2$.

Solution

▼ You can evaluate any polynomial when given values of the variables.

Example 7 Evaluate each polynomial for $m = 8$ and $p = -3$.

a. $3m - 2p$ **b.** $m^2 + 3m - 6$ **c.** $3p^2 - 4m + 15$

Solution   **a.** $3m - 2p = 3(8) - 2(-3)$
$= 24 - (-6)$
$= 24 + 6$
$= 30$

b. $m^2 + 3m - 6 = 8^2 + 3(8) - 6$
$= 64 + 24 - 6$
$= 82$

c. $3p^2 - 4m + 15 = 3(-3)^2 - 4(8) + 15$
$= 3(9) - 4(8) + 15$
$= 27 - 32 + 15$
$= 10$

If you can jump 3 ft on Earth, you can jump 10 ft on Mercury.
Let j = height to which you can jump on Earth. What polynomial would express the height to which you could jump on Mercury?

1. Find the meaning of the prefixes used for the expressions: monomial, binomial, trinomial, and polynomial. Do the prefixes reflect the expressions they represent? What would you call a polynomial with four terms?

2. Is $y^2 + 3y + \frac{7}{y}$ a trinomial? Explain.

CLASS EXERCISES

Which of the following are monomials?

1. $2 + x$ **2.** $18ab^2$ **3.** $\frac{4}{b}$ **4.** 1

Identify each expression as a monomial, binomial, or trinomial.

5. $3xy + 4y^3$ **6.** $0.8x$ **7.** $1.7y^2 + 2.4y - 9$ **8.** 658

Write the polynomial represented by each model.

9.   **10.**

Model each polynomial.

11. $3x^2 + 2x + 4$ **12.** $5x^2 + 3^2$ **13.** $2a^2 + a + 7$

Evaluate each polynomial for $a = 2$ and $b = 4$.

14. $5a + 7b$ **15.** $2a^2 - b + 4$ **16.** $ab^2 + 5$

WRITTEN EXERCISES

Which of the following are monomials?

1. $2x$ **2.** $-0.3y + 9.35$ **3.** $\frac{a}{3}$ **4.** 8

How many terms are in each expression?

5. $-x^2 + 3x$ **6.** 5 **7.** $27 + x - 4xy$

8. $16 - 3xy + c + x^2$ **9.** x **10.** $x^2yz - 1$

Identify each expression as a monomial, binomial, or trinomial.

11. $3x^2 + 2x$ **12.** 21 **13.** $7p^2$ **14.** $1 + 4x - xy$

15. $5x$ **16.** $56 - x$ **17.** $4.5 + 3.7a$ **18.** $x^2 + 7x + 4$

Model each polynomial.

19. $2x^2 + x + 4$ **20.** $x^2 + 3x + 1$ **21.** $4x^2 + 2x$

22. $3x^2 + 5$ **23.** $2x + 6$ **24.** $4x^2 + 3x$

Write the polynomial represented by each model.

25.   **26.**

27.

28.

29. *WRITE* at least five words that begin with mono-, bi-, tri-, or poly-.
Give the meaning of each word.

MENTAL MATH Evaluate each polynomial for $a = 1$, $b = 2$, and $c = -1$.

30. $4a + b$ **31.** $a^2 + 2a + 3$ **32.** $b^2 + 6$

33. $3c + b$ **34.** $c^2 + c - 1$ **35.** $a^2 + c$

CALCULATOR Evaluate each polynomial for $d = 12$, $e = -11$,
and $m = 15$.

36. $2d^2 + d$ **37.** $d^2 + 3d + 7$ **38.** $3d + 4e$

39. $m^2 - 2m$ **40.** $e^2 + 4e - 6$ **41.** $8d + 7m$

Critical Thinking

EXPLORING CONCLUSIONS

For each Given, tell whether or not the Conclusions are possible.

1. Given: $x - 7 < 0$
$x + 3 > 0$

Conclusions:

a. $x = 0$

b. $x = -1$

c. $x < 7$ and $x > -3$

d. $x > 7$

e. $x < -7$

2. Given: $3y < 100$

$\frac{y}{2} > 5$

Conclusions:

a. $y = 5$

b. $y = -5$

c. $y < 0$

d. $y \geq 0$

e. $y > 10$ and $y < 33\frac{1}{3}$

3. Given: $a^2 > 90$
$a + 3 < 20$

Conclusions:

a. $a < 20$

b. $a > -10$

c. $a = 7$

d. $a = 12$

e. $a < -10$

4. Given: $n^2 + 6 > 30$
$n + 6 > 5$

Conclusions:

a. $n > 0$

b. $n < 0$

c. $n = 0$

d. $n > 5$

e. $n < 5$

MIXED REVIEW

Simplify.

1. $x^2 x^3$ **2.** $(4m^2)^3$

Are the events dependent or independent?

3. $P(A) = \frac{3}{7}$ $P(B) = \frac{1}{3}$
$P(A \text{ and } B) = \frac{1}{7}$

4. $P(A) = \frac{5}{6}$ $P(B) = \frac{2}{5}$
$P(A \text{ and } B) = \frac{5}{24}$

Simplify.

5. $2x^2 + 3x^2 + x^2$

6. $3(x + 3) - 2x - x$

Solve.

7. Four class officers and their advisor want to stand side-by-side for a photograph. How many poses are possible?

13-2 Adding and Subtracting Polynomials

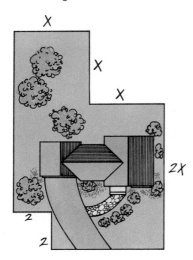

▼ The figure at the left represents a lawn. You can express the area of the lawn by the polynomial $4x^2 - 4 + x^2$ or simplify it as $5x^2 - 4$.

▼ You can model addition of polynomials.

Example 1 Use models to find $(2x^2 + 3x + 7) + (x^2 + x + 3)$.

Solution
$2x^2 + 3x + 7$

$x^2 + x + 3$

The sum is $3x^2$ + $4x$ + 10.

▼ You can add polynomials using number properties to combine like terms.

Example 2 Find $(5y^2 + 3y + 9) + (2y^2 + 5y - 7)$.

Solution
$(5y^2 + 2y^2) + (3y + 5y) + (9 - 7)$	Group like terms.
$(5 + 2)y^2 + (3 + 5)y + (9 - 7)$	Use the distributive property.
$7y^2 + 8y + 2$	

THINK How would you use the associative and commutative properties to group like terms?

▼ You can add polynomials in a column by aligning like terms and then combining them.

Example 3 Find the sum of $2z^2 + 5xz - x^2$ and $4z^2 - 3xz + x^2$.

Solution

$$\begin{array}{r} 2z^2 + 5xz - x^2 \\ + \ 4z^2 - 3xz + x^2 \\ \hline 6z^2 + 2xz + 0 = 6z^2 + 2xz \end{array}$$

Align like terms.
Add the terms in each column.

▼ You can model subtraction of polynomials.

Example 4 Use models to find $(4x^2 + 5x) - (2x^2 + 4x)$.

Solution
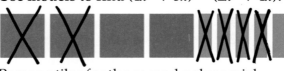
$4x^2 + 5x$

Remove tiles for the second polynomial.
Count the remaining tiles.

The difference is $2x^2 + x$.

▼ You can subtract polynomials by adding the opposite of each term in the second polynomial.

Example 5   Find $(5x - 9 + y) - (2x + 4 - 3y)$.

Solution $5x - 9 + y + (\text{-}2x) + (\text{-}4) + 3y$ Add the opposite of the second polynomial.

$5x + (\text{-}2x) - 9 + (\text{-}4) + y + 3y$ Group like terms.
$(5 - 2)x \quad - \quad 9 - 4 \quad + (1 + 3)y$ Use the distributive property.

$\qquad 3x \qquad - \quad 13 \quad + \quad 4y$

THINK Why is subtracting a polynomial the same as adding its opposite?

▼ You can use these methods to add and subtract polynomials when solving equations.

Example 6   **a.** Write a polynomial for the perimeter of the polygon. Simplify.

        b. If $P = 26$ and $b = 3$, find a.

Solution   **a.** $4a + b + b + a + a + b + a + b$
$\quad 7a + 4b$ Combine like terms.

     b. $\quad 7a + 4b = 26$ Write an equation.
$\qquad 7a + 4(3) = 26$ Substitute values.
$\qquad\quad 7a + 12 = 26$
$\qquad\qquad\quad 7a = 14$
$\qquad\qquad\quad\ a = 2$

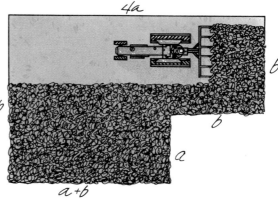

CLASS EXERCISES

Use a model to find each sum.

1. $(x^2 + 3x + 1) + (x^2 + x + 6)$

2. $(x^2 + 5x + 2) + (3x^2 + x + 1)$

Find each sum.

3. $(3x - 2y) + (5x + 4y)$

4. $(x^2 + 3x - 7) + (x^2 - 6x - 9)$

5. $\quad\ 5a + 7b$
$\underline{+\ \text{-}3a + 2b}$

6. $x^4 + 3x^3 - x^2 + \ x - 2$
$\underline{+ \qquad 7x^3 + x^2 - 5x - 9}$

Use a model to find each difference.

7. $(2x^2 + 3x) - (x^2 + 2x)$

8. $(x^2 + 3x + 5) - (x^2 + x + 2)$

Find each difference by adding opposites.

9. $(8j - 3k + 6m) - (\text{-}2j + 3m)$

10. $(\text{-}11a^2 + 2a - 1) - (7a^2 + 4a - 1)$

11. $(9x^2 - 4y + 5z) - (-4x^2 - 15z)$

THINK AND DISCUSS

1. Describe the three methods you could use to add polynomials. Which do you prefer? Explain.

2. Explain how you could use a column format to subtract polynomials.

3. What is true about the sum of a polynomial and its opposite?

4. Compare and contrast the methods for adding whole numbers with those for adding polynomials. Then repeat for the subtraction methods.

12. Three numbers are consecutive multiples of 4.

    a. Write an expression for their sum. Use polynomials for each term. Then simplify the expression.

    b. Find the numbers if the sum is 108.

Find the area of each polygon.

1.

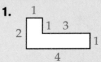

2.

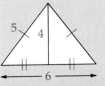

State the number of terms in each polynomial.

3. $8yz + 1$

4. $5 + 4xy - z$

Simplify.

5. $6x + 3(x - 2) + 8x$

6. $2(12x + 3 - 10y)$

7. A student participates in a walk for charity. His friends pledged a total of $3.20 for each mile he walked. The student earned $22.80 for the charity. How many miles did he walk?

WRITTEN EXERCISES

Use a model to find each sum.

1. $(x^2 + 3x - 2) + (3x^2 + 2x + 4)$

2. $(x^2 + 2x + 1) + (x^2 + 3x + 4)$

Find each sum by combining like terms.

3. $3x + 2 + (\text{-}4x + 3)$ **4.** $5x^2 + 3x + 7 + (7x - 2)$

5. $\text{-}4x^2 + 2x - 1 + (x^2 - x + 8)$

6. $7x^3 + 4x^2 + 3x - 1 + (8x^3 - 10x + 18)$

7. $x^2 + 4x - 2$
   $+\ 8x^2 - 3x + 7$
   $\overline{}$

8. $xy + 5x - 2y + 4$
   $+\ 2xy - 3x - 3y - 8$
   $\overline{}$

9. $x^3 + 5x^2 + 3x - 2$
   $+\ x^3 - 2x + 6$
   $\overline{}$

10. $4x^2 - 5xy + 7$
   $+\ 8x^2 + 3xy - 3y - 4$
   $\overline{}$

Use a model to find each difference.

11. $(5x + 9) - (2x + 1)$ **12.** $(3x^2 + x + 7) - (2x^2 + x + 2)$

Subtract each by adding the opposite of the second polynomial.

13. $(6y - 8) - (2y + 7)$ **14.** $(x^2 - 3x - 9) - (5x - 4)$

15. $(mn^2 + 4m - n^2) - (\text{-}3mn^2 + 2m + n^2)$

16. $(6a^2b + 5ab^2 - 8) - (2a^2b - 3ab^2 + 1)$

17. $(4a^2 + 3ab + b) - (2a^2 - 2ab - b)$

18. $(7p^2q^2 + 5pq - 8) - (4pq - 5)$

Add or subtract.

19. $(3m - 8) + (2m + 1)$ **20.** $(8j^2 + 2j) - (6j^2 + j)$

21. $(ab + 4) + (3ab + 6)$ **22.** $(13d^2q - 3dq^2) + (2d^2q + 5dq^2)$

23. $(w^2 + 5w) + (2w - 6)$ **24.** $(11t^2 + 2) - (3t^2 + 2)$

25. $(x^2 - 5x - 9) + (\text{-}4x^2 - 3x + 17)$

26. $(ab + b - 4a) + (\text{-}2ab + 6b + 2a)$

27. $(y - 3x + 1) + (5x + 9 + y)$

28. $(-3x^4y^3 - 5xy + 2) + (x^4y^3 + x^2 + xy + 1)$

29. $(9a^7 - 7a^4 + a^2 - 8) + (8a^7 + 15a^4 + 12)$

30. $(m^3n - 3m^2n^2 + 8mn - 6) + (m^3n + 3m^2n^2 + 8mn + 6)$

31. $(4a^3b^2 - 9a^2b + 2ab + 11) + (7a^3b^2 - 6a^2b - 4ab + 12)$

32. WRITE a paragraph explaining how you can use the commutative, associative, and distributive properties in the addition and subtraction of polynomials.

Write an expression for each phrase. Use the same variable in each term of the expression.

33. the sum of three consecutive multiples of 2

   a. Simplify the expression.

   b. Find the numbers if their sum is 36.

34. the sum of four consecutive even numbers

   a. Simplify the expression.

   b. Find the numbers if their sum is 84.

35. the sum of five consecutive multiples of 5

   a. Simplify the expression.

   b. Find the numbers if their sum is 375.

Write the perimeter of each figure as a polynomial. Simplify.

36.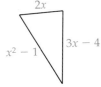

37.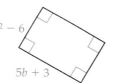

38. $2a^2 - 1$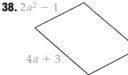

39. The sum of the interior angles of a convex polygon with n sides is $180(n - 2)$. Find the sum of the interior angles for each polygon.

   a. square   **b.** pentagon   **c.** hexagon   **d.** decagon

40. Use the article at the right.

   a. Write a polynomial to represent the amount of fuel the space shuttle burns in m minutes.

   b. Write the speed of the space shuttle in miles per hour. Round to the nearest whole mile. *Hint:* 5,280 ft = 1 mi.

   c. The air distance from New York to Paris is 3,624 mi. Suppose you could fly from New York to Paris on the space shuttle. How long would the trip take? Round to the nearest tenth of an hour. What is the percent of change from Lindbergh's flight? Round to the nearest percent.

Exploring Takes Energy

Charles Lindbergh's historic flight from New York to Paris in 1927 took 33.5 h. Lindbergh's plane, the *Spirit of St. Louis,* had no front window. An extra tank of gas carrying 450 gal of gas weighing 4,000 lb took the window's place. Today's space shuttle uses about 8,000 lb of fuel per minute at liftoff alone. In flight, the space shuttle flies at a speed of 3,700 ft/s at an altitude 100 mi above Earth.

OBJECTIVE:
To multiply a
polynomial by a
monomial.

13-3 *Multiplying a Polynomial by a Monomial*

▼ You can write a polynomial to describe the area of the rectangle at the left. You can use a model to illustrate both the area and a way to simplify the resulting expression.

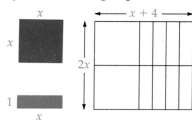

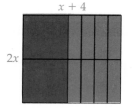

$$2x(x + 4) = 2x^2 + 8x$$

▼ You can use the distributive property to find the product of a monomial and a binomial.

Example 1 **Simplify $3x(x - 4)$.**

Solution $3x(x) + 3x(-4)$ Use the distributive property.
$3x^2 - 12x$ Simplify.

▼ You can also use the distributive property to find the product of a monomial and a polynomial with more than two terms.

Example 2 **Simplify $-2x(z^2 - 3x + y - 7)$.**

Solution $-2x(z^2) - 2x(-3x) - 2x(y) - 2x(-7)$
$-2xz^2 + 6x^2 - 2xy + 14x$

▼ You can use the rules of exponents to simplify the product of a monomial and a polynomial.

Example 3 **Simplify $3x^2(8x^2 - 5xy + 2y^3)$.**

Solution $3x^2(8x^2) + 3x^2(-5xy) + 3x^2(2y^3)$
$3(8)x^2x^2 + 3(-5)x^2xy + 3(2)x^2y^3$
$24x^4 - 15x^3y + 6x^2y^3$

FLASHBACK

When multiplying powers with the same base, add exponents.

The expression $-2(8t^2 - 70t)$, where t equals time in seconds, represents the height in feet at which a fireworks burst will explode. At what height would a burst explode after 7s?

CLASS EXERCISES

Use a model to find each product.

1. $2x(x + 4)$ **2.** $x(2x + 3)$ **3.** $3x(x + 1)$

4. $x(x + 5)$ **5.** $2x(x + 3)$ **6.** $2x(3x + 1)$

Use the distributive property to find each product.

7. $3x(x + 5)$ **8.** $-4xy(2x - 3y)$

9. $5x(-3x^2 + 2x)$ **10.** $4x(7x^6 - 3x^5 + 2x^2 + 1)$

11. $xy(x^2 + 2xy + y^2)$ **12.** $3x^2y(2x^2 - xy + y^2)$

Use the distributive property to find each product. Then evaluate the polynomial for $x = 5$ and $y = 7$.

13. $x^2(y + 7)$ **14.** $-2x(3x + xy - y^2)$

15. $2x^2(y + 3)$ **16.** $2y(x + y)$

Write an expression for the area of each shaded region.

17.

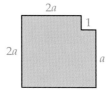

18.

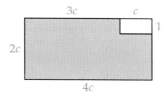

WRITTEN EXERCISES

Use a model to find each product.

1. $2x(x + 6)$ **2.** $x(2x + 6)$ **3.** $2x(3x - 1)$

4. $3x(2x + 4)$ **5.** $x(5x + 3)$ **6.** $2x(4x + 7)$

7. MENTAL MATH Complete each exercise using two different methods. First substitute the value for the variable, then multiply. Next, multiply the polynomial first, then substitute the value for the variable. Evaluate each of the following for $x = 1$, $y = -1$, and $z = 2$.

    a. $3x(-6y + z)$ **b.** $y^2(x - y)$ **c.** $5z(3x + y^2)$ **d.** $2x^2(z^2 - y^2)$

    e. WRITE a paragraph telling which method of solving the expressions above you found to be the easiest. Explain.

CALCULATOR Find each product. Then evaluate the expression for $x = 12$ and $y = -15$.

8. $2x^2(x^2 + y^2)$ **9.** $-4xy(xy - x^2)$ **10.** $x^2(5x + y^2 - y)$

Use the distributive property to find each product.

11. $2x(4x - 1)$

12. $x(x^2 + 3x)$

13. $x^2(2x - 5)$

14. $x^2(x^2 - 9)$

15. $y^2(y + 2y^2 - 3)$

16. $-3(2x^2 - 3x - 1)$

17. $5xy(x + 5 - y)$

18. $5a^2bc^2(abc - a^2b^2c^2 + 6a^2bc)$

19. $-3xy(2x^2y + xy + y^2 - 3)$

20. $4z(2z^6 - 3z^5 - 12z^2 + 8)$

21. $8xyz(12x^2y^2 + 3x^3z^5)$

22. $-2x^2b^2(-4xb^3 + 3x^3b^2)$

23. $12x^2(x + y^2 + z)$

24. $-4x^2y(25x^5y^2z + 8x^3y)$

25. $\frac{1}{2}y(x + xy^2 + 5)$

26. $3y\left(x^2 - xy - \frac{1}{3}x\right)$

27. $7x^2(2x^2 + y^2 - xy)$

28. $4x^2(x^2 + xy - y^2)$

29. $3x(x^2 + 5) + 2x(x - 3)$

30. $2y(-y + 4) + 3(y - 5)$

Solve. Use only one variable for each expression.

31. Assume e is an even integer. Write an expression to represent the product of e and the next consecutive even integer. Simplify.

32. Assume m is a multiple of 6. Write an expression to represent the product of m and the next consecutive integer that is a multiple of 6. Simplify.

33. The width of a rectangle is $\frac{1}{2}$ the length plus 7. Write an expression to represent its area. Then simplify the expression.

34. The length of a rectangle is 5 less than 4 times its width. Write an expression to represent its area. Simplify.

35. The base length of a triangle is $8x$. The triangle's height is twice that plus 5. Write an expression for the area of the triangle. Simplify.

36. The height of an isosceles triangle is $\frac{1}{3}$ its base less 3. Write an expression to represent its area. Simplify.

37. Express the number 792 in expanded form. Let $x = 10$. Write a polynomial to represent the number. Then write a polynomial in x to represent 40. Find the product of the two polynomials. Simplify it and substitute 10 for x. Is your answer equal to 40(792)?

Write an expression for the area of the shaded region.

38.

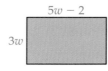

39.

40.

41.

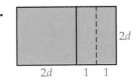

Exploring Mind-reading Tricks

OBJECTIVE:
To explore algebraic
expressions.

MATERIALS

- Algebra tiles or colored
paper

- Math journal to record
work

■ You have probably heard of mind-reading tricks. Most such tricks are simple applications of algebraic expressions.

1. Think of a number. Add 4. Multiply by 2. Subtract 6. Divide by 2. Subtract your original number. What is your final result?

   a. **Model** each step of the process with algebra tiles. The number you think of is the variable. Use the rectangle to represent this number. Use positive tiles to represent the units.

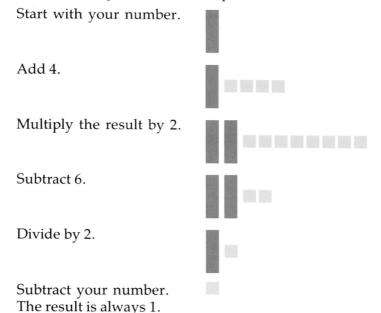

   Start with your number.

   Add 4.

   Multiply the result by 2.

   Subtract 6.

   Divide by 2.

   Subtract your number.
   The result is always 1.

   b. Use a variable to replace the tiles.

Start with your number.	n
Add 4.	$n + 4$
Multiply the result by 2.	$2(n + 4) = 2n + 8$
Subtract 6.	$2n + 8 - 6 = 2n + 2$
Divide by 2.	$\frac{2n + 2}{2} = n + 1$
Subtract your number.	$n + 1 - n = 1$

   The result is always 1.

2. **Explore** Use algebra tiles and then variables to find the result of another trick.

   Think of a number. Triple it. Add 14. Subtract 5. Divide by 3. Subtract your original number. What do you get?

   a. **Write** an equation to summarize your exploration of the trick.

   b. Make up a mind-reading trick of your own and try it on a classmate. Then explain how the trick works.

13-4 Multiplying Binomials

NOTES & QUOTES

Isaac Newton (1642–1727) invented the binomial theorem, a formula for finding the product of the expression $(x + y)^2$. By the age of 23, Newton also had made discoveries about the nature of light, had invented calculus, and had established the theory of universal gravitation. When hailed for his achievements, Newton modestly replied, "If I have seen a little farther than others, it is because I have stood on the shoulders of giants."

DISCUSS the meaning of Newton's famous quote.

▼ Suppose a is an even integer. You can represent the product of the next two consecutive odd integers, $a + 1$ and $a + 3$, by the expression $(a + 1)(a + 3)$.

You can use a model to help find the product.

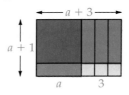

$$(a + 1)(a + 3) = a^2 + 4a + 3$$

▼ If you think of one binomial as a single expression, you can use the distributive property twice to multiply two binomials.

Example 1 Multiply $(x - 3)(x + 4)$.

Solution	$(x - 3)x + (x - 3)4$	Multiply the first binomial by each term in the second.
	$x(x) - 3(x) + x(4) - 3(4)$	Multiply each binomial and monomial.
	$x^2 - 3x + 4x - 12$	Combine like terms.
	$x^2 + x - 12$	Simplify.

▼ The FOIL method is another way to find the product of two binomials.

1. Multiply the First terms in each binomial.
2. Multiply the Outside terms in each binomial.
3. Multiply the Inside terms in each binomial.
4. Multiply the Last terms in each binomial.
5. Add the products.

Example 2 Multiply $(x + 2)(x + 6)$.

Solution

Outside
First
$(x + 2)$ $(x + 6)$
Inside
Last

First   Outside   Inside   Last
$x(x) + $ $x(6)$ $ + $ $2(x)$ $ + 2(6)$

$x^2 + 6x + 2x + 12$ Combine like terms.
$x^2 + 8x + 12$ Simplify.

▼ When you use FOIL to multiply the sum and difference of the same terms, or to square a binomial, the product has interesting characteristics.

Example 3 Multiply $(a + 5)(a - 5)$.

Solution $(a + 5)(a - 5) = a^2 - 5a + 5a - 25$
$$= a^2 - 25$$

Example 4 Multiply.

   a. $(a + 7)^2$ **b.** $(a - 3)^2$

Solution   **a.** $(a + 7)(a + 7) = a^2 + 14a + 49$
   b. $(a - 3)(a - 3) = a^2 - 6a + 9$

The examples lead to the following rules for finding special products.

Product of **$(a + b)(a - b)$**	To find the product of the sum and difference of two terms, square the first term and subtract the square of the second term. $$(a + b)(a - b) = a^2 - b^2$$

Squaring **Binomials**	To square a binomial, square the first term then add or subtract twice the product of the two terms and add the square of the second term. $$(a + b)^2 = a^2 + 2ab + b^2$$ $$(a - b)^2 = a^2 - 2ab + b^2$$

> **FLASHBACK**
> The square of a number is the product of the number and itself.

CLASS EXERCISES

Find each product using models.

1. $(x + 2)(x + 1)$ **2.** $(x + 1)(x + 4)$
3. $(x + 2)(x + 2)$ **4.** $(x + 2)(x + 3)$

Find each product using the distributive property.

5. $(x + 3)(x - 2)$ **6.** $(x + 7)(x + 9)$ **7.** $(y - 2)(y - 4)$

Find each product using the FOIL method.

8. $(a - 9)(a + 1)$ **9.** $(x + 3)(x - 4)$ **10.** $(x - 7)(x + 5)$

Find each product.

11. $(x + 5)^2$ **12.** $(x - 2)(x + 2)$ **13.** $(x - 5)^2$

> ▼
> **THINK AND DISCUSS**
> **1.** How is using FOIL similar to using the distributive property? Which method do you prefer?
> **2.** Does the product of two binomials always have three terms? Could it have two? four? more than four? Explain.

WRITTEN EXERCISES

Find each product using models.

1. $(x + 1)(x + 6)$ **2.** $(x + 2)(x + 4)$ **3.** $(a + 1)(a + 7)$

Find each product using the distributive property.

4. $(a - 1)(a + 6)$ **5.** $(a + 3)(a - 2)$ **6.** $(y - 16)(y + 20)$

7. $(a + 3)(a + 8)$ **8.** $(x + 4)(2x + 1)$ **9.** $(x + a)(y + b)$

Find each product using FOIL.

10. $(y + 2)(y + 8)$ **11.** $(x + 1)(x + 12)$ **12.** $(x - 8)(x - 3)$

13. $(3 + x)(5 - x)$ **14.** $(3x + 1)(2x - 4)$ **15.** $(2a + b)(4c - 2d)$

Find each product.

16. $(y + 5)^2$ **17.** $(x - 3)(x + 3)$ **18.** $(a - 8)(a + 8)$

19. $(b - 7)^2$ **20.** $(y - 10)^2$ **21.** $(2a + 5)(2a - 5)$

22. $(a + 7)(a - 8)$ **23.** $(2a + 1)^2$ **24.** $(a - 15)(a + 15)$

25. $(x - 21)(x + 36)$ **26.** $(x - 5)(x - 8)$ **27.** $(3a + 4)(a - 2)$

28. $(x - 2)(x + 11)$ **29.** $(x + 1.3)(x - 4.8)$ **30.** $(3x + y)(x^2 + 2)$

31. $(b - 1)^3$ **32.** $(x + 1)(x^2 + 2x - 3)$ **33.** $-4(2a + 1)(a - 3)$

MENTAL MATH Find each product mentally.

34. $(x - 1)^2$ **35.** $(x + 1)^2$ **36.** $(x + 3)^2$

37. $(x - y)(x + y)$ **38.** $(x + 1)(x - 1)$ **39.** $(x + 2)(x + 2)$

Write an expression for the area of each rectangle. Simplify the expression.

40.
$x + 3$ ⎤
         $2x + 1$

41.
$2x + 4$ ⎤
         $5x + 3$

42.
$4x - 5$ ⎤
         $3x + 1$

43.
$10x - 2$ ⎤
         $2x + 1$

Solve. Write an expression to represent each problem. Use one variable in each expression. Then simplify each expression.

44. Assume e is an even integer. Find the product of the next two consecutive even integers.

45. Assume w is an integer that is a multiple of 3. Find the product of the previous two consecutive integers.

46. The base of a parallelogram is $w + 5$ centimeters. The height is 2 cm less. Find the area of the parallelogram.

47. The side of a square is $(t - 6)$ meters. Find the area.

48. Two right triangles are joined to form a rectangle. The base of the triangle is m units. The height of the triangle is $m + 2$ units. Find the area of the rectangle.

Solve each equation.

49. $3(x + 5) - 2(x + 6) = 5$

50. $4(a - 3) + 5(a + 7) = 14$

51. $-(w + 7) - 6(w + 6) = -43$

52. $5(b - 6) + 4(6 - b) = -8$

53. *DATA FILE 8 (pp. 312–313)* By about how many miles does the center of population move each year?

54. *DATA FILE 10 (pp. 404–405)* The area of Rhode Island is about 1,055 mi². About how long does it take to destroy an area of rain forests equal to the area of Rhode Island?

> **FLASHBACK**
> $27{,}878{,}400 \text{ ft}^2 = 1 \text{ mi}^2$
> $1 \text{ acre} = 43{,}560 \text{ ft}^2$

TEST YOURSELF

Is each a monomial, binomial, trinomial, or not a polynomial?

1. $4x$

2. $5y + 6$

3. $\dfrac{7}{w}$

4. $m^2 + 3m - 7$

5. $186.5p$

6. $3g + g^2$

7. $14v7v$

8. $\dfrac{a}{3}$

Evaluate each polynomial for $x = 7$, $y = 10$, and $z = -5$.

9. $x^2 + 5x - 3$

10. $y^2 + z$

11. $z^2 + 5z - x$

12. $x^2 - y^2$

13. $y^2 - z + x$

14. $z^2 + x^2 - y^2$

Add or subtract.

15. $(7a + 3) + (4a - 3)$

16. $(p + 7) + (p^2 + 5)$

17. $(3ab^2 + 9) + (2a + b)$

18. $(rs - 6) - (r^2s^2 + 10)$

19. Write an expression for the area of square that has sides of length $a^2 + b$. Simplify the expression.

20. *WRITE* a sentence explaining how to use the FOIL method to find the product of two polynomials.

Practice

CAREER

Help Wanted: Finance Manager

A Bachelor's degree in accounting or finance, or a business degree with emphasis on accounting or finance is required.

For more information, write: American Financial Services Association, 919 18th St. NW, Suite 300, Washington, DC, 20006.

Financial managers plan and analyze operations in a business. They evaluate a company's performance and determine the company's monetary needs. Financial managers use formulas to compile data to make decisions.

PROJECT

Analyze the cost of running a car wash. Decide what materials you will need and what they will cost. Use the information to decide on a price to charge per car.

Tell how many terms are in each of the following expressions. Then identify each as a monomial, binomial or trinomial.

1. $3x^2 + x$

2. xy

3. $5x + 3$

4. $7x^2 + x + 4$

5. 72

6. $2xy + x + y$

Add or subtract.

7. $(2r^2 - 5) + (4r^2 + 2)$

8. $(5ab - 2) - (ab + 6)$

9. $(-8d + 2) - (-4d + 3)$

10. $(6c^2 - 3a) + (-5c^2 - 2a)$

11. $(-7x^2y - 2xy + 7) - (5x^2 + 4xy - 6)$

12. $(3mn^2 - mn + 6) + (4mn^2 + mn - 2)$

13. $(5rt^2 + 4r^2t - 2t) - (3rt^2 - 2r^2t - 4t)$

14. $(2jk^2 + 5jk + j - 4) + (jk^2 + 3jk - j - 1)$

Use the distributive property to find each product.

15. $3x(7y + 2)$

16. $-6xy(4x^2 - 2y^2)$

17. $5xy(4x + 3y)$

18. $7ab^2(a - b + 4)$

19. $2a^2b^2(5a^2 - 5b^2)$

20. $6x^2y(7x^2 + 3y^2 + 2xy - 5)$

21. $4cd(2c + 3d - 6)$

22. $3x^2yz(4x + 5y + 6z - 2)$

Find each product.

23. $(x + 5)^2$

24. $(x - 7)(2x + 9)$

25. $(x - 1.5)(x - 3)$

26. $(2x + 3)^2$

27. $(x + 5)(x - 5)$

28. $(2x - 4)(2x + 4)$

29. $(x - 5)^2$

30. $(4x - 10)(x - 8)$

31. $(x^2 - 2)(x - 5)$

32. $(x + 1)(x + 1)$

33. $(6x + 2)(2x + 6)$

34. $(x^2 - x)(x^2 - 8)$

35. $(-5x + 2)^2$

36. $9(x + 4)(x - 2)$

37. $(10x^2 - 2)(3x^2 + x)$

38. $9(x + 4)^2$

39. $3(x + 6)(x^2 - 4x)$

40. $\left(\frac{1}{2}x - 67\right)\left(\frac{1}{3}x + 12\right)$

Evaluate each polynomial for $x = 3$, $y = -2$, and $z = 1$.

41. $x^2 + 4$

42. $3x^2 - 2y + z$

43. $4x^2y^2 - 4x + 8$

44. $7xy - 3z$

45. $-3z^2y + 2xy$

46. $-x^2 + 2y - z + 8$

47. $30x^5 - 10z^{10}$

48. $-22xyz^3$

49. $2x^2 + y - 50$

50. $25x^3 + 5y^2 + 10z - 1$

51. $z^5 + x^2 - y$

52. $5x^2 - 2y^2$

53. $y^2 + xyz$

54. $3x + z^2$

55. $y^2 - z + x^2$

56. $(x + y)^2$

OBJECTIVE:
To solve systems of equations using matrices.

13-5 *Using Matrices*

■ You can use a *matrix* to solve a system of linear equations.

| **Matrix** | A matrix is an array of numbers written in brackets. |

■ The matrix of a system of two linear equations in two variables is square and is made up of the coefficients from each equation.

Example 1 **Determine the matrix of coefficients for the system of linear equations.**

$$3x + 5y = 13$$
$$2x + 3y = 8$$

Solution $\begin{bmatrix} 3 & 5 \\ 2 & 3 \end{bmatrix}$ Write the coefficients for x in one column and the coefficients for y in the other column.

■ A *determinant* is real number value associated with a square matrix.

THINK How is evaluating a determinant similar to cross multiplication?

| **Determinant** | We define the determinant (D) of a square matrix as $D = \begin{vmatrix} a_1 & b_1 \\ a_2 & b_2 \end{vmatrix} = a_1 b_2 - a_2 b_1.$ |

THINK How do you know whether a matrix or a determinant is being shown?

Example 2 **Find the determinant of the matrix below.**

$$\begin{bmatrix} 8 & 3 \\ 4 & 5 \end{bmatrix}$$

Solution $D = \begin{vmatrix} 8 & 3 \\ 4 & 5 \end{vmatrix} = 8(5) - 4(3) = 28$

■ You can use *Cramer's rule* and determinants to find the solution of a system of equations.

| **Cramer's Rule** | Cramer's rule uses the following determinants. $D = \begin{vmatrix} a_1 & b_1 \\ a_2 & b_2 \end{vmatrix} \quad D_x = \begin{vmatrix} c_1 & b_1 \\ c_2 & b_2 \end{vmatrix} \quad D_y = \begin{vmatrix} a_1 & c_1 \\ a_2 & c_2 \end{vmatrix}$ The x value of the solution is $\frac{D_x}{D}$ and the y value is $\frac{D_y}{D}$. The letter c in each matrix represents the constant term in each equation. |

Example 3 Solve the system of equations using Cramer's rule.

$$3x + y = 5$$
$$2x + 3y = 8$$

Solution
1. Solve for D. $D = \begin{vmatrix} 3 & 1 \\ 2 & 3 \end{vmatrix} = 3(3) - 2(1) = 7$

2. Solve for D_x. $D_x = \begin{vmatrix} 5 & 1 \\ 8 & 3 \end{vmatrix} = 5(3) - 8(1) = 7$

3. Solve for D_y. $D_y = \begin{vmatrix} 3 & 5 \\ 2 & 8 \end{vmatrix} = 3(8) - 2(5) = 14$

4. Solve for x and y.

$$x = \frac{D_x}{D} = \frac{7}{7} = 1 \qquad y = \frac{D_y}{D} = \frac{14}{7} = 2$$

The solution of the system of equations is $(1,2)$.

THINK How could you check to make sure that $(1,2)$ is the solution?

CLASS EXERCISES

Determine the matrix of coefficients for each system of equations. Evaluate the determinant of each matrix.

1. $2x + 6y = 22$
  $4x + 3y = 17$

2. $x + 2y = 3$
  $3y - x = 2$

3. $-4y + 6x = 16$
  $-2x + 3y = -2$

4. What will be the value of the determinant if all elements in one column are zero?

■■■■■■ Decision Making ■ **DECISION MAKING** ■ Decision Making ■ Decision Making ■ Decision Making ■

USING MATRICES

■ You can solve real life problems using matrices.

■ **COLLECT DATA**

1. a. Visit a travel agent and find the prices of a round-trip coach ticket to Paris and to Mexico City. Record the data in a chart like the one below.

City	Travel Cost	Hotel Cost
Paris		
Mexico City		

  b. Your travel agent will be able to recommend a hotel in the area. Record the price of the hotel in your chart.

2. Look in the newspaper and find the exchange rate from dollars to francs and from dollars to pesos.

WRITTEN EXERCISES

Write the matrix of coefficients for each system of linear equations.

1. $x + 2y = 16$
$2x + 3y = 26$

2. $y = 2x$
$-x + y = 1$

3. $y = -3x + 17$
$2y + 6 = 2x$

Evaluate each determinant.

4. $\begin{vmatrix} 3 & 4 \\ 2 & 9 \end{vmatrix}$

5. $\begin{vmatrix} 8 & 4 \\ -6 & -2 \end{vmatrix}$

6. $\begin{vmatrix} -7 & -2 \\ 0 & 11 \end{vmatrix}$

Solve each system of linear equations using Cramer's rule.

7. $2x + 4y = 12$
$3x + 5y = 14$

8. $-4x + 7y = 1$
$25 = 2x + 5y$

9. $x + 2y = 3$
$3y - x = 2$

Write a system of linear equations for each situation. Solve using Cramer's rule.

10. At the grocery store, one box of laundry detergent and two bottles of fabric softener cost $7.75. Two boxes of laundry detergent and one bottle of fabric softener cost $8.75. Find the cost of each product.

11. A manufacturer sells packages of pens and pencils. A package of 3 pens and 5 pencils costs $1.65. A package of 5 pens and 10 pencils costs $3.00. Find the price of one pen and two pencils.

■ *Decision Making* ■ *Decision Making* ■ *Decision Making* ■ *Decision Making* ■

■ **ANALYZE DATA**

3. Which city is less expensive to visit? Why might this be true?

4. How much would a meal cost in United States dollars if it costs $16 in Mexico City?

5. Write a system of linear equations using the collected data.

■ **MAKE DECISIONS**

6. A travel agency offers a package deal to Freeport, Bahamas. The four day-three night package is $590 per person. The seven day-six night package is $815 per person. Each price includes the cost of airfare and hotel.

   a. Write a system of linear equations for the situation.

   b. Solve the system using Cramer's rule.

   c. Find the cost of each airfare per person.

   d. Find the cost of the hotel per night.

$590 PER PERSON
4 DAYS 3 NIGHTS
$815 PER PERSON
7 DAYS 6 NIGHTS

THE BAHAMAS

HOTEL AND AIR INCLUDED

OBJECTIVE:
To solve problems using one or more strategies.

13-6 *Using Multiple Strategies*

■ Sometimes you may need to use more than one strategy to solve a problem.

PROBLEM

A rancher bought 104 ft of fencing to make a rectangular corral. The rancher wants the corral to have the greatest possible area. What dimensions should the rancher use?

SOLUTION

READ ▶ What do you want to find?

the base and height of a rectangle with $P = 104$ ft and the greatest possible area

What do you know?

$A = bh$
$P = 2b + 2h$
$\quad = 104$ ft

PLAN ▶ Decide on strategies.

1. Draw a diagram to represent the information.
2. Use guess and test.
3. Make a table.

SOLVE ▶ Draw a diagram.

Choose some possible dimensions. Make a table to organize your data.

Look for a pattern. Guess some higher numbers and see how long the area continues to increase.

b	h	P(ft)	A(ft²)
10	42	104	420
11	41	104	451
12	40	104	480
20	32	104	640
22	30	104	660
24	28	104	672
26	26	104	676
28	24	104	672

The corral with the greatest area is a square that is 26 ft on a side.

LOOK BACK ▶ Describe the pattern.

As the dimensions of the rectangle get closer to those of a square, the area approaches the greatest possible area.

CLASS EXERCISES

Solve.

1. A gardener wants to fence in the greatest possible area using 200 ft of fencing. What should be the base length and height of the garden?

2. **CALCULATOR** A circle and a square both have an area of 144 square units. Use 3.14 for π.

   a. What is the circumference of the circle? Round to the nearest tenth.

   b. What is the perimeter of the square?

   c. Which figure is the most economical if purchasing fencing materials to surround the figure?

   d. Fencing material is $6.80/unit. How much is saved by choosing the most economical figure?

WRITTEN EXERCISES

 Use a CALCULATOR where appropriate.

Solve.

1. A student playing a computer chess game gets 5 points every time he wins the game. The computer gets 3 points every time it wins the game. They play 128 games and end with a tie score. How many games did the computer win?

2. Two people on bicycles leave home at 10 A.M. and ride towards each other. Their homes are 56 mi apart. The first cyclist pedals at 16 mi/h. The second pedals at 12 mi/h. At what time will they meet?

3. A painter places an 8.5-ft ladder against a wall. The bottom of the ladder is 4 ft from the base of the wall. How high up on the wall does the ladder reach?

4. There are 27 white cubes assembled to form a large cube. The outside surface of the large cube is then painted red. The large cube is then separated into a set of smaller cubes. How many of the small cubes will have exactly two red faces?

5. A student weighs his hamsters two at a time. Together, Sandy and White Ears weigh 209 g. White Ears and Sport weigh 223 g together. Sandy and Sport weigh 216 g together. How much does each hamster weigh?

6. A grocer is arranging cans in a pyramid. She uses 9 cans on each side of the base of the pyramid. How many cans will be in the pyramid?

7. A room has an area of 1,025 ft² and a 10-ft ceiling. Occupancy guidelines recommend at least 200 ft³ per person. What should be the maximum number of people allowed in the room?

8. A man who won the lottery gave his daughter half of the money. He gave his brother half as much as he gave his daughter and kept $3.8 million for himself. How much did the man win?

9. A student has $8 to spend on a phone call to a friend. The cost of a call is $.34 for the first minute and $.24 for each additional minute. How long can she talk to her friend?

10. A student decided to purchase a new telephone. He could choose from 8 different models, 2 different cord lengths, and 4 different colors. How many possible choices did he have if he can choose only one of each model, cord length, and color.

11. How many different angles can you find in the figure?

12. A clerk starts working at a beginning salary of $10,400 with an annual increase of $400. The clerk hires an assistant at a starting salary of $9,600 per year with an annual increase of $600. At this rate, in how many years will the assistant be earning more money than the clerk?

13. A lot measures 50 ft by 100 ft. The house on the lot measures 25 ft by 50 ft. What is the area of the lawn?

14. A bus left Freetown at noon traveling 40 mi/h. A car left Freetown at 1:30 P.M. traveling 60 mi/h.

 a. At what time did the car catch up with the bus?

 b. How many miles from Freetown were the car and the bus when they met?

15. A student spends $\frac{1}{3}$ of her money on a movie and $\frac{1}{6}$ of the remaining amount on a snack after the movie. She now has $16. How much money did she originally have?

16. A boy jogs in the park every other day. His sister jogs every third day. They both jogged together on April 2. How many more days in April can they jog together if they maintain this schedule?

17. In how many different ways can you give change from a $100 bill for a $78 purchase if the customer will accept no more than seven singles?

18. *DATA FILE 12 (pp. 486–487)* A base runner tried to steal a base 73 times during the baseball season. Approximately how many times was the base runner out?

Problem Solving Practice

READ
PLAN
LOOK BACK
SOLVE

PROBLEM SOLVING STRATEGIES

Draw a Diagram
Make a Table
Look for a Pattern
Guess and Test
Write an Equation
Simplify the Problem
Work Backwards
Account for All Possibilities
Make an Organized List
Solve by Graphing
Make a Model
Simulate the Problem

Solve. Use an appropriate strategy or combination of strategies.

1. There are 7 roads from Mayville to Scottsburg and 4 roads from Scottsburg to Dunlap. How many possible routes can you take from Mayville to Dunlap if you go through Scottsburg?

2. A singles tennis court is 75% as wide as a doubles tennis court. The singles court is 27 ft wide. How wide is the doubles court?

3. A student's average grade for six math quizzes is 85. He received these grades on five math quizzes: 82, 88, 94, 72, 88. What grade did he receive on the other quiz?

4. There are 48 students in the band. Of these students, 24 have blonde hair, and 18 have blue eyes. There are 16 students who do *not* have blonde hair or blue eyes.

  a. How many students have both blonde hair and blue eyes?

  b. How many students do *not* have blond hair?

  c. How many students do *not* have blue eyes?

5. An astronaut's spacesuit weighs 10.02 lb on the moon. This is 16.7% of its weight on Earth. How much does the spacesuit weigh on Earth?

6. A student weighs 10 lb more than his sister. Together they weigh 260 lb. How much does each weigh?

7. The area of rectangle A exceeds the area of square B by 24 yd^2. Find the dimensions of each figure.

w | A | $w + 8$ w | B | w

8. A student has 4 one-dollar bills, 2 five-dollar bills, and 5 ten-dollar bills. What is the probability that he will select the following bills at random?

  a. a one-dollar bill, then a ten-dollar bill

  b. a ten-dollar bill, then a five-dollar bill

  c. two ten-dollar bills

9. One hot chocolate for each of the 29 students on a field trip would cost $21.75. The bill for hot chocolate was $27.75. How many students had two hot chocolates?

10. *DATA FILE 13 (pp. 534–535)* About how much carbon is released per year by the 17 million people of Texas? Express your answer in pounds using scientific notation.

Chapter 13 Review

Write an explanation for each of the following.

1. Explain the term monomial and write two examples.

2. Explain the term polynomial and write two examples.

3. Explain how to use the distributive property to find $x(2x - 1)$.

4. Explain how you use FOIL to find the product of $(x + 3)(2x + 1)$.

5. Explain how to find the product of $(a + b)(a - b)$.

6. Explain the phrase *square a binomial* and write an example.

Polynomials   13-1

To name a polynomial, count the number of terms.

Write the polynomial for each model. Then write the name of each polynomial.

7.    8.    9.

Evaluate each polynomial for $a = 1$ and $b = -2$.

10. $3b^2 - ab + 1$ 11. $a^2b + 3b - a$ 12. $b^3 + ab^2 + 3b$

Adding and Subtracting Polynomials   13-2

To add or subtract polynomials, use models, number properties, or align like terms in columns.

To add polynomials, combine like terms.

To subtract polynomials, add the opposite of each term in the second polynomial.

Use a model to find each sum or difference.

13. $(5x^2 + 3x) + (2x^2 + x)$

14. $(3x^2 + 2x + 4) - (x^2 - x + 3)$

Add or subtract.

15. $(3x + 2y) + (5x + 3y)$ 16. $(5m - 3n) - (2m - n)$

17. $(4a^2 + 6b) + (2a^2 - 3b)$ 18. $(-r^2 + 2s) - (2r^2 - 3s)$

19. $(3c^2 + 5c - 2) - (-c^2 + 3c - 1)$ 20. $(a^2b + b^2 - a) + (a^2b - 2b^2 + 3a)$

Multiplying a Polynomial by a Monomial

To multiply a polynomial by a monomial, you can use models, or you can use the distributive property. Use the rules of exponents to simplify the product.

Use a model to find each product.

21. $2x(x + 5)$

22. $3x(2x + 1)$

Use the distributive property to find each product.

23. $x(x - 5)$

24. $3x(x + 2)$

25. $2x(x - 2)$

26. $4x(x^2 + 3x)$

27. $-5x(-2x^2 + 2x - 3)$

28. $-2xy(x^2 - xy + y^2)$

Multiplying a Polynomial by a Binomial

To multiply a polynomial by a binomial, you can use a model, you can use the distributive property twice, or you can use the FOIL method. FOIL means: multiply the First terms, Outside terms, Inside terms, and Last terms. Then add the products.

Write a multiplication expression for the model. Simplify.

29.

30.

Find each product.

31. $(x - 1)^2$

32. $(a + 3)^2$

33. $(y - 2)(y + 2)$

34. $(b + 3)(b - 2)$

35. $(m + 5)(m - 3)$

36. $(2n - 4)(n + 5)$

Problem Solving

To solve a problem, use an appropriate strategy or combination of strategies.

37. The number of bacteria doubles each minute. A bottle is completely filled after 5 minutes. After how many minutes was the bottle half full?

38. Fourteen boxes contain 152 classic and rock CDs. There are 10 classic CDs in a box and 12 rock CDs in a box. How many boxes contain each kind of CD?

39. The number 72 can be divided into three numbers in the ratio 1 to 2 to 3. Find these three numbers.

40. A gardener plans to use 196 ft of fencing to enclose a garden. What is the largest possible area of the garden?

Chapter 13   Test

Use a model to represent each polynomial.

1. $3x + 2x^2 + 3$

2. $3x^2 + 2x + 1$

Write the polynomial represented by each model.

3.

4.

Identify each expression as a monomial, binomial, or trinomial.

5. $7x - 5$

6. $-3x^2 + 3x + 1$

7. $x^2 + 9$

8. x^2

Evaluate each polynomial for $a = 2$ and $b = -3$.

9. $7a + 3b$

10. $a^2 - b^2 + 1$

11. $(b - 1)^2$

12. $a^2 + 2b - 5$

Find each sum.

13. $2x^3 - 3x^2 + x - 1$
    $+ \ x^3 + 2x^2 - 3x + 2$

14. $5x^3 + 2x^2 - 3x + 5$
    $+ \ 2x^3 - 5x^2 + 6x - 9$

Add or subtract.

15. $(5x^2 - 2x) - (3x^2 + x)$

16. $(3x^2 + 5x - 3) + (x^2 - 2x + 1)$

17. $(7x^2 + 5x + 3) - (4x^2 + 7x)$

18. $(9x^2 - 4x - 8) + (3x^2 + 6x + 3)$

19. $(-x^2 + 3x + 4) + (2x^2 - 5x + 1)$

20. $(2x^2 - 3x + 4) - (x^2 - 2x - 1)$

Find each product.

21. $(x + 3)^2$

22. $(x - 2)^2$

23. $x(3x^2 - 2x + 5)$

24. $2x(x^2 + 3x - 2)$

25. $3x^2(x + 2y - 1)$

26. $xy(x^2 - 2y + y^2)$

27. $(x - 2)(x + 3)$

28. $(x + 2)(x - 5)$

29. $(2x - 3)(x + 4)$

Solve.

30. The width of a rectangle is $\frac{1}{3}$ the length plus 5. The perimeter is 34. Find the length and the width.

31. A pair of jeans are on sale for 35% off the original price. The sale price is $19.50. What is the original price?

32. The sum of three consecutive multiples of 4 is 60. What is the product of the three multiples?

33. Two students are chosen at random to do a project together. There are 15 girls and 10 boys in the class. What is the probability that both students chosen for the project are boys?

Chapters 1–13   Cumulative Review

Choose the correct answer. Write A, B, C, or D.

1. Add $(3x^2 + 2x - 5) + (2x^2 - 3x + 1)$.
   - **A.** $5x^2 + 5x + 6$
   - **B.** $5x^2 - x - 4$
   - **C.** $x^2 + 5x - 6$
   - **D.** not given

2. Find the volume of a cone, $r = 4$, $h = 12$.
   - **A.** 16π
   - **B.** 192π
   - **C.** 64π
   - **D.** not given

3. Multiply $(x - 2)(x - 3)$.
   - **A.** $x^2 - 5x + 6$
   - **B.** $x^2 - 5x - 6$
   - **C.** $x^2 - 5x - 5$
   - **D.** not given

4. Find the mode of the following data:
   31, 29, 31, 23, 35, 34, 19, 35, 23, 29, 35.
   - **A.** 23
   - **B.** 29
   - **C.** 35
   - **D.** not given

5. Find a solution of $x - 2y = 3$ and $3x + y = 2$.
   - **A.** (1,-1)
   - **B.** (-1,1)
   - **C.** (3,2)
   - **D.** not given

6. Find the circumference of a circle with $r = 3$.
   - **A.** 3π
   - **B.** 6π
   - **C.** 9π
   - **D.** not given

7. Write the fraction for $37\frac{1}{2}\%$.
   - **A.** $\frac{1}{2}$
   - **B.** $\frac{75}{2}$
   - **C.** $\frac{3}{8}$
   - **D.** not given

8. A set of (d) dimes and (n) nickels is worth $3.20. There are 52 coins. How many of each coin are there?
   - **A.** 12 n, 40 d
   - **B.** 40 n, 12 d
   - **C.** 26 n, 26 d
   - **D.** not given

9. Solve $-3x + 1 < 25$.
   - **A.** $x < -8$
   - **B.** $x > -8$
   - **C.** $x > 8$
   - **D.** not given

10. 32% of $b = 10{,}000$. Find b.
    - **A.** 3,200
    - **B.** 31,250
    - **C.** 3,125
    - **D.** not given

11. Multiply $(a - b)^2$.
    - **A.** $a^2 - 2ab + b^2$
    - **B.** $a^2 + 2ab + b^2$
    - **C.** $a^2 + 2ab - b^2$
    - **D.** not given

12. Find the distance Joe traveled if he traveled 50 mi/h for $2\frac{1}{2}$ h.
    - **A.** 150 mi
    - **B.** 100 mi
    - **C.** 250 mi
    - **D.** not given

13. What is the probability of tossing heads twice with a fair coin?
    - **A.** $\frac{1}{2}$
    - **B.** 1
    - **C.** $\frac{1}{4}$
    - **D.** not given

14. Find the next number. 0, -1, $\sqrt{1}$, -2, $\sqrt{4}$, -3, . . .
    - **A.** $\sqrt{5}$
    - **B.** $\sqrt{9}$
    - **B.** $\sqrt{7}$
    - **D.** not given

15. Write 568,000,000 in scientific notation.
    - **A.** 5.68×10^6
    - **B.** 56.8×10^7
    - **C.** 5.68×10^8
    - **D.** not given

16. Write the expression for the model.

    - **A.** $2(x^2 + 2x) + 3$
    - **B.** $2x^2 + 2x + 3$
    - **C.** $x^2 + 2x + 3$
    - **D.** not given

Write an integer.

1. opposite of 4
2. opposite of -8
3. $|10|$
4. $|-6|$

Compare. Use <, >, or =.

5. $5 \;\blacksquare\; -1$
6. $-7 \;\blacksquare\; -3$
7. $-2 \;\blacksquare\; -2$
8. $-9 \;\blacksquare\; 0$

Find each answer.

9. $-11 + 1$
10. $-4 - (-9)$
11. $-3(-3)$
12. $44 \div (-4)$
13. $28 \cdot (-4)$
14. $-64 \div (-8)$
15. $98 - (-12)$
16. $-52 + (-11)$
17. $-2 + (-7) + 15$
18. $-2 \cdot 10 \cdot (-4)(-1)$
19. $120 \div (-4) \div 10 \div (-1)$
20. $9 \cdot 7 \div (4 - 1)$
21. $5 + 7 \cdot 3 + 1$
22. $3(12 + 6) - 9 \cdot 6$
23. $|12 - (-5)|3$
24. $1 + (-4) \cdot (-7) + 10 - 2$
25. $30 - 7 \cdot 2(22 - 12) \div 5$

Write an expression for each word phrase.

26. a number increased by eight
27. the product of negative seven and x
28. twelve less than the absolute value of negative three
29. the opposite of the quantity seven less than y
30. three times the sum of negative eight and twelve
31. the absolute value of the difference of negative three and ten
32. the quotient of twenty-five and negative five, minus two
33. ten times the quantity seventeen minus negative eleven

Evaluate each expression for the given values of the variables.

34. $4a + 7$, for $a = -2$
35. $8m + 13 + 6n$, for $m = 5$, $n = 3$
36. $7|x - y| + y$, for $x = 3$, $y = 11$
37. $-14 - 2(a - b)$, for $a = 6$, $b = 4$

Solve.

38. A group of children line up in a row. The first child takes 1 step forward. The second child takes 2 steps forward. The third child takes 5 steps, the fourth takes 14, and so on. Following this pattern, how many steps will the next two children take?

39. Concert tickets cost $20 and concert T-shirts cost $12.
   a. Write an expression for the cost of x tickets and y shirts.
   b. Find the cost of 4 tickets and 6 shirts.
   c. How many tickets can you buy for $60? how many T-shirts?

40. **DATA FILE 1 (pp. 2–3)** The air temperature is 5°F. What is the maximum wind speed, in miles per hour, before there is an increased danger of frostbite?

41. After being kicked forward 20 m, a ball is pushed backward 7 m. Describe the position of the ball using an integer.

Replace each variable with the given value. State whether the equation is true or false.

1. $17 - a = 7$, $a = 8$

2. $4 + m = 2m + 8$, $m = -4$

3. $8 - 2q = 3q + 1$, $q = 0$

4. $-x + 3 = 2x$, $x = 1$

5. $4x + y = 20$, $x = -4$, $y = 5$

6. $3a = 2b - 9c$, $a = -3$, $b = 0$, $c = 1$

Which of the numbers -1, 0, 1, 3, 5 is a solution?

7. $0 = 121y$

8. $-8 = 2m - 18$

9. $4n = 3n - (-3)$

10. $x(3 - 8) = 5(-x)$

Evaluate.

11. $26 + 8 + 10$

12. $33 \cdot 2 \cdot 5 + 7$

13. $5(8 - 3)$

14. $6[8 - 2 - (-7)]$

15. $5[(-8) + 17 - (2)3]$

16. $510 \div (-5) \cdot 2$

17. $5(8 \div 8) - 33 \cdot 2$

18. $18 + 7 \cdot 4 - 3 \div (-1)$

19. $4(3 + 7) \div 2$

Simplify each expression.

20. $-3(2c)$

21. $41 - 2(m + 1) - m$

22. $3(a + b + 2c)$

23. $3q + 2(q + 1)$

24. $(8 \div 4)r - 3r$

25. $8 + (3s + 2)(-2)$

Solve each equation.

26. $x - 33 = 0$

27. $j + (-22) = 4$

28. $14 = z - 9$

29. $z(3 - 1) = 40$

30. $5q = 26 - 1$

31. $2|n| = 10$

Write an equation for each word sentence.

32. Twice the sum of a number and one is twenty-two.

33. Negative three divided by negative one is three.

34. The sum of three and four times a number x is equal to $6x$.

35. The product of two numbers is the absolute value of negative twenty-four.

Solve.

36. Terry's age is half Bobby's age. The sum of their ages is 36. How old are Terry and Bobby?

37. *DATA FILE 2 (pp. 52–53)* A lightning flash is seen 7 s before the thunder is heard. How far away is the lightning?

38. There are 10 children on a school bus. At the next stop, 5 get on and 1 gets off. Then x get on and none get off. This leaves a total of $3x$ children on the bus. Solve for x. How many children are on the bus?

39. There are twice as many golf balls as ping-pong balls. If 9 golf balls are taken away, there will be the same amount of golf balls and ping-pong balls. How many golf balls and ping-pong balls are there altogether?

Order from greatest to least.

1. 2.012, 2.12, 2.011   **2.** -0.03, -0.33, -3   **3.** 0.00004, 1.00009, 0.000045   **4.** 278, 2.78, 27.8

Round each decimal to the indicated place.

5. 0.38, nearest tenth   **6.** -3.089, nearest hundredth   **7.** 238.079, nearest whole number

Estimate using the technique which seems best.

8. -42.039 ÷ 10.99   **9.** $3.74 + $12.12 + $3.00   **10.** -97.3 + (-33.9776) + (-28.0549)

11. 83.6 + 7.98 + (-2.09)   **12.** 397 ÷ 1.9   **13.** $238.01 + $449.99 + $302.55

Use estimation to place the decimal point in each answer.

14. 4.003 · 0.64 = 256192   **15.** 4.32 ÷ 0.02 = 216   **16.** 12.38 + 8.02 + 10.99 = 3139

17. -28 ÷ 0.24 = -116667   **18.** 23.05 · 0.07 = 16135   **19.** 525.1324 ÷ 5.2 = 100987

Evaluate each expression for $a = 3.02$ and $b = -12.3$.

20. $a + b$ **21.** $a - b$ **22.** $2a - b$ **23.** $\frac{a - b}{2}$

24. $\frac{2(a + b)}{4}$ **25.** $\frac{-a - b}{5 \div (-1)}$ **26.** $5b - 2a$ **27.** $|a| + |b|$

Solve each equation using any method.

28. $a + 0.03 = 3.75$ **29.** $48.9 + y = 50$ **30.** $q - 4.099 = 2.33$

31. $m - (-1.2) = 3.09$ **32.** $5m = -95$ **33.** $0.5 = \frac{x}{33}$

34. $y \div 0.3 = -15$ **35.** $98.53 = 0.9853n$ **36.** $3.3x = 13.2$

Write an equation for each problem.

37. Three hundredths times a number is equal to the opposite of three and one hundredth.

38. x is equal to four hundred ninety-five and seventy-three hundredths.

39. The absolute value of negative nine tenths is equal to two times a number.

40. Five divided by two and five hundredths is equal to q.

Solve.

41. A student is assigned pages 38–130. The student reads a page every 20 s. How long will it take the student to finish the assignment?

42. A painter can paint one window in 17 min. There are 7 windows to paint. How long will it take? Round to the nearest hour.

43. A pound of peanuts costs $2.87. How many whole pounds can be bought with $20?

44. **DATA FILE 3 (pp. 96–97)** A collector spent $7.24 on proof sets in 1936. How much profit would the collector make if he sold them all in 1965?

Evaluate.

1. 4^5

2. $(-2)^4$

3. -2^4

4. -12^0

5. $5x^2 \cdot 3x$

6. $-(2mn)^3$

7. $(4y^4)^3$

8. $(x^2)(x^3)(-x^1)$

9. $[5 + (-7)]^4$

10. $-2(-3 + 4)^5$

11. y^3 for $y = 2$

12. x^4 for $x = -1$

13. $-q^5$ for $q = 1$

14. $(2y)^2$ for $y = -2$

15. $-(a^0bc)$ for $a = 2$, $b = 3$, $c = 4$

16. $(r + 2s + t)^2$ for $r = 3$, $s = -1$, $t = 5$

17. $x^2 + 3x + y^2$ for $x = 7$, $y = -8$

Find the value of a.

18. $4^a = 64$

19. $a^5 = 1$

20. $11^a = 1$

21. $6^a = 36$

22. $a^4 = 625$

23. $3^3 = a$

Write each answer in scientific and standard notation.

24. $(4 \times 10^3)(3 \times 10^2)$

25. $1.32 \times 40{,}000$

26. $(1.4 \times 10^5)2.32$

27. $7(2.6 \times 10^6)$

State which of the numbers 2, 3, 4, 5, or 9 are divisors.

28. 25

29. 72

30. 18

31. 135

32. 24,270

Find the GCF of each set of numbers.

33. 58, 34

34. 21, 63

35. 18, 36, 38

36. $35x^3y^2$, $70x^6y^4$

37. $27a^2b^2$, $9ab^2$

Find the LCM of each set of numbers.

38. 60, 12

39. 55, 100

40. 16, 20, 36

41. $12a^5b$, $6ab$

42. x^4y^3, $200x^2y^4$

Solve.

43. *DATA FILE 4 (pp. 138–139)* How many babies are born in 10 s? How many people die in 10 s? Round to the nearest integer.

44. A professional basketball player runs 8 mi in an average game. About how many miles does a player run during games in a season of 82 games?

45. A popcorn popper pops 2 kernels/s for 10 s. After 10 s it pops 4 kernels/s for 20 s. After 20 s it pops 6 kernels/s for 30 s, and so on. At the end of 2 min and 30 s, how many kernels have popped?

46. There are 5 children who want to play a game. Only 2 can play the game at a time. In how many different ways can the children be paired?

47. Find one pair of numbers that satisfies both conditions.

  a. their product is 80

  b. their LCM is 20

48. Find one pair of numbers that satisfies both conditions.

  a. their sum is 40

  b. their GCF is 5

Write in lowest terms.

1. $\frac{7}{14}$ **2.** $\frac{xyz}{2xz}$ **3.** $\frac{4mn}{20mn}$ **4.** $\frac{25x}{75y}$ **5.** $\frac{3xy}{9xy}$ **6.** $\frac{12abc}{144ab}$

Write each decimal as a fraction or mixed number in lowest terms.

7. 0.2 **8.** 4.1 **9.** 20.08 **10.** 0.17 **11.** 0.005 **12.** 1.125

Write as a decimal.

13. $\frac{4}{10}$ **14.** $\frac{11}{20}$ **15.** $\frac{3}{5}$ **16.** $\frac{5}{8}$ **17.** $\frac{3}{4}$ **18.** $\frac{1}{3}$

Order from least to greatest.

19. $\frac{8}{4}, \frac{1}{2}, -\frac{3}{4}$ **20.** $-\frac{15}{20}, -\frac{3}{10}, -\frac{4}{5}$ **21.** $\frac{2^2}{5}, 2\frac{3}{10}, \frac{9}{10}$ **22.** $\frac{a}{3}, \frac{a}{6}, \frac{3a}{2}$ for $a > 0$ **23.** $\frac{xy}{15}, \frac{-xy}{5}, \frac{3xy}{10}$ for $xy > 0$

Find each answer. Write in lowest terms.

24. $\frac{5}{6} + \frac{3}{8}$ **25.** $\frac{2}{3} - 1\frac{1}{2}$ **26.** $\frac{x}{4} - \frac{x}{10}$ **27.** $\frac{8}{9}x + \left(\frac{-3}{6}x\right)$

28. $-5 + \left(-\frac{5}{10}\right)$ **29.** $8 - \frac{2}{4}$ **30.** $\frac{1}{4} \cdot \frac{5}{9}$ **31.** $\frac{8}{11} \div \frac{7}{9}$

32. $2\frac{3}{4} \cdot \frac{3}{7}$ **33.** $\frac{3x}{5} \cdot \frac{7x}{9}$ **34.** $5\frac{4}{7} \div \left(\frac{-3}{14}\right)$ **35.** $\frac{4}{5} + 1\frac{2}{15}$

36. $\frac{7}{8}q - \frac{5}{5}q$ **37.** $\left(\frac{3}{8}\right)\left(-2\frac{3}{4}\right) - \frac{1}{2}$ **38.** $\frac{9}{11} \div \frac{3}{4} \div \frac{2}{7}$ **39.** $\frac{-1}{3} \div (-3)$

Simplify.

40. $\frac{15y^7}{33y^3}$ **41.** $\frac{a^3b^2c^0}{abc}$ **42.** $\frac{9m^7n^2}{3m^3n}$ **43.** $\frac{-y^3z^5}{y^4z^5}$ **44.** $\frac{16q^2m^3}{12q^4m}$

Solve each equation. Write in lowest terms.

45. $h + 3\frac{1}{3} = 4\frac{7}{9}$ **46.** $x - |-3.1| = 8\frac{1}{4}$ **47.** $c + \left(\frac{-3}{8}\right) = -\frac{7}{10}$ **48.** $d + \frac{3}{7} = -2\frac{3}{14}$

49. $\frac{3}{10}c = \frac{3}{4}$ **50.** $-\frac{7}{6}z = -4$ **51.** $\frac{-9}{10}q = 4$ **52.** $\frac{-5}{9}y = -\frac{3}{6}$

Solve.

53. *DATA FILE 4 (pp. 138–139)* How many millions of people speak Chinese, Spanish, German, or Arabic?

54. You have $20.50 in quarters, dimes, nickels, and pennies. You have an equal number of each coin. How many of each coin do you have?

55. Four children are told to line up and hold hands as they cross the street. How many different ways can they line up?

56. A ball is pushed down a flight of 50 stairs. The ball rolls down four stairs per second. How long will it take the ball to roll down $\frac{4}{5}$ of the stairs?

Write each ratio as a fraction in lowest terms.

1. $2:6$ **2.** $9:3$ **3.** $7:28$ **4.** $25:45$

5. 3 people out of 27 are wearing hats.   **6.** 18 dogs out of 81 have fleas.

7. 6 out of the 30 TVs are on sale.   **8.** 7 out of the 31 athletes made the team.

Write a proportion to describe each situation. Then solve.

9. An athlete swims 20 laps in 30 min; x laps in 2 hours.

10. 38 lb of soil cost $3.20; 95 lb cost y dollars.

11. 20 stamps cost 95¢; z stamps cost 19¢.

12. A car can travel 282 mi on 14 gal of gas; m miles on 42 gal of gas.

Write a ratio and percent for each.

13. 17 questions right out of 20

14. 12 questions right out of 18

15. 40 questions wrong out of 120

16. 2 questions wrong out of 20

Solve.

17. What percent of 80 is 36?   **18.** Find 39% of 66.   **19.** 33% of q is 109. What is q?

20. What percent of 33 is 99?   **21.** Find 23% of 28.   **22.** 75% of k is 15. What is k?

Find each percent of change. Round to the nearest tenth.

23. from 18 to 12   **24.** from 88 to 125   **25.** from 15.5 to 25.5   **26.** from 100 to 88

27. from 2.4 to 8.6   **28.** from 11 to 17   **29.** from 92 to 98   **30.** from 34 to 49

Solve.

31. An athlete must swim 18 laps. The athlete swims $\frac{1}{2}$ of the laps and then swims $\frac{1}{3}$ of those remaining. How many laps are left?

32. A florist cuts a wire into three pieces. The first piece is 20% of the second. The third piece is 110% of the second. The wire is 23 cm long. Find the length of each piece.

33. There are 10 girls and 15 boys. What percent of the group is boys?

34. *DATA FILE 6 (pp. 230–231)* What percent of teens study an average of more than 2 h a day?

35. In a town with 12,000 residents, 2 out of 10 voted in the last election. How many residents voted?

36. In a sample of 2,500 ballpoint pens, 15 were found to be defective. How many pens would you expect to be defective in a shipment of 10,000 pens?

37. *DATA* Use the data on page 130. Find the percent of change in the price of a loaf of bread and a half gallon of milk from 1890 to 1980.

38. A salesperson earns $800 per week plus 5% commission on sales over $10,000. How much would the salesperson earn in a week when sales were $25,000?

Solve each equation. Check.

1. $3x + (-12) = x$

2. $2m + -3m - 8 = 26$

3. $4(-y + 2) = -1$

4. $-0.2 - q = 9q$

5. $\frac{3}{4}x - \frac{1}{2}x = 5$

6. $32 = 4(a - 2) + 10$

7. $4(b - 2.1) = b + 0.6$

8. $\frac{1}{4}(x - 8) = \frac{3}{4}x$

9. $48 = \frac{1}{2}(8x - 14) + 15$

Graph each inequality on a number line. Write each inequality as a word sentence.

10. $y < 9$

11. $-3 > q$

12. $0.009 \geq p$

13. $a \geq -2$

14. $c > 99$

15. $c < -99$

16. $n < 7.3$

17. $h \geq -1.2$

18. $-11 \leq b$

Solve each inequality.

19. $y + 3 \geq 9$

20. $y - 3 > -7$

21. $\frac{y}{4} \leq -9$

22. $3q > 0$

23. $-9x \leq -5$

24. $\frac{x}{7} \geq -3$

25. $19 - 3x > -2$

26. $-314 \leq x + 1$

27. $\frac{1}{2}(x - 6) \leq 22$

28. $-5(a - 3) \leq 45$

29. $-\frac{x}{3} + 3 \geq -27$

30. $\frac{2}{3}(4a + 12) \geq \frac{1}{3}(6a - 10)$

Write an inequality to describe the situation. Solve.

31. When a is divided by 8, the result is at most 13. Find a.

32. Four less than n is greater than negative six. Find n.

33. Five less than seven times p is at least twenty-three. Find p.

34. Three times q plus negative twenty-two is less than q. Find q.

Solve.

35. Each month Gil saves $22.27. How long does it take him to save $267.24?

36. Four times a number is fifty-two minus forty. Find the number.

37. A student buys three movie tickets for $6.60 each. The student pays with $20. What is the change?

38. You open a book. The product of the two page numbers is 9,702. What are the page numbers?

39. Nita has test scores of 92, 84, and 87. She needs a 90 average to get an A. What is the lowest score she can get on her next test and still have an A average?

40. *DATA FILE 7 (pp. 272–273)* Estimate which is greater using the figures from 1987: the total of passengers boarding at Chicago/O'Hare, Atlanta, and Miami or the total boarding in Denver, Los Angeles, and San Francisco.

In which quadrant or on which axis does each point fall?

1. $(-3,18)$ **2.** $(0,44)$ **3.** $(22,3)$ **4.** $(-18,-5)$ **5.** $(-0.33,-5)$

Solve for y in terms of x. Find four solutions of each equation.

6. $5y - 10x = 15$ **7.** $4 - y = \frac{1}{2}x$ **8.** $2x + 2y = -4$

9. $\frac{1}{2}y - x = 12$ **10.** $-4x - 0.5y = 4$ **11.** $\frac{1}{3}y - x = 1$

Graph each equation. Name the slope, x-intercept, and y-intercept.

12. $y = -8$ **13.** $y = 2x - 5$ **14.** $x = y$

15. $x + y = 5$ **16.** $-y + 3x = \frac{1}{2}$ **17.** $\frac{1}{4}x + y = -3$

Solve each system by graphing. Check your solutions.

18. $y = x + 4$ **19.** $2x + y = 3$ **20.** $y = -3$
  $y = x - 2$ $-2y = 14 - x$ $2x + 3y = 6$

Solve each inequality for y in terms of x. Write three ordered pairs that are solutions of the inequality.

21. $3x - y < 5$ **22.** $-x + 4y + 12 \geq 0$

23. $x - 5 + 3y < 44 + 2y + 3x$ **24.** $-x > 2y - 5(x + y)$

Graph each inequality.

25. $y > 7$ **26.** $x + 3y < 2$ **27.** $4x + 4y > 10$

28. $x - \frac{1}{3}y \leq \frac{1}{3}$ **29.** $\frac{3}{4}x - \frac{1}{4}y \leq \frac{1}{4}$ **30.** $3x + 6y > 15$

Solve.

31. At a party 20 guests consume 5 bags of popcorn and 10 gal of juice. At this rate, how much popcorn and juice will 28 guests consume?

32. A line has a slope of $\frac{2}{5}$ and passes through the point $(-10,7)$. Find the equation of the line. State the quadrants which the line will pass through.

33. Find two consecutive numbers such that the greater number times 3 is 9 less than 5 times the lesser number.

34. *DATA FILE 5 (pp. 180–181)* Write a ratio in lowest terms to compare the number of violas to the number of second violins.

35. A train that is 500 m long is traveling at a speed of 125 km/h. How long will it take the train to entirely pass through a tunnel that is 2 km long?

36. Shoes are $10 off. A customer buys three pairs of shoes for $110. What percent did the customer save on the total purchase? Round to the nearest whole number.

Tell whether each angle is acute, right, obtuse, or straight.

1. 2°   **2.** 75°   **3.** 99°   **4.** 90°   **5.** 180°   **6.** 77°

Find the measure of a complement and a supplement of each angle, if possible.

7. 90°   **8.** 1°   **9.** 45°   **10.** 33°   **11.** 140°   **12.** 101°

Draw a figure to fit each description.

13. a concave octagon   **14.** an obtuse triangle   **15.** a quadrilateral   **16.** a convex rhombus

Find the measure of the third angle of a triangle that has two angles with the given measures.

17. 30°, 60°   **18.** $x°$, $x°$ **19.** 40°, 60°   **20.** 60°, 60°   **21.** 39°, 57°   **22.** $(x + 2)°$, $(x - 4)°$

Find each radius or diameter.

23. $r = 29.3$ cm   **24.** $d = 40$ yd   **25.** $d = 78$ in.   **26.** $r = 10$ km   **27.** $r = 228.5$ m

ABCDE ≅ *MNOPQ*. **Tell whether each statement is true or false.**

28. $\angle A \cong \angle P$ **29.** $\overline{AB} \cong \overline{MN}$ **30.** $\angle D \cong \angle P$ **31.** $\overline{CE} \cong \overline{OP}$ **32.** $\angle B \cong \angle N$ **33.** $\angle A \cong \angle M$

Find the circumference. Use 3.14 for π.

34.

6 cm

35.

102 ft

36.

0.35 in.

Find the perimeter of each figure.

37. a regular hexagon with side 2.8 in.

38. a parallelogram with sides 4 ft and 7 ft

39. an equilateral triangle with side 9 m

40. a figure with sides 4 cm, 8 cm, 12 cm, and 12 cm

Solve.

41. Sol and Julia run a race. Sol runs 7.3 mi/h. Julia runs 6.8 mi/h. After 2 h, how far apart will they be?

42. A coat is on sale for 75% off the regular price. If the sale price is $60, what was the original price?

43. Carlos wants to trim a circular carpet in his house. The carpet has a diameter of 20 yd. How much trim does he need? Use 3.14 for π.

44. *DATA FILE 9 (pp. 360–361)* At St. Andrew's golf club a golfer takes a break after the 13th hole. If the golfer has a score of 57, what must the golfer average on the remaining holes to receive a score of par?

Find the area of each parallelogram with the given base and height. Round to the nearest tenth.

1. $b = 6.3$ cm, $h = 2.9$ cm
2. $b = 13$ ft, $h = 19$ ft
3. $b = 0.8$ m, $h = 1.1$ m
4. $b = 55$ in., $h = 22$ in.
5. $b = 17x$, $h = 33x$
6. $b = x$, $h = 2x$

Find the area of each circle with the given diameter or radius. Round to the nearest tenth. Use 3.14 for π.

7. $r = 8.1$ cm
8. $d = 0.39$ in.
9. $r = 13.2$ m
10. $r = 0.75$ in.
11. $r = 5.6$ m
12. $d = 16z$
13. $r = 14.5$ cm
14. $d = 5.5x$

Find each surface area. Use 3.14 for π.

15. a rectangular prism with base edges 7 in. and 9 in., and height 5 in.
16. a cylinder with radius 7 cm and height 12 cm
17. a square pyramid with edge 59 m and slant height 66 m
18. a cone with radius 9 cm and slant height 15 cm
19. a sphere with radius 12 in.
20. a hemisphere with radius 5 cm

Find each volume. Use 3.14 for π.

21. a triangular prism with base 4 ft, height 7 ft, and a prism height of 10 ft
22. a rectangular prism with length 3 in., width 8 in., and height 9 in.
23. a cylinder with $r = 11$ cm and $h = 6$ cm
24. a cone with radius 9 m and height 13 m
25. a square pyramid with side 5 cm and height 12 cm
26. a sphere with radius 10 in.

Solve.

27. A dress is on sale for 20% off the original price of $89. Another dress not on sale costs $61. Which dress costs less?

28. Ten players line up to shoot baskets. Each player makes at least 60% of her shots. Altogether, there were 300 attempts. What's the smallest number of baskets made?

29. A juice can has radius 1.1 in. and height 4.2 in. What is the volume of the can? Round to the nearest unit. Use 3.14 for π.

30. **DATA FILE 10 (pp. 404–405)** What is the area in square meters of the black bear's home range? Use 3.14 for π.

Find each square root. If necessary, use your calculator. Round decimal answers to the nearest thousandth.

1. $\sqrt{51}$

2. $\sqrt{36}$

3. $\sqrt{144}$

4. $\sqrt{\dfrac{16}{36}}$

5. $\sqrt{49x^2}$

6. $\sqrt{101.101}$

7. $\sqrt{(a+b)^2}$

8. $\sqrt{a^4 b^{12} c^8}$

Determine whether each is a Pythagorean triple.

9. 3, 4, 5

10. 9, 7, 12

11. $2\sqrt{12}$, 5, $\sqrt{37}$

12. 6, 7, 8

13. 5, 12, 13

14. $3x^2$, $4x^2$, $5x^2$

Find the missing length.

15.

16.

17.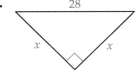

18.

19.

20.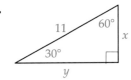

State the trigonometric ratio using the given values.

21. tan $k°$

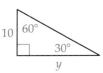

22. sin $x°$

23. cos $a°$

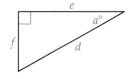

Solve.

24. The diameter of a circular ring is 18 yd. What is the circumference of the ring? What is the area? Use 3.14 for π.

25. At takeoff, an airplane forms a 44° angle with the runway. How many miles will the airplane fly before reaching an altitude of 28,000 ft? Round to the nearest mile.

26. It takes Jonathan 1 min 20 s to walk around the track. Twelve laps equal 1 mile. How long will it take Jonathan to walk 1 mile?

27. *DATA FILE 7 (pp. 272–273)* It is 12 A.M. in Fairbanks, Alaska. What time is it in Chicago, Illinois?

**Find the mean, median, mode, and range of each of the following.
Round to the nearest tenth.**

1. 13, 12, 15, 13, 9, 6, 5   **2.** 28, 1, 5, 6, 9, 1, 3, 10, 1   **3.** 100, 100, 100, 100, 100, 0, 50

4.

x	f
8	5
9	2
10	3
11	1

5. Make a line plot for the table in Exercise 4.

**Make a stem and leaf plot for each set of data. Then find the median
and the mode for each set of data.**

6. 30, 15, 19, 35, 20, 20   **7.** 10, 16, 22, 13, 25, 13, 13, 10

8. 11, 55, 30, 32, 55, 12, 13, 55   **9.** 33, 99, 82, 66, 72, 66

Make a box and whisker plot for each set of data.

10. 40, 43, 48, 48, 50, 66, 60, 61, 70, 69, 45, 46   **11.** 40, 11, 30, 12, 28, 17, 29, 19

Find the value of each factorial.

12. 8!   **13.** $\frac{5!}{4!}$ **14.** 5!   **15.** 6! − 3!

**Suppose you have a deck of 52 cards. Find the probability of
selecting each of the following. Cards will always be replaced. An
ace is not considered to be a face card.**

16. a red card   **17.** a heart   **18.** a king   **19.** a face card

20. a face card first and then an ace   **21.** the jack of hearts first and a king second

Solve.

22. ***DATA FILE 5 (pp. 180–181)*** If you choose one
musician at random from a symphony
orchestra, what is the probability that he or
she will play the cello?

23. A ball was thrown up a hill 22 ft. It then
rolled back 28 ft. Represent this as an
integer.

24. Find the probability of rolling one number
cube and getting a multiple of 2 first and a 3
second.

25. Find the volume of a sphere with radius
7.5 cm.

26. A right triangle has side lengths 5, $5\sqrt{3}$,
and 10. What are the angle measures?

27. The hypotenuse of a 45°-45°-90° triangle has
length 12. What is the length of each leg?

28. The sum of three consecutive even integers
is 30. Their mean is 10. Find the integers.

29. The sum of the squares of two consecutive
positive integers is 85. Find the integers.

Simplify.

1. $(x^2 + 3x + 4) + (2x^2 + x + 1)$

2. $(3x^2 + x + 5) + (x^2 + 2x + 1)$

3. $(mn^2 + 3n - 8) - (3mn^2 - m + n - 5)$

4. $18p^2q^2 + 19 - 18p$

5. $(a^3n^2 - 3a^2n + 5a - 9) - (4a^3n^2 + a^2n - a - 9)$

6. $(-3w^4y^5 - 18w^3y^4 + 2w^2y^3 - 3wy^2) + (3w^4y^5 + 18w^3y^4 - 2w^2y^3 + 3wy^2)$

Simplify.

7. $18x(4x^2 - 2x + 9)$

8. $-m^4(m^2 - 14m + 5)$

9. $\frac{1}{2}a(5a^5 - a^3 - 33)$

10. $4abc(a^4b + 10abc - 8)$

11. $(x + 1)(x + 3)$

12. $(x - 2)(x + 5)$

13. $(x - 9)(x + 9)$

14. $(x - 5)^2$

15. $(x + 2)(2x^2 + x + 1)$

16. $-5(x + 9)(x - 1)$

Write an expression using one variable to represent each product. Then simplify.

17. If m is an even integer, find the product of the next three consecutive even integers.

18. If w is a multiple of 5, find the product of the next two consecutive multiples of 5.

19. If z is a multiple of 4, find the product of the previous two consecutive multiples of 4.

20. If m is an integer, find the product of the next three consecutive integers.

Solve.

21. A ball has a diameter of 12 cm. Find the volume. Use 3.14 for π.

22. A car traveled 192 mi in 3 h. What was the car's average speed?

23. Ron has a choice of 3 sweaters, 2 pairs of pants, and 4 pairs of shoes. How many different outfits can Ron choose?

24. *DATA FILE 9 (pp. 360–361)* What is the average distance that a ball will go if hit with a club having a loft of 31°?

25. Three consecutive integers have a sum of 291. What is the sum of the largest and smallest of these integers?

26. Janet is four years older than Frank. The sum of their ages is 76. How old was Janet eight years ago?

27. A sock drawer contains 4 red socks, 3 green socks, 8 blue socks, and 10 black socks. What is the probability that a blue sock is chosen first and another blue sock second?

28. An average honeybee hive produces 350 oz of honey. How many honeybee hives would be needed to produce 2,275 oz of honey?

Table 1:   Squares and Square Roots

N	N^2	$\sqrt{N}$	N	N^2	$\sqrt{N}$
1	1	1	51	2,601	7.141
2	4	1.414	52	2,704	7.211
3	9	1.732	53	2,809	7.280
4	16	2	54	2,916	7.348
5	25	2.236	55	3,025	7.416
6	36	2.449	56	3,136	7.483
7	49	2.646	57	3,249	7.550
8	64	2.828	58	3,364	7.616
9	81	3	59	3,481	7.681
10	100	3.162	60	3,600	7.746
11	121	3.317	61	3,721	7.810
12	144	3.464	62	3,844	7.874
13	169	3.606	63	3,969	7.937
14	196	3.742	64	4,096	8
15	225	3.873	65	4,225	8.062
16	256	4	66	4,356	8.124
17	289	4.123	67	4,489	8.185
18	324	4.243	68	4,624	8.246
19	361	4.359	69	4,761	8.307
20	400	4.472	70	4,900	8.367
21	441	4.583	71	5,041	8.426
22	484	4.690	72	5,184	8.485
23	529	4.796	73	5,329	8.544
24	576	4.899	74	5,476	8.602
25	625	5	75	5,625	8.660
26	676	5.099	76	5,776	8.718
27	729	5.196	77	5,929	8.775
28	784	5.292	78	6,084	8.832
29	841	5.385	79	6,241	8.888
30	900	5.477	80	6,400	8.944
31	961	5.568	81	6,561	9
32	1,024	5.657	82	6,724	9.055
33	1,089	5.745	83	6,889	9.110
34	1,156	5.831	84	7,056	9.165
35	1,225	5.916	85	7,225	9.220
36	1,296	6	86	7,396	9.274
37	1,369	6.083	87	7,569	9.327
38	1,444	6.164	88	7,744	9.381
39	1,521	6.245	89	7,921	9.434
40	1,600	6.325	90	8,100	9.487
41	1,681	6.403	91	8,281	9.539
42	1,764	6.481	92	8,464	9.592
43	1,849	6.557	93	8,649	9.644
44	1,936	6.633	94	8,836	9.695
45	2,025	6.708	95	9,025	9.747
46	2,116	6.782	96	9,216	9.798
47	2,209	6.856	97	9,409	9.849
48	2,304	6.928	98	9,604	9.899
49	2,401	7	99	9,801	9.950
50	2,500	7.071	100	10,000	10

Table 2: Table of Trigonometric Ratios

Angle	Sine	Cosine	Tangent	Angle	Sine	Cosine	Tangent
1°	0.0175	0.9998	0.0175	46°	0.7193	0.6947	1.0355
2°	0.0349	0.9994	0.0349	47°	0.7314	0.6820	1.0724
3°	0.0523	0.9986	0.0524	48°	0.7431	0.6691	1.1106
4°	0.0698	0.9976	0.0699	49°	0.7547	0.6561	1.1504
5°	0.0872	0.9962	0.0875	50°	0.7660	0.6428	1.1918
6°	0.1045	0.9945	0.1051	51°	0.7771	0.6293	1.2349
7°	0.1219	0.9925	0.1228	52°	0.7880	0.6157	1.2799
8°	0.1392	0.9903	0.1405	53°	0.7986	0.6018	1.3270
9°	0.1564	0.9877	0.1584	54°	0.8090	0.5878	1.3764
10°	0.1736	0.9848	0.1763	55°	0.8192	0.5736	1.4281
11°	0.1908	0.9816	0.1944	56°	0.8290	0.5592	1.4826
12°	0.2079	0.9781	0.2126	57°	0.8387	0.5446	1.5399
13°	0.2250	0.9744	0.2309	58°	0.8480	0.5299	1.6003
14°	0.2419	0.9703	0.2493	59°	0.8572	0.5150	1.6643
15°	0.2588	0.9659	0.2679	60°	0.8660	0.5000	1.7321
16°	0.2756	0.9613	0.2867	61°	0.8746	0.4848	1.8040
17°	0.2924	0.9563	0.3057	62°	0.8829	0.4695	1.8807
18°	0.3090	0.9511	0.3249	63°	0.8910	0.4540	1.9626
19°	0.3256	0.9455	0.3443	64°	0.8988	0.4384	2.0503
20°	0.3420	0.9397	0.3640	65°	0.9063	0.4226	2.1445
21°	0.3584	0.9336	0.3839	66°	0.9135	0.4067	2.2460
22°	0.3746	0.9272	0.4040	67°	0.9205	0.3907	2.3559
23°	0.3907	0.9205	0.4245	68°	0.9272	0.3746	2.4751
24°	0.4067	0.9135	0.4452	69°	0.9336	0.3584	2.6051
25°	0.4226	0.9063	0.4663	70°	0.9397	0.3420	2.7475
26°	0.4384	0.8988	0.4877	71°	0.9455	0.3256	2.9042
27°	0.4540	0.8910	0.5095	72°	0.9511	0.3090	3.0777
28°	0.4695	0.8829	0.5317	73°	0.9563	0.2924	3.2709
29°	0.4848	0.8746	0.5543	74°	0.9613	0.2756	3.4874
30°	0.5000	0.8660	0.5774	75°	0.9659	0.2588	3.7321
31°	0.5150	0.8572	0.6009	76°	0.9703	0.2419	4.0108
32°	0.5299	0.8480	0.6249	77°	0.9744	0.2250	4.3315
33°	0.5446	0.8387	0.6494	78°	0.9781	0.2079	4.7046
34°	0.5592	0.8290	0.6745	79°	0.9816	0.1908	5.1446
35°	0.5736	0.8192	0.7002	80°	0.9848	0.1736	5.6713
36°	0.5878	0.8090	0.7265	81°	0.9877	0.1564	6.3138
37°	0.6018	0.7986	0.7536	82°	0.9903	0.1392	7.1154
38°	0.6157	0.7880	0.7813	83°	0.9925	0.1219	8.1443
39°	0.6293	0.7771	0.8098	84°	0.9945	0.1045	9.5144
40°	0.6428	0.7660	0.8391	85°	0.9962	0.0872	11.4301
41°	0.6561	0.7547	0.8693	86°	0.9976	0.0698	14.3007
42°	0.6691	0.7431	0.9004	87°	0.9986	0.0523	19.0811
43°	0.6820	0.7314	0.9325	88°	0.9994	0.0349	28.6363
44°	0.6947	0.7193	0.9657	89°	0.9998	0.0175	57.2900
45°	0.7071	0.7071	1.0000				

Glossary

A

absolute value (p. 5)   The absolute value of an integer is its distance from zero on a number line.

acute angle (p. 365)   An acute angle has measure less than 90°.

acute triangle (p. 374)   An acute triangle is one in which all angles have measure less than 90°.

adding two integers with different signs (p. 10)   To add two integers with different signs, find the *difference* of the absolute values of the addends. The sum has the sign of the integer with the greater absolute value.

adding two integers with the same sign (p. 10)   To add two integers with the same sign, add the absolute values of the integers. The sum has the same sign as the addends.

addition properties for inequalities (p. 296)

  1. If $a > b$, then $a + c > b + c$.
  2. If $a < b$, then $a + c < b + c$.

addition property of equality (p. 73)   You can add the same value to both sides of an equation.

  If $a = b$, then $a + c = b + c$.

additive identity (p. 59)   The additive identity is zero. $a + 0 = a$

adjacent angles (p. 366)   Two angles that have the same vertex and have a common side but no interior points in common form adjacent angles.

altitude (p. 407)   An altitude is a segment from one vertex of a polygon perpendicular to the line containing the opposite side, called the base.

angle (p. 365)   Two rays with a common endpoint form an angle.

area (p. 406)   Area is the amount of surface inside a region. We measure area in square units.

area of a circle (p. 414)   The area of a circle equals the product of π and the square of the radius (r). $A = \pi r^2$

area of a parallelogram (p. 407)   The area of a parallelogram equals the product of its base length (b) and its height (h). $A = bh$

area of a rectangle (p. 406)   The area of a rectangle equals the product of its base length (b) and its height (h). $A = bh$

area of a trapezoid (p. 411)   The area of a trapezoid equals half the product of the height (h) and the sum of the bases (b_1 and b_2). $A = \frac{1}{2}h(b_1 + b_2)$

area of a triangle (p. 410)   The area of a triangle equals half the product of the base length (b) and the height (h). $A = \frac{1}{2}bh$

associative property of addition (p. 58)   You can change the grouping and then add without changing the sum. $(a + b) + c = a + (b + c)$

associative property of multiplication (p. 59)   You can change the grouping and then multiply without changing the product. $(ab)c = a(bc)$

B

base (p. 141)   A base is a number used as a factor. For a^n, a is the base.

box and whisker plot (p. 502)   A box and whisker plot is an organization of data. It is especially useful to show the distribution of each 25% of data.

C

central angle (p. 377)   A central angle is an angle with the vertex at the center of a circle.

chord (p. 377)   A chord is a segment with endpoints on a circle.

circle (p. 377)   A circle ($\odot$) is the set of all points the same distance from a given point called the center.

circumference (p. 390)   The circumference (C) is the distance around a circle. Use the formula $C = \pi d$ to compute circumference.

common factor (p. 167)   The factors that are the same for a given set of numbers are the common factors. A common factor of 12 and 18 is 6.

common multiples (p. 168)   The multiples that are the same for a given set of whole numbers are the common multiples. A common multiple of 6 and 8 is 24.

commutative property of addition (p. 58)   You can add in any order without changing the sum. $a + b = b + a$

commutative property of multiplication (p. 58)   You can multiply in any order without changing the product. $a \cdot b = b \cdot a$

compatible numbers (p. 105)   Compatible numbers are two numbers that are easy to compute mentally.

complementary angles (p. 366)   Two angles are complementary angles if the sum of their measures is 90°.

composite number (p. 163)   A composite number is a whole number greater than one with more than two factors.

compound event (p. 522)   A compound event is a combination of two or more events.

cone (p. 421)   A cone is a space figure with one circular base and one vertex.

congruent polygons (p. 380)   Two polygons are congruent if there is a correspondence between their vertices such that the corresponding sides and corresponding angles are congruent.

converse of Pythagorean theorem (p. 462)   If $a^2 + b^2 = c^2$, then the triangle with sides a, b, and c is a right triangle.

convex and concave polygons (p. 370)   A polygon is convex if all points on the diagonals are inside the polygon. Otherwise, the polygon is concave.

coordinate plane (p. 316)   A coordinate plane is the plane which results when two perpendicular number lines intersect at their zero points. The number lines form a grid on the plane.

cosine ratio (p. 473)   In a right triangle, the cosine of $\angle A = \frac{\text{length of side adjacent to } \angle A}{\text{hypotenuse}}$.

counting principle (p. 508)   The counting principle states that the number of outcomes for an event with two or more stages equals the product of the number of outcomes at each stage.

cross products (p. 185)   Finding cross products is a method of checking equivalence of fractions or ratios.
$\frac{a}{b} = \frac{c}{d}$, if $a \cdot d = b \cdot c$

cylinder (p. 421)   A cylinder is a space figure with two circular, parallel, and congruent bases.

D

data base (p. 122)   A data base is a collection of information.

dependent events (p. 523)   Dependent events are events in which the outcome of one depends on the outcome of the other.

For two dependent events A and B, where B is dependent on A,

$P(A \text{ and } B) = P(A) \cdot P(B, \text{ given } A)$.

diagonal (p. 370)   A diagonal is a segment that joins two nonconsecutive vertices of a polygon.

diameter (p. 377)   A diameter is a chord that passes through the center of a circle. The diameter (d) is the length of such a segment.

direct variation (p. 353)   Direct variation means that as one factor increases the other factor also increases. We represent direct variation by an equation in the form $y = kx$, where k is not zero. k is the constant of variation.

distributive property of multiplication over addition (p. 62)   You can distribute a factor to each term inside a set of parentheses.
$a(b + c) = ab + ac \qquad (b + c)a = ba + ca$

distributive property of multiplication over subtraction (p. 62)   You can distribute a factor to each term inside a set of parentheses.
$a(b - c) = ab - ac \qquad (b - c)a = ba - ca$

dividing integers (p. 26)   To divide two integers, find the quotient of the absolute values of the integers. Then use these rules.

1. The quotient of two integers with the same sign is positive.
$(+) \div (+) = + \qquad (-) \div (-) = +$
2. The quotient of two integers with different signs is negative.
$(+) \div (-) = - \qquad (-) \div (+) = -$

dividing two rational numbers (p. 207)   For any two rational numbers $\frac{a}{b}$ and $\frac{c}{d}$,
$\frac{a}{b} \div \frac{c}{d} = \frac{a}{b} \cdot \frac{d}{c} \qquad b \neq 0, c \neq 0, d \neq 0$.

divisible (p. 159)   A number is divisible by a second number if the second number divides the first with no remainder.

divisible by 3 (p. 160)   A number is divisible by 3 if the sum of its digits is divisible by 3.

divisible by 9 (p. 160)   A number is divisible by 9 if the sum of its digits is divisible by 9.

division properties for inequalities (p. 297)

1. If c is positive and $a < b$, then $\frac{a}{c} < \frac{b}{c}$.
2. If c is positive and $a > b$, then $\frac{a}{c} > \frac{b}{c}$.
3. If c is negative and $a < b$, then $\frac{a}{c} > \frac{b}{c}$.
4. If c is negative and $a > b$, then $\frac{a}{c} < \frac{b}{c}$.

division property of equality (p. 76)   You can divide both sides of an equation by the same nonzero value.

If $a = b$, then $a \div c = b \div c$, $\frac{a}{c} = \frac{b}{c}$, $c \neq 0$.

E

equation (p. 54)   An equation is a mathematical sentence with an equal sign.

equiangular triangle (p. 374)   An equiangular triangle is a triangle in which all angles have equal measure.

equilateral triangle (p. 374)   An equilateral triangle is a triangle in which all sides have equal measure.

equivalent fractions (p. 184)   You can form equivalent fractions by multiplying or dividing the numerator and denominator by the same nonzero factor.

evaluate an expression (p. 44)   To evaluate an expression, replace each variable with a number. Then compute, following order of operations.

exponent (p. 141)   An exponent shows the number of times a base is used as a factor. For a^n, n is the exponent.

F

factor (p. 159)   One number is a factor of another if it divides that number with no remainder.

factorial (p. 509)   A factorial is the product of all whole numbers from n to 1. We write this as $n!$

FOIL method (p. 550)   Use the FOIL method to find the product of two binomials.

1. Multiply the **F**irst terms in each binomial.
2. Multiply the **O**utside terms in each binomial.
3. Multiply the **I**nside terms in each binomial.
4. Multiply the **L**ast terms in each binomial.
5. Add the products.

formula (p. 128)   A formula is an equation that shows the relationship between two or more variables.

frequency distribution (p. 492)   A frequency distribution is a listing of data that pairs each data item with the number of times it occurs.

front-end estimation (p. 105)   To use front-end estimation:

1. Add the front-end digits.
2. Adjust by estimating the sum of the remaining digits.
3. Add the two values.

G

greatest common factor (GCF) (p. 167)   The greatest common factor of a set of numbers is the greatest number that is a factor of the given numbers.

grouping symbols (p. 40)   Grouping symbols include parentheses, ( ), brackets, [ ], absolute value symbols, and a division bar. These are used to group expressions.

H

height (p. 407)   The height of a figure is the length of its altitude.

hypotenuse (p. 460)   The hypotenuse is the side of a right triangle opposite the right angle.

I

improper fraction (p. 188)   A fraction that has a numerator equal to or greater than the denominator is an improper fraction.

independent events (p. 522)   Independent events are events in which the outcome of one has no affect on the outcome of the other.

For two independent events A and B,

$P(\text{A and B}) = P(\text{A}) \cdot P(\text{B})$.

indirect variation (p. 353)   In indirect variation, one factor increases as the other factor decreases. The equation $xy = k$ represents an indirect variation. k is the constant of variation.

inequality (p. 292)   An inequality is a statement that two expressions are not equal.

integers (p. 4)   The whole numbers and their opposites form the set of integers.

$$\ldots, -4, -3, -2, -1, 0, 1, 2, 3, 4, \ldots$$
negative   zero   positive

inverse operations (p. 72)   Inverse operations are operations that undo each other. Addition and subtraction are inverse operations. Multiplication and division are inverse operations.

irrational numbers (p. 455)   Irrational numbers are numbers which we cannot express as either terminating or repeating decimals.

isosceles triangle (p. 374)   An isosceles triangle has at least two sides with equal measure.

L

lateral area of a cone (p. 430)   The lateral area (LA) of a cone equals half the product of the circumference (C) and slant height (l).
$$LA = \frac{1}{2} Cl$$

lateral area of a cylinder (p. 428)   The lateral area (LA) of a cylinder is the product of the circumference of the base (C) and the height of the cylinder (h).
$$A = Ch$$

lateral area of a prism (p. 427)   The lateral area (LA) of a prism is the product of the perimeter of the base (P) and the height of the prism (h).
$$A = Ph$$

least common denominator (LCD) (p. 196)   The least common denominator of two or more fractions is the LCM of the denominators.

least common multiple (LCM) (p. 168)   The least common multiple is the least number that is a common multiple of two or more given numbers.

legs of a right triangle (p. 460)   The legs of a right triangle are the two sides that form the right angle.

like terms (p. 66)   Like terms have the same variable(s).

line (p. 362)   A line continues without end in opposite directions. We denote line AB by $\overleftrightarrow{AB}$.

line plot (p. 492)   A line plot shows data on a number line. You place an $\times$ for each response above the category of the response.

line symmetry (p. 381)   A figure is said to have line symmetry if a line can be drawn through the figure so that one side is a mirror image of the other.

linear equation (p. 324)   A linear equation is an equation for which the graph is a line. The standard form of a linear equation is $Ax + By = C$, where A, B, and C are real numbers and A and B are not both equal to zero.

locating a point on the coordinate plane (p. 316)   To locate $P(x, y)$ on the coordinate plane:
1. Begin at origin.
2. Locate x on the x-axis.
3. Move up or down the absolute value of y units.

lowest terms (p. 185)   When a fraction is in lowest terms, the only common factor of the numerator and denominator is 1.

M

mean (p. 27)   The mean is the sum of a set of numbers divided by the number of items in the set.

measures of central tendency (p. 488)   The measures of central tendency are statistics used to describe data characteristics. These measures are mean, median, and mode.

median (p. 488)   The median is the middle value in a set of data.

mixed number (p. 188)   A mixed number is a number that includes an integer and a fraction.

mode (p. 488)   The mode is the data item that occurs most often.

monomial (p. 538)   A monomial is a real number, a variable, or the product of a real number and one or more variables.

multiple (p. 159)   A multiple of a number is the product of that number and any other whole number.

multiplication properties for inequalities (p. 297)
1. If c is positive and $a < b$, then $ac < bc$.
2. If c is positive and $a > b$, then $ac > bc$.
3. If c is negative and $a < b$, then $ac > bc$.
4. If c is negative and $a > b$, then $ac < bc$.

multiplication property of equality (p. 77)   You can multiply both sides of an equation by the same value. If $a = b$, then $ac = bc$.

multiplicative identity (p. 59)   The multiplicative identity is one. $a \cdot 1 = a$

multiplying integers (p. 22)   To multiply two integers, find the product of the absolute values of the integers. Then use these rules.
1. The product of two integers with the same sign is positive.
   $(+)(+) = +$ $(-)(-) = +$
2. The product of two integers with different signs is negative.
   $(+)(-) = -$ $(-)(+) = -$

N

negative exponents (p. 212)   For any nonzero integers a and n: $a^{-n} = \frac{1}{a^n}$.

numerical coefficient (p. 66)   A numerical coefficient is a number that is multiplied by a variable.

numerical expression (p. 34)   A numerical expression names a number. A numerical expression does not contain variables.

O

obtuse angle (p. 365)   An obtuse angle is an angle with measure between 90° and 180°.

obtuse triangle (p. 374)   An obtuse triangle has one obtuse angle.

open equation (p. 54)   An open equation is an equation that contains one or more variables.

opposites (p. 4)   Opposites are two integers the same distance from zero on a number line, but in opposite directions.

order of operations (p. 40)

1. Do all operations within grouping symbols.
2. Evaluate powers.
3. Multiply and divide from left to right.
4. Add and subtract from left to right.

ordered pair (p. 316)   An ordered pair is a pair of numbers (x,y) assigned to a point on a coordinate plane.

origin (p. 316)   The origin is the intersection point of the x- and y-axes in a coordinate plane. The coordinates of the origin are $(0,0)$.

P

parallel lines (p. 363)   Two lines are parallel if they lie in the same plane and do not intersect.

parallel planes (p. 363)   Two planes are parallel if they do not intersect.

parallelogram (p. 371)   A parallelogram is a quadrilateral with two pairs of opposite parallel sides.

percent (p. 245)   A percent is a ratio that compares a number to 100.

percent equation (p. 256)   Use a triangle to solve percent problems.

percent of change (p. 260)   Use the following formula to find percent of change.

$$\text{percent of change} = \frac{\text{amount of change}}{\text{original amount}}$$

perimeter (p. 390)   Perimeter is the distance around a figure.

pi (π) (p. 389)   Pi is the ratio of the circumference of a circle to its diameter.

plane (p. 362)   A plane is a flat surface with no thickness that continues without end in all directions.

point (p. 362)   A point represents a position in space.

polygon (p. 370)   A polygon is a closed plane figure such that no two segments with a common endpoint are collinear and segments intersect only at the endpoints.

polyhedron (p. 420)   A polyhedron is a space figure in which all faces are polygons.

polynomial (p. 538)   A polynomial is a monomial or a sum or difference of monomials.

prime factorization (p. 164)   Prime factorization is an expression showing a composite number as a product of its prime factors.

prime number (p. 163)   A prime number is a whole number greater than 1 with exactly two factors, 1 and the number itself.

principal square root (p. 454)   The principal square root of a number is its positive square root. The principal square root is denoted by the symbol $\sqrt{}$.

prism (p. 420)   A prism is a polyhedron with two parallel bases that are congruent polygons and sides that are parallelograms.

probability (p. 512)   Probability is the likelihood that a certain event, or set of outcomes, will occur.

$$P(\text{E}) = \frac{\text{number of favorable outcomes}}{\text{total number of possible outcomes}}$$

product of $(a + b)(a - b)$ (p. 551)   To find the product of the sum and difference of two terms, square the first term and subtract the square of the second term.

$$(a + b)(a - b) = a^2 - b^2$$

product of two rational numbers (p. 206)   For any two rational numbers $\frac{a}{b}$ and $\frac{c}{d}$,

$$\frac{a}{b} \cdot \frac{c}{d} = \frac{a \cdot c}{b \cdot d}, \ b \neq 0, d \neq 0.$$

proportion (p. 233)   A proportion is a statement that two ratios are equal. If two ratios are equal, their cross products are equal.

a is to b as c is to d

$a : b : : c : d, \frac{a}{b} = \frac{c}{d}, b \neq 0, d \neq 0$

proportions and percents (p. 252)   To find the ratio of a number to 100, use the following formula.

$\frac{\text{part}}{\text{whole}} = \frac{n}{100}$

pyramid (p. 420)   A pyramid is a polyhedron with triangular sides that meet at a vertex. The base of a pyramid is a polygon.

Pythagorean theorem (p. 461)   In any right triangle with legs a and b, and hypotenuse c,

$a^2 + b^2 = c^2$.

Q

quadrant (p. 316)   A quadrant is one of four sections into which the x- and y-axes divide the coordinate plane.

quadrilateral (p. 371)   A quadrilateral is a polygon with four sides.

R

radius (p. 377)   A radius is a segment that has endpoints at the center of a circle and on the circle. The radius (r) is the length of such a segment.

range (p. 489)   The range of a set of data is the difference between the greatest and least values in the set.

rate (p. 234)   A rate is a ratio that compares quantities in different units. A unit rate compares a quantity to one.

ratio (p. 233)   A ratio is a comparison of two quantities by division.

a to b; $a : b$; $\frac{a}{b}$; $b \neq 0$

rational number (p. 192)   A rational number is a number you write in the form $\frac{a}{b}$, where a is any integer, and b is a nonzero integer.

ray (p. 362)   A ray is part of a line with only one endpoint that continues without end in one direction. We denote ray AB as $\overrightarrow{AB}$.

rectangle (p. 371)   A rectangle is a parallelogram with four right angles.

regular polygon (p. 371)   A polygon is regular if the measures of all sides and all angles are equal.

rhombus (p. 371)   A rhombus is a parallelogram with all sides equal.

right angle (p. 365)   A right angle is an angle that measures 90°.

right triangle (p. 374)   A right triangle is a triangle with one right angle.

rule of a power raised to a power (p. 145)   To raise a power to a power, multiply the exponents.

$(a^m)^n = a^{m \cdot n}$

rule of a product raised to a power (p. 146)   To raise a product to a power, raise each factor to the power and then use the rule of exponents for multiplication. $(ab)^m = a^m b^m$

rule of exponents for division (p. 211)   To divide numbers or variables with the *same* base, subtract exponents.

$\frac{a^m}{a^n} = a^{m-n}, a \neq 0$

rule of exponents for multiplication (p. 145)   To multiply numbers or variables with the *same* base, add exponents. $a^m \cdot a^n = a^{m+n}$

S

sample space (p. 512)   The set of possible outcomes is the sample space.

scalene triangle (p. 374)   A scalene triangle is a triangle that has no sides equal.

scientific notation (p. 149)   A number is in scientific notation when it is written as the product of a number greater than or equal to 1 and less than 10, and a power of 10.

segment (p. 362)   A segment is part of a line with two endpoints. We denote segment AB by $\overline{AB}$.

similar figures (p. 384)   Two figures are similar ($\sim$) if corresponding angles are congruent and corresponding sides are in proportion.

similar triangles (p. 385)   Two triangles are similar if two angles of one are congruent to two angles of another.

simplify an expression (p. 67)   To simplify an expression, replace it with an equivalent expression that contains no like terms or parentheses.

sine ratio (p. 473)   In a right triangle, the sine of $\angle A = \frac{\text{length of side opposite } \angle A}{\text{hypotenuse}}$.

skew lines (p. 363)   Skew lines are lines that do not lie in the same plane and do not intersect.

slant height (p. 430)   A slant height of a cone or a pyramid is the height of a face.

slope (p. 330)   The slope of a line is the ratio of the vertical change in y to the corresponding horizontal change in x. Use the following formula to calculate slope.

$$\text{slope} = \frac{\text{difference in } y \text{ coordinates}}{\text{difference in } x \text{ coordinates}}$$

slope-intercept form (p. 331)   A linear equation in the form $y = mx + b$ is in slope-intercept form. The slope is m and the y-intercept is b.

solution (p. 55)   A solution is a number that replaces a variable to make an open equation true.

solution of a system of linear equations (p. 340)   A solution of a system of linear equations is any ordered pair of numbers that satisfies all equations in the system.

solving a multi-step equation (p. 279)   To solve a multi-step equation:

1. Remove parentheses using the distributive property.
2. Combine like terms.
3. Undo addition or subtraction.
4. Undo multiplication or division.

solving a simple two-step equation (p. 275)   To solve a simple two-step equation:

1. Undo addition or subtraction.
2. Undo multiplication or division.

solving proportions (p. 237)   To solve a proportion:

1. Write the cross products.
2. Solve the equation.

sphere (p. 421)   A sphere is the set of all points in space that are the same distance from a given point called the center.

square (p. 371)   A square is a parallelogram that is both a rectangle and a rhombus.

square root (p. 454)   The square root of a number, n, is a if $a^2 = n$.

squaring binomials (p. 551)   To square a binomial, square the first term. Then add or subtract twice the product of the two terms and add the square of the second term.

$$(a + b)^2 = a^2 + 2ab + b^2$$
$$(a - b)^2 = a^2 - 2ab + b^2$$

stem and leaf plot (p. 498)   A stem and leaf plot is an organization of data that groups data into categories based on place values.

subtracting integers (p. 15)   To subtract an integer, add its opposite.

subtraction properties for inequalities (p. 296)

1. If $a > b$, then $a - c > b - c$.
2. If $a < b$, then $a - c < b - c$.

subtraction property of equality (p. 72)   You can subtract the same value from both sides of an equation.

If $a = b$, then $a - c = b - c$.

supplementary angles (p. 366)   Two angles are supplementary angles if the sum of their measures is 180°.

surface area (p. 427)   Surface area (SA) is the sum of the areas of the base(s) and the side(s). Surface area is measured in square units.

surface area of a sphere (p. 431)   The surface area of a sphere equals the product of 4π and the square of the radius (r).

$$A = 4\pi r^2$$

system of linear equations (p. 340)   A system of linear equations is two or more linear equations using the same variables.

system of linear inequalities (p. 349)   A system of linear inequalities is two or more linear inequalities using the same variables.

T

tangent ratio (p. 473)   In a right triangle, the tangent of $\angle A = \frac{\text{length of side opposite } \angle A}{\text{length of side adjacent to } \angle A}$.

term (p. 66)   A term is a part of an expression. Terms are separated by addition and subtraction symbols.

tessellation (p. 397)   A tessellation is a design that covers a plane with no gaps and no overlaps.

trapezoid (p. 371)   A trapezoid is a quadrilateral with exactly one pair of parallel sides.

triangle (p. 371)   A triangle is a polygon that has three sides.

triangle, 30°-60°-90° (p. 470)   In a 30°-60°-90° triangle, the lengths of the sides have the following relationships.

hypotenuse = 2(shorter leg)
longer leg = shorter leg ($\sqrt{3}$)
shorter leg = $\frac{\text{longer leg}}{\sqrt{3}}$

triangle, 45°-45°-90° (p. 469) In a 45°-45°-90° right triangle, the lengths of the sides have the following relationships.

hypotenuse = $\sqrt{2} \cdot$ leg

leg = $\dfrac{\text{hypotenuse} \cdot \sqrt{2}}{2}$

trigonometric ratio (p. 473) A trigonometric ratio is a ratio of the measures of two sides of a right triangle.

V

variable (p. 34) A variable is a symbol (usually a letter) that stands for a number.

variable expression (p. 34) A variable expression is an expression that contains at least one variable.

vertex (p. 365) The vertex of an angle is the common endpoint of the two rays forming the angle.

vertical angles (p. 366) Two intersecting lines form two pairs of vertical angles. The measures of vertical angles are equal.

volume (p. 437) Volume is the measure of the space inside a space figure. We measure volume in cubic units.

volume of a cone and a pyramid (p. 440) The formula for the volume of the cone and pyramid is base area (B) times one-third the height (h).

$V = \dfrac{1}{3} Bh$

volume of a cylinder or a prism (p. 437) The volume (V) of a prism or a cylinder is base area (B) times the height (h).

$V = Bh$

volume of a sphere (p. 441) The volume (V) of a sphere with radius r is $V = \frac{4}{3} \pi r^3$.

X

x-axis (p. 316) The x-axis is the horizontal number line on a coordinate plane.

x-intercept (p. 325) The x-intercept is the x-coordinate of a point where a graph crosses the x-axis.

Y

y-axis (p. 316) The y-axis is the vertical number line on a coordinate plane.

y-intercept (p. 325) The y-intercept is the y-coordinate of a point where a graph crosses the y-axis.

Z

zero as an exponent (p. 211) Any nonzero number with zero as an exponent equals 1.

$a^0 = 1$ for all $a \neq 0$.

Selected Answers

CHAPTER 1

Integers and Expressions

1-1 pages 6–7
Written Exercises 1. 110 **3.** -300 **5.** -8 **13.** -6 **15.** 3
17. 4 **19.** -9 **21.** -12,500; -15,617; 0 **23.** -2 **25.** -8
27. 8 **33.** > **35.** < **37.** < **39.** = **41.** zero
43. negative **53. a.** -27°; **b.** -20°; -71°
Mixed Review 1. 907 **2.** 814 **3.** 1,088 **4.** 42
5. 7,872 **6.** 13

1-2 pages 12–13
Written Exercises 1. -20 + 18 = -2; still owe $2
3. -10 + (-2) + 8 + (-5) + (-13) + 1 = -21; temp. is 21°
below. **5.** -9 **7.** 4 **9.** 9 **11.** -8 **13.** -40 **15.** -847
17. -5 **19.** 0 **21.** 3 **23.** -13 **25.** 15 **27.** -13 **29.** 4
31. -6 **33.** 9 **35.** -6 < 2 **37.** -2 + (−7) = −9
39. 3 + (−8) = −5 **41.** < **43.** < ; < **45.** 10-yd loss
Mixed Review 1. -8 **2.** 12 **3.** 10 **4.** 16 **5.** < **6.** >
7. 12 **8.** -13
Critical Thinking 1. -7, 525, -47 **2.** -19, -50, -198
3. -7, -78, -47 **4.** all neg. **5.** -47, -19, -7; -5, -25, -40

1-3 pages 15–17
Written Exercises 1. 3 − (-2) = 5 **3.** 3 − 5 = -2
5. 3,000 − 600 **7.** -5 **9.** -16 **11.** -60 **13.** 150 **15.** 66
17. -196 **19.** 178 **21.** 913 **23.** -31 **25.** 25 **27.** -175
29. -422 **31.** 15 **33.** 191 **35.** -101 **37.** 56 **39.** 356
41. 38 **43.** 16; 20; 24; 28; 28 **45.** -7, -6, -1, -3, -8; -15
47. a. The temperature decreases.; **b.** 24°; **c.** decrease;
d. 21,000 m **49.** -15 **57.** 180 **59.** -70 **61.** 2,400
63. -3,600
Mixed Review 1. -29 **2.** 65 **3.** 7 **4.** -6
5. -6, -7, -8, or -9 **6.** -6 **7.** -925 ft

1-4 pages 20–21
Written Exercises 1. 78 students
3. 4, 3, 1, 16, 15, 1; 9, 8, 1, 25, 24, 1; **a.** 11 · 11; 1
b. subtract 1; 2,208; **c.** add 1; 4,225
5. 1810 and 1820; 467,174 people **7. a.** $59; $21; **b.** 10
Critical Thinking 1. 107 **2.** 234 **3.** 37

1-5 pages 24–25
Written Exercises 1. -60 **3.** -30 **5.** 21 **7.** 20 **9.** A
11. B **13.** 4,661 **15.** 46,354 **17.** 15 **19.** -96
21. -220 **23.** 12,288 **25.** -200 **27.** -56 **29.** -7 **31.** 0
33. -26 **35.** -81 **37.** -19 **39.** 8(-5) = -40
41. 6(−9) = −54 **43.** > **45.** = **47. a.** -$36; **b.** $40
49. -3 and -4 **51.** 5 and -1 **53. a.** 5,000 ft at 40°; **b.** no
Mixed Review 1. < **2.** > **3.** < **4.** -11 **5.** 3,003
6. |-20| **7.** 6 **8.** 180°

1-6 pages 27–29
Written Exercises 1. -9(10) = -90 **3.** 8(7) = 56 **5.** -7
7. -5 **9.** -9 **11.** 126 **13.** 56 **15.** 4 **17.** 19 **19.** -1
21. -15 **23.** -384 **25.** -59 **27.** -225 **29.** -80 **31.** -35
33. 64 **35.** 3,375 **37.** -9 **39.** -42(3); -126
41. -25 − 200; -225 **43.** $3 **45.** 0 **47.** < **49.** <
55. -15 **57.** 2 ft/s
Mixed Review 1. -45 **2.** 24 **3.** -48 **4.** 30
5. 13, 18, 23 **6.** 25, 36, 49
Test Yourself 1. > **2.** < **3.** = **4.** 8 **5.** -85 **6.** -12
7. -8 **8.** 20 **9.** -45 **10.** 8 **11.** 3 **12.** 44

Practice page 30
1. 55 **3.** -23 **5.** -19 **7.** 133 **9.** -334 **11.** 141
13. -100 **15.** 63 **17.** -89 **19.** -62 **21.** -238 **23.** -224
25. -705 **27.** 63 **29.** -84 **31.** -162 **33.** 375 **35.** -896
37. 288 **39.** -496,000 **41.** -9 **43.** -6 **45.** -5 **47.** 37
49. -37 **51.** 153 **53.** 8 **55.** 142 **57.** -20 **59.** -3
61. 0 **63.** 55 **65.** 10 **67.** -1

1-7 page 33
Written Exercises 1. 90 C **3.** 230 C **5.** 120 C
7. -580 C **9.** 660 C; about 5 h **11.** 900 C; 18,000 C

1-8 pages 36–37
Written Exercises 1. $3x − 3$ **3.** $3z + (-2)$ **9.** 23(-9)
11. $-6 − 8$ **13.** $19 + m$ **15.** $12x$ **17.** $n ÷ (-1)$
19. $g · 4r$ **21.** $10a$ **23.** $t + 200$ **33. a.** 7 · 1; **b.** 7 · 4;
c. $7w$ **35. a.** 15 − 3; **b.** 15 − p; **c.** 15 + 10; **d.** 15 + f
37. $d − 20$ **41. a.** (2 · 25) + (4 · 12); **b.** $25j + 12t$ **43.** b
45. d
Mixed Review 1. -5 **2.** 20 **3.** 0 **4.** -23 **5.** 100 **6.** 8
7. $2.95

1-9 pages 41–43
Written Exercises 1. addition **3.** subtraction inside
absolute value symbols **5.** -1 **7.** 3 **9.** 4 **11.** -20
13. -30 **15.** -13 **17.** 243 **19.** 4 **21.** -394 **23.** -8
25. -2[(7 + 8) ÷ 5 + 5] = -16 **27.** >
29. (7 + 4) · 6 = 66 **31.** 3 · (8 − 2 + 5 − 12) = -3
33. no **35.** yes **37.** 25 h **39.** Alice 103; Ray 118
41. A possible answer is [-6 + (-8)](6 + 4) − 2
45. 5 + (4)(9); 41 **47.** 17 − (25 ÷ 5); 12
49. 130 + (116 − 8); 238 **55.** 74 + 5*9 + -7 = 112
57. 70 + 8*-9 = -2 **59.** 2,087*37 − 1,951 = 75,268
61. Yes, computers follow order of operations.
Mixed Review 1. $6n$ **2.** $x − 6$ **3.** $a + |-7|$ **4.** <
5. < **6.** < **7.** 36

1-10 pages 45–46
Written Exercises 1. -24 **3.** -5 **5.** -12 **7.** 11 **9.** 21
11. 7 **13.** 20 **15.** -35 **17.** 21 **19.** 1 **21.** 425 **23.** 18
25. 117 **27.** A possible answer is 2. **29.** 8, -8 **31.** -6
33. 0 **35.** 3 **37. a.** 265m; **b.** 1,590; **c.** 381,600
39. a. 14m; **b.** 350 C **41.** $400 **43.** 6, 12, -12, 36, 4
45. 55 **47. a.** 13; **b.** 24

Mixed Review 1. -54 2. -48 3. -5 4. -24
5. the sum of 6 and a number
6. twice the quantity of a number minus 2
7. the opposite of 12 times a number 8. 83

Problem Solving Practice page 47
1. **a.** Each month the interest increases by a penny
more than the previous month.; **b.** May $1.04, $105.10;
June $1.05, $106.15; July $1.06, $107.21; August $1.07,
$108.28 3. thermosphere, mesosphere, stratosphere,
troposphere 5. -39°F

Chapter 1 Review pages 48–49
1. grouping symbols; order of operations 2. opposite
3. integers 4. absolute value
5. variable expression; variable 6. mean 7. > 8. >
9. = 10. < 11. < 12. > 13. -7 14. 12 15. -9
16. 14 17. -12 18. -16 19. -27 20. -15 21. -1
22. -42 23. -5 24. 72 25. 7 26. -3 27. -165
28. $x - 25$ 29. $3rn$ 30. $y + 2$ 31. 36 32. 33 33. 25
34. 24 35. 3 36. 4 37. 19 38. 6 39. 16 40. 14
41. -450 42. 16 43. $112 44. She will gain weight.

Chapter 1 Cumulative Review page 51
1. A 3. C 5. D 7. B 9. B 11. B 13. A 15. D

CHAPTER 2

Solving Equations

2-1 pages 56–57
Written Exercises 1. yes 3. yes 5. open 7. false
9. false 11. true 13. true 15. true 17. false
19. true 21. yes 23. yes 25. yes 27. no 29. yes
31. 0 33. -2 35. 4 37. > 39. < 41. > 43. 30; 48
45. 15; 28 47. $0 \cdot (-7) = -7$; false
49. $15 + n = 50$; open 51. $(-7) + 12 = -5$; false
53. $3 \cdot 32 = 96$; true 57. $13b = f$
Mixed Review 1. -1 2. 10 3. -3 4. 13
5. 13, 21, 34 or 12, 17, 23 6. 15, 8, 3 7. 12h

2-2 pages 60–61
Written Exercises 1. c 3. d 5. f 7. d 9. c
11. $z \cdot 25$ 13. $5(a + b)$ 15. $3 \cdot (25 \cdot 4)$ 17. $4(ab)$
19. 47,000 21. 2,800 23. 100 25. 3; 7 27. 730; 270
29. 58 31. 60 33. 60,000 35. **a.** No, it would change
the order of operations. **b.** Yes, it does not matter in
what order you multiply 6, 5, and -4.
Mixed Review 1. true 2. open 3. no 4. yes 5. no
6. yes 7. $3 \cdot (4 - 7) + 6 = -3$ 8. 4 and 9

2-3 pages 64–65
Written Exercises 1. $4(w + 7)$ 3. $7(x + y + 5)$ 5. -4
7. c 9. -w 11. -9; $-9(x + y)$ 13. e; $(b - c - d)e$
15. -1; $-1(a + b)$ 17. w, y 19. -2, -4 21. 5, -2
23. 1,120 25. 5,075 27. -12 29. -30 31. 7 33. 285
35. 16 37. 3,098 mi
Mixed Review 1. C 2. AI 3. A 4. MI 5. <
6. = 7. < 8. 605

Critical Thinking 1. **a.** 3; **b.** 0; **c.** 1 2. **a.** =; **b.** yes
3. yes 4. yes; zero 5. It is an operation which is
associative and commutative. It has an identity of zero.

2-4 pages 68–69
Written Exercises 1. 2; 5, 8; 5a, 8a; none
3. 2; 2; none; -7 5. 2; -7; none; 3
7. 4; 6, 4, 1; 6ab, 4ba, ab; 8 9. 9a 11. 5b 13. A
15. D 17. A 19. 5a 21. 6; 4; 10 23. 1m 25. 6a
27. $54k + 5$ 29. $5g + 15$ 31. $8x - 32w$ 33. -83x
35. $44a - 59b + 19c$ 37. -12y; 60 39. $3y + 2z - 16$; -17
41. $6x + 7x + 14$; $13x + 14$
43. $3x + 2x + 189$; $5x + 189$
Mixed Review 1. 7 2. 3 3. 5 4. 3 5. -4 6. 86
7. 46
Test Yourself 1. yes 2. no 3. no 4. C 5. A
6. MI 7. C 8. C 9. D 10. 50b 11. 173 12. 18y
13. 9a 14. -2 15. $16w - 6$

2-5 pages 74–75
Written Exercises 1. $x = 2$ 3. $w = -2$ 5. $-2 = x - 3$; 1
7. -5 9. -54 11. 626 13. 82 15. -13 17. 10,221
19. 41 21. 39 23. -11 25. -300 27. 0 29. 308
31. 1,364,615 33. 77,098 35. 500 37. 65 39. -20
41. 1,598 43. 25 45. $b - a$ 47. $d + 5 = 17$; $d = 12$
49. $20 + d = 150$; $d = 130$
51. $5,200 = 2,680 + h$; $h = 2,520$
53. $700 = 119 + p$; $p = 581$ million
Mixed Review 1. 3 2. 3 3. $4x + 4$ 4. $2q + 6$ 5. 3
6. 12 7. 512 min

2-6 pages 77–79
Written Exercises 1. $g = 4$ 3. $h = -3$ 5. yes 7. no
9. $8 = 4x$; 2 11. -15 13. 6 15. -4 17. 5 19. 52
21. -16 23. 300 25. -24 27. 42 29. -15,000
31. 382,300 33. -42,336 35. -1,586 37. -768 39. -8
41. 504 43. 15 45. 31 47. 11 49. 0 51. 875,000
53. 12d 55. -6, 6 57. $\frac{b}{a}$ 59. $b + a$
Mixed Review 1. -11 2. 17 3. -19 4. $a - 3 + b$
5. $7(9 - w)$ 6. $|-8 + q|$ 7. 60 s or 1 min
Critical Thinking 1. they get thinner 2. where all of the
lines meet 3. All of the dot is on the missing piece.
4. 2 5. 3

2-7 pages 81–82
Written Exercises 1. c 3. $n - 24 = -9$ 5. $15c = 30$
9. $x + 46 + 54 = 150$; 50 mm
Mixed Review 1. 515 2. 540 3. Divide each side by 5.
4. Subtract 5 from each side. 5. Add 5 to each side.
6. Multiply each side by 5. 7. 1,028 ft
Test Yourself 1. 20 2. -68 3. -34 4. 32 5. -23
6. -13 7. $n + 12 = 20$; 8 8. $(c - 6) - 3 = -10$; -1

2-8 page 86
Written Exercises 1. 12, 84 and 8, 56 3. 11, 12
5. -2, -3, -4 7. 12:40 P.M. 9. -10
11. 30 ft, 40 ft, 50 ft

2-9 pages 88–89
Written Exercises   1. $2,860,000,000
3. a. about 2 billion lb; **b.** about 16 billion kW · h
5. $325,000

Practice page 90
1. open   **3.** true   **5.** open   **7.** no   **9.** yes   **11.** no
13. A   **15.** C   **17.** MI   **19.** -476   **21.** 216   **23.** -22
25. 26   **27.** -16   **29.** -15k **31.** 5g + 8
33. 4x + 4y − 4z **35.** -3w + 4   **37.** 27   **39.** 12   **41.** 9
43. -39   **45.** 3,072   **47.** n + 5 = -123; -128

Problem Solving Practice page 91
1. a. 4; **b.** 8; **c.** yes; 16; 2   **3. a.** total wages for each
employee; **b.** = SUM(B2:B4); =SUM(D2:D4); place in
B5 and D5, respectively   **5. a.** $260; **b.** 1$\frac{1}{2}$ h

Chapter 2 Review pages 92–93
1. f   **2.** a   **3.** e   **4.** i   **5.** k   **6.** j   **7.** b   **8.** c   **9.** d
10. g   **11.** h   **12.** 547   **13.** 80   **14.** 700   **15.** 6,500
16. 115   **17.** 192   **18.** 80   **19.** 0   **20.** 8x + 5y
21. 9a + 16   **22.** x = -1   **23.** x = 3   **24.** a = 35
25. x = 11   **26.** y = 480   **27.** n = 20   **28.** x = -1
29. x = 2   **30.** m = -72   **31.** b = 12   **32.** c = 288
33. k = 18   **34.** 2x + 28 = 54   **35.** x − 17 = 12
38. 5 pkgs of 15 plates; 4 pkgs of 20 plates   **39.** 80
billion lb

Chapters 1–2 Cumulative Review page 95
1. B   **2.** C   **3.** C   **4.** D   **5.** A   **6.** A   **7.** A   **8.** C
9. C   **10.** B   **11.** B   **12.** D   **13.** C   **14.** C   **15.** B
16. B

CHAPTER 3

Decimals and Equations

3-1 pages 102–103
Written Exercises   5. 512.73 km/h   **11.** >   **13.** =
15. >   **17.** >   **19.** 4.5, 4.05, 4.049
21. 3.003, 0.3002, 0.30, 0.030008, 0.03   **29.** 0.8   **31.** 0.36
33. 365,987   **37. a.** lesser; **b.** greater; **c.** when the digit to
the right is greater than the digit to the left   **39.** If the
absolute value of a negative number is less than the
absolute value of another negative number, the first
number is greater than the second number.
Mixed Review   1. -5   **2.** 3   **3.** -9   **4.** -45   **5.** 3 and 7
6. d − 40 = 182; $222

3-2 pages 106–107
Written Exercises   1. 0.25   **3.** 60   **5.** 40   **7.** -18,000
9. 300   **11.** 8   **13.** 27   **15.** 3   **17.** 4   **19.** 0.02
21. $2,000   **23.** 0.23   **25.** 200   **27.** -20   **29.** 22.4256
31. 213.76   **33.** 109.571   **35.** 67.3436   **37.** yes
39. food   **41.** $2   **43.** $3,200   **45.** about 3,500 yd
Mixed Review   1. -0.88   **2.** 4.13   **3.** 24   **4.** -2   **5.** -108
6. 11   **7.** 36

3-3 pages 109–110
Written Exercises   1. 11.5 h   **3.** 14.375 h   **5.** -7.8
7. 15.1   **9.** 6.14   **11.** -20.62   **13.** -25.48   **15.** -14.965
17. -3.07   **19.** -25   **21.** -20.44   **23.** 3.001   **25.** 7.69
27. -40.416w **29.** -0.8m **31.** 7.6x
33. 17.247a − 24.228   **35.** -1.8102x **37.** -90   **39.** 3
41. a. 12.3a − 1.08; **b.** 102.2523   **43.** $21.67
Mixed Review   1. $200   **2.** 20,000   **3.** -5   **4.** 0.1   **5.** 4
6. 35   **7.** $.22
Critical Thinking   1. 0.125 ÷ 0.625 = 0.2; 0.2 ÷ 0.125 =
1.6; 1.6 ÷ 0.2 = 8   **2.** 2.5 and 2; 2 ÷ 2.5 = 0.8; 0.8 ÷ 2 =
0.4; 0.4 ÷ 0.8 = 0.5; 0.5 ÷ 0.4 = 1.25; 1.25 ÷ 0.5 = 2.5;
2.5 ÷ 1.25 = 2; 2 ÷ 2.5 = 0.8; By following the pattern,
you arrive at the numbers you began with; no.
3. 2 and -0.2; -0.2 ÷ 2 = -0.1; -0.1 ÷ (-0.2) = 0.5; 0.5 ÷
(-0.1) = -5; -5 ÷ 0.5 = -10; -10 ÷ (-5) = 2; 2 ÷ (-10) =
-0.2; -0.2 ÷ 2 = -0.1; By following the
pattern, you arrive at the numbers you began with;
no.   **4.** By following this pattern, you arrive at the
numbers you began with. It does not matter whether
you use decimals, whole numbers, positive numbers,
or negative numbers.

3-4 pages 112–114
Written Exercises   1. -13.391   **3.** 1.63   **5.** -0.3698
7. -0.0233   **9.** 12.58   **11.** 1.032   **13.** 13.31   **15.** -23.12
17. 4.66   **19.** 2   **21.** 60,392.0034   **23.** 7.131   **25.** 3.9
27. 0   **29.** -5.4   **31.** 2.9   **33.** 0.4   **35.** -59.9
37. a. apple, grapefruit, orange, grape; **b.** blue
39. b − c = a **41.** x = 0.08 and y = -0.05
43. n − 0.058 = 0.58; 0.638
45. 1.0099 = n + 2; n = -0.9901
47. 3 + n = 8.16; n = 5.16
Mixed Review   1. 7.629   **2.** -1.6642   **3.** -2.46   **4.** 4.754
5. -39.56x **6.** -0.28y **7.** $1.82
Test Yourself   1. <   **2.** =   **3.** >   **4.** -9.7   **5.** 4.3
6. 18.0   **7.** 0.3   **8.** 24   **9.** 250   **10.** -13.34   **11.** 3.8
12. -1.2   **13.** x − 0.09   **14.** -12.56y **15.** -6.71
16. 0.111

3-5 pages 116–118
Written Exercises   1. -2.44   **3.** 0.044   **5.** 1.2   **7.** 42.6
9. 0.374   **11.** -14.85   **13.** -5.4   **15.** 86.7   **17.** 3.0772
19. -708   **21.** 0.048308   **23.** 194.0   **25.** -42.1   **27.** 9.50
29. 236.03   **31.** 36.9   **33.** -0.2   **35.** -6   **37.** x = zy
39. x = yz **41.** 0.004n = 0.88; 220
43. $\frac{n}{-2.35}$ = 400.9; -942.115   **47. a.** $2,537.50; **b.** 205;
c. yes
Mixed Review   1. 1.446   **2.** 84.72   **3.** 0   **4.** 0.111
5. -1,056   **6.** -360   **7.** 14
Critical Thinking   1. The outside shape becomes shaded
inside; the shaded shape inside becomes the outside
shape.   **2.** c and d

Practice page 119
1. sixty-seven hundredths

3. six hundred thirty-seven and four ten-thousandths
5. 215.74 **7.** 42.07 **9.** > **11.** < **13.** > **15.** =
17. = **19.** 20 **21.** 1 **23.** $56 **25.** 6.62 **27.** -94
29. -41.706 **31.** -1 **33.** $x = 7.75$ **35.** $a = 0$
37. $z = 30$ **39.** $t = -1.2$ **41.** $y = 42.71$ **43.** $j = -4.036$
45. $x = -1.94$ **47.** $r = -18.57$ **49.** $m = np$ **51.** $m = \frac{n}{p}$
53. $m = \frac{p}{n}$

Problem Solving Practice page 124
1. Christine, Lisa, Nicole, JoAnn **3.** 8.2 mi
5. 276.8 m **7.** on; off **9.** 1.2 h

3-6 pages 126–128
Written Exercises 1. 66.8 g **3.** water:ethyl alcohol,
gasoline; mercury:copper, gasoline, ethyl alcohol,
rubber, and iron **5.** 110 g **7.** 0.917 g/cm³ **9.** 1,050 g

3-7 pages 129–131
Written Exercises 1. 87°F **3.** 52°F **5.** 465.85 mi
7. 1,704 cm **9.** 6,700 mi; high **11.** 0.347 **13.** 0.366
15. 0.345 **17.** Cobb, Hornsby, Jackson, Browning,
Delahanty, Keeler **19.** $536.25 **21.** $683.98
23. -128.2°F **25.** $.43 **27. a.** 7.875; 64.05;
b. $.32 and $2.56; **c.** $116.48 **31.** $V = IR$; $R = \frac{V}{I}$
Mixed Review 1. -30.67 **2.** -2.236 **3.** 34 **4.** ⁻33.8
5. 4.03 **6.** $2,600
Test Yourself 1. 2.68 **2.** -0.186875 **3.** 20.24372
4. 77.26952 **5.** 40 **6.** 3.03 **7.** $a = \frac{c}{b}$ **8.** $a = b - c$
9. $a = cb$ **10. a.** 168; **b.** 11; **c.** 9.7 h

3-8 page 133
Written Exercises 1. 87 **3.** 23,471.4 **5.** 23
7. 8 airplanes; 16 spaceships **9.** 717

Chapter 3 Review pages 134–135
1. F, hundredths **2.** F, estimating **3.** T **4.** T
5. F, variables **6.** < **7.** = **8.** > **9.** < **10.** <
11. 0.25 **12.** 0.5 **13.** 0.25 **14.** 53 **15.** 0.75 **16.** $24
17. 0.2 **18.** 12,905 **19.** $79 **20.** -1.1 **21.** 0.4
22. 4.1 **23.** 11 **24.** $4.5a + 3.1$ **25.** $\frac{x}{2}$ **26.** $8a + 13ab$
27. -5 **28.** 0.55 **29.** 7.35 **30.** 11 **31.** 10 **32.** 7.3
33. 3 **34.** 3.8 **35.** 192.5 mi **36.** 36 ft **37.** 9.125 h
38. 1,400 children **39.** 10.5 g/cm³

Chapters 1–3 Cumulative Review page 137
1. B **2.** C **3.** A **4.** B **5.** C **6.** D **7.** A **8.** C
9. A **10.** A **11.** A **12.** B **13.** C **14.** B

CHAPTER 4

Number Theory

4-1 pages 142–144
Written Exercises 1. 8^3 **3.** $2r^4s^2$ **5.** x^2y^2z **7.** n^{30}
9. a^a **11.** $(a + 1)^3$ **13. a.** 1; **b.** 1,000,000 **15. a.** -16;
b. 1 **17.** 36 **19.** -4 **21.** 1 **23.** 7 **25.** 9 **27.** >
29. = **31.** < **33.** > **35.** d
37. (-1) raised to an even power is positive; 1

39. The power tells you the number of zeros in the
product. $10^6 = 1,000,000$; $10^{10} = 10,000,000,000$
41. a. 0, 1, 0; 4, 4, 1; 8, 16, 16; 12, 64, 81; 16, 256, 256
b. $n = 2, 4$; $n = 3$; $n = 0, 1$, $n > 4$ **43.** $n = 0$ **45.** $x =$
any pos. value **47.** $x = 3$ **49. a.** It is half as tall.; yes;
b. Each bar is twice as tall as the previous bar.
Mixed Review 1. 19.5 **2.** -19 **3.** 123.75 mi **4.** 280 km
5. 285.75 mi **6.** $4x - 2y$ **7.** $-3w - 7$ **8.** 83
Critical Thinking 2. 8; 27; 64 **3.** 1; 8; 27; 64 **4.** 1,000

4-2 pages 146–148
Written Exercises 1. -8 **3.** 8 **5.** x^9 **7.** $10x^9$ **9.** 72
11. $-x^8$ **13.** $16a^6$ **15.** $1,296y^{12}$ **17.** $-27y^{12}$ **19.** -8
21. 531,441 **23.** 9 **25.** 17 **27.** -216
29. F; add exponents; $x^5 \cdot x^3 = x^8$ **31.** T; $1 = 1$
33. T; $(r^2)^3$ is positive, so the opposite is less than 0.
35. no **37.** no **39.** no **41.** yes **43.** < **45.** <
47. < **49.** 3^{50}; $2^{75} = (2^3)^{25}$ and $3^{50} = (3^2)^{25}$ **51.** $x = 2$
53. a. 1,024; **b.** 10^3; **c.** 2^3; **d.** $2^{10} \cdot 2^{10}$; **e.** $2^{20} \cdot 2^3$
Mixed Review 1. 4 **2.** 360 **3.** $-5a^3b^2$ **4.** $-14c^2d^3$
5. -12 **6.** 6 **7.** -1 **8.** 8
Critical Thinking 1. the two numbers diagonally above
it in the preceding row **2.** 1, 6, 15, 20, 15, 6, 1 **3.** 8
4. 1,048,576

4-3 pages 150–152
Written Exercises 1. Ex: 6.25×10^8; 62.5×10^7;
625×10^6 **3.** 6×10^{13} **5.** 6.382×10^7 **7.** 100,000
9. 7,654 **11.** 600.32 **13.** 4,060 **15.** 1.5×10^5; 150,000
17. 9.9×10^{12}; 9,900,000,000,000
19. 4.7×10^6; 4,700,000 **21.** 3 **23.** 8.45 **25.** 0.000845
27. 2.49×10^{21} **29.** 7.89×10^{20} **31.** 3.22×10^{30}
33. 7×10^8 **37.** 5.79×10^7, 1.082×10^8, 1.496×10^8,
2.279×10^8, 7.783×10^8, 1.427×10^9, 2.869×10^9,
4.497×10^9, 5.9×10^9 **39.** 4.06×10^{13} km **43.** 7.6×10^8
Mixed Review 1. multiplicative identity
2. commutative prop. for addition **3.** additive identity
4. distributive property **5.** $3m^7$ **6.** n^6 **7.** $25y^3$
8. 2^5 or 32
Test Yourself 1. a^2b^3 **2.** $4x^3y$ **3.** 64 **4.** 144 **5.** -243
6. 1 **7.** -625 **8.** 512 **9.** 1×10^4 **10.** 1×10^5
11. 1×10^7 **12.** 7.5×10^4 **13.** 8.54×10^5
14. 1.645123×10^6

4-4 pages 154–155
Written Exercises 1. 1.3125×10^{10}
3. a. 2.8×10^8; **b.** about 1,393 da
5. 7.3×10^8 **7.** 7.498×10^6

Practice page 158
1. $3^2 \cdot 5^3$ **3.** $(-3a)^5$ **5.** 512 **7.** -243 **9.** 64 **11.** 16
13. 40,353,607 **15.** 256 **17.** -147 **19.** 6,561
21. 8,388,608 **23.** b^3 **25.** k^{13} **27.** c^{11} **29.** y^6
31. $243r^{15}$ **33.** $405m^{10}$ **35.** 104 **37.** 200 **39.** -81
41. -16,384 **43.** 240,000,000 **45.** 10,000,000
47. 98,367.5 **49.** 3.392×10^6 km **51.** 5.88×10^{21}
53. 1×10^{19} m

4-5 pages 161–162
Written Exercises 1. yes 3. yes 5. yes 7. no
9. yes 11. yes 13. 1, 2, 3, 5, 6, 10, 15, 30 15. 1, 5, 11, 55 17. 1, 29 19. 12, 24, 36, 48, 60 21. 25, 50, 75, 100, 125 23. 2, 3, 5, 9 25. 2, 3 27. 5 29. 3
31. **a.** 78, no, no, 96, yes, yes; **b.** If the last two digits are divisible by 4, the number is divisible by 4. 33. 7
35. odd 37. yes
Mixed Review 1. $n - 5 = -24$ 2. $3n - 10 = 57$ 3. -23
4. 36 5. -19 6. 3.48×10^6 7. 2.5×10^2 8. 95°F
Test Yourself 1. 9,604 2. 12,300
3. 28,560,000,000,000,000 4. 9.65×10^6 5. 5.48×10^2
6. 3×10^6 7. 1, 3, 9, 27 8. 1, 3, 5, 9, 15, 45
9. 1, 2, 3, 4, 5, 6, 10, 12, 15, 20, 30, 60 10. 3, 5, 9
11. 2, 3, 5 12. 3, 9 13. 4^4 14. 17^3 15. z^4 16. 20
17. 50 18. 29 19. -9

4-6 pages 165–166
Written Exercises 1. composite 3. prime
5. composite 7. $5^2 \cdot 17$ 9. $2 \cdot 3 \cdot 31$ 11. $3^2 \cdot 5^2 \cdot 7$
13. 1,056 15. 9,274,720 17. $3^3 \cdot 23$ 19. $11 \cdot 23$
21. even 23. 6, 14, 21, 42 25. 841; 960
27. **a.** China; **b.** Brazil
29. **a.** 3, 5; 5, 7; 11, 13; 17, 19; 29, 31; 41, 43; 59, 61;
b. They are all odd.; **c.** yes
Mixed Review 1. 1, 2, 4, 8 2. 8, 16, 24, 32
3. 1, 2, 3, 4, 6, 9, 12, 18, 36 4. -9 5. 45 6. 4
7. -57 to $-59°F$
Critical Thinking 1. They are all located in columns 2, 4, and 6.
2. They are all located in columns 3 and 6.
3. They are in diagonal lines going from right to left, starting with 5, 30, 60, and 90. 4. 7
5. The multiples of 11 are multiples of 2, 3, 5, or 7.
6. They are all primes. All other numbers are crossed out because they are multiples of 2, 3, 5, and 7.
7. 2, 3, 5, 7, 11, 13, 17, 19, 23, 29, 31, 37, 41, 43, 47, 53, 59, 61, 67, 71, 73, 79, 83, 89, 97, 101, 103, 107, 109, 113, 127, 131, 137, 139, 149, 151, 157, 163, 167, 173, 179, 181, 191, 193, 197, 199; Stop at 13 on the sieve.

4-7 pages 169–170
Written Exercises 1. 7 3. 13 5. x^2y 7. $30a$ 9. 3
11. 60 13. 1,260 15. $24a^3b^2$ 17. 180 19. 4; 96
21. 5; 37,800 23. If a is the LCM of 8 and x, then a is divisible by both 8 and x. Since $8 = 2^3$, a is divisible by 2^3. 25. 2 times per minute 27. 2 tables that seated 5 people; 7 tables that seated 8 people 29. 21 ft. 31. 59
Mixed Review 1. $2^2 \cdot 3$ 2. $3 \cdot 41$ 3. 1, 2, 3, 4, 6, 12
4. 12, 24, 36, 48 5. 4 6. -11.4 7. -16 8. 8, 3

4-8 pages 173–174
Written Exercises 1. 9 3. 17 5. 24 7. 4; the last digits of the powers of 8 form this pattern: 8, 4, 2, 6
9. 63 tickets 11. They are all prime numbers. 13. $5

Problem Solving Practice page 175
1. every 21,000 mi 5. 16 (including a plain pizza)
9. **a.** 1950 **b.** 1700–1749

Chapter 4 Review pages 176–177
1. b 2. d 3. h 4. f 5. a 6. c 7. e 8. g 9. 8
10. 1 11. 27 12. 25 13. 16 14. a^5 15. $8a^6$
16. $ab^3 + ab^2$ 17. a^4b^2 18. a^3b^7 19. 4.65×10^8
20. 1.36×10^7 21. 1.28×10^3 22. 5.09×10^6
23. 210,000 24. 61,300,000 25. 1,050 26. 835
27. T 28. T 29. T 30. F 31. F 32. T
33. $3 \cdot 5^2$ 34. $2^2 \cdot 3 \cdot 5 \cdot 7$ 35. $2^2 \cdot 3^3$ 36. $3^2 \cdot 5 \cdot 17$
37. $2^2 \cdot 3 \cdot 19$ 38. $5 \cdot 7 \cdot 17$ 39. 4 40. 8 41. 9
42. $3x^2$ 43. 36 44. 56 45. 105 46. $60x^2y^3$
47. $198ab^3c^2$ 48. 45

Chapters 1–4 Cumulative Review page 179
1. C 2. B 3. B 4. A 5. C 6. D 7. C 8. B 9. C
10. A 11. C 12. D 13. B 14. C 15. C 16. A

CHAPTER 5

Rational Numbers and Expressions

5-1 pages 186–187
Written Exercises 1. $\frac{3}{13}$
3. $\frac{1}{2}$; one-fourth; five-sevenths; $\frac{5}{7}$ 5. $\frac{6}{10}$ or $\frac{3}{5}$ 17. 2
19. 6 21. 1 23. 4 25. $\frac{1}{5}$ 27. $\frac{2}{3}$ 29. $\frac{1}{3}$ 31. $\frac{c}{3}$ 33. $\frac{1}{2t}$
37. $\frac{3}{4}$ 39. $\frac{3a^2}{5}$ 41. $\frac{2pq}{3}$ 43. $\neq$ 45. $=$ 47. $\frac{2}{5}$
Mixed Review 1. 1, 2, 4, 8, 16, 32 2. 1, 3, 9, 27
3. 2, 3; $2^2 \cdot 3^2$ 4. 2, 3; $2 \cdot 3^3$ 5. 200 6. 70
7. GCF 6; LCM 36 8. $-54°F$

5-2 pages 190–191
Written Exercises 1. **a.** $\frac{11}{4}$; **b.** $2\frac{3}{4}$ 5. $\frac{13}{8}$ 7. $\frac{47}{8}$ 9. $\frac{20}{3}$
11. $\frac{31}{11}$ 13. $5\frac{2}{9}$ 15. $4\frac{3}{5}$ 17. $1\frac{8}{11}$ 19. $3\frac{1}{3}$ 21. $\frac{4}{5}$ 23. $5\frac{3}{20}$
25. $2\frac{1}{2}$ 27. $6\frac{1}{20}$ 29. 0.28 31. 0.625
33. $0.\overline{5}$ 35. 5.375
37. 0.18, $\frac{18}{100}$; 5.73, five and seventy-three hundredths; 0.9, $\frac{9}{10}$ 39. **a.** $\frac{15}{104}$; **b.** $\frac{7}{52}$; **c.** $\frac{7}{104}$; **d.** $\frac{33}{52}$ 41. yes
43. yes
Mixed Review 1. $>$ 2. $<$ 3. $\frac{2}{3}$ 4. $\frac{3}{a}$ 5. 0.6 6. 1.5
7. 3.485×10^{10}

5-3 pages 194–195
Written Exercises 1. $\frac{9}{4}$ 3. $-1\frac{1}{5}$ 5. $\frac{3}{5}$ 11. $\frac{4}{9}, \frac{4}{9}$
13. $-1\frac{2}{3}, 1\frac{2}{3}$ 15. a; c 17. $\frac{4}{5}$ 19. -4 21. $\frac{a}{2b}$ 23. $\frac{a}{4b}$
25. always 27. sometimes 29. negative 31. negative
33. yes 35. yes, yes, yes, yes; yes, no, no, no; yes, no, no, no; yes, yes, yes, yes; yes, yes, yes, no
Mixed Review 1. 0 2. -6 3. -5 4. $-\frac{3}{8}$ 5. $\frac{2a^2}{5}$ 6. 0.8
7. -3.25 8. $\frac{1}{2}, \frac{1}{2}, \frac{3}{8}, \frac{1}{4}$
Test Yourself 1. $\frac{4}{5}$ 2. $\frac{3}{4}$ 3. $\frac{3}{10}$ 4. $\frac{a^2}{3}$ 5. $\frac{35n^3}{4}$ 11. $-\frac{2}{3}, \frac{2}{3}$
12. $2\frac{5}{6}, 2\frac{5}{6}$ 13. $-1\frac{7}{16}, 1\frac{7}{16}$ 14. $2\frac{3}{4}, 2\frac{3}{4}$

5-4 page 198
Written Exercises 1. $<$ 3. $<$ 5. $<$ 7. $<$ 9. $<$
11. $<$ 13. $=$ 15. $<$ 17. $<$ 19. $<$ 21. $<$

23. $-\frac{5}{12}, -\frac{3}{8}, -\frac{1}{4}$ 25. $-\frac{11}{15}, -\frac{7}{10}, -\frac{13}{20}, -\frac{7}{12}$
27. $-2\frac{7}{8}, -2\frac{9}{16}, 2\frac{3}{50}, 2\frac{19}{25}$ 33. $x < 2.5$ 35. $\frac{1}{14}$
Mixed Review 1. 7 2. 10.58 3. $7\frac{1}{3}$ 4. $1\frac{2}{5}$ 5. $2\frac{7}{9}$
6. -14 7. -2.375 8. 192.5 mi

5-5 pages 201–202
Written Exercises 5. $\frac{1}{3}+\frac{1}{2}=\frac{5}{6}$ 7. $1\frac{7}{24}$ 9. $-\frac{4}{9}$ 11. $2\frac{1}{2}$
13. $9\frac{2}{9}$ 15. $\frac{7}{18}y$ 17. $-4\frac{5}{8}$ 19. 16 21. 150
23. 75 25. $29\frac{2}{3}$ 27. yes 29. no 31. C 33. >
35. > 37. < 39. 42 ft 41. $\frac{1}{4}, \frac{5}{4}$ 43. $\frac{1}{12}, \frac{7}{12}, \frac{1}{4}, \frac{3}{4}$
Mixed Review 1. $-3\frac{1}{5}, 3\frac{1}{5}$ 2. $-5\frac{8}{11}$ 3. $-\frac{7}{10}, \frac{7}{-10}$
4. -20 5. < 6. when $y > 4$ 7. 60 8. $150

5-6 page 204
Written Exercises 1. 7 3. $15\frac{3}{16}$ ft 5. 12 y 7. a. $0.\overline{1}$;
b. $0.\overline{2}$; c. $0.\overline{3}$; d. $0.\overline{4}$; e. $0.\overline{5}$; f. $0.\overline{6}$
9. $3\frac{2}{3}, 4\frac{5}{12}, 5\frac{1}{6}$

Practice page 205
1. $\frac{1}{5}$ 3. $\frac{2}{3}$ 5. $\frac{3}{5}$ 7. $\frac{3y}{7}$ 9. $\frac{1}{3}$ 11. $\frac{2}{3m}$ 13. $\frac{13}{5}$
15. $\frac{14}{3}$ 17. $\frac{33}{4}$ 19. $\frac{247}{12}$ 21. $2\frac{2}{5}$ 23. $6\frac{1}{4}$ 25. $6\frac{5}{8}$
27. $8\frac{1}{7}$ 29. $-2\frac{3}{8}, 2\frac{3}{8}$ 31. $18\frac{2}{3}, 18\frac{2}{3}$ 33. $13\frac{5}{9}, 13\frac{5}{9}$
35. $-\frac{11}{15}, \frac{11}{15}$ 37. < 39. > 41. > 43. 1 45. $1\frac{1}{9}$
47. $-\frac{3}{8}$ 49. $-6\frac{1}{4}$ 51. $1\frac{11}{24}$ 53. $6\frac{23}{30}$ 55. $6\frac{3}{7}$ 57. -11
59. $30\frac{5}{16}$

5-7 page 208
Written Exercises 1. $\frac{1}{3}$ 3. 8 5. $\frac{2}{11}$ 7. $\frac{15}{16}$ 9. $-\frac{a}{10}$
11. $5\frac{5}{6}$ 13. 1 15. $\frac{3}{4}$ 17. 39 19. -8 21. -60 23. $1\frac{1}{2}$
25. 130 27. > 29. < 31. = 33. $-1\frac{8}{15}$ 35. $-\frac{9}{10}$
37. a. 200; b. 500; c. 12
Mixed Review 1. 1.4 2. 9.9 3. $\frac{1}{2}$ 4. $\neq$ 5. 0.325
6. 6 7. 5 8. Paul

5-8 pages 213–214
Written Exercises 1. $\frac{1}{36}$ 3. 1 5. $\frac{3}{8}$ 7. $\frac{1}{25}$ 9. a^{-3}
11. $\frac{1}{2}x^7$ 13. x^2y^{-10} 15. $5b^4c^5$ 17. $5m^2$ 19. $\frac{3y^2}{x^3}$
21. a. -25 b. 25 c. $\frac{1}{25}$ d. $\frac{1}{25}$ 23. $\frac{1}{25a^2}$ 25. $a^{10}b^{-15}$ or $\frac{a^{10}}{b^{15}}$
27. $9a^4b$ 29. a. The numbers decrease by 1.; b. The
numbers decrease by a power of 3. 1, $\frac{1}{3}$, $\frac{1}{9}$; c. They are
values of the powers of 3.; d. They are the values of the
powers of 2. 31. T 33. F 35. T 37. T
39. 1,580,000,000,000,000,000 41. $\frac{13}{20}$
Mixed Review 1. $\frac{7}{10}$ 2. $\frac{3}{8}$ 3. $-1\frac{1}{8}$ 4. $6\frac{1}{6}$ 5. 5 6. -12
7. -5.2 8. 34
Critical Thinking 1. If n is the exponent, the decimal
point moves to the left $|n|$ places. 2. 1.2, 0.12, 0.012,
$1.2 \times 10^{-3} = 0.0012$ 3. 0.00037 4. 23 5. Writing long
strings of zeros takes too much space and can be
confusing to read.

5-9 pages 216–217
Written Exercises 1. $x + \frac{3}{5} = \frac{7}{10}; \frac{1}{10}$ 3. $-\frac{1}{2}$ 5. $5\frac{3}{8}$ 7. $\frac{13}{24}$
9. $-1\frac{7}{40}$ 11. $\frac{23}{24}$ 13. $2\frac{19}{20}$ 15. 6.1 17. 5 19. 6 21. $\frac{1}{5}$
23. $-8\frac{1}{8}$ 25. $-1\frac{5}{12}$ 27. x must be less than zero
because the sum will be less than zero. 29. yes
31. $b + 3\frac{3}{16} = 5\frac{11}{16}, 2\frac{1}{2}$ lb 33. $h + 1\frac{5}{8} = 68\frac{1}{2}, 66\frac{7}{8}$ in.
Mixed Review 1. T 2. $3\frac{8}{13}$ 3. < 4. > 5. $\frac{31}{150}$
6. a^{-4} 7. $x^{-2}y^5$ 8. $3\frac{1}{8}$

5-10 pages 219–221
Written Exercises 1. $1\frac{5}{16}$ 3. $\frac{81}{10}$ or $8\frac{1}{10}$ 5. -12 7. $\frac{1}{2}$
9. 4 11. -0.8 13. neg · neg = pos
15. pos · neg = neg 17. $\frac{25}{9}, -\frac{25}{9}$ 19. no solution
21. no solution 23. $\frac{5}{8}d = 12; d = 19.2$ 25. $a = \frac{5}{6}, b = 1\frac{1}{3}$,
$a < b$ 27. 350 29. $\frac{1}{15}$ 33. whole 35. multiplication
37. $\frac{7}{8}$ 39. 64 41. $2\frac{5}{7}$ 43. $\frac{7}{11}$ 45. $\frac{7}{20}$ 47. No; the
chart does not tell the number of cans recycled in any
year. 49. $\frac{9}{10}$
Mixed Review 1. $-9\frac{1}{3}$ 2. $1\frac{1}{8}$ 3. $11\frac{1}{9}$ 4. 6.1 5. $\frac{29}{36}$
6. 2.2 7. < 8. 126
Test Yourself 1. $\frac{23}{24}$ 2. $10\frac{1}{4}$ 3. $-\frac{7}{8}$ 4. $2\frac{7}{16}$ 5. $-1\frac{5}{9}$
6. $-\frac{27}{32}$ 7. $16\frac{7}{8}$ 8. no solution 9. no solution 10. $\frac{1}{9}$
11. 1 12. 27 13. $\frac{8}{5}$ 14. $5n$ 15. $\frac{3}{a^3}$ 16. $\frac{8x^2}{y^3}$ 17. $\frac{b^6}{a^5}$

5-11 page 224
Written Exercises 1. 62.625 3. 77.125 5. 88.875
7. $3.625 9. a. DQ $2,805.00, MCJ $5,036.25, EDL
$5,992.50, JMB $23,778.75, BBH $27,030.00; b. DQ $510,
MCJ $630, EDL $450, JMB $340, BBH $1,380
11. The commission is figured on different amounts.

Problem Solving Practice page 225
1. 27th 3. 1,223 or 2,486 5. Lena 7. $5.26 11. $\frac{3}{4}$ lb

Chapter 5 Review pages 226–227
1. equivalent fractions 2. lowest terms
3. rational number 4. least common denominator
5. exponents 6. 6 7. 6 8. 8 9. 4 10. 25
11. $3\frac{3}{4}$; 3.75 12. $1\frac{1}{2}$; 1.5 13. $2\frac{2}{5}$; 2.4 14. $2\frac{5}{6}$; $2.8\overline{3}$
15. $2\frac{5}{8}$; 2.625 16. $\frac{3}{5}$ 17. $2\frac{3}{8}$ 18. $5\frac{1}{4}$ 19. $\frac{7}{10}$ 20. $\frac{7}{20}$
21. < 22. > 23. = 24. > 25. $3\frac{1}{12}$ 26. $7\frac{2}{15}$
27. $15\frac{5}{12}$ 28. $6\frac{11}{24}$ 29. 6 A.M. 30. $19,937.50
31. $\frac{9}{10}$ 32. 9 33. 6 34. $\frac{1}{2}$ 35. $\frac{1}{x^5}$ 36. $\frac{6}{a}$ 37. $2m^4$
38. $\frac{2}{b}$ 39. $\frac{3y^3}{x^2}$ 40. $1\frac{2}{15}$ 41. $3\frac{1}{3}$ 42. $-3\frac{1}{8}$ 43. $1\frac{1}{3}$

Chapters 1–5 Cumulative Review page 229
1. C 2. C 3. B 4. B 5. D 6. C 7. B 8. D 9. C
10. A 11. D 12. A 13. C 14. C 15. D 16. B

Ratios, Proportions, and Percent

6-1 pages 235–236
Written Exercises **1.** $\frac{3}{8}$ **3.** $\frac{8}{11}$ **5.** $\frac{3}{5}$ **7.** $\frac{5}{2}$ **9.** $\frac{1}{5}$ **11.** $\frac{1}{6}$
13. $\frac{1}{4}$ **15.** $\frac{1}{7}$ **17.** 3 to 2; 2 to 3; 2 to 5 **25.** $\neq$
27. =; prop. **29.** $\neq$ **31.** $\neq$ **33.** $\neq$ **35.** =; prop.
37. 6 gal/min **39.** 0.18 hits/time at bat
41. 4.375 mi/h **43.** 0.3 hits/time at bat
45. 50 to 2; 2 to 50; 2 to 48 **47.** $\frac{4}{24} \stackrel{?}{=} \frac{6}{30}$; no
49. $\frac{2}{1.69} \stackrel{?}{=} \frac{5}{3.98}$; no, 2 for $1.69 is $.85 each;
5 for $3.98 is $.80 each. **51. a.** 300 to 70; 300 : 70; $\frac{300}{70}$;
b. $9.00/pt **c.** $22/gal
Mixed Review **1.** $\frac{7}{13}$ **2.** $\frac{13}{19} > \frac{19}{28}$ **3.** $x = -14$ **4.** $x = -2\frac{1}{4}$
5. yes **6.** no **7.** 1,239 mi

6-2 pages 238–240
Written Exercises **1.** $a = 20$ **3.** $c = 20$ **5.** $e = 19.2$
7. $g = 133.\overline{3}$ **9.** $j = 17.5$ **11.** $m = 16.9$ **13.** $x = 1$
15. $\frac{4}{1.85} = \frac{24}{t}$; $11.10 **17.** $\frac{5}{18.6} = \frac{8}{v}$; $v = 29.76$ min
19. $\frac{6}{2.25} = \frac{y}{\$10}$; $y = 26.67$ lb **21.** $\frac{3}{1} = \frac{x}{4}$; $x = 12$ bags
23. $\frac{3}{\$9.60} = \frac{15}{p}$; $p = $48 **25.** $\frac{3}{750} = \frac{x}{10,000}$; $x = 40$ defects
29. $\frac{7}{3}$ **31.** $-\frac{2}{7}$ **33.** no **35.** no **37.** $\frac{30}{100}$ **39.** $\frac{12}{1}$
41. 15; 1 **43.** 32; 8; 32; 16 **45.** 15 s **47.** 360 times
49. 42,048,000 times
Mixed Review **1.** F **2.** T **3.** $\frac{6}{11}$ **4.** $\frac{25}{14}$ **5.** yes **6.** yes
7. $67.97
Critical Thinking **1.** even numbers **2.** prime numbers
3. odd numbers **4.** the even primes
5. the odd primes **6.** yes; yes
7. No; Two is the only even prime.

6-3 pages 242–243
Written Exercises **1.** 1 in. : 10 ft **3.** 20 ft
5. Yes; the scale of the dance floor is 10 : 8.$\overline{3}$. **7.** N
9. 4.5 in. **11.** 14.4 ft

6-4 pages 246–248
Written Exercises **1.** 75% **3.** 62.5% **5.** 58.3%
7. 140% **9.** 33% **11.** 6% **13.** 4.5% **15.** 188%
17. 79% **19.** 30% **21.** 68% **23.** 111% **25.** 22.2%
27. 43.8% **29.** 80% **31.** 25% **33.** $\frac{1}{10}$; 10%
35. 0.75; 75% **37.** $\frac{1}{4}$; 0.25 **39.** 112% **41.** 60%
43. 47.2% **45.** 25% **47.** < **49.** < **51.** < **53.** >
55. yes **57.** No; 100% is a perfect grade. **59.** 100
61. 10 **63.** week **65.** $\frac{5}{12}$ **67.** $\frac{3}{4}$
Mixed Review **1.** $x = 47$ **2.** $x = -0.175$ **3.** $x = 68.75$
4. $x = 1,820$ **5.** $\frac{1}{4} = 25\%$ **6.** $\frac{11}{14} = 78.6\%$ **7.** 93

Practice page 249
1. $\frac{2}{5}$ **3.** $\frac{2}{5}$ **5.** $\frac{3}{7}$ **7.** $\neq$ **9.** =; prop. **11.** =; prop.
13. =; prop. **15.** $a = 2$ **17.** $c = 12$ **19.** $e = 2.25$
21. $g = 2$ **23.** 180% **25.** 37.5% **27.** 76.7% **29.** 55%
31. 6.7% **33.** 85% **35.** 62.5% **37.** 12.5% **39.** 0.225
41. 0.736 **43.** $\frac{1}{3}$; 0.$\overline{3}$; 33.3% **45.** $\frac{1}{3}$, 0.$\overline{3}$, 33.3%

47. $\frac{2}{3}$, 0.$\overline{6}$, 66.7% **49.** $\frac{16}{27}$, 0.$\overline{592}$, 59.3% **51.** >
53. = **55.** > **57.** = **59.** >

6-5 pages 253–255
Written Exercises **1.** 52% **3.** 107.8 **5.** 33.3% **7.** 9
9. 31.5 **11.** 35% **13.** 20 **15.** 175% **17.** = **19.** >
21. < **23.** = **25.** > **27.** 20% **29.** 25% **31.** 24
33. 12 **35.** 18.5% **37.** 44.5 **39.** 84.2 **41.** 132 **43.** 42
45. 8% **47.** $1,200 **49.** You can't tell who got the
better deal without knowing the original price.
51. It makes sense. **53.** 15% tip: $30.00; 20% tip: $22.50
Mixed Review **1.** 52 **2.** 39 **3.** $258\frac{1}{3}\%$ **4.** 452.3%
5. 8% **6.** 4,560% **7.** 38%
Test Yourself **1.** $\frac{1}{3}$ **2.** $\frac{1}{20}$ **3.** $5.78 **4.** $1.75 **5.** 75%
6. 89% **7.** 87.5% **8.** 3% **9.** 0.7% **10.** 5.4
11. $n = 100$

6-6 pages 257–259
Written Exercises **1.** $15\% = \frac{x}{115}$; $0.15 \cdot 115 = x$;
$17.25 = x$ **3.** 55% **5.** $46\frac{2}{3}$ **7.** 60 **9.** 225%
11. 21.6 **13.** 2.4 **15.** 64% **17.** 22.5 **19.** 81
21. 50% **23.** 100 **25.** 22 **27.** 20% **29.** 100 **31.** 12.5
33. $33\frac{1}{3}\%$ **35.** 46.2% **37.** 13.3 **39.** 100 **41.** $39.38
43. no **45.** $25; $18.75 **47.** $240,000,000
49. 1,442,100
Mixed Review **1.** 52 **2.** 150 **3.** 12.5% **4.** 21
5. 0.62 **6.** 0.899 **7.** $15.00
Critical Thinking **1.** a and c

6-7 pages 261–263
Written Exercises **1.** 32% **3.** 137.5% **5.** 16.7%
7. 20.8% **9.** 150% **11.** 166.7% **13.** 20% increase
15. 10% decrease **17.** 86 **19.** 58.3 **21.** 24.1%; I
23. 83.1%; D **25.** 69.3%; D **27.** 27.7% **29.** 29.6%
31. +13.6% **33.** +393.8% **35.** 1936: 1,175%; 1937:
2,087.5%; 1940: 2,300%; 1955: 445.5%; 1961: 566.7%
37. a. +44%, +27%, +90%, -28%, -28% **b.** no
Mixed Review **1.** 8 **2.** 3,600 **3.** < **4.** > **5.** 20.25
6. 98.5%
Test Yourself **1.** 39.6 **2.** 52.5 **3.** 20% **4.** 65
5. $66\frac{2}{3}\%$ **6.** 150 **7.** 32% **8.** 38.9%

6-8 pages 265–266
Written Exercises **1.** $\frac{1}{4}$ **3.** 34 in. **5.** 54 post holes
7. 5 cm **9.** 1 **11.** $1\frac{7}{8}$ mi **13.** 47 students
15. a. 28; **b.** 46 ft × 46 ft

Problem Solving Practice page 267
1. 4 **3.** 1 **5.** $700 **7. a.** 2.3% **b.** no

Chapter 6 Review pages 268–269
1. false; ratio **2.** true **3.** true **4.** false; percent
5. true **6.** =; prop. **7.** $\neq$ **8.** =; prop. **9.** $\neq$ **10.** $\neq$
11. 50 mi/h **12.** 23 mi/gal **13.** 90 words/min
14. $1.89/lb **15.** $n = 35$ **16.** $x = 12$ **17.** $a = 49$
18. $y = 3$ **19.** $m = 126$ **20.** 187.5 km **21.** 0.5 cm
22. 5% **23.** 98% **24.** 145% **25.** 75% **26.** 62.5%

SELECTED ANSWERS

27. 12% 28. 6 29. $x = 150$ 30. $33\frac{1}{3}$% 31. $a = 200$
32. 204 33. 5% 34. 18.2% 35. 2.7 36. $y = 80$
37. $33\frac{1}{3}$% 38. 25% 39. 75% 40. 20% 41. 75%
42. 50% 43. 21.4%

Chapters 1–6 Cumulative Review page 271
1. C 2. A 3. C 4. B 5. D 6. A 7. D 8. B
9. B 10. A 11. C 12. C

CHAPTER 7

Equations and Inequalities

7-1 pages 277–278
Written Exercises 1. 6 3. 47 5. -324 7. 12 9. 54
11. -70 13. -3 15. -2 17. -7 19. 85 21. 10 23. 60
25. 30 27. 5 29. $167,645.1\overline{6}$ 31. -43.375 35. C; 4
39. $3n - 7 = 19$ 41. $2 = 12n - 4; \frac{1}{2}$ 43. $8d + 36 = 78$;
5.25 45. $30 = 3n - 9$; 13 47. $x = \frac{c - b}{a}$ 49. $8.50
Mixed Review 1. 20 2. 4 3. 18 4. $6.30 5. 96
6. $3m + 5$ 7. $15 - 5x$ 8. 96°

7-2 pages 281–282
Written Exercises 1. $2\frac{3}{4}$ 3. $-2\frac{1}{2}$ 5. 31 7. 12 9. 5
11. $-3\frac{5}{18}$ 13. -12 15. $4\frac{2}{3}$ 17. $\frac{5}{7}$ 19. $3\frac{1}{3}$ 21. 3 23. 6
25. 74.2 27. 40.4 29. $1.\overline{3}$ 33. a; $70
35. $p + p + 13 = 171$; 79 37. $p - 0.2p = 53$; $66.25
39. $3(n - 8) = 36$; 20 41. Step 2 should be
$3x - 3 - 5 = 14$; $x = 7\frac{1}{3}$.
Mixed Review 1. 24 2. 30 3. $-17\frac{1}{3}$ 4. 64 5. $\frac{1}{4}n - 10$
6. $12n - 5n$ 7. $27.15
Test Yourself 1. -2 2. 162 3. 6 4. -3 5. -1
6. $185 - 11x + 40 = 93$; $12

Problem Solving Practice page 283
1. 28 3. 30 5. 120 cm 7. 4 9. 1,295 m and 1,575 m
11. 74 and 75 13. 15 min

7-3 pages 285–286
Written Exercises 1. $8n - \frac{1}{2}n = 16$
3. $n + (n - 5) = 114.90$, where n = price of boots;
$59.95
5. $c + c + 0.45 = 0.95$; $.25 7. $8.75 + 1.25t = 12.50$; 3
9. $x - 0.75x = 175$; 700 11. $15x = 240$; 16
13. $\frac{2}{3}s - \frac{2}{5} = \frac{11}{45}; \frac{29}{30}$ 15. 8 17. increased danger
19. 18 bu
Critical Thinking 1. 10:00 2. 11:00 3. 7 h
4. a. clocktime − (5)(groups of 5 in clocktime); b. 1:00;
c. 2:00

7-4 pages 289–290
Written Exercises 1. $4m + 5 = 21$; 4 3. 3 5. 1 7. 4
9. -4 11. 6 13. -10 15. 4 17. $-4\frac{2}{3}$ 19. 4 21. $2\frac{2}{3}$
23. 3 25. yes 27. yes 29. $2.\overline{69}$
31. $x + x + 1 + x + 2 = 165$; 54, 55, and 56
33. $\frac{1}{2}n + 1 = \frac{2}{3}n - 1$; 12 35. $2n - 8 = 3n - 16$; 8
37. $2(35) - x = 47$; $x = 23$
Mixed Review 1. $2(n + 4)$ 2. $c + 14$ 3. $3n - 6 = 12$; 6
4. $56 = 6x + 8$; 8 5. = 6. = 7. $93

7-5 pages 294–295
Written Exercises 1. true 3. true 5. false 7. true
9. false 17. $x \leq 2$ 31. $3 < 10$ 33. $p > 0$ 35. $p \leq 30$
37. $3x < 15,000$ 39. $x < -10$; $x \geq -5$ 41. < 43. <
45. = 47. > 49. > 51. $m > 5$ 53. $b \geq 15$
55. $s \leq 50$ 57. a. $5,140; $6,500; $4,400; $2,925; $7,700;
$2,550; b. Yes, if the program was input
correctly.; c. They determine how the IF command
decides what tax rate to use.
Mixed Review 1. $x = 17$ 2. $x = -5.\overline{6}$ or $-5\frac{2}{3}$ 3. $2n - 4$
4. $14 - x$ 5. 0 6. $3n + 6$ 7. 2 cups

7-6 pages 298–299
Written Exercises 1. same 3. reversed
5. Divide by -3. 7. Mult. by 3. 9. yes 11. no
13. $8 \leq x$ 15. $x > 0$ 17. $x > 4$ 19. $x < -8$
21. $x > -12$ 23. $21 \leq g$ 25. hydroelectric and oil
27. 28
Mixed Review 1. 5 2. 1 5. $1\frac{4}{5}$ 6. $-\frac{8}{9}$ 7. 76 and 88
Test Yourself 1. 5 2. 7 3. -4 4. 8 5. $y > -4$
6. $y < 4$ 7. $s < 42$ 8. $h > \frac{1}{21}$ 9. $-8 \geq k$ 10. $y > -12$
11. $n - 7 > -2$; $n > 5$ 12. $\frac{n}{-4} \geq 30$; $n \leq -120$
13. $-8 \geq \frac{n}{-3}$; $n \geq 24$

7-7 pages 301–303
Written Exercises 1. Sub. 8. 3. Sub. 7. 5. $x > 3$
7. $x \geq 6$ 9. $x > 5$ 11. $x \leq 1\frac{2}{5}$ 13. $x > 4\frac{4}{5}$ 15. $x \leq -5$
17. $x > 3$ 19. $x \geq -72$ 21. $x > -7$ 23. $x < 3$
25. $x > 2$ 27. $x < 60$ 29. $x < 4$ 31. b; $n \geq -18$
33. $2n - 5 \geq 13$; $n \geq 9$
35. $\frac{x + 88 + 91 + 85}{4} \geq 90$; $x \geq 96$ 37. 3
41. a. 24,000 acres; b. 39.1
Mixed Review 1. $2n = n + 5$; 5 2. $2n - 5 = 121$; 63
3. $x \leq -3$ 4. $x \leq 32$ 5. $x = 18$ 6. $x = 5$
7. $7\frac{1}{2}$ m, $12\frac{1}{2}$ m
Critical Thinking 2. D 3. A 4. D 5. C 6. B

Practice page 304
1. 6 3. 4 5. 243 7. 19 9. 3 11. 12 13. $6\frac{6}{7}$ 15. 13
17. 10 19. -3 21. 26 23. 6 25. 8 33. $x > -4$
35. $x > -18$ 37. $x \leq 3$ 39. $x \geq 4$ 41. $x > 2$
43. $x \leq 14$ 45. $x \geq 15$ 47. $22x + 47 = 201$; 7
49. $x + x + 1 + x + 2 + x + 3 = -490$; -121, -122, -123,
and -124

7-8 page 307
1. $520.50 3. $999.24 5. 9 7. 11.75 9. 47.08
11. a. $630; b. $266.39

Chapter 7 Review pages 308–309
1. operations 2. distributive 3. combine
4. not equal 5. negative 6. equation 7. $x = 1$
8. $x = 2$ 9. $a = 5$ 10. $x = 12$ 11. $n = 3$ 12. $b = 18$
13. $x = 7$ 14. $x = -10$ 15. $x = \frac{1}{3}$ 16. $x = -1$
17. $x = 14$ 18. $x = -\frac{2}{3}$ 19. $3n - 2(n + 5) = 3$; $n = 13$
20. $2(x + 12) + 3x = 144$; $x = 24$ 21. $x = -2$ 22. $x = 4$
23. $n = -10$ 24. c 25. a 26. b 27. d 28. $x < -5$

29. $x \geq -3$ **30.** $x < -4$ **31.** $x \leq -8$ **32.** $x \leq 5$
33. $y > 4$ **34.** $b < -9$ **35.** $a < 12$

Chapters 1–7 Cumulative Review page 311
1. B **2.** C **3.** A **4.** C **5.** A **6.** C **7.** C **8.** B
9. D **10.** C **11.** C **12.** A **13.** B **14.** D

CHAPTER 8

Graphing in the Coordinate Plane

8-1 pages 318–319
Written Exercises **1.** Q **3.** M **5.** (2,-3) **7.** (-5,0)
17. (3,0)(0,3)(-3,0)(0,-3) **19.** IV **21.** II **23.** I
25. y-axis **27.** III **29.** parallelogram **31.** triangle
33. (0,-5)
Mixed Review **1.** 2 **2.** 8 **3.** $x < -7$ **4.** $x \leq 9$ **5.** 3
6. -35 **7.** 12 in., 19 in.
Critical Thinking **3. a.** (2,1)(2,3)(-1,3)(-1,1);
b. (-2,-1)(-2,-3)(1,-3)(1,-1); **c.** (2,-1)(2,-3)(-1,-3)(-1,-1);
d. (-4,2)(-4,6)(2,6)(2,2) **4.** When the x-coordinate is
multiplied by -1, the figure slides to the right 1 unit.
When the y-coordinate is multiplied by -1, the figure
is reflected over the x-axis. When each coordinate is
multiplied by -1, the figure slides to the right 1 unit and
is reflected over the x-axis. When each coordinate is
multiplied by 2, the figure moves up 1 unit and each side
is twice the length of the original figure.

8-2 pages 322–323
Written Exercises **1.** no **3.** yes **5.** yes **7.** yes **9.** no
11. -1 **13.** 2 **15.** 11.5 **17.** $y = 3x + 5$ **19.** $y = \frac{3}{2}x - 5$
21. $y = -\frac{1}{6}x$ **23.** $y = -\frac{1}{2}x - \frac{5}{2}$ **25.** $y = \frac{2}{3}x - 4$
27. $y = -\frac{1}{4}x + 4$ **29. b.** 1,092.6 kg/cm² **c.** 2,838.4 kg/cm²
Mixed Review **1.** -16 **2.** -8 **4.** neg., neg. **6.** (0,8)
7. 7:17 A.M.
Test Yourself **1.** F **2.** G **3.** H **4.** E **5.** (-1,3)
6. (3,3) **7.** (4,-2) **8.** (-4,-4) **9.** $y = -\frac{3}{2}x + 2$
10. $y = -\frac{1}{2}x - 3$ **11.** $y = -\frac{1}{3}x + \frac{7}{3}$

8-3 pages 326–327
Written Exercises **1.** $\frac{1}{2}x + y = -3$ **3.** -6 and -3 **5.** $-1\frac{1}{3}$; 4
7. 0; 0 **9.** $y = -x + 2$ **11.** $y = -5$ **21.** $x = -1$ **23.** $y =$
-6 **25.** $x - y = 3$; 3 and 0 **27.** $x + y = 6$; 2 oranges and
4 apples **29.** $2x = y$; 4 and 8 **31.** $2x + 2y = 12$; width is
1 and length is 5.
Mixed Review **1.** 4 **2.** 4 **3.** $y = -\frac{2}{5}x + \frac{11}{5}$
4. $y = -\frac{3}{2}x - 6$ **7.** 34 and 35

8-4 pages 332–333
Written Exercises **1.** $\frac{2}{3}$; -2 **3.** $\frac{4}{3}$; -4 **5.** $\frac{1}{3}$; 4 **7.** 0
9. $\frac{10}{3}$ **11.** -2 **19.** $y = 2x + 1$; 2; 1
21. $y = -2x - 3$; -2; -3 **23.** $y = \frac{3}{4}x + \frac{1}{4}$; $\frac{3}{4}$; $\frac{1}{4}$
31. b. The lines are parallel. **c.** They are the same.
d. When two lines have the same slope and different
y-intercepts, they are parallel.
33. $0x + 1y = 6$ **35.** $1x + 0y = -3$

Mixed Review **1.** 80 **2.** 252 **3.** yes **4.** yes **5.** no
6. yes **7.** yes **8.** no **9.** 20%

8-5 pages 335–336
Written Exercises **1. b.** 50°F; **c.** 20°C **3.** 64°F **5.** 3
7. $2.11 **9.** 35 ft **11. a.** $27; **b.** $150
13. 18 quarters and 14 dimes **15.** 20 mi

Problem Solving Practice page 337
1. 12 quarters and 5 dimes **3.** 48 **5.** 36, 37, 38
7. 65 in. or 5 ft 5 in. **9.** 4 ft × 4 ft and 16 ft × 16 ft
11. $27.26 **13.** $1.18

8-6 pages 342–343
Written Exercises **1.** yes **3.** no **5.** (1,5) **7.** (2,1)
9. (2,2) **11.** (3,1) **13.** no solution **15.** (3,4)
17. $x + y = 55$; $x - y = 15$; 20 and 35
19. $x + y = 144$; $x = 3y$; 108 m and 36 m
21. $x + y = 16$; $5x + 10y = 100$; 12 five-point questions
and 4 ten-point questions **23.** parallel **25.** 1850
Mixed Review **1.** $3x^2$ **2.** $\frac{5xy^3}{2}$ **3.** 1; 0 **4.** $-\frac{2}{3}$; 4
5. $x < 3$ **6.** $x \geq -3$ **7.** $75
Test Yourself **1.** 10; 4 **2.** $-\frac{2}{3}$; 2 **3.** -2; 10 **4.** no slope
5. $-\frac{1}{2}$ **6.** $\frac{2}{11}$ **7.** $y = -2x + 7$; -2; 7 **8.** $y = -\frac{2}{3}$; 0; $-\frac{2}{3}$
9. $y = -\frac{1}{3}x + \frac{2}{3}$; $-\frac{1}{3}$; $\frac{2}{3}$ **10.** (-2,8) **11.** infinite
12. (3,-2)

8-7 pages 346–347
Written Exercises **1.** no **3.** no **5.** no **7.** no
9. $y > \frac{5}{2}x - 5$ **11.** $y < -\frac{1}{3}$ **13.** $y \leq |x| - 4$
15. $y \leq -x + 5$ **19. a.** infinite; **b.** no solution
Mixed Review **1.** 0.075; 7.5% **2.** $0.\overline{2}$; $22.\overline{2}$% **3.** (1,1)
4. (6,2) **6.** below **7.** 12%
Critical Thinking **1.** A and D **2.** C **3.** A **4.** A and C

8-8 pages 350–351
Written Exercises **1.** $2x + y = 3$; solid **3.** $y = -2$; solid
5. $x - 4y = 1$; dotted **7.** $5x - 3y = 2$; dotted
9. $x = 9$; solid **11.** $3x + y = 2$; dotted **13.** no
15. yes **17.** no **19.** yes **21.** no **37.** $x - y > 3$
39. $0.05x + 0.10y < 1$ **47.** $x + y \leq 10$; $y > 2x$
Mixed Review **1.** infinite **2.** no solution **3.** one
6. a. 8; **b.** 5; **c.** (shirts,sweaters); (1,4)(1,3)(1,2)(1,1)(2,3)
(2,2)(2,1)(3,3)(3,2)(3,1)(4,2)(4,1)(5,1)(6,1)

Practice page 352
1. I **3.** IV **5.** (-4,-3) **7.** $y = -3x - 10$ **9.** $y = -2x + 4$
11. 0; 0 **19.** -1 **21.** $\frac{6}{5}$ **23.** $x = 6$ **25.** $y = \frac{1}{4}x - 3$; $\frac{1}{4}$; -3
27. (2,4) **29.** (1,2) **31.** $y > -\frac{4}{5}x - \frac{6}{5}$

8-9 pages 353–355
Written Exercises **1.** direct; 30 **3.** direct; 8.5 **5.** 27.5 lb
7. 1,156 cycles/s **9.** 3 h

Chapter 8 Review pages 356–357
1. false; an ordered pair **2.** true **3.** false; x-axis
4. false; m; b **5.** false; is not part of **6.** (1,-3)
7. (-2,1) **8.** (-3,-3) **9.** (2,2) **10.** (1,2) **11.** (2,-2)

12. (3,3) **13.** yes **14.** no **15.** yes **16.** yes **17.** 2
18. $\frac{3}{2}$ **19.** -1 **20.** 0 **21.** $y = 2x + 3$; 2; 3
22. $y = -\frac{1}{2}x - 2$; $-\frac{1}{2}$; -2 **23.** $y = -x + 5$; -1; 5
24. $y = -5x + \frac{5}{2}$; -5; $\frac{5}{2}$ **25.** 22 liters **26.** yes **27.** no
28. yes

Chapters 1–8 Cumulative Review page 359
1. B **2.** C **3.** A **4.** C **5.** D **6.** A **7.** A **8.** B
9. D **10.** C **11.** B **12.** B **13.** B **14.** A **15.** A
16. B

CHAPTER 9

Algebra in Geometry and Measurement

9-1 page 364
Written Exercises **1.** $\overline{BZ}$, $\overline{BT}$, $\overline{BM}$, $\overline{MT}$, $\overline{ZM}$, $\overline{ZT}$
3. $\overrightarrow{DC}$, $\overrightarrow{DB}$, $\overrightarrow{DA}$ **5.** an infinite number; one
7. a. The intersection of two planes is a line.;
b. the intersection of a floor and wall
9. $2x + 3 = 8x$; 4 **11.** true **13.** true
Mixed Review **2.** $6\frac{1}{2}$ **3.** 34% **4.** 92¢ **5.** $x = 2$
6. a = 64 **7.** 4

9-2 pages 367–368
Written Exercises **1.** obtuse **3.** straight **5.** acute
7. if the sum of their measures is 180°
9. $\angle SRB$ and $\angle WRQ$; $\angle WRA$ and $\angle TRB$
11. 45°; 135° **13.** 70° **15.** 120° **17.** 73° **19.** 22°
21. acute **23.** right **25.** obtuse **27.** acute **29.** none;
90° **31.** none; 65° **33.** 47°; 137° **35.** $(110 - y)°$;
$(200 - y)°$
Mixed Review **1.** $y = \frac{1}{4}x + 2$ **2.** $y = -x + 12$
3. $\overline{AB}$ and $\overline{RM}$ **4.** intersecting **5.** $24.74

9-3 page 372
Written Exercises **1.** F **3.** F **5.** F **7.** T
9. rectangle $ABCD$; polygon $ABCD$
11. quad. $QRTS$; polygon $QRTS$
13. convex; triangle **19.** 3, 4
Mixed Review **1.** 6.25 **2.** 1.024 **3.** 60° **4.** 47° **5.** B
6. $a > \frac{11}{3}$ **7.** $y = 17$ **8.** Joe 13; Ellen 6

9-4 pages 375–376
Written Exercises **1.** acute **3.** right **5.** isosceles **7.** T
9. T **11.** T **13.** F **19.** 90° **21.** 50° **23.** 90° **25.** 90°
27. 60° **29.** $(80 - x)°$ **31.** obtuse
Mixed Review **1.** $6^2 + (18 + 9) \cdot -2 = -18$
2. $(150 + 17) \cdot 10 = 1,670$ **5.** 0.235 **6.** 0.059
7. 100 for $121.50
Critical Thinking **1. b.** 4 **2.** T **3.** F **4.** T
5. You can make an inductive conclusion after trying
numerous examples, but you cannot prove the
conclusion true. If you have proved the statement to be
false, you are done once you find a counterexample.

9-5 pages 378–379
Written Exercises **1.** F **3.** T **5.** T **7.** 85 in. **9.** 35 cm
11. $250x$ ft **13.** 31.5 in. **15.** 0.29 cm **17.** 45,044.5 mi
19. a. no; **b.** no; C and D are not on the circle.
Mixed Review **1.** 9 **2.** 15 **3.** 149 **4.** 49,990
5. $m\angle 1 = 100°$; $m\angle 2 = 60°$ **6.** 672,000 km

9-6 pages 381–382
Written Exercises **1.** B **3.** $\overline{EF} \cong \overline{LM}$; $\overline{FG} \cong \overline{MN}$;
$\overline{HG} \cong \overline{ON}$; $\overline{EH} \cong \overline{LO}$; $\angle F \cong \angle M$; $\angle G \cong \angle N$; $\angle H \cong \angle O$;
$\angle E \cong \angle L$; $EFGH \cong LMNO$ **5.** 40° **7.** 3.5 **9.** 4.5 **11.** T
13. T **15.** F **17.** $m\angle 3 = 80°$; $m\angle 4 = 80°$ **23.** yes
Mixed Review **1.** 32.34 **3.** 27 mm **4.** $1\frac{3}{4}$ in. **5.** 5
6. 3 **7.** acute **8.** 25
Test Yourself
1. Answers may vary. $\overleftrightarrow{WY}$, $\overleftrightarrow{VU}$, $\overleftrightarrow{ZX}$; $\overrightarrow{MZ}$, $\overrightarrow{MX}$, $\overrightarrow{MY}$;
$\overline{WM}$, $\overline{UM}$, $\overline{ZX}$; $\angle XMY$, $\angle VMX$, $\angle ZMU$
2. parallelogram **3.** acute **4.** $\overline{AB} \cong \overline{CD}$; $\overline{BD} \cong \overline{BD}$;
$\overline{BC} \cong \overline{AD}$; $\angle BAD \cong \angle DCB$; $\angle ABD \cong \angle CDB$;
$\angle CBD \cong \angle ADB$ **5.** 52 ft **6.** 30 in. **7.** 31 m
8. 11.1 cm

9-7 pages 386–387
Written Exercises **3.** $\frac{MO}{RT} = \frac{OR}{RY} = \frac{ER}{YS} = \frac{ME}{TS}$ **5.** $x = 5$
7. $z = 5.8\overline{3}$ **9.** yes; $\overline{PQ} \leftrightarrow \overline{QS}$; $\overline{PR} \leftrightarrow \overline{ST}$; $\overline{RQ} \leftrightarrow \overline{TQ}$
13. 53.4 cm **15.** A possible answer is 24.5 in. × 21 in.
Mixed Review **1.** 0.375 **2.** $0.41\overline{6}$ **3.** $\overline{AB} \cong \overline{XY}$;
$\overline{BC} \cong \overline{YZ}$; $\overline{AC} \cong \overline{XZ}$; $\angle A \cong \angle X$; $\angle B \cong \angle Y$; $\angle C \cong \angle Z$
4. 9 **5.** 36 **6.** 1.44 **7.** 10
Critical Thinking card 1 is a triangle; card 2 is a circle;
card 3 is a square

Practice page 388
1. 55° **3.** 75° **5.** 33°, 123° **7.** 47°, 137° **9.** 74°, 164°
11. none; 1° **13.** 90° **15.** 72° **17.** 45° **19.** 44°
21. 113.6 m **23.** 0.19 km **25.** 134,770 mi **27.** chords:
$\overline{LK}$, $\overline{JI}$; $\overline{GJ}$, $\overline{KH}$ diameters: $\overline{GJ}$, $\overline{KH}$; radii: $\overline{OH}$, $\overline{OJ}$, $\overline{OK}$, $\overline{OG}$;
central angles: $\angle GOH$, $\angle HOJ$, $\angle JOK$, $\angle KOG$
29. $\overline{YX} \cong \overline{TS}$, $\overline{XZ} \cong \overline{SU}$, $\overline{ZY} \cong \overline{UT}$, $\angle Y \cong \angle T$, $\angle X \cong \angle S$,
$\angle Z \cong \angle U$

9-8 pages 392–393
Written Exercises **1.** 36 ft **3.** 7 yd 1 ft **5.** 240 **7.** 19
9. 56.52 ft **11.** 8.4 mi **13.** $5a$ yd, $2.5a$ yd
15. ≈$0.8x$ units, ≈$0.4x$ units **17.** 22.0 **19.** 2.0
21. $1\frac{5}{7}$ **23.** $568\frac{6}{7}$ **25.** 27 **27.** 6 **29.** $2a + 2b = P$
Mixed Review **1.** 20 **2.** 93% **3.** 2.5
4. $\frac{AB}{HI} = \frac{BC}{IJ} = \frac{CD}{JK} = \frac{DA}{KH}$ **5.** 26.62 **6.** 169 **7.** 27
Test Yourself **1.** 6 **2.** 33.4 **3.** 94.2

9-9 page 395
Written Exercises **1.** about 8 **3.** 13
5. a. sun = 324 in.; moon = 0.825 in.
b. sun = 34,875 in.; moon = 90 in.

Problem Solving Practice page 396
1. positive **3.** 13 games **5.** 309 mi
7. 13 **9.** 13,455.33 yen; 52.42 pounds; 516.8 francs
11. $17,340.00 **13.** $90; $60

9-10 pages 399–400
Written Exercises 1. yes **3.** no **7.** yes

Chapter 9 Review page 400
2. $\overleftrightarrow{AB} \parallel \overleftrightarrow{CD}$ **3.** Answers may vary. $\overleftrightarrow{AB}$, $\overleftrightarrow{CD}$, $\overleftrightarrow{EF}$
4. Answers may vary. $\overrightarrow{AE}$; $\overrightarrow{EB}$; $\overrightarrow{EF}$; $\overrightarrow{FD}$; $\overrightarrow{CF}$ **5.** Answers
may vary. $\overrightarrow{EF}$, $\overrightarrow{CD}$, $\overrightarrow{BA}$, $\overrightarrow{AB}$, $\overrightarrow{EB}$, $\overrightarrow{FD}$, $\overrightarrow{FC}$, $\overrightarrow{EA}$, $\overrightarrow{FE}$
6. acute **7.** supplementary **8.** $\cong$ **9.** 120° **10.** 125°
11. F **12.** T **13.** F **14.** T **15.** T **16.** T **17.** right
18. obtuse **19.** acute **20.** 60° **21.** 50 cm **22.** 20 cm
23. 7 in. **24.** 8.4 cm **25.** 15 ft **26.** 4.5 ft **27.** $\overline{AB} \cong$
$\overline{WX}$; $\overline{BC} \cong \overline{XY}$; $\overline{CD} \cong \overline{YZ}$; $\overline{AD} \cong \overline{WZ}$; $\angle A \cong \angle W$; $\angle B \cong$
$\angle X$; $\angle C \cong \angle Y$; $\angle D \cong \angle Z$ **28.** $x = 9$ **29.** $y = 5.4$
30. 84 in. **31.** 471 cm

Chapters 1–9 Cumulative Review page 403
1. C **2.** B **3.** C **4.** B **5.** A **6.** B **7.** A **8.** A **9.** C
10. C **11.** B **12.** B **13.** B **14.** D **15.** C **16.** B

CHAPTER 10

Area and Volume Formulas

10-1 pages 408–409
Written Exercises 7. 7.02 cm² **9.** 237.16 in.²
11. 154.8 cm² **13.** 5.5 cm **15.** 15x **17.** 540 ft²
19. 58.79 km² **21.** 577.5 cm² **23.** 42x² sq. units
25. 32 ft **27.** 49 cm² **29.** 96 ft **31.** 9 ft² **33.** $5\frac{1}{3}$ ft
Mixed Review 1. 1.474×10^3 **2.** $\frac{4}{81}$ **3.** $>$ **4.** 6 and 7
5. 50.24 **6.** 180° **7.** 22.5 ft

10-2 pages 412–413
Written Exercises 1. 39.36 m² **3.** 441 in.²
5. 161.7 cm² **7.** 750 cm² **9.** 1,394.64 ft²
11. 119.7 cm² **13.** 1.4 cm² **15.** 3.2 cm²
17. 81x² sq. units **19.** 1.5 ft **21.** T **23.** F **25.** T
Mixed Review 1. 180 cm² **2.** 764 mm² **3.** 121.7%
4. 1.4352×10^{10} **5.** 18.84x **6.** −5 **7.** $\frac{15}{16}$ **8.** 10

10-3 pages 415–416
Written Exercises 1. 121π mi²; 379.94 mi²
3. 0.36π in.²; 1.13 in.² **5.** 2.56π ft²; 8.04 ft²
7. 25πx² sq. units; 78.5x² sq. units **9.** 4.41πx² sq. units;
13.85x² sq. units **11.** e **13.** c **15.** b **17.** 1 circle of
radius 4 is larger. Area is 50.24. Area of 4 circles is
12.56. **19.** 50.24 cm² **21. b.** approximately 6 units
23. 16 in. **25.** 32.7 cm and 84.9 cm² **27.** 116.8 m and
1,086.3 m² **29.** 54.6 m and 237.7 m² **31.** 9.14 sq. units
33. 20π sq. units or 62.8 sq. units **35. a.** 6,280 ft²;
b. 9 ft²; **c.** 698 yd² **37. a.** The circumference is doubled,
tripled.; **b.** No. The area is multiplied by 4.

Mixed Review 1. 60° **2.** 11 **3.** 8 **4.** 144 **5.** 60 **6.** 70
7. 67.5 **8.** 280 ft²
Test Yourself 1. πr^2 **2.** $\frac{1}{2}bh$ **3.** bh **4.** $\frac{1}{2}h(b_1 + b_2)$
5. bh **6.** 35.75 cm² **7.** 286 ft² **8.** 910 in.²
9. 961.625 mm² **10.** 10.92 ft² **11.** 1,808.64 ft²

10-4 pages 422–423
Written Exercises 1. pentagonal prism
3. triangular prism **5.** triangular pyramid **9.** T
11. F **13.** F **15.** rectangles, octagons **17.** 4
19. pentagonal prism, pentagons **21.** rectangular prism
23. sphere **27.** square pyramid
Mixed Review 1. $9a^2\pi$ square units **2.** 8x square units
3. 25π in.² **4.** 35 cm² **5.** −13 **6.** −7 **7.** $1\frac{2}{5}$ **8.** 5:00 A.M.
9. 20°; acute
Critical Thinking 2. Pattern A: triangle, circle, square,
square; Pattern B: circle, square, square, triangle;
Pattern C: square, square, triangle, circle.
3. Pattern D: square, triangle, circle, square. **4.** C

10-5 page 426
Written Exercises 1. Use 2 strings of different lengths
with equal weights on the end. Test the time of swings.
3. 200 **5.** 7,042.6 m **7.** 7 **9.** $\frac{2}{15}$ **11.** 65

10-6 page 429
Written Exercises 1. 1,078 sq. units **3.** 602.88 sq. units
5. 1,056 mm² **7.** 475.2 cm² **9. a.** 6 sq. units, 24 sq.
units, 54 sq. units; **b.** quadrupled; nine times larger
11. 16 gal
Mixed Review 1. $6x^3$ **2.** $4a^2 + 7a$ **3.** $1\frac{1}{9}$ **4.** 12 **5.** 256
6. 144π or 452.16 **7.** 112 **8.** 1,500 bels **9.** 219.8 cm

10-7 page 432
Written Exercises 1. 5,600 ft² **3.** 1,040 m²
5. 1,714.44 m² **7.** 2,826 in.² **9.** 4,578.12 m²
11. radii $\frac{2}{5}$; areas $\frac{4}{25}$; Ratio of areas is the square of the
ratio of the radii. **13.** 28.26 m²
Mixed Review 1. 22 **2.** −8 **3.** $2.99 **4.** $3\frac{1}{5}$ **5.** 79.2 cm
6. 25.8 in. **7.** 1.024×10^9 **8.** Both figures have a
hexagon for a base. The sides of the prism are
rectangles. The sides of the pyramid are triangles.

10-8 pages 434–435
Written Exercises 1. b. 125.25 ft²; yes; **c.** $626.25;
$1,252.50

Practice page 436
1. 29.2 m² **3.** 30.6 ft² **5.** 44.2 yd² **7.** 126 m² or
1,260,000 cm² **9.** 4,750 mm² **11.** 11,040 in.²
13. triangular pyramid **15.** 52 ft² **17.** 848 cm²
19. 1,256 m² **21.** 1,865.16 m² **23.** 5,024 mm²

10-9 pages 439–440
Written Exercises 1. 637 in.³ **3.** 27a³ **5.** 720 mm³
7. 6,782.4 ft³ **9.** 5,803.72 cm³ **11.** 8,138.88 in.³
13. 128 ft³ **15.** $\frac{1}{2}$; doubles the volume
17. 5,878.08 mm³ **19.** πx^3 **21.** 320 ft³

Mixed Review 1. $(180 - 3x)°$ **2.** $\frac{2}{5}$ **3.** 94.2 cm **4.** 3
5. 3.136×10^{13} square units **6.** 391.2 in.² **7.** 263.76 ft²
8. 22
Test Yourself 1. 680 mm² **2.** 477.28 m² **3.** 1,400 cm²
4. 19,292.16 ft³ **5.** 36,000 cm³ **6.** 1,200 in.³
7. $6x^3$ cu. units **8.** $12.56x^3$ cu. units **9.** $50x^3$ cu. units

10-10 pages 443–444
Written Exercises 1. 904.32 cm³ **3.** 847.8 ft³ **5.** 300 ft³
7. The box from theater A holds 3 times more. **9.** 4 m
11. 5 ft **13.** ≈12.27 in.³ **15. a.** 480.42 in. or 40.035 ft;
b. 73,504.3 in.² or 510.45 ft²;
c. ≈1,874,000 in.³ or ≈1,085 ft³ **17.** $88,565,333\frac{1}{3}$ ft³
Mixed Review 1. 61,544 mm³ **2.** 43.332 in.
3. 533.8 in.² **4.** 1.2×10^5 **5.** -1 **6.** 8 **7.** $\frac{43}{72}$
8. 2,167.5 cm³
Critical Thinking 3. a. $\frac{2}{3}$; **b.** $\frac{2}{3}$; **c.** $\frac{2}{3}$; **d.** $\frac{4}{9}$ **5.** $\frac{5}{8}$, $\frac{25}{64}$

Problem Solving Practice page 445
1. 704 in.³ **3.** 21 **5.** 27
7. Juan picked 15 bushels. Kimo picked 5 bushels.
9. Teresa, Fran, Vivian, Clara, Marie, Cindy
11. 12 ft × 20 ft

Chapter 10 Review pages 446–447
1. area **2.** polygons **3.** triangles **4.** prism
5. cylinder **6.** cone, vertex **7.** sphere, center **8.** faces
9. slant height **10.** volume **11.** 49 cm² **12.** 27 in.²
13. 30 ft² **14.** 15 cm² **15.** 78.5 m² **16.** 200.96 mm²
17. 56.52 m² **18.** 37.68 in.² **19.** square pyramid
20. triangular prism **21.** cylinder **22.** 13 in. × $24\frac{1}{2}$ in.
23. 164 cm² **24.** 62.8 in.² **25.** 84 cm² **26.** 216 m²
27. 310.86 in.³ **28.** 384 cm³ **29.** 18 ft³ **30.** 904.32 cm³

Chapters 1–10 Cumulative Review page 449
1. B **2.** A **3.** C **4.** A **5.** D **6.** C **7.** C **8.** A
9. B **10.** C **11.** B **12.** B **13.** A **14.** A

CHAPTER 11

Right Triangles in Algebra

11-1 pages 456–457
Written Exercises 1. false **3.** false **5.** true **7.** true
9. 256 **11.** $\frac{4}{9}$ **13.** $25x^6$ **15.** 81 **17.** 100 **19.** 8 **21.** 7
23. $\frac{4}{5}$ **25.** 7.035 **27.** $4y^5$ **29.** 16 **31.** 4.472 **33.** ⑦, 8
35. ②, 3 **37.** ⑫, -3 **39.** ④, 5 **41.** rational
43. irrational **45.** rational **47.** rational **49.** 7.071
51. 9.950 **53.** 6.557 **55.** 7.348
Mixed Review 1. 403.44 cm² **2.** 0.00254 m³ **3.** $n \leq \frac{7}{8}$
4. $x \geq -13\frac{1}{2}$ **5.** $-\frac{4}{7}$ **6.** $x = 16\frac{1}{3}$ **7.** 1,502% **8.** $12
Critical Thinking 1. You keep getting 6.85 and 6.86. Go
halfway between the numbers to get 6.855. **2.** 4.359
3. Calculators and computers can calculate square roots
instantly.

11-2 page 459
Written Exercises 1. lost $8 **3.** 4 h; 12 mi; 6 mi **5.** -3
7. 3:02 P.M.

11-3 pages 463–464
Written Exercises 1. 5 **3.** $\frac{9}{25}$ **5.** 7.937 **7.** 5.657
9. $\overline{AC}$ and $\overline{CB}$; $\overline{AB}$ **11.** 10 **13.** 9
15. $50^2 + 120^2 = x^2$; $x = 130$
17. $x^2 + (6\sqrt{5})^2 = 18^2$; $x = 12$
19. $11^2 + x^2 = \sqrt{202}^2$; $x = 9$
21. $3^2 + 7^2 = h^2$; $x = 4.62$ **23.** yes **25.** no **27.** no
29. yes for $p > 0$ **31.** $\sqrt{2}$, $\sqrt{3}$, 2, $\sqrt{5}$, $\sqrt{6}$, $\sqrt{7}$
33. 106 ft **35.** 21.21 in. **37.** 14.1 ft **39. a.** 21.63 in.;
b. 461.44 in.³
Mixed Review 1. $25ab^2$ **2.** xy **3.** yes **4.** 33°; 123°
5. 58°; 148° **6.** 4 **7.** 256 **8.** 36°F

11-4 pages 467–468
Written Exercises 1. 27 **3.** 3 **5.** $x = 8.602$
7. $x = 9.487$ **9.** $x = 10.5$ **11.** $x = 12$; $y = 15$
13. $x = 36$; $y = 69.97$ **15.** 43.75 ft
17. a. 611.45 ft; **b.** 570,025 ft²
Mixed Review 1. yes **2.** no **3.** 8.96×10^{12} **4.** 6
5. 38 **6.** $\frac{4}{2x} = \frac{1}{8} \cdot 12$; $x = 1\frac{1}{3}$ **7.** $\frac{6x}{2} = x + 4$; $x = 2$
8. $0.02 \times 50 = x$; 1
Test Yourself 1. $x = 8$ **2.** $x = 8.5$ **3.** $x = 14.7$
4. 8.062 cm **5.** 7.5 ft

11-5 pages 471–472
Written Exercises 1. 9; $9\sqrt{2}$ **3.** 4; 4 **5.** $2\sqrt{3}$; 4
7. $7\sqrt{3}$; 14 **9.** $x = \frac{27}{\sqrt{2}}$ **11.** $x = \frac{14}{\sqrt{3}}$; $y = \frac{28}{\sqrt{3}}$
13. a. 8.5 in.; **b.** 433.5 in² **15.** $26\sqrt{3}$ in. **17.** 55.04 cm²
19. 51 in.
Mixed Review 1. -12 **2.** 10 **3.** $x = 4.75$ **4.** $-16x^6$
5. 6 **6.** pentagon **7.** 27% **8.** $33.32
Critical Thinking Lisa–bedroom; Nicole–bathroom;
Robert–living room; Eric–family room; JoAnn–kitchen

11-6 pages 475–476
Written Exercises 1. 0.1736 **3.** 0.2679 **5.** 0.9781
7. 84° **9.** 63° **11.** $\sqrt{3}$ **13.** $\tan z° = \frac{f}{e}$ **15.** $\sin y° = \frac{d}{c}$
17. $x \approx 54$; $y \approx 36$; $z = 1.27$
19. $x = 68$; $y = 9.90$; $z = 10.68$ **21.** $x \approx 28$; $y \approx 62$
23. 13.3 mi **25.** 41 ft
Mixed Review 1. 3.4 ft **2.** 11.56 ft² **3.** 8 in.; $8\sqrt{3}$ in.
4. 0 **5.** acute **6.** 5 m **7.** -13, -14, -15
Test Yourself 1. 30°-60°-90° **2.** 45°-45°-90° **3.** neither
4. $x = 11$ **5.** $x = 3$; $y = 6$; $z = 60$ **6.** $x = 56$; $y = 8.09$;
$z = 14.48$

11-7 page 479
Written Exercises 11. a. $m\angle A \approx 23°$; $m\angle B \approx 67°$

Practice page 480
1. 13 **3.** $\frac{9}{2}$ **5.** $\frac{x}{y}$ **7.** $20x^3$ **9.** $11c^2$ **11.** 1 **13.** 3
15. 10 **17.** rational **19.** rational **21.** no **23.** no
25. no **27.** yes **29.** 45°-45°-90° **31.** neither
33. $x = 24$ **35.** $y = 10$ **37.** $y = 15$ **39.** $a = 5$

Problem Solving Practice page 481
1. 42 **3.** 35°, 58°, and 87° **5.** 1.36 min **7.** 12
9. 657 cm³ **11.** 8, 18, and 22

Chapter 11 Review pages 482–483
1. g 2. d 3. f 4. b 5. a 6. h 7. c 8. i 9. e
10. 14 11. $8p$ 12. 1.732 13. $x-2$ 14. 25 15. 6
16. 18 17. 5 18. 15 19. 25 20. 6.708 21. 39 22. 9
23. 25 24. 32 25. 18 26. $8\sqrt{3}$ 27. 20 28. $x=25$;
$y=45.315$; $z=21.13$ 29. $x=70$; $y=26.312$; $z=9.576$
30. $x=68$; $y=24.752$; $z=26.695$ 31. $x=50$;
$y=51.424$; $z=61.28$ 32. 13.610 ft 33. $2°$

Chapters 1–11 Cumulative Review page 485
1. A 2. B 3. D 4. B 5. B 6. C 7. A 8. C
9. B 10. A 11. A 12. B

CHAPTER 12

Statistics and Probability

12-1 pages 490–491
Written Exercises 1. 4.8, 5, 5, 4
3. 21.5, 22.5, no mode, 10.3 5. 2, 2, 2, 4
7. 4.5, 4.5, 2, 6 9. 84.2, 84, 84, 16
11. 101, 101, 101, 8 13. a. 10; 8; 3 b. The median.
It is not influenced by the extreme of 30 points.
25. a. The mean, because it is the highest average.;
b. 87 c. 90
Mixed Review 1. 33.2 in.^{2} 2. 360 ft^2 3. $\frac{4}{5}$ 4. $\frac{3}{4}$
5. 3rd and 4th 6. 1st and 2nd 7. $7.16

12-2 pages 494–495
Written Exercises 1. 4; 4 3. 3.5; 1 and 6 5. 3.5, 2
7. 7.3, 7, 6 9. 25.8, 25, 25 11. 4, 4
13. 17.5, 15 and 20 15. c. 4.1, 3, 2 17. b. 2.7, 2, 0
21. a. men 40–44, women 30–34; b. Total number
entered. Divide by 2 to find middle number. Add
numbers entered one group at a time. Start at the top
until the middle number is reached or surpassed. Find
corresponding age. Men: 35–39. Women 35–39.
Mixed Review 1. -5.5 2. 62.5%, 0.625
3. 15.7, 16, 16 and 18 4. 14.4, 15, no mode 5. 5
6. $-\frac{7}{8}$ 7. 156

12-3 pages 500–501
Written Exercises 1. 774, 768 and 785 3. 82, 74
5. 11.65, 11.8 7. Set A: 62.5, 63; Set B: 57, no mode
9. Set E: 5.85, no mode; Set F: 6.45, no mode
11. a. 0; c. 10, 12, and 15; d. 13 13. 6, 7, 8, 9
15. Class A: 79.5, 74, 79 and 96; Class B: 84, 99
Mixed Review 1. 6,-6 2. 37.5 in.^{2} 3. 2 4. 2
5. 18, 9, 27 6. 46, 23, 69 7. 852.375; 803.5; 774
Critical Thinking 1. A change in the groupings of the
horizontal scale changes heights on the vertical scale.
2. The shape of the graph is changed, giving a
different impact.

12-4 pages 504–505
Written Exercises 5. $220, $50 7. 75% 9. no
17. 7.76, 7.7, 7.4, mean

Mixed Review 1. 118 2. 37.5% 3. 79, 25 4. 79.4
5. 79 7. 120
Test Yourself 1. 65.3, 66, 45, 42

12-5 pages 510–511
Written Exercises 1. 120 3. 3,628,800 5. 60
7. 30,240 9. 479,001,600 11. 360,360 13. 6 15. 90
17. T 19. F 21. 12 23. 80 25. 440 27. a. 7; b. 6;
c. 5; d. 210 29. 36 31. 18
Mixed Review 1. 1×10^{11} 2. 1×10^{-4} 3. 19 5. $\frac{1}{3}$
6. $\frac{5}{11}$ 7. $28.50
Critical Thinking 1. 2 2. red

12-6 pages 514–515
Written Exercises 1. $\frac{1}{2}$ 3. $\frac{7}{11}$ 5. $\frac{6}{11}$ 7. $\frac{4}{25}$ 9. $\frac{3}{7}$
11. a. $\frac{6}{13}$; b. $\frac{13}{25}$; c. $\frac{24}{49}$; d. Yes. The sample space is
different for each question. 13. a. $\frac{4}{25}$; b. $\frac{21}{25}$; c. Any
prime number has 1 or more digits. 15. a. $\frac{1}{7}$; b. $\frac{2}{7}$;
c. $\frac{5}{14}$; d. $\frac{1}{7}$; e. $\frac{1}{14}$; f. 1 17. a. $\frac{1}{5}$; b. $\frac{1}{5}$; c. $\frac{1}{10}$; d. $\frac{1}{5}$; e. $\frac{1}{5}$;
f. The event of having the digit 0 as the last digit is not
included. 19. 15 21. $\frac{1}{3}$
Mixed Review 1. 9 2. $\frac{2}{5}$ 3. 720 4. 840 5. 7.25
7. $5x = 850$; 170 tickets

12-7 pages 519–520
Written Exercises 3. $\frac{5}{16}$ 5. $\frac{19}{25}$ 7. $\frac{1}{31}$ 9. 98 11. $67.50
13. 2 15. Yes. The circumference of the hole is 3.14 in.
17. 78.6%

Practice page 521
1. 16, 13, 6 and 7, 30 3. 4, 4, 4, 6 5. 3.75, 5, 6
7. Set A: 23.5, 23 Set B: 22, no mode 9. The data for
Set A is spread out. Set B data is consistent, staying close
to the median, which is 9. 11. 4! 13. $\frac{25!}{22!}$ 15. 720
17. 2,450 19. $\frac{1}{9}$ 21. $\frac{4}{9}$ 23. 1

12-8 pages 524–525
Written Exercises 1. independent 3. dependent 5. $\frac{1}{10}$
7. $\frac{1}{12}$ 9. Dependent $\frac{5}{82}$ 11. dependent a. $\frac{9}{56}$; b. $\frac{3}{28}$
13. 24; No. The class is small enough to ask each
person for his/her preference. 15. $\frac{2}{5}$
Mixed Review 1. 195 2. 132 3. $\frac{1}{2}$ 4. $\frac{1}{6}$ 5. $48n$
6. $29n - 5$ 7. 5 y, 15 y
Test Yourself 1. 30.3, 30, 28 and 35 2. 20 3. $\frac{1}{36}$
4. $\frac{1}{11}$

Problem Solving Practice page 526
1. 105 ft 3. 24 5. 32 students 7. 5 and 6
9. 160, 160, 160, 80 or 112, 112, 224, 112 11. 69

12-9 pages 528–529
Written Exercises 1. 496 3. 315 5. a. 240; b. 400;
c. 600; d. 192, 320, 480; e. $1,240

Chapter 12 Review pages 530–531
1. false, mode 2. true 3. true 4. false, independent
5. false, factorial 6. 7.46, 8, 8, 4
7. 115.56, 115, no mode, 37 10. 6 11. 5,040

12. 12   **13.** 1,680   **14.** 35   **15.** $\frac{1}{5}$ **16.** $\frac{2}{5}$ **17.** $\frac{1}{5}$ **18.** $\frac{4}{5}$
19. $\frac{2}{25}$ **20.** $\frac{1}{10}$

Chapters 1–12 Cumulative Review page 533
1. B   **2.** C   **3.** A   **4.** C   **5.** B   **6.** A   **7.** B   **8.** D
9. B   **10.** C   **11.** A   **12.** A   **13.** A   **14.** C

CHAPTER 13

Polynomials

13-1 pages 540–541
Written Exercises   1. monomial   **3.** monomial   **5.** 2
7. 3   **9.** 1   **11.** binomial   **13.** monomial
15. monomial   **17.** binomial   **25.** $x^2 + 3$
27. $x^2 + 2x + 3$ **31.** 6   **33.** -1   **35.** 0   **37.** 187
39. 195   **41.** 201
Mixed Review   1. x^5 **2.** $64m^6$ **3.** independent
4. dependent   **5.** $6x^2$ **6.** 9   **7.** 120 poses
Critical Thinking   1. a. yes; **b.** yes; **c.** yes; **d.** no; **e.** no
2. a. no; **b.** no; **c.** no; **d.** no; **e.** yes   **3. a.** no; **b.** no;
c. no; **d.** yes; **e.** yes   **4. a.** no; **b.** no; **c.** no; **d.** yes;
e. no

13-2 pages 544–545
Written Exercises   1. $4x^2 + 5x + 2$ **3.** $-x + 5$
5. $-3x^2 + x + 7$ **7.** $9x^2 + x + 5$ **9.** $2x^3 + 5x^2 + x + 4$
11. $3x + 8$ **13.** $4y - 15$ **15.** $4mn^2 + 2m - 2n^2$
17. $2a^2 + 5ab + 2b$ **19.** $m - 9$ **21.** $4ab - 10$
23. $w^2 + 7w - 6$ **25.** $-3x^2 - 8x + 8$ **27.** $-8x + 10$
29. $17a^7 + 8a^4 + a^2 + 4$ **31.** $11a^3b^2 - 15a^2b - 2ab + 23$
33. $2a + (2a + 2) + (2a + 4)$; **a.** $6a + 6$; **b.** 10, 12, 14
35. $5a + (5a + 5) + (5a + 10) + (5a + 15) + (5a + 20)$;
a. $25a + 50$; **b.** 65, 70, 75, 80, 85   **37.** $8b^2 + 10b - 6$
39. a. 360; **b.** 540; **c.** 720; **d.** 1,440
Mixed Review   1. 5 sq. units   **2.** 12 sq. units   **3.** 2   **4.** 3
5. $17x - 6$ **6.** $24x + 6 - 20y$ **7.** 7.125 mi

13-3 pages 547–548
Written Exercises   1. $2x^2 + 12x$ **3.** $6x^2 - 2x$ **5.** $5x^2 + 3x$
7. a. 24; **b.** 2; **c.** 40; **d.** 6   **9.** $-4x^2y^2 + 4x^3y$; -233,280
11. $8x^2 - 2x$ **13.** $2x^3 - 5x^2$ **15.** $2y^4 + y^3 - 3y^2$
17. $5x^2y + 25xy - 5xy^2$ **19.** $-6x^3y^2 - 3x^2y^2 - 3xy^3 + 9xy$
21. $96x^3y^3z + 24x^4yz^6$ **23.** $12x^3 + 12x^2y^2 + 12x^2z$
25. $\frac{1}{2}xy + \frac{1}{2}xy^3 + \frac{5}{2}y$ **27.** $14x^4 + 7x^2y^2 - 7x^3y$
29. $\frac{2}{3}x^3 + \frac{2}{3}x^2 + 9x$ **31.** $e(e + 2)$; $e^2 + 2e$
33. $l\left(\frac{1}{2}l + 7\right)$; $\frac{1}{2}l^2 + 7l$ **35.** $\frac{1}{2}(8x)(16x + 5)$; $64x^2 + 20x$
37. $7 \times 10^2 + 9 \times 10 + 2$; $7x^2 + 9x + 2$; $4x$;
$(7x^2 + 9x + 2)4x = 28x^3 + 36x^2 + 8x$;
$28(10)^3 + 36(10)^2 + 8(10) = 31{,}680 = 40(792)$; yes
39. $8a^2 + a$ **41.** $4d^2 + 4d$
Mixed Review   1. 2.75   **2.** 27.52 m²   **3.** $3x^2 + 7x + 6$
4. $-9x^2 - 5x + 13$ **5.** x^4 **6.** x^{10} **7.** $449

13-4 pages 552–553
Written Exercises   1. $x^2 + 7x + 6$ **3.** $a^2 + 8a + 7$
5. $a^2 + a - 6$ **7.** $a^2 + 11a + 24$ **9.** $xy + xb + ay + ab$

11. $x^2 + 13x + 12$ **13.** $15 + 2x - x^2$
15. $8ac - 4ad + 4bc - 2bd$ **17.** $x^2 - 9$
19. $b^2 - 14b + 49$ **21.** $4a^2 - 25$ **23.** $4a^2 + 4a + 1$
25. $x^2 + 15x - 756$ **27.** $3a^2 - 2a - 8$
29. $x^2 - 3.5x - 6.24$ **31.** $b^3 - 3b^2 + 3b - 1$
33. $-8a^2 + 20a + 12$ **35.** $x^2 + 2x + 1$ **37.** $x^2 - y^2$
39. $x^2 + 4x + 4$ **41.** $10x^2 + 26x + 12$ **43.** $20x^2 + 6x - 2$
45. $(w - 1)(w - 2) = w^2 - 3w + 2$
47. $(t - 6)^2 = t^2 - 12t + 36$ **49.** $x = 2$ **51.** $w = 0$
53. about 50 mi
Mixed Review   1. 2   **2.** 13.5   **3.** $6x^2 + 2x$
4. $-5x^3 + 10x^2$ **5.** 20   **6.** 6   **7.** 72 ft by 72 ft
Test Yourself   1. monomial   **2.** binomial   **3.** not a
polynomial   **4.** trinomial   **5.** monomial   **6.** binomial
7. monomial   **8.** monomial   **9.** 81   **10.** 95   **11.** -7
12. -51   **13.** 112   **14.** -26   **15.** $11a$
16. $p^2 + p + 12$ **17.** $3ab^2 + 2a + b + 9$
18. $-r^2s^2 + rs - 16$ **19.** $(a^2 + b)(a^2 + b) = a^4 + 2a^2b + b^2$

Practice page 554
1. 2; binomial   **3.** 2; binomial   **5.** 1; monomial
7. $6r^2 - 3$ **9.** $-4d - 1$ **11.** $-7x^2y - 6xy - 5x^2 + 13$
13. $2rt^2 + 6r^2t + 2t$ **15.** $21xy + 6x$ **17.** $20x^2y + 15xy^2$
19. $10a^4b^2 - 10a^2b^4$ **21.** $8c^2d + 12cd^2 - 24cd$
23. $x^2 + 10x + 25$ **25.** $x^2 - 4.5x + 4.5$ **27.** $x^2 - 25$
29. $x^2 - 10x + 25$ **31.** $x^3 - 5x^2 - 2x + 10$
33. $12x^2 + 40x + 12$ **35.** $25x^2 - 20x + 4$
37. $30x^4 + 10x^3 - 6x^2 - 2x$ **39.** $3x^3 + 6x^2 - 72x$ **41.** 13
43. 140   **45.** -6   **47.** 7,280   **49.** -34   **51.** 12   **53.** -2
55. 12

13-5 page 557
Written Exercises   1. $\begin{bmatrix} 1 & 2 \\ 2 & 3 \end{bmatrix}$ **3.** $\begin{bmatrix} 3 & 1 \\ -2 & 2 \end{bmatrix}$
5. 8   **7.** (-2,4)   **9.** (1,1)   **11.** One pen and two pencils
cost $.60.

13-6 pages 559–560
Written Exercises   1. 80 games   **3.** 7.5 ft
5. Sandy = 101 g; White Ears = 108 g; Sport = 115 g
7. 51 people   **9.** 32.9 min   **11.** 10 angles   **13.** 3,750 ft²
15. $28.80   **17.** 6 ways

Problem Solving Practice page 561
1. 28 possible routes   **3.** 86   **5.** 60 lb
7. A is 3 yd by 11 yd; B is 3 yd by 3 yd
9. 8 students

Chapter 13 Review pages 562–563
1. A monomial is a real number, variable, or the
product of a real number and one or more variables.
Examples: $6x^2$; $3x$.   **2.** A polynomial is a monomial or a
sum or difference of monomials. Examples: $5x - 2$;
$12x^2 - 6x - 5$.   **3.** Multiply x by each term within the
parentheses. $x(2x - 1) = x \cdot 2x - x \cdot 1 = 2x^2 - x$
4. Multiply the first terms, $x \cdot 2x$, the outer terms, $x \cdot 1$,
the inner terms, $3 \cdot 2x$, and the last terms, $3 \cdot 1$.
Then add the products. $2x^2 + x + 6x + 3 = 2x^2 + 7x + 3$
5. Square the first term and subtract the square of the

second term. $(a + b)(a - b) = a^2 - b^2$ **6.** To square a binomial like $(a + b)^2$ or $(a - b)^2$, square the first term. Add or subtract twice the product of the two terms and add the square of the last term.
$(a + b)^2 = a^2 + 2ab + b^2$; $(a - b)^2 = a^2 - 2ab + b^2$
7. $2x^2 + 3x$; binomial **8.** $x^2 + 2x + 4$; trinomial
9. $3x^2$; monomial **10.** 15 **11.** -9 **12.** -10
13. $7x^2 + 4x$ **14.** $2x^2 + 3x + 1$ **15.** $8x + 5y$
16. $3m - 2n$ **17.** $6a^2 + 3b$ **18.** $-3r^2 + 5s$
19. $4c^2 + 2c - 1$ **20.** $2a^2b - b^2 + 2a$ **21.** $2x^2 + 10x$
22. $6x^2 + 3x$ **23.** $x^2 - 5x$ **24.** $3x^2 + 6x$ **25.** $2x^2 - 4x$
26. $4x^3 + 12x^2$ **27.** $10x^3 - 10x^2 + 15x$
28. $-2x^3y + 2x^2y^2 - 2xy^3$
29. $(x + 2)(x + 2) = x^2 + 4x + 4$
30. $(x + 2)(x + 3) = x^2 + 5x + 6$ **31.** $x^2 - 2x + 1$
32. $a^2 + 6a + 9$ **33.** $y^2 - 4$ **34.** $b^2 + b - 6$
35. $m^2 + 2m - 15$ **36.** $2n^2 + 6n - 20$ **37.** 4 min
38. 8 classic; 6 rock **39.** 12, 24, 36 **40.** $2,401 \text{ ft}^2$

Chapters 1–13 Cumulative Review page 565
1. B **2.** C **3.** A **4.** C **5.** A **6.** B **7.** C **8.** B
9. B **10.** B **11.** A **12.** D **13.** C **14.** B **15.** C
16. B

CHAPTER 1

Extra Practice

page 566
1. -4 **3.** 10 **5.** $>$ **7.** $=$ **9.** -10 **11.** 9 **13.** -112
15. 110 **17.** 6 **19.** 3 **21.** 27 **23.** 51 **25.** 2 **27.** $-7x$
29. $-(y - 7)$ **31.** $|-3 - 10|$ **33.** $10[17 - (-11)]$
35. 71 **37.** -18 **39. a.** $20x + 12y$; **b.** \$152; **c.** 3; 5
41. $+13$

CHAPTER 2

Extra Practice

page 567
1. false **3.** false **5.** false **7.** 0 **9.** 3 **11.** 44 **13.** 25
15. 15 **17.** -61 **19.** 20 **21.** $-3m + 39$ **23.** $5q + 2$
25. $-6s + 4$ **27.** $j = 26$ **29.** $z = 20$ **31.** $n = 5$ or $n = -5$
33. $-3 \div (-1) = 3$ **35.** $xy = |-24|$ **37.** 2,422 m **39.** 27

CHAPTER 3

Extra Practice

page 568
1. 2.12, 2.012, 2.011 **3.** 1.00009, 0.000045, 0.00004
5. 0.4 **7.** 238 **9.** \$19 **11.** 90 **13.** \$1,000 **15.** 216
17. -116.667 **19.** 100.987 **21.** 15.32 **23.** 7.66
25. -1.856 **27.** 15.32 **29.** $y = 1.1$ **31.** $m = 1.89$
33. $x = 16.5$ **35.** $n = 100$ **37.** $0.03x = -3.01$
39. $|-0.9| = 2x$ **41.** 31 min **43.** 6

CHAPTER 4

Extra Practice

page 569
1. 1,024 **3.** -16 **5.** $15x^3$ **7.** $64y^{12}$ **9.** 16 **11.** 8
13. -1 **15.** -12 **17.** 134 **19.** 1 **21.** 2 **23.** 27
25. 5.28×10^4; 52,800 **27.** 1.82×10^7; 18,200,000
29. 2,3,4,9 **31.** 3,5,9 **33.** 2 **35.** 2 **37.** $9ab^2$
39. 1,100 **41.** $12a^5b$ **43.** 45; 15 **45.** 1,100
47. 20 and 4

CHAPTER 5

Extra Practice

page 570
1. $\frac{1}{2}$ **3.** $\frac{1}{5}$ **5.** $\frac{1}{3}$ **7.** $\frac{1}{5}$ **9.** $20\frac{2}{25}$ **11.** $\frac{1}{200}$ **13.** 0.4
15. 0.6 **17.** 0.75 **19.** $-\frac{3}{4}, \frac{1}{2}, \frac{8}{4}$ **21.** $\frac{2^2}{5}, \frac{9}{10}, 2\frac{3}{10}$
23. $\frac{-xy}{5}, \frac{xy}{15}, \frac{3xy}{10}$ **25.** $-\frac{5}{6}$ **27.** $\frac{7}{18}x$ **29.** $7\frac{1}{2}$ **31.** $\frac{72}{77}$
33. $\frac{7x^2}{15}$ **35.** $1\frac{14}{15}$ **37.** $-1\frac{17}{32}$ **39.** $\frac{1}{9}$ **41.** $\frac{a^2b}{c}$ **43.** $\frac{-1}{y}$
45. $1\frac{4}{9}$ **47.** $\frac{-13}{40}$ **49.** $2\frac{1}{2}$ **51.** $-4\frac{4}{9}$
53. 1,205 million people **55.** 24

CHAPTER 6

Extra Practice

page 571
1. $\frac{1}{3}$ **3.** $\frac{1}{4}$ **5.** $\frac{1}{9}$ **7.** $\frac{1}{5}$ **9.** $\frac{20}{30} = \frac{x}{120}$; $x = 80$
11. $\frac{20}{95} = \frac{z}{19}$; $z = 4$ **13.** $\frac{17}{20}$; 85% **15.** $\frac{40}{120}$; $33\frac{1}{3}\%$
17. 45% **19.** $330.\overline{30}$ **21.** 6.44 **23.** -33.3%
25. $+64.5\%$ **27.** $+258.3\%$ **29.** $+6.5\%$ **31.** 6 **33.** 60%
35. 2,400 **37.** bread: $+4,533\%$; milk: $+679\%$

CHAPTER 7

Extra Practice

page 572
1. $x = 6$ **3.** $y = 2\frac{1}{4}$ **5.** $x = 20$ **7.** $b = 3$ **9.** $x = 10$
19. $y \geq 6$ **21.** $y \leq -36$ **23.** $x \geq \frac{5}{9}$ **25.** $x < 7$
27. $x \leq 50$ **29.** $x \leq 90$ **31.** $\frac{a}{8} \leq 13$; $a \leq 104$
33. $7p - 5 \geq 23$; $p \geq 4$
35. 12 months **37.** \$.20
39. 97

CHAPTER 8

Extra Practice

page 573
1. II **3.** I **5.** III **7.** $y = -\frac{1}{2}x + 4$ **9.** $y = 2x + 24$

11. $y = 3x + 3$ 13. 2; $2\frac{1}{2}$; -5 15. -1; 5; 5
17. $-\frac{1}{4}$; -12; -3 19. $(4, -5)$ 21. $y > 3x - 5$
23. $y < 2x + 49$ 31. 7 bags of popcorn and 14 gal of juice   33. 6 and 7   35. 1 min 12 s

CHAPTER 9

Extra Practice

page 574

1. acute   3. obtuse   5. straight   7. not possible; 90
9. 45; 135   11. not possible; 40   17. 90   19. 80   21. 84
23. $d = 58.6$ cm   25. $r = 39$ in.   27. $d = 457$ m
29. true   31. false   33. true   35. 640.56 ft   37. 16.8 in.
39. 27 m   41. 1 mi   43. 62.8 yd

CHAPTER 10

Extra Practice

page 575

1. 18.3 cm²   3. 0.9 m²   5. $561x^2$ 7. 206 cm²   9. 547.1 m²
11. 98.5 m²   13. 660.2 cm²   15. 286 in.²   17. 11,269 m²
19. 1,808.64 in.²   21. 140 ft³   23. 2,279.64 cm³
25. 100 cm³   27. the \$61 dress   29. 16 in.³

CHAPTER 11

Extra Practice

page 576

1. 7.141   3. 12   5. $7x$ 7. $a + b$ 9. yes   11. no   13. yes
15. $x = 4\sqrt{2}$ 17. $x = 14\sqrt{2}$ 19. $x = 9\sqrt{2}$
21. $\frac{n}{m}$ 23. $\frac{e}{d}$ 25. 8 mi   27. 3 A.M.

CHAPTER 12

Extra Practice

page 577

1. 10.4; 12; 13; 10   3. 78.6; 100; 100; 100   7. 13; 13
9. 69; 66   13. 5   15. 714   17. $\frac{1}{4}$ 19. $\frac{3}{13}$ 21. $\frac{1}{676}$ 23. -6
25. 1,766.25 cm³   27. $6\sqrt{2}$ 29. 6 and 7

CHAPTER 13

Extra Practice

page 578

1. $3x^2 + 4x + 5$ 3. $-2mn^2 + m + 2n - 3$
5. $-3a^3n^2 - 4a^2n + 6a$ 7. $72x^3 - 36x^2 + 162x$
9. $\frac{5}{2}a^6 - \frac{1}{2}a^4 - \frac{33}{2}a$ 11. $x^2 + 4x + 3$ 13. $x^2 - 81$
15. $2x^3 + 5x^2 + 3x + 2$
17. $(m + 2)(m + 4)(m + 6)$; $m^3 + 12m^2 + 44m + 48$
19. $(z - 4)(z - 8)$; $z^2 - 12z + 32$ 21. 904.32 cm³
23. 24   25. 194   27. $\frac{7}{75}$

page 616   1. hundred-thousandths   3. hundredths
5. hundred millions   7. 0.0041   9. 0.000008   11. 0.012
13. 6 hundredths   15. eleven hundred-thousandths
17. twelve thousandths   19. forty two ten-thousandths
page 617   1. <   3. >   5. <   7. =   9. <   11. >   13. 0.23, 0.231, 2.31, 3.21, 23.1   15. 0.002, 0.02, 0.22, 0.222, 2.22
17. 0.007, 0.07, 0.7, 0.71, 0.72   19. 7, 7.0324, 7.3, 7.3246, 7.3264   **page 618**   1. 105,000   3. 79,528,000   5. 4,312,000
7. 3   9. 101   11. 82.0   13. 20.4   15. 130.0   17. 96.40
19. 4.23   21. 7.06   23. 1520   25. 4.2   27. 400   29. 8.1
31. 410   33. 2.58   35. 19   37. 7,700   39. 980,000,000
41. 0.00377   43. 12.8   45. 21,000   **page 619**   1. 3.67
3. 7.312   5. 36.127   7. 1.6   9. 13.95   11. 60.21
13. 34.023   15. 39.95   17. 25.73   19. 31.95   21. 7.045
23. 6.21   25. 7.511   27. 2.825   29. 3.55   31. 1.434
33. 10.37   35. 0.32   37. 28.22   39. 37.002   41. 12.403
43. 747.1109   45. 11.36   47. 39.101   **page 620**   1. 5.328
3. 2.15   5. 5.168   7. 0.38912   9. 1.1424   11. 2.07828
13. 0.48   15. 0.364   17. 6.5658   19. 41.16   21. 1.26
23. 12.15   25. 12.05   27. 4.8018   29. 18.012   **page 621**
1. 0.027   3. 0.072   5. 0.0025   7. 0.00248   9. 0.00891
11. 0.00165   13. 0.0376   15. 0.081   17. 0.00072
19. 0.0009   21. 0.04   23. 0.000376   25. 0.012   27. 0.092
29. 0.072   31. 0.01812   33. 0.007   **page 622**   1. 2.56
3. 0.776   5. 8.79   7. 0.11   9. 0.184   11. 2.07   13. 8.76
15. 0.0169   17. 0.0147   19. 0.561   21. 0.868   23. 2.551
25. 3.98   27. 0.025   29. 0.0014   **page 623**   1. 560   3. 52
5. 2367   7. 0.0009   9. 8   11. 0.001803   13. 13700
15. 0.47   17. 0.236   19. 0.00041   21. 423   23. 502
25. 27   27. 0.4   29. 0.065   31. 26   33. 0.0003   35. 15.8
page 624   1. 84   3. 452   5. 32   7. 31.1   9. 3.1   11. 26
13. 31   15. 16   17. 44   19. 2.8   21. 3.6   23. 1.24   25. 58.3   27. 31.4   29. 3.96   31. 0.53   33. 9.5   35. 1.6   37. 3.58   39. 0.243   41. 3.44   43. 1.86   45. 3.77   **page 625**
1. 0.046   3. 0.075   5. 0.0095   7. 0.0025   9. 0.085
11. 0.015   13. 0.0035   15. 0.07   17. 0.0021   19. 0.00015
21. 0.006   23. 0.009   25. 0.0035   27. 0.033   29. 0.073
31. 0.0056   **page 626**   1. 2   3. 10   5. 12   7. 24
9. 3   11. 16   13. 30   15. 21   17. $\frac{5}{6}$ 19. $\frac{3}{4}$ 21. $\frac{4}{5}$
23. $\frac{1}{2}$ 25. $\frac{3}{7}$ 27. $\frac{3}{5}$ 29. $\frac{11}{12}$ 31. $\frac{3}{4}$ 33. $\frac{3}{7}$ 35. $\frac{2}{9}$
37. $\frac{1}{2}$ 39. $\frac{4}{7}$ **page 627**   1. $1\frac{2}{5}$ 3. $3\frac{1}{4}$ 5. $1\frac{3}{10}$ 7. $2\frac{5}{8}$
9. $3\frac{2}{5}$ 11. $4\frac{1}{4}$ 13. $5\frac{2}{5}$ 15. $3\frac{3}{4}$ 17. $1\frac{1}{3}$ 19. $4\frac{1}{2}$ 21. $5\frac{1}{2}$
23. $4\frac{1}{4}$ 25. $\frac{3}{2}$ 27. $\frac{13}{12}$ 29. $\frac{16}{7}$ 31. $\frac{23}{8}$ 33. $\frac{26}{5}$ 35. $\frac{37}{4}$
37. $\frac{63}{8}$ 39. $\frac{24}{7}$ 41. $\frac{31}{10}$ **page 628**   1. $1\frac{2}{5}$ 3. $\frac{4}{7}$ 5. $1\frac{1}{5}$
7. $\frac{3}{8}$ 9. $\frac{3}{5}$ 11. 1   13. $4\frac{2}{5}$ 15. $1\frac{1}{3}$ 17. $8\frac{1}{4}$ 19. $11\frac{1}{2}$
21. 11   23. $4\frac{3}{5}$ 25. $\frac{3}{4}$ **page 629**   1. $\frac{9}{20}$ 3. 4   5. $\frac{5}{12}$
7. $\frac{1}{25}$ 9. $\frac{1}{16}$ 11. $3\frac{5}{9}$ 13. $7\frac{1}{2}$ 15. $43\frac{3}{4}$ 17. $1\frac{3}{8}$ 19. $\frac{7}{8}$
21. $1\frac{3}{8}$ 23. $\frac{1}{81}$ 25. 6   27. $\frac{9}{40}$ 29. $1\frac{3}{4}$ 31. $\frac{2}{5}$ 33. $11\frac{3}{4}$
35. $3\frac{4}{7}$ **page 630**   1. 6   3. 5   5. 3   7. 12   9. >   11. <
13. <   15. >   17. >   19. <   21. >   23. >   25. >   27. <
29. >   31. <   33. >

Index

INDEX

Hypotenuse, 460, 461, 469, 470
Hypothesis, exploring a, 444

Number patterns, 18
  exploring, 144
Number relationships, exploring, 250–251
Number sentences, models, 8
Numbers
  compatible, 105
  mixed, 188, 200, 206, 218
  natural, 195
  negative, 4, 8, 10, 300
  prime and composite, 163
  rational, 192–202
  relatively prime, 167
  square, 140
Numerator, 183, 185
Numerical expressions, 34–47, 54
  evaluating, 40–46

O

One-step inequalities, 296–299
Open equation, 54, 73
Operations
  inverse, 26, 72
  order of, 40–43, 56, 208
  properties of, 58–61
Opposite, 4
  integers, 4–5, 8, 9, 74
  solving equations, 112
  square/square roots, 452
Order of operations, 40–43, 56, 208
Ordered pairs, 316, 317, 320, 340
Origin, 316
Ounces, 260

P

Parallel lines, 363
Parallel planes, 363
Parallelograms
  area, 407–409, 414
  diagonal, 410
Pascal's triangle, 148
  exploring, 516–517
Pattern blocks, 182
Patterns, 19–21
  exploring, 424, 457
  in division, 110
  in scientific notation, 214
  number, 18, 144
  repeating decimal, 189
Percent(s), 244–248
  and decimals, 244, 245–246
  and equations, 256–259
  and fractions, 245
  as ratio, 244, 245, 253
  estimating, 244, 247

Percent(s) (cont.)
  exploring, 244
  models, 244
  of change, 260–263
  proportions and, 245, 252–255
Perfect number, 161
Perimeter, 327, 390–393
Periodic table, 296
Pi (π), 389, 390, 391, 414, 431
  exploring, 389
Pick's theorem, exploring, 418–419
Planes
  parallel, 363
  properties, 362
  symbol, 362. *See also* Coordinate plane
Point
  center of circle, 377
  intersections as, 363
  properties, 362
  symbol, 362
Polygons, 370–372
  convex and concave, 370
  naming, 371
  regular, 371
Polyhedrons, 420
Polynomials, 536–541
  addition and subtraction, 542–545
  exploring, 536–537
  multiplication by monomials, 546–548
Pound, 260
Powers, 141, 145, 146, 546,
  of ten, 149
Prime factorization, 163–166, 167
Prime numbers, 163
  classification, 166
Principal square root, 454
Prisms, 420
  base, 420
  lateral area, 427
  surface area, 427
  types, 420
  volume, 437–440, 441
Probability, 512–515
  dependent events, 523
  exploring, Pascal's triangle, 516–517
  independent events, 522
  Monte Carlo simulation, 518–519
Problem solving applications
  buying a car, 305–307
  direct and indirect variation, 353–355
  ecology, 87–89
  fitness and health, 31–33
  making predictions, 527–529
  parade floats, 433–435

Problem solving applications (cont.)
  precision drawing, 477–479
  scale drawing, 241–243
  simulations, 518–519
  stock market, 222–224
  tessellations, 397–399
  using matrices, 555–557
  using the metric system, 125–127
  water resources, 153–155
Problem solving practice, 47, 91, 124, 175, 225, 267, 283, 337, 396, 445, 481, 526, 561
Problem solving strategies
  account for all possibilities, 172–174
  draw a diagram, 264–266, 394–395
  guess and test, 85–86
  look for a pattern, 19–21
  make a model, 425–426
  multiple strategies, 558
  simplify the problem, 132
  simulating a problem, 458–459, 518–520
  solve by graphing, 334–337
  working backwards, 203–204
  writing equations, 284–286
Product, 22, 34, 146
Projects, 6, 7, 12, 29, 30, 39, 75, 82, 84, 89, 90, 113, 119, 123, 131, 144, 151, 152, 155, 158, 187, 191, 205, 214, 220, 232, 235, 239, 240, 249, 263, 299, 304, 319, 323, 333, 336, 351, 364, 383, 387, 388, 409, 423, 429, 436, 439, 480, 497, 504, 505, 507, 515, 521, 525, 554
Properties
  addition and subtraction for inequalities, 296
  addition and subtraction of equality, 72–75, 111
  algebraic, 287
  associative, 58–59, 108
  commutative, 58–59, 108
  distributive, 62–65, 108, 279, 288, 546, 550
  identity, 59
  line, 362
  multiplication and division for inequalities, 297
  multiplication and division of equality, 76–79, 115
  plane, 362
  point, 362
  ray, 362
  segment, 362
Proportions, 233–236, 384
  and percents, 245, 252–255
  same units, 237

INDEX

INDEX

Acknowledgments

PHOTO CREDITS

KEY TO PHOTO SOURCE ABBREVIATIONS
Bruce Coleman, Inc.= BC; Freelance Photographers Guild
= FPG; Ken Karp = KK; Russ Lappa = RL; Larry Lawfer
= LL; Picture Cube = PC; PhotoEdit = PE; Photo
Researchers, Inc. = PR; Tom Stack & Associates = TSA;
Stock Market = SM; Tony Stone Worldwide = TSW;
Woodfin Camp & Associates = WC.

KEY TO PHOTO POSITION ON TEXT PAGE
T=Top; **M**=Middle; **B**=Bottom; **L**=Left; **R**=Right.

Back Cover: Top, James H. Carmichael/BC; Center, PR;
Bottom, Hank Morgan/PR.

Front Matter: i T, Photo by Mark Richards; **i B,** Hank
Morgan/PR; **vi TR,** Patrick Aventurier/Gamma-Liaison;
vi BL, Rolf Sorensen/TSW; **vii TMR,** Nancy Sheehan;
vii TR, Chris Hackett/The Image Bank; **viii TL,** Tony
Freeman/PE; **ix TL,** David Ball/SM; **ix BR,** TSW; **x MR,**
J. J. Raynal/PR; **xi TM,** Brownie Harris/SM; **xi BL,**
European Space Agency/PR.

CHAPTER ONE 2, Annie Griffiths/BC; **2-3,** PR; **3,** Rolf
Sorensen/TSW; **4,** Keith Lanpher; **9,** Richard Haynes;
13, David Madison/BC; **17,** David Austen/TSW; **23,**
Greg Vaughn/TSA; **30,** Thomas Braise/SM; **33,** FPG; **40,**
Bob Daemmrich/TSW; **42,** Photo by Mark Richards; **47,**
Jack Finch/PR.

CHAPTER TWO 52 M, Armando Jenik/The Image Bank;
52 B, Carl Roessler/Animals Animals; **52 MR,** Carl
Roessler/FPG; **52-53,** John L. Pontier/Animals Animals;
53, FPG; **61 T,** Clyde H. Smith/FPG; **61 (inset),** Lee Foster/
FPG; **67,** The Granger Collection; **69,** Peter Menzel; **71,**
LL; **76,** Michael Melford/The Image Bank; **80,** LL/PC;
89, Arnold John Kaplan/PC; **90,** Brownie Harris/SM.

CHAPTER THREE 96, Patrick Aventurier/Gamma-
Liaison; **96-97,** Nancy Sheehan; **97 T, B,** Nancy Sheehan;
98, LL; 99, Meral Dabcovich; **100,** Jack Dermid/BC; **102,**
The Granger Collection; **111,** FPG; **115,** Steve Ogden/TS;
119, Pete Saloutos/SM; **120,** Peter Steiner/SM; **124,**
TSW; **127 T,** Bob and Clara Calhoun/BC; **127 B,** Meral
Dabcovich; **129,** UPI/Bettmann Newsphotos; **133,** Doug
Armand/TSW.

CHAPTER FOUR 139 T, Peter Miller/The Image Bank;
139 BR, Chris Hackett/The Image Bank; **139 (inset),**
Nancy Sheehan; **141,** Robert Knauft/PR; **144,**
M. Richards/PE; **150,** FPG; **152,** NASA; **155,** KK; **156,**
Michal Heron/WC; **167, 168,** KK.

CHAPTER FIVE 180, Milton Feinberg/PC; **180-181,**
Dave Schaefer/PC; **181, LL; 181 T,** Richard Anders/
FPG; **181 B,** Phil Degginger/BC; **183,** Richard Haynes;
187, LL; 189, KK; **192,** Kim Taylor/BC; **195,** Sarah
Putnam/PC; **196,** Mackson/FPG; **198,** Photo by Mark
Richards; **199,** Franz Lazi/FPG; **205,** Michael Keller/
FPG; **206,** TSW; **211,** Chris Bjornberg/PR; **213,** Photo by
Mark Richards; **214,** Thomas Kitchin/TS; **218,** Meral
Dabcovich; **223,** Alan Klehr/TSW; **228,** Ken Karp.

CHAPTER SIX 230, Tony Freeman/PE; **231,** David
Young-Wolff/PE; **232,** KK; **236,** Kindra Clineff PC; **237,**
Zur Veroffentlichung/FPG; **240,** Robert Huntzinger/SM;
243 T, LL; **243 B,** Nancy Sheehan; **245,** Michal Heron/
WC; **248,** Brian Seed/TSW; **249,** Steve Liss/Gamma-
Liaison; **250-251,** Richard Hutchings/ InfoEdit; **252,**
Martin Rogers/TSW; **259,** LL; **260,** Richard Laird/FPG;
265, Nancy Sheehan; **266,** Joe Baraban/SM.

CHAPTER SEVEN 272, John Blaustein/WC; **272-273,**
Joe Tower/SM; **273,** Chris Sorenson/SM; **274,** Richard
Haynes; **276,** J. H. Robinson/PR; **279,** Tom Campbell/
FPG; **282,** T. J. Florian/Rainbow; **284,** Scott Deitrich/
TSW; **292,** Gary Buss/FPG; **295,** Frank Siteman/PC;
296, Novosti/Science Photo Library/PR; **300,** Jon
Feingersh/TSA; **303,** Alan Carey/PR; **304,** Dick Luria/
FPG; **307,** Charles West/SM.

CHAPTER EIGHT 312, Tom Bean/SM; **312-313,** The
Granger Collection; **313,** Jeffry Myers/FPG; **314 (all),**
RL; **315,** Richard Haynes; **318,** Keith Olson/TSW; **320,**
TSW; **323,** Charles Seaborn/WC; **329,** Cathlyn Melloan/
TSW; **333,** Wesley Bocxe/PR; **335,** Peter Gridley/FPG;
336, David Young-Wolff/PE; **337,** David Young-
Wolff/PE; **338, 339 L,** Lily Yamamoto; **339 R,**
European Space Agency/Science Photo Library/PR;
344, Tony Freeman/PE; **346,** All photos by Mark
Richards; **352,** Richard Hutchings/PR; **354,** J.
Mejuto/FPG; **355,** KK.

CHAPTER NINE **361,** Henley and Savage/TSW; **360-361,** Nancy Sheehan; **360,** David Ball/SM; **362,** D. Wilder/TSA; **367,** S.L. Craig/BC; **369 (all),** RL; **370,** John Lamb/TSW; **374,** David Ball/PC; **377 T,** Stanley Rowin/PC; **377 B,** Dr. Jeremy Burgess/Science Photo Library/PR; **380,** Tony Freeman/PE; **383 L,** Ray Coleman/PR; **383 M,** Brian Parker/TSA; **383 R,** Michael Keller/SM; **384,** Dan McCoy/Rainbow; **388,** Paulette Brunner/TSA; **389,** FPG; **394,** Vandystadt/PR; **395,** Michael Dunn/SM; **397,** Art Resource; **399,** Aga Khan Program Archives, M.I.T., Photo by George J. Kostaras, 1983.

CHAPTER TEN **404,** FPG; **404-405,** FPG; **405,** TSW; **406,** RL; **411,** Tom Tracy/FPG; **414,** David Ball/PC; **415,** Meral Dabcovich; **417,** Photo by Mark Richards; **418, 419 (all),** RL; **421,** Richard Haynes; **430,** Hugh Sitton/TSW; **431 L,** Frank Cezus/FPG; **431 R,** Bob Brudd/TSW; **432,** Alan Smith/TSW; **434,** R. B. Sanchez/SM; **435 T,** Joe Sohn/SM; **436,** Dan McCoy/Rainbow; **439,** Photo by Mark Richards; **440,** The Granger Collection; **441,** Tom Tracy/FPG; **443,** RL; **445,** José Carrillo/TSW.

CHAPTER ELEVEN **450,** Tom Sanders/SM; **450-451,** J. J. Raynal/PR; **451,** Richard Burda/FPG; **455,** RL; **457,** Bill Sanderson/Science Photo Library/PR; **458,** John Terence Turner/FPG; **459,** Henley and Savage/TSW; **461,** Photoworld/FPG; **468,** K&G Photo/FPG; **477,** David Jeffrey/The Image Bank; **479,** Stock Imagery; **480,** Bill Losh/FPG; **482,** J. J. Raynal/PR.

CHAPTER TWELVE **486 T,** Tim Davis/Duomo; **486 B,** **487,** David Madison/Duomo; **491,** Morris Lane/SM; **492,** David Conklin/PE; **503,** Mitchell Layton/Duomo; **504,** David Weintraub/PR; **507 T, B,** Richard Haynes; **508,** David Madison/Duomo; **513,** KK; **514,** Bob Peterson/FPG; **521,** Tom Tracy/FPG; **527,** Bonnie L. Lange/Stock Imagery; **528,** Alan Carey/PR; **529,** KK.

CHAPTER THIRTEEN **534,** FPG; **535,** Stock Imagery; **537,** Richard Haynes; **545 T,** The Bettmann Archive; **545 B,** Robert P. Morrison/FPG; **546 T, B,** John Gillmoure/SM; **550,** The Granger Collection; **554,** Ed Lettau/FPG; **560,** KK; **561,** NASA/SB/FPG.

ILLUSTRATION CREDITS

Technical art by York Graphic Services, Inc., Synergy 2000 Series.

Bob Barner: 42, 86, 148, 198, 213, 281, 346, 417, 439

Eliot Bergman: 12, 25, 31, 53, 84, 103, 113, 128, 138, 139, 154, 181, 191, 221, 255, 259, 267, 299, 378, 396

Boston Graphics, Inc.: 17, 18, 27, 79, 150, 230, 231, 242, 264, 316, 360, 413, 423, 451, 465, 476, 486, 496, 500, 534, 545

John W. Cataldo: 450

Donald Doyle: 246

Function Thru Form, Inc., Guilbert Gates and Kathleen Katims: 241, 272, 312, 313, 404

Andrea Grassi: Decision Making logo, 458: figure icons, 313: Statue of Liberty icon

Mark Herman: 44, 110, 173, 217, 275, 319, 334, 363, 425, 433, 442, 469, 489, 557

Fran Jarvis: 507: spinner, 460: grid designs, 487: 511: 534

Barbara Maslen: 21, 32, 63, 104, 117, 151, 184, 219, 278, 343, 390, 506, 515, 524

Eve Melnechuk: Problem Solving logo

Terry Presnall: Calculator logo, computer logo, 2, 6, 10, 11, 19, 20, 29, 34, 52, 66, 88, 96, 101, 107, 111, 130, 131, 145, 153, 163, 172, 180, 204, 215, 230, 231, 232, 233, 239, 246, 247, 263, 273, 290, 312, 317, 361, 383, 385, 387, 416, 460, 487, 495, 499, 502, 519, 522, 534, 542, 543

Susan Spellman: 121, 287, 345, 517, 539, 559

Gary Torrisi: 2, 14, 46, 58, 72, 156, 157, 158, 210, 225, 330, 364, 404, 405, 420, 428, 438, 464, 497, 510, 535, 552

C. A. Trachok: 43, 75, 82, 100, 108, 123, 170, 174, 286, 351, 487, 511, 520

Cameron Wasson: 37, 54, 114, 203, 220, 235, 250, 251, 264, 285, 347, 426, 444, 453, 472, 509, 523, 538, 557

Any photo or illustration acknowledgment inadvertently omitted will be amended upon notification.

Skills Handbook

Contents

Skills Handbook

Decimals and Place Value

Each digit in a whole number or a decimal has both a place and a value. The value of any place is one tenth the value of the place to its left. The chart below can help you read and write decimals.

billions	hundred millions	ten millions	millions	hundred thousands	ten thousands	thousands	hundreds	tens	ones	.	tenths	hundredths	thousandths	ten-thousandths	hundred-thousandths	millionths
2	4	0	1	2	6	2	8	3	0	.	7	5	0	1	9	1

■ EXAMPLE

a. **What is the value of the digit 8 in the number above?**
The digit 8 is in the hundreds place.
So, its value is 8 hundreds.

b. **Write 2.006 in words.**

The digit 6 is in the thousandths place.
The answer is two and six thousandths.

c. **Write five and thirty-four ten-thousandths as a decimal.**
Ten-thousandths is 4 places to the right of the decimal point.
So, the decimal will have 4 places after the decimal point.
The answer is 5.0034.

EXERCISES *On Your Own*

Use the chart above. Write the value of each digit.

1. the digit 9

2. the digit 7

3. the digit 5

4. the digit 6

5. the digit 4

6. the digit 3

Write a decimal for the given words.

7. forty-one ten-thousandths

8. eighteen and five hundred four thousandths

9. eight millionths

10. seven and sixty-three hundred-thousandths

11. twelve thousandths

12. sixty-five and two hundred one thousandths

Write each decimal in words.

13. 0.06

14. 4.7

15. 0.00011

16. 0.9

17. 0.012

18. 0.000059

19. 0.0042

20. 6.029186

Comparing and Ordering Decimals

To compare two decimals, use the symbols > (is greater than), < (is less than), or = (is equal to). When you compare, start at the left and compare the digits.

■ EXAMPLE 1

Use >, <, or = to compare the decimals.

a. **0.1 ■ 0.06**
   1 tenth > 0 tenths, so
   0.1 > 0.06

b. **2.4583 ■ 2.48**
   5 hundredths < 8 hundredths,
   so 2.4583 < 2.48

c. **0.30026 ■ 0.03026**
   3 tenths > 0 tenths, so
   0.30026 > 0.03026

■ EXAMPLE 2

Draw number lines to compare the decimals.

a. **0.1 ■ 0.06**

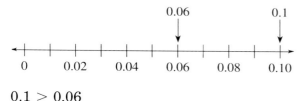

0.1 > 0.06

b. **2.4583 ■ 2.48**

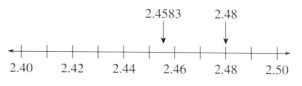

2.4583 < 2.48

EXERCISES *On Your Own*

Use >, <, or = to compare the decimals. Draw number lines if you wish.

1. 0.003 ■ 0.02
2. 84.2 ■ 842
3. 0.162 ■ 0.106
4. 0.0659 ■ 0.6059

5. 2.13 ■ 2.99
6. 3.53 ■ 3.529
7. 02.01 ■ 02.010
8. 0.00072 ■ 0.07002

9. 0.458 ■ 0.4589
10. 8.627 ■ 8.649
11. 0.0019 ■ 0.0002
12. 0.19321 ■ 0.19231

Write the decimals in order from least to greatest.

13. 2.31, 0.231, 23.1, 0.23, 3.21

14. 1.02, 1.002, 1.2, 1.11, 1.021

15. 0.02, 0.002, 0.22, 0.222, 2.22

16. 55.5, 555.5, 55.555, 5.5555

17. 0.07, 0.007, 0.7, 0.71, 0.72

18. 2.78, 2.7001, 2.701, 2.71, 2.7

19. 7, 7.3264, 7.3, 7.3246, 7.0324

20. 0.0101, 0.0099, 0.011, 0.00019

Rounding

When you round to a particular place, look at the digit to the right of that place. If it is 5 or more, the digit in the place you are rounding to will increase by 1. If it is less than 5, the digit in the place you are rounding to will stay the same.

■ EXAMPLE

a. Round 1.627 to the nearest whole number.
The digit to the right of the units place is 6, so 1.627 rounds up to 2.

b. Round 12,034 to the nearest thousand.
The digit to the right of the thousands place is 0, so 12,034 rounds down to 12,000.

c. Round 2.7195 to the nearest hundredth.
The digit to the right of the hundredths place is 9, so 2.7195 rounds up to 2.72.

d. Round 0.060521 to the nearest thousandth.
The digit to the right of the thousandths place is 5, so 0.060521 rounds up to 0.061.

EXERCISES *On Your Own*

Round to the nearest thousand.

1. 105,099   2. 10,400   3. 79,527,826   4. 79,932   5. 4,312,349

Round to the nearest whole number.

6. 135.91   7. 3.001095   8. 96.912   9. 101.167   10. 299.9

Round to the nearest tenth.

11. 82.01   12. 4.67522   13. 20.397   14. 399.95   15. 129.98

Round to the nearest hundredth.

16. 13.458   17. 96.4045   18. 0.699   19. 4.23   20. 12.09531

Round to the place of the underlined digit.

21. 7.0615   22. 5.77125   23. 1,522   24. 0.91952   25. 4.243

26. 236.001   27. 352   28. 3.495366   29. 8.07092   30. 0.6008

31. 409   32. 23,951,888   33. 2.5784   34. 862   35. 19.32

36. 918   37. 7,735   38. 25.66047   39. 983,240,631   40. 27

41. 0.003771   42. 0.0649   43. 12.777   44. 1,759,230   45. 20,908

Adding and Subtracting Decimals

You add or subtract decimals just as you do whole numbers. You line up the decimal points and then add or subtract. If you wish, you can use zeros to make the columns even.

■ EXAMPLE

Find each sum or difference.

a. 37.6 + 8.431

$$
\begin{array}{r} 37.6 \\ +\ 8.431 \\ \hline \end{array} \rightarrow
\begin{array}{r} 37.600 \\ +\ 8.431 \\ \hline 46.031 \end{array}
$$

b. 8 − 4.593

$$
\begin{array}{r} 8 \\ -4.593 \\ \hline \end{array} \rightarrow
\begin{array}{r} 8.000 \\ -4.593 \\ \hline 3.407 \end{array}
$$

c. 8.3 + 2.99 + 17.5

$$
\begin{array}{r} 8.3 \\ 2.99 \\ +17.5 \\ \hline \end{array} \rightarrow
\begin{array}{r} 8.30 \\ 2.99 \\ +17.50 \\ \hline 28.79 \end{array}
$$

EXERCISES *On Your Own*

Find each sum or difference.

1. $\begin{array}{r} 39.7 \\ -36.03 \\ \hline \end{array}$ **2.** $\begin{array}{r} 1.08 \\ -0.9 \\ \hline \end{array}$ **3.** $\begin{array}{r} 6.784 \\ +0.528 \\ \hline \end{array}$ **4.** $\begin{array}{r} 5.01 \\ -0.87 \\ \hline \end{array}$ **5.** $\begin{array}{r} 13.02 \\ +23.107 \\ \hline \end{array}$

6. $\begin{array}{r} 8.634 \\ +1.409 \\ \hline \end{array}$ **7.** $\begin{array}{r} 2.1 \\ -0.5 \\ \hline \end{array}$ **8.** $\begin{array}{r} 8.23 \\ -3.1 \\ \hline \end{array}$ **9.** $\begin{array}{r} 1.0 \\ 5 \end{array}$ **10.** $\begin{array}{r} 2.6 \\ +0.003 \\ \hline \end{array}$

11. $\begin{array}{r} 0.1 \\ 58.21 \\ +\ 1.9 \\ \hline \end{array}$ **12.** $\begin{array}{r} 12.2 \\ 3.06 \\ +\ 0.5 \\ \hline \end{array}$ **13.** $\begin{array}{r} 9.42 \\ 3.6 \\ +21.003 \\ \hline \end{array}$ **14.** $\begin{array}{r} 15.22 \\ 7.4 \\ +\ 8.125 \\ \hline \end{array}$ **15.** $\begin{array}{r} 3.7 \\ 20.06 \\ +16.19 \\ \hline \end{array}$

16. 76.39 − 8.47

17. 8.7 + 17.03

18. 32.403 + 12.06

19. 20.5 + 11.45

20. 8.9 − 4.45

21. 1.245 + 5.8

22. 3.9 + 6.57

23. 14.81 − 8.6

24. 11.9 − 2.06

25. 3.45 + 4.061

26. 8.29 + 4.3

27. 7.06 − 4.235

28. 6.02 + 4.005

29. 7.05 − 3.5

30. 1.18 + 3.015

31. 2.304 − 0.87

32. 5.002 − 3.45

33. 6.8 + 3.57

34. 0.23 + 0.091

35. 0.5 − 0.18

36. 8.3 + 2.99 + 17.52

37. 9.5 + 12.32 + 6.4

38. 4.521 + 1.8 + 3.07

39. 3.602 + 9.4 + 24

40. 11.6 + 8.05 + 5.13

41. 7.023 + 1.48 + 3.9

42. 57 + 0.6327 + 189.007

43. 741 + 6.08 + 0.0309

44. 0.045 + 16.32 + 8.6

45. 4.27 + 6.18 + 0.91

46. 3.856 + 14.01 + 1.72

47. 11.45 + 3.79 + 23.861

Multiplying Decimals

Multiply decimals as you would whole numbers. Then place the decimal point in the product. To do this, add the number of decimal places in the factors.

■ **EXAMPLE 1**

Multiply 0.068 × 2.3.

Step 1: Multiply.

```
  0.068
× 2.3
  204
+1360
 1564
```

Step 2: Place the decimal point.

```
  0.068   ←— three decimal places
× 2.3     ←— one decimal place
  204
+1360
 0.1564   ←— four decimal places
```

■ **EXAMPLE 2**

Find each product.

a. **3.12 × 0.9**

```
  3.12
× 0.9
  2.808
```

b. **5.75 × 42**

```
   5.75
×   42
  11 50
+230 00
 241.50
```

c. **0.964 × 0.28**

```
  0.964
× 0.28
  7712
+19280
 0.26992
```

EXERCISES *On Your Own*

Multiply.

1.
```
  1.48
× 3.6
```

2.
```
 191.2
× 3.4
```

3.
```
 0.05
× 43
```

4.
```
 0.27
× 5
```

5.
```
 1.36
× 3.8
```

6.
```
 6.23
×0.21
```

7.
```
 0.512
× 0.76
```

8.
```
 0.04
× 7
```

9.
```
 0.136
× 8.4
```

10.
```
     3
×0.05
```

11. 2.07×1.004

12. 0.12×6.1

13. 3.2×0.15

14. 0.74×0.23

15. 2.6×0.14

16. 0.77×51

17. 9.3×0.706

18. 71.13×0.4

19. 0.42×98

20. 6.3×85

21. 45×0.028

22. 76×3.3

23. 9×1.35

24. 4.56×7

25. 5×2.41

26. 704×0.3

27. 8.003×0.6

28. 42.2×0.9

29. 0.6×30.02

30. 0.05×11.8

Zeros in a Product

When you multiply with decimals, you may have to write one or more zeros to the left of a product before you can place the decimal point.

■ EXAMPLE 1

Multiply 0.06 × 0.015.

Step 1: Multiply.

$$\begin{array}{r} 0.015 \\ \times\ 0.06 \\ \hline 90 \end{array}$$

Step 2: Place the decimal point.

$$\begin{array}{r} 0.015 \\ \times\ 0.06 \\ \hline 0.00090 \end{array}$$

← The product should have 5 decimal places, so you must write three zeros before placing the decimal point.

■ EXAMPLE 2

a. **0.02 × 1.3**

$$\begin{array}{r} 1.3 \\ \times 0.02 \\ \hline 0.026 \end{array}$$

b. **0.012 × 2.4**

$$\begin{array}{r} 2.4 \\ \times 0.012 \\ \hline 48 \\ +240 \\ \hline 0.0288 \end{array}$$

c. **0.022 × 0.051**

$$\begin{array}{r} 0.051 \\ \times 0.022 \\ \hline 102 \\ +1020 \\ \hline 0.00112 \end{array}$$

EXERCISES *On Your Own*

Multiply.

1. $\begin{array}{r} 0.03 \\ \times\ 0.9 \\ \hline \end{array}$

2. $\begin{array}{r} 0.06 \\ \times\ 0.5 \\ \hline \end{array}$

3. $\begin{array}{r} 2.4 \\ \times 0.03 \\ \hline \end{array}$

4. $\begin{array}{r} 7 \\ \times 0.01 \\ \hline \end{array}$

5. $\begin{array}{r} 0.05 \\ \times 0.05 \\ \hline \end{array}$

6. $\begin{array}{r} 0.016 \\ \times\ 0.12 \\ \hline \end{array}$

7. $\begin{array}{r} 0.031 \\ \times\ 0.08 \\ \hline \end{array}$

8. $\begin{array}{r} 0.03 \\ \times\ 0.2 \\ \hline \end{array}$

9. $\begin{array}{r} 0.27 \\ \times 0.033 \\ \hline \end{array}$

10. $\begin{array}{r} 0.014 \\ \times\ 0.25 \\ \hline \end{array}$

11. 0.003×0.55

12. 0.01×0.74

13. 0.47×0.08

14. 0.76×0.1

15. 0.3×0.27

16. 0.19×0.05

17. 0.018×0.04

18. 0.43×0.2

19. 0.03×0.03

20. 4.003×0.02

21. 0.5×0.08

22. 0.06×0.7

23. 0.047×0.008

24. 0.05×0.06

25. 0.03×0.4

26. 0.05×0.036

27. 0.4×0.23

28. 0.3×0.017

29. 0.3×0.24

30. 0.67×0.09

31. 3.02×0.006

32. 0.31×0.08

33. 0.14×0.05

34. 0.07×0.85

Dividing Decimals by Whole Numbers

When you divide a decimal by a whole number, the decimal point in the quotient goes directly above the decimal point in the dividend. You may need extra zeros to place the decimal point.

■ EXAMPLE 1

Divide 2.432 ÷ 32.

Step 1: Divide.

$$
\begin{array}{r}
76 \\
32\overline{)2.432} \\
-2\,24 \\
\hline
192 \\
-192 \\
\hline
0
\end{array}
$$

Step 2: Place the decimal point.

$$
\begin{array}{r}
0.076 \\
32\overline{)2.432} \\
-2\,24 \\
\hline
192 \\
-192 \\
\hline
0
\end{array}
$$

←— You need two extra zeros to get the decimal point in the correct place.

■ EXAMPLE 2

a. 37.6 ÷ 8

$$
\begin{array}{r}
4.7 \\
8\overline{)37.6} \\
-32 \\
\hline
5\,6 \\
-5\,6 \\
\hline
0
\end{array}
$$

b. 39.33 ÷ 69

$$
\begin{array}{r}
0.57 \\
69\overline{)39.33} \\
-34\,5 \\
\hline
4\,83 \\
-4\,83 \\
\hline
0
\end{array}
$$

c. 4.482 ÷ 54

$$
\begin{array}{r}
0.083 \\
54\overline{)4.482} \\
-4\,32 \\
\hline
162 \\
-162 \\
\hline
0
\end{array}
$$

EXERCISES *On Your Own*

Divide.

1. $7\overline{)17.92}$
2. $5\overline{)16.5}$
3. $9\overline{)6.984}$
4. $6\overline{)91.44}$
5. $4\overline{)35.16}$

6. $56\overline{)8.848}$
7. $22\overline{)2.42}$
8. $26\overline{)1723.8}$
9. $83\overline{)15.272}$
10. $39\overline{)26.91}$

11. $14.49 \div 7$
12. $10.53 \div 9$
13. $17.52 \div 2$
14. $37.14 \div 6$

15. $0.1352 \div 8$
16. $0.0324 \div 9$
17. $0.0882 \div 6$
18. $0.8682 \div 6$

19. $12.342 \div 22$
20. $29.792 \div 32$
21. $22.568 \div 26$
22. $11.340 \div 36$

23. $45.918 \div 18$
24. $79.599 \div 13$
25. $59.7 \div 15$
26. $74.664 \div 12$

27. $2.1 \div 84$
28. $89.378 \div 67$
29. $0.0672 \div 48$
30. $171.031 \div 53$

Multiplying and Dividing by Powers of Ten

You can use shortcuts to multiply or divide by powers of ten.

When you multiply by	Move the decimal point	When you divide by	Move the decimal point
10,000	4 places to the right	10,000	4 places to the left
1,000	3 places to the right	1,000	3 places to the left
100	2 places to the right	100	2 places to the left
10	1 place to the right	10	1 place to the left
0.1	1 place to the left	0.1	1 place to the right
0.01	2 places to the left	0.01	2 places to the right
0.001	3 places to the left	0.001	3 places to the right

■ EXAMPLE

Multiply or divide.

a. **0.7×0.001**
   Move the decimal point 3 places to the left.
   0.000.7
   $0.7 \times 0.001 = 0.0007$

b. **$0.605 \div 100$**
   Move the decimal point 2 places to the left.
   0.00.605
   $0.605 \div 100 = 0.00605$

EXERCISES *On Your Own*

Multiply or divide.

1. $10,000 \times 0.056$ 2. 0.001×0.09 3. 5.2×10 4. $0.03 \times 1,000$

5. $236.7 \div 0.1$ 6. $45.28 \div 10$ 7. $0.9 \div 1,000$ 8. $1.07 \div 0.01$

9. 100×0.08 10. $1.03 \times 10,000$ 11. 1.803×0.001 12. 4.1×100

13. $13.7 \div 0.001$ 14. $203.05 \div 0.01$ 15. $4.7 \div 10$ 16. $0.05 \div 100$

17. 23.6×0.01 18. $1,000 \times 0.12$ 19. 0.41×0.001 20. 0.01×6.2

21. $42.3 \div 0.1$ 22. $0.4 \div 10,000$ 23. $5.02 \div 0.01$ 24. $16.5 \div 100$

25. $0.27 \div 0.01$ 26. 1.05×0.001 27. 10×0.04 28. $2.09 \div 100$

29. 0.65×0.1 30. $0.03 \div 100$ 31. $2.6 \div 0.1$ 32. $12.6 \times 10,000$

33. $0.3 \div 1,000$ 34. 0.01×6.7 35. 100×0.158 36. $23.1 \div 10$

Dividing Decimals by Decimals

To divide with a decimal divisor, multiply it by the smallest power of ten that will make the divisor a whole number. Then multiply the dividend by that same power of ten.

■ **EXAMPLE**

Find each quotient.

a. $3.348 \div 6.2$
Multiply by 10.

$$
\begin{array}{r}
0.54 \\
6.2.\overline{)3\,3.48} \\
-3\,1\,0 \\
\hline
2\,48 \\
-2\,48 \\
\hline
0
\end{array}
$$

b. $2.4885 \div 0.35$
Multiply by 100.

$$
\begin{array}{r}
7.11 \\
0.35.\overline{)2\,48.85} \\
-2\,45 \\
\hline
3\,8 \\
-3\,5 \\
\hline
35 \\
-35 \\
\hline
0
\end{array}
$$

c. $0.0576 \div 0.012$
Multiply by 1,000.

$$
\begin{array}{r}
4.8 \\
0.012.\overline{)0\,057.6} \\
-48 \\
\hline
9\,6 \\
-9\,6 \\
\hline
0
\end{array}
$$

EXERCISES *On Your Own*

Divide.

1. $3.2\overline{)268.8}$

2. $1.9\overline{)123.5}$

3. $0.3\overline{)135.6}$

4. $2.3\overline{)170.2}$

5. $7.9\overline{)252.8}$

6. $5.7\overline{)10.26}$

7. $2.3\overline{)71.53}$

8. $3.1\overline{)16.12}$

9. $7.8\overline{)24.18}$

10. $6.3\overline{)14.49}$

11. $134.42 \div 5.17$

12. $89.96 \div 3.46$

13. $160.58 \div 5.18$

14. $106.59 \div 6.27$

15. $62.4 \div 3.9$

16. $260.4 \div 8.4$

17. $316.8 \div 7.2$

18. $162.4 \div 2.9$

19. $1.512 \div 0.54$

20. $3.225 \div 0.43$

21. $2.484 \div 0.69$

22. $511.5 \div 5.5$

23. $0.992 \div 0.8$

24. $4.53 \div 0.05$

25. $3.498 \div 0.06$

26. $59.2 \div 0.8$

27. $2.198 \div 0.07$

28. $14.28 \div 0.7$

29. $1.98 \div 0.5$

30. $26.36 \div 0.04$

31. $3.922 \div 7.4$

32. $23.52 \div 0.98$

33. $71.25 \div 7.5$

34. $114.7 \div 3.7$

35. $0.832 \div 0.52$

36. $1.125 \div 0.09$

37. $9.666 \div 2.7$

38. $1.456 \div 9.1$

39. $0.4374 \div 1.8$

40. $2.3414 \div 0.46$

41. $0.07224 \div 0.021$

42. $0.1386 \div 0.18$

43. $0.16926 \div 0.091$

44. $0.6042 \div 5.3$

45. $2.3374 \div 0.62$

46. $1.0062 \div 0.078$

Zeros in Decimal Division

When you are dividing by a decimal, sometimes you need to use extra zeros in the dividend or the quotient, or both.

■ **EXAMPLE 1**

Divide 0.045 ÷ 3.6.

Step 1: Multiply by 10.

$$3.6.\overline{)0.0.45}$$

Step 2: Divide.

$$
\begin{array}{r}
125 \\
3.6.\overline{)0.0.4500} \\
-36 \\
\hline
90 \\
-72 \\
\hline
180 \\
-180 \\
\hline
0
\end{array}
$$

Step 3: Place the decimal point.

$$
\begin{array}{r}
0.0125 \\
3.6.\overline{)0.0.4500} \\
-36 \\
\hline
90 \\
-72 \\
\hline
180 \\
-180 \\
\hline
0
\end{array}
$$

■ **EXAMPLE 2**

Find each quotient.

a. **0.4428 ÷ 8.2**
   Multiply by 10.

$$
\begin{array}{r}
0.054 \\
8.2.\overline{)0.4.428}
\end{array}
$$

b. **0.00434 ÷ 0.07**
   Multiply by 100.

$$
\begin{array}{r}
0.062 \\
0.07.\overline{)0.00.434}
\end{array}
$$

c. **0.00306 ÷ 0.072**
   Multiply by 1,000.

$$
\begin{array}{r}
0.0425 \\
0.072.\overline{)0.003.0600}
\end{array}
$$

EXERCISES *On Your Own*

Divide.

1. $0.05\overline{)0.0023}$
2. $0.02\overline{)0.000162}$
3. $0.12\overline{)0.009}$
4. $2.5\overline{)0.021}$

5. $0.0019 \div 0.2$
6. $0.9 \div 0.8$
7. $0.000175 \div 0.07$
8. $0.142 \div 0.04$

9. $0.0017 \div 0.02$
10. $0.003 \div 0.6$
11. $0.0105 \div 0.7$
12. $0.034 \div 0.05$

13. $0.00056 \div 0.16$
14. $0.0612 \div 7.2$
15. $0.217 \div 3.1$
16. $0.052 \div 0.8$

17. $0.000924 \div 0.44$
18. $0.05796 \div 0.63$
19. $0.00123 \div 8.2$
20. $0.0954 \div 0.09$

21. $0.0084 \div 1.4$
22. $0.259 \div 3.5$
23. $0.00468 \div 0.52$
24. $0.104 \div 0.05$

25. $0.00063 \div 0.18$
26. $0.011 \div 0.25$
27. $0.3069 \div 9.3$
28. $0.00045 \div 0.3$

29. $0.6497 \div 8.9$
30. $0.00246 \div 0.06$
31. $0.00168 \div 0.3$
32. $0.00816 \div 3.4$

Writing Equivalent Fractions

If you multiply or divide both numerator and denominator of a
fraction by the same number, you get an equivalent fraction.

■ **EXAMPLE 1**

a. Find the missing number in $\frac{5}{6} = \frac{20}{\blacksquare}$.

$$\overset{\times 4}{\frac{5}{6} = \frac{20}{\blacksquare}}$$

$$\underset{\times 4}{\frac{5}{6} = \frac{20}{24}}$$

b. Find the missing number in $\frac{12}{30} = \frac{\blacksquare}{15}$.

$$\overset{\div 2}{\frac{12}{30} = \frac{\blacksquare}{15}}$$

$$\underset{\div 2}{\frac{12}{30} = \frac{6}{15}}$$

To write a fraction in simplest form, divide both numerator and
denominator by the greatest common factor.

■ **EXAMPLE 2**

a. Write $\frac{6}{15}$ in simplest form.

3 is the greatest common factor.

$$\frac{6}{15} = \frac{6 \div 3}{15 \div 3} = \frac{2}{5}$$

The simplest form of $\frac{6}{15}$ is $\frac{2}{5}$.

b. Write $\frac{36}{42}$ in simplest form.

6 is the greatest common factor.

$$\frac{36}{42} = \frac{36 \div 6}{62 \div 6} = \frac{6}{7}$$

The simplest form of $\frac{36}{42}$ is $\frac{6}{7}$.

EXERCISES *On Your Own*

Find each missing number.

1. $\frac{1}{3} = \frac{\blacksquare}{6}$

2. $\frac{3}{4} = \frac{\blacksquare}{16}$

3. $\frac{18}{30} = \frac{6}{\blacksquare}$

4. $\frac{2}{3} = \frac{\blacksquare}{21}$

5. $\frac{3}{4} = \frac{9}{\blacksquare}$

6. $\frac{3}{10} = \frac{9}{\blacksquare}$

7. $\frac{4}{5} = \frac{\blacksquare}{30}$

8. $\frac{2}{3} = \frac{8}{\blacksquare}$

9. $\frac{33}{55} = \frac{\blacksquare}{5}$

10. $\frac{27}{72} = \frac{9}{\blacksquare}$

11. $\frac{2}{3} = \frac{\blacksquare}{24}$

12. $\frac{11}{12} = \frac{55}{\blacksquare}$

13. $\frac{3}{5} = \frac{18}{\blacksquare}$

14. $\frac{60}{72} = \frac{10}{\blacksquare}$

15. $\frac{7}{8} = \frac{\blacksquare}{24}$

Write each fraction in simplest form.

16. $\frac{12}{36}$

17. $\frac{25}{30}$

18. $\frac{14}{16}$

19. $\frac{27}{36}$

20. $\frac{21}{35}$

21. $\frac{40}{50}$

22. $\frac{24}{40}$

23. $\frac{32}{64}$

24. $\frac{15}{45}$

25. $\frac{27}{63}$

26. $\frac{44}{77}$

27. $\frac{45}{75}$

28. $\frac{60}{72}$

29. $\frac{77}{84}$

30. $\frac{12}{24}$

31. $\frac{24}{32}$

32. $\frac{7}{21}$

33. $\frac{18}{42}$

34. $\frac{35}{49}$

35. $\frac{18}{81}$

36. $\frac{6}{18}$

37. $\frac{28}{56}$

38. $\frac{10}{25}$

39. $\frac{16}{28}$

Mixed Numbers and Improper Fractions

A fraction, such as $\frac{10}{7}$, in which the numerator is greater than or equal to the denominator is an improper fraction. You can write an improper fraction as a mixed number that shows the sum of a whole number and a fraction.

Sometimes it is necessary to do the opposite and write a mixed number as an improper fraction.

■ EXAMPLE

a. Write $\frac{11}{5}$ as a mixed number.

$$\frac{11}{5} \rightarrow \begin{array}{r} 2 \leftarrow \text{whole number} \\ 5\overline{)11} \\ -10 \\ \hline 1 \leftarrow \text{remainder} \end{array}$$

$$\frac{11}{5} = 2\frac{1}{5} \leftarrow \text{whole number} + \frac{\text{remainder}}{\text{denominator}}$$

b. Write $2\frac{5}{6}$ as an improper fraction.

$$2\frac{5}{6} = 2 + \frac{5}{6}$$
$$= \frac{12}{6} + \frac{5}{6} \leftarrow \text{Write 2 as } \frac{12}{6}.$$
$$= \frac{12+5}{6} \leftarrow \text{Add the numerators.}$$
$$2\frac{5}{6} = \frac{17}{6}$$

EXERCISES *On Your Own*

Write each improper fraction as a mixed number.

1. $\frac{7}{5}$ 2. $\frac{9}{2}$ 3. $\frac{13}{4}$ 4. $\frac{21}{5}$ 5. $\frac{13}{10}$ 6. $\frac{49}{5}$

7. $\frac{21}{8}$ 8. $\frac{13}{7}$ 9. $\frac{17}{5}$ 10. $\frac{49}{6}$ 11. $\frac{17}{4}$ 12. $\frac{5}{2}$

13. $\frac{27}{5}$ 14. $\frac{12}{9}$ 15. $\frac{30}{8}$ 16. $\frac{37}{12}$ 17. $\frac{8}{6}$ 18. $\frac{19}{12}$

19. $\frac{45}{10}$ 20. $\frac{15}{12}$ 21. $\frac{11}{2}$ 22. $\frac{20}{6}$ 23. $\frac{34}{8}$ 24. $\frac{21}{9}$

Write each mixed number as an improper fraction.

25. $1\frac{1}{2}$ 26. $2\frac{2}{3}$ 27. $1\frac{1}{12}$ 28. $3\frac{1}{5}$ 29. $2\frac{2}{7}$ 30. $4\frac{1}{2}$

31. $2\frac{7}{8}$ 32. $1\frac{2}{9}$ 33. $5\frac{1}{5}$ 34. $4\frac{7}{9}$ 35. $9\frac{1}{4}$ 36. $2\frac{3}{8}$

37. $7\frac{7}{8}$ 38. $1\frac{5}{12}$ 39. $3\frac{3}{7}$ 40. $6\frac{1}{2}$ 41. $3\frac{1}{10}$ 42. $4\frac{6}{7}$

Adding and Subtracting Fractions with Like Denominators

When you add or subtract fractions with the same denominator, add or subtract the numerators and then write the answer over the denominator.

■ EXAMPLE 1

Add or subtract. Write the answers in simplest form.

a. $\frac{5}{8} + \frac{7}{8}$

$\frac{5}{8} + \frac{7}{8} = \frac{5+7}{8} = \frac{12}{8} = 1\frac{4}{8} = 1\frac{1}{2}$

b. $\frac{11}{12} - \frac{2}{12}$

$\frac{11}{12} - \frac{2}{12} = \frac{11-2}{12} = \frac{9}{12} = \frac{3}{4}$

To add or subtract mixed numbers, add or subtract the fractions first. Then add or subtract the whole numbers.

■ EXAMPLE 2

Add or subtract. Write the answers in simplest form.

a. $3\frac{4}{6} + 2\frac{5}{6}$

$\begin{aligned} 3\frac{4}{6} \\ + 2\frac{5}{6} \\ \hline 5\frac{9}{6} = 5 + 1 + \frac{3}{6} = 6\frac{1}{2} \end{aligned}$

b. $6\frac{1}{4} - 1\frac{3}{4}$

$\begin{aligned} 6\frac{1}{4} && 5\frac{5}{4} \end{aligned}$ ← Rewrite 1 unit as as $\frac{4}{4}$ and add it to $\frac{1}{4}$.

$\begin{aligned} - 1\frac{3}{4} && \rightarrow && - 1\frac{3}{4} \\ \hline && && 4\frac{2}{4} = 4\frac{1}{2} \end{aligned}$

EXERCISES *On Your Own*

Add or subtract. Write the answers in simplest form.

1. $\frac{4}{5} + \frac{3}{5}$

2. $\frac{2}{6} - \frac{1}{6}$

3. $\frac{2}{7} + \frac{2}{7}$

4. $\frac{7}{8} + \frac{2}{8}$

5. $1\frac{2}{5} - \frac{1}{5}$

6. $\frac{3}{6} - \frac{1}{6}$

7. $\frac{6}{8} - \frac{3}{8}$

8. $\frac{2}{9} + \frac{1}{9}$

9. $\frac{4}{5} - \frac{1}{5}$

10. $\frac{5}{9} + \frac{7}{9}$

11. $9\frac{1}{3} - 8\frac{1}{3}$

12. $8\frac{6}{7} - 4\frac{2}{7}$

13. $3\frac{1}{10} + 1\frac{3}{10}$

14. $2\frac{2}{9} + 3\frac{4}{9}$

15. $4\frac{5}{12} - 3\frac{1}{12}$

16. $9\frac{5}{9} + 6\frac{7}{9}$

17. $5\frac{7}{8} + 2\frac{3}{8}$

18. $4\frac{4}{7} - 2\frac{1}{7}$

19. $9\frac{3}{4} + 1\frac{3}{4}$

20. $8\frac{2}{3} - 4\frac{1}{3}$

21. $8\frac{7}{10} + 2\frac{3}{10}$

22. $1\frac{4}{5} + 3\frac{3}{5}$

23. $7\frac{1}{5} - 2\frac{3}{5}$

24. $4\frac{1}{3} - 1\frac{2}{3}$

25. $4\frac{3}{8} - 3\frac{5}{8}$

26. $5\frac{1}{12} - 2\frac{7}{12}$

Multiplying and Dividing Fractions

To multiply fractions, multiply the numerators and the denominators. To divide fractions, multiply by the reciprocal of the divisor.

■ EXAMPLE

Multiply. Write the answers in simplest form.

a. $\dfrac{8}{9} \times \dfrac{3}{10} = \dfrac{\overset{4}{\cancel{8}}}{9} \times \dfrac{\overset{1}{\cancel{3}}}{\underset{5}{\cancel{10}}} = \dfrac{4}{15}$

b. $3\dfrac{1}{8} \times 1\dfrac{3}{4} = \dfrac{25}{8} \times \dfrac{7}{4}$

$= \dfrac{175}{32} = 5\dfrac{15}{32}$ ← Rewrite as a mixed number.

Divide. Write the answers in simplest form.

c. $\dfrac{2}{3} \div \dfrac{4}{5} = \dfrac{2}{3} \times \dfrac{5}{4}$

$= \dfrac{2}{3} \times \dfrac{5}{\underset{2}{\cancel{4}}} = \dfrac{5}{6}$

d. $3\dfrac{1}{8} \div 1\dfrac{3}{4} = \dfrac{25}{8} \div \dfrac{7}{4}$

$= \dfrac{25}{\underset{2}{\cancel{8}}} \times \dfrac{\overset{1}{\cancel{4}}}{7} = \dfrac{25}{14} = 1\dfrac{11}{14}$ ← Rewrite as a mixed number.

EXERCISES *On Your Own*

Multiply. Write the answers in simplest form.

1. $\dfrac{3}{4} \times \dfrac{3}{5}$

2. $\dfrac{2}{3} \times \dfrac{3}{4}$

3. $6 \times \dfrac{2}{3}$

4. $\dfrac{3}{4} \times \dfrac{5}{6}$

5. $\dfrac{5}{8} \times \dfrac{2}{3}$

6. $\dfrac{9}{16} \times \dfrac{2}{3}$

7. $\dfrac{3}{10} \times \dfrac{2}{15}$

8. $\dfrac{3}{4} \times \dfrac{1}{6}$

9. $\dfrac{1}{4} \times \dfrac{5}{20}$

10. $\dfrac{9}{10} \times \dfrac{1}{3}$

11. $1\dfrac{1}{3} \times 2\dfrac{2}{3}$

12. $\dfrac{3}{5} \times 2\dfrac{3}{4}$

13. $2\dfrac{1}{4} \times 3\dfrac{1}{3}$

14. $\dfrac{1}{4} \times 3\dfrac{1}{3}$

15. $6\dfrac{1}{4} \times 7$

16. $1\dfrac{3}{4} \times 2\dfrac{1}{5}$

17. $2\dfrac{3}{4} \times \dfrac{1}{2}$

18. $3\dfrac{4}{5} \times 2\dfrac{1}{3}$

Divide. Write the answers in simplest form.

19. $\dfrac{5}{8} \div \dfrac{5}{7}$

20. $\dfrac{5}{7} \div \dfrac{5}{8}$

21. $\dfrac{3}{4} \div \dfrac{6}{11}$

22. $\dfrac{1}{9} \div \dfrac{1}{9}$

23. $\dfrac{1}{9} \div 9$

24. $\dfrac{9}{10} \div \dfrac{3}{5}$

25. $\dfrac{2}{3} \div \dfrac{1}{9}$

26. $\dfrac{4}{5} \div \dfrac{5}{6}$

27. $\dfrac{1}{5} \div \dfrac{8}{9}$

28. $\dfrac{7}{8} \div \dfrac{1}{3}$

29. $4\dfrac{1}{5} \div 2\dfrac{2}{5}$

30. $6\dfrac{1}{4} \div 4\dfrac{3}{8}$

31. $2\dfrac{1}{3} \div 5\dfrac{5}{6}$

32. $1\dfrac{1}{2} \div 4\dfrac{1}{2}$

33. $15\dfrac{2}{3} \div 1\dfrac{1}{3}$

34. $10\dfrac{1}{3} \div 2\dfrac{1}{5}$

35. $6\dfrac{1}{4} \div 1\dfrac{3}{4}$

36. $6\dfrac{2}{3} \div 3\dfrac{1}{8}$

Working with Integers

Quantities less than zero can be written using negative integers. For example, a temperature of 5 degrees below zero can be written as −5. Positive integers are used for quantities greater than zero.

■ EXAMPLE 1

Write an integer for each situation.

   a. 10 degrees above zero   **b. a loss of $20**   **c. 15 yards lost**

     +10, or 10   −20   −15

A number line can be used to compare integers. The integer to the right is greater.

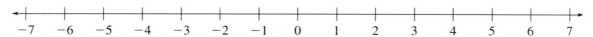

■ EXAMPLE 2

Compare. Use >, <, or =.

  a. 0 ■ −3   **b. −2 ■ −6**   **c. −7 ■ 3**

    0 is to the right, so   −2 is to the right,   −7 is to the left,
    it is greater.   so it is greater.   so it is less.
    0 > −3   −2 > −6   −7 < 3

EXERCISES *On Your Own*

Write an integer for each situation.

  1. 6 yards gained   **2.** 10 yards lost   **3.** 5 steps forward   **4.** 4 steps backward

  5. find $3   **6.** lose $8   **7.** 12 floors up   **8.** 4 floors down

Compare. Use >, <, or =.

  9. 0 ■ −1   **10.** −9 ■ 0   **11.** −3 ■ 3   **12.** 7 ■ −3   **13.** 0 ■ 1

  14. 3 ■ 0   **15.** 1 ■ −4   **16.** −2 ■ −9   **17.** 6 ■ −1   **18.** 3 ■ −10

  19. −7 ■ 3   **20.** 4 ■ 6   **21.** −16 ■ −25 **22.** −15 ■ −12 **23.** 7 ■ −8

  24. 2 ■ 3   **25.** −7 ■ −8   **26.** 35 ■ −40   **27.** −30 ■ −20 **28.** 25 ■ −25

  29. 9 ■ −9   **30.** −6 ■ −5   **31.** −23 ■ −15 **32.** −17 ■ −19 **33.** −15 ■ −25